Finite Mathematics

Lawrence E. Spence
Illinois State University

HARPER & ROW, PUBLISHERS, New York
Cambridge, Hagerstown, Philadelphia, San Francisco,
London, Mexico City, São Paulo, Sydney

Sponsoring Editor: Sharmon Hilfinger/Don Shauger
Project Editor: Molly Scully/Cynthia Indriso
Designer: Paula Schlosser
Assistant Production Manager: Marian Hartsough
Senior Production Manager: Kewal K. Sharma
Compositor: Syntax International Pte. Ltd.
Printer and Binder: R. R. Donnelley & Sons Company
Art Studio: J & R Services
Cover: Sculpture in the Hirshorn Garden; photo by M. Osborne, The Image Bank West, San Francisco; design by Paula Schlosser.

Finite Mathematics

Copyright © 1981 by Lawrence E. Spence

Portions of this work were published as a preliminary edition under the title *Finite Mathematics for Business and Social Sciences*. Copyright © 1979 by Lawrence E. Spence

All rights reserved. Printed in the United States of America. No part of this book may be used or reproduced in any manner whatsoever without written permission except in the case of brief quotations embodied in critical articles and reviews. For information address Harper & Row, Publishers, Inc., 10 East 53rd Street, New York, N.Y. 10022.

Library of Congress Cataloging in Publication Data
Spence, Lawrence E
    Finite mathematics.

    Includes index.
    1. Mathematics—1961–   I. Title.
QA39.2.S682   510   80-25884
ISBN 0-06-046369-4

Contents

Preface ix

1 Introduction 1

2 Linear Functions 6
    2.1 Functions **6**
    2.2 Linear Functions and the Straight Line **16**
    2.3 Market Equilibrium and Break-Even Analysis **25**
    *2.4 Further Applications of Linear Functions **35**
Chapter Review **42**

3 Matrices and Systems of Linear Equations 45
    3.1 Matrices **45**
    3.2 Matrix Addition and Scalar Multiplication **51**
    3.3 Matrix Multiplication **57**
    *3.4 Incidence Matrices **68**
    3.5 Systems of Two Linear Equations in Two Unknowns **77**
    3.6 Gaussian Elimination **85**
    *3.7 Some Applications of Systems of Linear Equations **94**
    3.8 The Inverse of a Matrix **105**
Chapter Review **113**

* A section number preceded by an asterisk indicates that the section may be omitted without loss of continuity.

4 Linear Programming 117

- 4.1 Systems of Linear Inequalities 117
- 4.2 Mathematical Models Involving Systems of Linear Inequalities 126
- 4.3 Geometric Solution of Linear Programming Problems 134
- 4.4 An Introduction to the Simplex Method 140
- 4.5 The Simplex Method 147
- 4.6 Artificial Variables and Minimization Problems 157
- *4.7 Duality 171

Chapter Review 177

5 An Introduction to Statistics 181

- 5.1 Frequency Distributions 181
- 5.2 Measures of Central Tendency and Measures of Dispersion 189
- 5.3 The Normal Distribution 196
- 5.4 Linear Regression 203

Chapter Review 211

6 Sets and Techniques for Counting 215

- 6.1 Introduction to Set Theory 215
- 6.2 Venn Diagrams and Counting 220
- 6.3 The Multiplication Principle 228
- 6.4 Permutations and Combinations 232

Chapter Review 240

7 Probability 243

- 7.1 Sample Spaces and Elementary Properties of Probability 243
- 7.2 Probability of the Complement and Union of Events 257
- 7.3 Conditional Probability and the Probability of the Intersection of Events 264
- 7.4 Binomial Experiments 274
- 7.5 Bayes' Formula 279
- 7.6 Expected Value 288

Chapter Review 294

8 Markov Chains 298

- 8.1 Transition Matrices 298
- 8.2 Regular Markov Chains 308
- 8.3 Absorbing Markov Chains 316
- *8.4 Some Applications Involving Absorbing Markov Chains 324

Chapter Review 331

Contents vii

9 Game Theory 336
9.1 Matrix Games 336
9.2 Strictly Determined Games 349
9.3 Geometric Solution of $2 \times m$ Matrix Games 353
9.4 Solution of $m \times n$ Matrix Games 361
Chapter Review 370

10 The Difference Equation $y_n = ay_{n-1} + b$ 374
10.1 Arithmetic Progressions 374
10.2 Geometric Progressions 380
10.3 Interest 385
10.4 First-Order Linear Difference Equations 391
10.5 Annuities 397
*10.6 Economic Applications 403
*10.7 Mathematical Models of Learning 409
Chapter Review 413

11 Graph Theory 417
11.1 Graphs and Their Representations 417
11.2 Paths and Circuits 424
11.3 Coloring Problems 435
11.4 Digraphs 444
Chapter Review 453

Appendix 458
Table 1 Areas Under the Standard Normal Distribution 459
Table 2 Compound Interest 460
Table 3 Present Value of a Dollar 464
Table 4 Amount of an Annuity 468
Table 5 Present Value of an Annuity 472

Answers to Odd-Numbered Exercises 476

Index 527

Preface

This book is intended to introduce topics from finite mathematics to first-year college students who have completed $1\frac{1}{2}$ years of high school algebra or the equivalent. Whenever possible, applications to business and the social sciences have been included. Finding suitable applications is difficult because meaningful applications often require a deeper knowledge of mathematics or some other discipline than the typical first-year college student possesses. For this reason a few of the applications require more background than is assumed otherwise. These are denoted by the heading "Application" and may be omitted without loss of continuity. In any case, since their primary purpose is to illustrate how a particular mathematical concept arises in the context of some real-world problem, the reader who studies these applications need not be overly concerned with their technical aspects. Items denoted by the heading "Example," however, are intended to demonstrate specific mathematical techniques or results, and so the reader should attempt to understand them completely.

There is ample material in the book for a four-semester-hour or a two-quarter course. Chapter 1 provides an overview of the types of problems considered in later chapters and is intended to be read by students outside of class. The body of the book is contained in Chapters 2–11, and the accompanying diagram shows the logical dependencies that exist among these chapters.

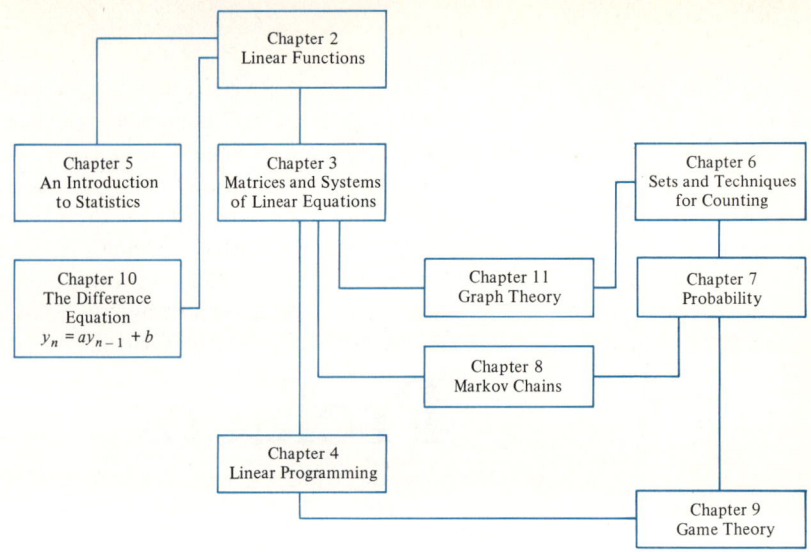

Sample outlines for different types of courses that can be taught from this book are shown in the table below.

	For students in Business and Economics	For students in the other Social Sciences
Semester hours	*Chapters*	*Chapters*
3	2–4, 6, 7, 10	2, 3, 5–7, 11
		2, 3, 6–8, 11
4	2–7, 9, 10	2, 3, 5–8, 10, 11
	2–7, 10, 11	
	2–4, 6–10	
	2–4, 6–8, 10, 11	

Answers to the odd-numbered exercises and the chapter review exercises appear on pages 476–526. Complete solutions to these exercises and practice chapter tests are available in a solutions manual. In addition, an instructor's manual that includes answers to the even-numbered exercises can be obtained from the publisher.

I am deeply indebted to Kenneth N. Berk (Illinois State University), Daniel A. Moran (Michigan State University), and their students for class testing much of the manuscript and to John L. Leonard (University of Arizona), George D. Parker (Southern Illinois University at Carbondale), and Michael D. Grady (Loyola Marymount University) for reviewing the manuscript. Their comments have contributed significantly to this book.

Special thanks are due as well to Janet Eardley (Illinois State University), who, in addition to preparing the solutions manual, made many suggestions that strengthened the exercises in this book. I appreciate also the help of Teresa Ling (University of California, Berkeley), who helped to verify the accuracy of the answers by working all of the odd-numbered exercises.

Preparing the manuscript was made considerably easier because of the fine typing by Patricia McCarney, who typed the entire first draft, and by Marilyn Parmantie, who assisted her in typing the revisions. I am grateful also for the constant support and encouragement that I received during the production process from Sharmon Hilfinger, Molly Scully, Cynthia Indriso and the rest of the staff at Harper & Row.

Lawrence E. Spence

1
Introduction

The use of mathematics in the physical sciences has a long and distinguished history, but the use of mathematics in other disciplines is very much more recent. With the increasing quantification of business and many of the social sciences, mathematical concepts and techniques are being used more frequently in these fields. Thus the education of students of business, economics, and psychology often includes required courses in mathematics, and, to a lesser degree, students of sociology, anthropology, and political science also study mathematics.

The purpose of this book is to present a variety of mathematical topics that have proved to be useful in the fields of business and the social sciences. These topics, which have come to be called *finite mathematics*, do not form a unified body of material in the way that, for example, the calculus does. Consequently the reader will often find it necessary to reorient himself or herself at the beginning of a new chapter. There are, however, certain common threads woven throughout the book: linear equations and matrices, which are discussed in Chapters 2 and 3, occur frequently in later chapters; linear programming, introduced in Chapter 4, recurs in Chapter 9; and Chapters 5–9 all involve the concept of probability either explicitly or implicitly.

Whenever possible, applications of the mathematics under consideration in some area of business or social science are included. Hopefully these applications will serve to convince the skeptical reader that mathematics can be used to solve significant problems in these disciplines. Unfortunately, realistic problems, which by their nature are usually quite complex, typically require advanced concepts (both mathematical and nonmathematical) that are beyond the scope of this book. Thus the absence of an application for a particular topic may signify only that further knowledge is required before the topic can be put to meaningful use. With further study, however, a reader might encounter applications of such topics.

Yet it is only fair to say that every topic in this book has not proved equally useful in business and the social sciences. Linear programming, for example, has found frequent use in the former but little use in the latter. Conversely, graph theory has proved to be much more important to the social sciences than to business. However, other topics such as statistics and probability are used constantly in both.

Although mathematical techniques can certainly be used to solve specific problems in business and the social sciences, they are often used to analyze general types of problems or commonly occurring situations. The use of mathematics in these settings often involves finding a representation of the problem or situation in mathematical terms. Such a representation, called a *mathematical model*, involves not only a mathematical structure but also a correspondence between the mathematics and its real-world context.

mathematical model

Mathematical models used in the physical sciences are often very accurate representations of reality. The equation $s = \frac{1}{2}gt^2$, for example, has proved to describe quite accurately the distance s traveled during time t by an object falling freely in a vacuum. (Here g denotes the acceleration due to gravity, approximately 32 feet per second per second.) Moreover, mathematical models of the orbits of heavenly bodies have enabled astronomers to predict their future locations with great precision.

In business and the social sciences, however, real-world problems are often more complex than in the physical sciences, involving many more variables than can reasonably be incorporated into a tractable model. Consequently mathematical models in these disciplines frequently provide only crude approximations to reality, but even these crude approximations may produce useful predictions of a general nature that would otherwise be unavailable. And even if a mathematical model is unable to provide valid predictions, it often proves useful by leading to a precise statement of the problem under consideration, by specifying the assumptions being made, by identifying relevant variables, or by suggesting additional problems requiring further study.

It is important to note that the reasons for using a model in business are often different than they are in the social sciences. Whereas the use of a model in business is most often for decision making, a model in the social sciences is often employed solely to understand better some complicated process or pattern of behavior. Thus a businessperson typically relies on a mathematical model in order to select the course of action that seems most likely to accomplish certain objectives, but a social scientist frequently seeks a mathematical model only to help codify certain empirical knowledge. Mathematical theories of learning, for example, have been developed for the purpose of understanding rather than decision making.

Learning to construct and test models is a valuable skill for both the businessperson and the social scientist. Unfortunately, it is a skill that is difficult to acquire, and this book will not be concerned with the modeling process. Several well-known mathematical models will be discussed and used, however. In Chapter 3, for example, a model for allocating service charges in accounting and the Leontief input-output model for a simplified economy are discussed, and various mathematical models of learning, including the Bower all-or-none model, are introduced in Chapters 8 and 10. In addition, a variety of mathematical techniques will be presented and used to solve problems such as the following.

PROBLEM 1

Having stopped production of an unprofitable item, a manufacturer has additional production capacity that can be used for the manufacture of two new products. Both these products require time on a lathe and a milling machine: Each unit of the first product requires 1 hour on a lathe and 3 hours on a milling machine, whereas each unit of the second product requires 2 hours on a lathe and 2 hours on a milling machine. Because of the current production schedule for other products, a lathe is available for at most 14 hours per week and a milling machine is available for at most 18 hours per week. The manufacturer expects to be able to sell as many units of either new product as can be produced, and the anticipated profit is $20 per unit for the first product and $30 per unit for the second. Under these conditions, how many units of each new product should be made in order to earn a maximum profit?

PROBLEM 2

Scores on the 1960 revision of the Stanford-Binet intelligence test are normally distributed with a mean of 100 and a standard deviation of 16. What percentage of the population will have IQ scores in the superior range (120–140)?

PROBLEM 3

A factory employs its workers on three shifts; the first shift employs 60% of the workers, the second shift employs 30% of the workers, and the third shift employs 10% of the workers. Management has found that the absentee rate for the first shift is 1.5% but increases to 5% for the second shift and 6% for the third shift. What percentage of the absentees are employed on each of the three shifts?

PROBLEM 4

Suppose that $40,000 is borrowed to purchase a house, that interest is to be charged monthly at an annual rate of 9%, and that the debt is to be repaid in 25 years by equal monthly payments. How large should each payment be?

PROBLEM 5

Suppose that New York City is considering seven new routes for garbage trucks that will visit 12 heavily used locations as listed below.

Route A: The Empire State Building, Madison Square Garden, the New York Stock Exchange, and Grand Central Station
Route B: Lincoln Center, the Bronx Zoo, Columbia University, and Yankee Stadium
Route C: The Statue of Liberty, Lincoln Center, Yankee Stadium, and Grand Central Station
Route D: The New York Public Library, Madison Square Garden, the New York Stock Exchange, and Grand Central Station
Route E: The Brooklyn Botanic Garden, Shea Stadium, the Bronx Zoo, and Madison Square Garden
Route F: Columbia University, the Empire State Building, Yankee Stadium, and the Bronx Zoo
Route G: Shea Stadium, the New York Public Library, the Statue of Liberty, and the Brooklyn Botanic Garden

Is it possible to schedule these routes on Monday, Tuesday, and Wednesday in such a way that no location is visited twice on the same day?

References

1. Apostel, Leo, "Towards the Formal Study of Models in the Non-Formal Sciences," in *The Concept and the Role of the Model in Mathematics and Natural and Social Sciences*, H. Freudenthal, ed. New York: Gordon and Breach, 1961.
2. Bass, Frank M. et al., *Mathematical Models and Methods in Marketing.* Homewood, Ill.: Irwin, 1961.
3. Bishir, John W. and Donald W. Drewes, *Mathematics in the Behavioral and Social Sciences.* New York: Harcourt Brace Jovanovich, 1970.
4. Clarke, David L., ed., *Models in Archaeology.* London: Methuen, 1972.
5. Committee on Support of Research in the Mathematical Sciences of the National Research Council, ed., *The Mathematical Sciences: A Collection of Essays.* Cambridge, Mass.: MIT Press, 1969.

6. Fagen, Richard R., "Some Contributions of Mathematical Reasoning to the Study of Politics," *Am. Polit. Sci, Rev.*, vol. 55 (1961), pp. 888–900.
7. Festinger, Leon, "The Relevance of Mathematics to Controlled Experimentation in Sociology," *Int. Soc. Sci. Bull.*, vol. 6 (1954), pp. 622–627.
8. Fiorina, Morris P., "Formal Models in Political Science," *Am. J. Polit. Sci.*, vol. 19 (1975), pp. 133–159.
9. Hirstein, I. N., "Some Mathematical Methods and Techniques in Economics," *Q. Appl. Math.*, vol. 11 (1953), pp. 249–261.
10. Hodson, F. R., D. G. Kendall, and P. Tautu, eds., *Mathematics in the Archaeological and Historical Sciences.* Edinburgh: Edinburgh University Press, 1971.
11. Hull, John, John Mapes, and Brian Wheeler, *Model Building Techniques for Management.* Westmead, England: Saxon House, 1976.
12. Kaplan, Abraham, "Sociology Learns the Language of Mathematics," *Commentary*, vol. 14, no. 3 (September 1952), pp. 274–284.
13. Kemeny, John G. and J. Laurie Snell, *Mathematical Models in the Social Sciences.* New York: Blaisdell, 1962.
14. Lave, Charles A. and James G. March, *An Introduction to Models in the Social Sciences.* New York: Harper and Row, 1975.
15. Mattessich, Richard, "Mathematical Models in Business Accounting," *Account. Rev.*, vol 33, no. 3 (July 1958), pp. 472–481.
16. Rivett, Patrick, *Principles of Model Building.* London: Wiley, 1972.
17. Samuelson, Paul A., "Economic Theory and Mathematics–An Appraisal," *Am. Econ. Rev. Pap. Proc.*, vol. 42, no. 2 (May 1952), pp. 56–69.
18. Springer, Clifford H., Robert E. Herlihy, and Robert I. Beggs, *Advanced Methods and Models.* Homewood, Ill.: Irwin, 1965.

2

Linear Functions

Every discipline is concerned with the relationships that exist among variable quantities. An economist, for example, may be interested in the effect of supply and demand on the price of an item, a sociologist may be interested in the effect of increases in population and unemployment on the crime rate, and a businessperson may be interested in the effect of increases in the cost of labor and raw materials on profits. The use of mathematics in such situations provides a method for describing these relationships precisely.

One of the simplest types of relationships that can exist between a pair of variable quantities is a linear relationship. Yet despite this simplicity, many relationships of interest are linear or, at least, approximately linear. In this chapter we discuss how to describe linear relationships algebraically, but the problem of approximating a linear relationship will be deferred until Section 5.4.

2.1 Functions

As mentioned above, the most important use of mathematics in many disciplines is to describe the relationships among variable quantities. Such descriptions involve the concept of a function.

function
By a *function* we mean a rule that associates with a given input value exactly one output value. Although we are most often concerned with the situation where the input and output values are real numbers, we also need to consider ordered pairs (x, y) or, more generally, ordered n-tuples $(x_1, x_2, \ldots, x_n)$ as possible inputs.

Functions that arise in mathematics can often be described by equations expressing the output values in terms of the input values. For example,

$$y = 2x$$

is an equation relating the quantities x and y, which expresses that the value of y equals twice the value of x. Thus for each input value x we have a rule (multiply x by 2) for determining the output value y; hence y is a function of x. In this context x is called the *independent variable*, and y is called the *dependent variable* because its value depends on the value given to x.

independent variable
dependent variable

To denote that a dependent variable y is a function f of an independent variable x, we write

$$y = f(x)$$

Here $f(x)$, read "f of x," represents the output value associated with the input value x.

EXAMPLE 1

For the function f defined by the equation $f(x) = 3x - 2$, f associates the output value $3x - 2$ with the input value x. Thus

$$f(-5) = 3(-5) - 2 = -17$$
$$f(0) = 3(0) - 2 = -2$$

and

$$f(4) = 3(4) - 2 = 10$$

EXAMPLE 2

In the United States, temperature readings are frequently reported both in degrees Fahrenheit and in degrees Celsius. A simple functional relationship exists between these two scales of measurement that permits a reading on one scale to be converted to a reading on the other. For example, the Fahrenheit reading F expressed as a function of the Celsius reading C is

$$F(C) = \tfrac{9}{5}C + 32$$

Thus $F(10) = 50$ and $F(30) = 86$; so Celsius temperatures of 10 and 30° correspond to Fahrenheit temperatures of 50 and 86°, respectively.

EXAMPLE 3

If $1000.00 is deposited in an account paying 8% interest compounded quarterly, the value of the account at any later time will be a function of the number of quarters the money has been on deposit. Specifically, after n quarters the value of the account in dollars, $A(n)$, is given by[1]

$$A(n) = 1000(1.02)^n$$

Hence after 1 quarter the value of the account is $1020.00, and after 2 quarters the value of the account is $1040.40.

EXAMPLE 4

The gross national product of a country is the total value of the goods and services it produces during a year. The gross national product G can be approximated as the sum of the country's consumption c, investment spending i, and government expenditure e. In this approximation G is treated as a function of the three independent variables c, i, and e; symbolically

$$G(c, i, e) = c + i + e$$

This function assigns to each ordered triple (c, i, e) a real number, namely, the sum of its coordinates. Thus, for example, if $c = \$963$ billion, $i = \$205$ billion, and $e = \$331$ billion (as was the case in 1975 for the United States), then the gross national product for the year is

$$C(963, 205, 331) = \$963 + \$205 + \$331 = \$1499 \text{ billion}$$

Although there is a difference between the function and the equation that defines the function, this distinction is usually ignored for convenience of expression. Thus we speak of "the function $g(x) = x^2 - 3x + 5$" rather than "the function g defined by the equation $g(x) = x^2 - 3x + 5$." It is also convenient to display the independent variable(s) when referring to a function; thus we normally speak of "the function $g(x)$" rather than "the function g."

Since we are interested primarily in functions of one independent variable, we restrict our attention to such functions for the remainder of this chapter.

For many purposes it is useful to have a geometric representation of a function. Such a representation allows us to estimate where a function is increasing, where it assumes a maximum or minimum value, and so forth. By the *graph of a function* $y = f(x)$ we mean the collection of ordered pairs (a, b) that satisfy $y = f(x)$ when a is substituted for x and b is substituted for y. By plotting enough of these pairs, we can obtain a geometric representation of the function.

Before we actually graph a function, let us recall how ordered pairs are plotted. A *rectangular* (or *Cartesian*) *coordinate system* consists of a pair of perpendicular lines, one horizontal and one vertical. The horizontal line is usually called the *x axis* and chosen with its positive direction to the right, and the vertical line is usually called the *y axis*

graph of a function

rectangular coordinate system
x axis
y axis

[1] We shall see how this formula is obtained in Section 10.3.

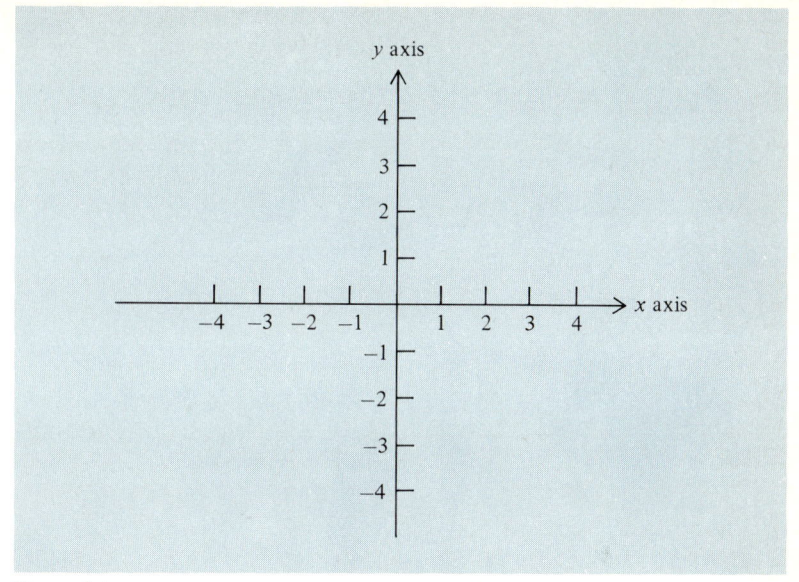

Figure 2.1

and chosen with its positive direction upward. On each line a unit of length is chosen; it is not necessary that the same unit of length be used on each axis. (See Figure 2.1.)

For each ordered pair of real numbers (a, b) we can associate a unique point P in the plane by the following method. Draw a line perpendicular to the x axis through the point corresponding to the number a, and likewise draw a line perpendicular to the y axis through the point corresponding to the number b. The point of intersection P of these two lines is called the point with *coordinates* (a, b). (See Figure 2.2.) The number a is called the *first coordinate* (or x coordinate) of P, and the number b is called the *second coordinate* (or y coordinate) of P. It is customary to refer to "the point (a, b)" rather than to "the point with coordinates (a, b)."

coordinates
first coordinate
second coordinate

EXAMPLE 5

The points $(-7, -4)$, $(-3, 5)$, $(0, -2)$, $(3, 0)$, $(4, -3)$, and $(6, 2)$ are plotted in Figure 2.3.

To graph the function $f(x) = x^2 - 6x + 8$, we must plot the ordered pairs (x, y) satisfying the equation $y = f(x)$, that is, $y = x^2 - 6x + 8$. Since there is an infinite number of such pairs, it is impossible to plot all of them. Instead, we plot enough points to indicate the general shape of the graph and then approximate the graph by drawing a smooth curve through the points that were plotted. In order to determine pairs that satisfy $y = f(x)$, we need only substitute arbitrary values for the independent variable x and compute the corresponding

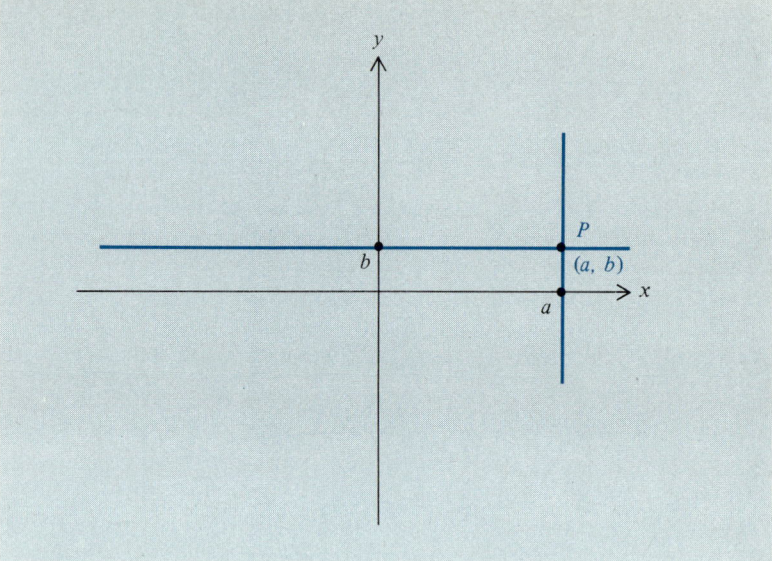

Figure 2.2

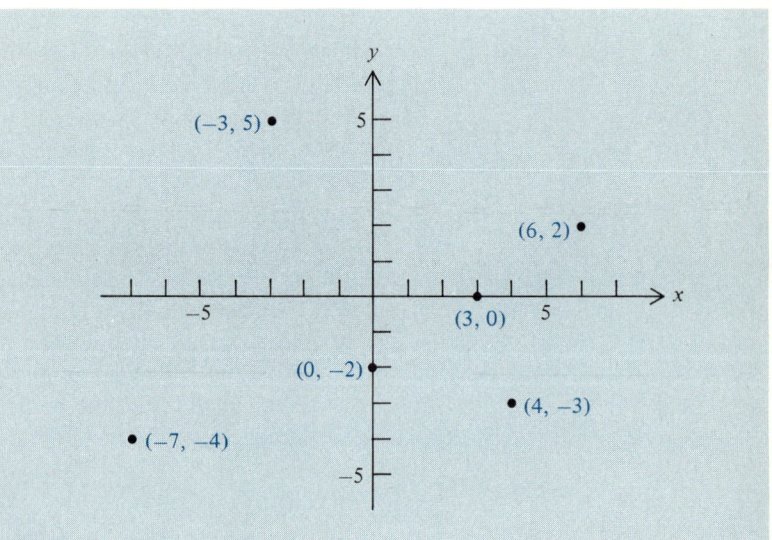

Figure 2.3

values of the dependent variable y. If we substitute the integers from -1 through 7 for x, we obtain the following table of values.

x	-1	0	1	2	3	4	5	6	7
y	15	8	3	0	-1	0	3	8	15

Plotting these nine ordered pairs (x, y) and connecting them with a smooth curve, we obtain the graph in Figure 2.4.

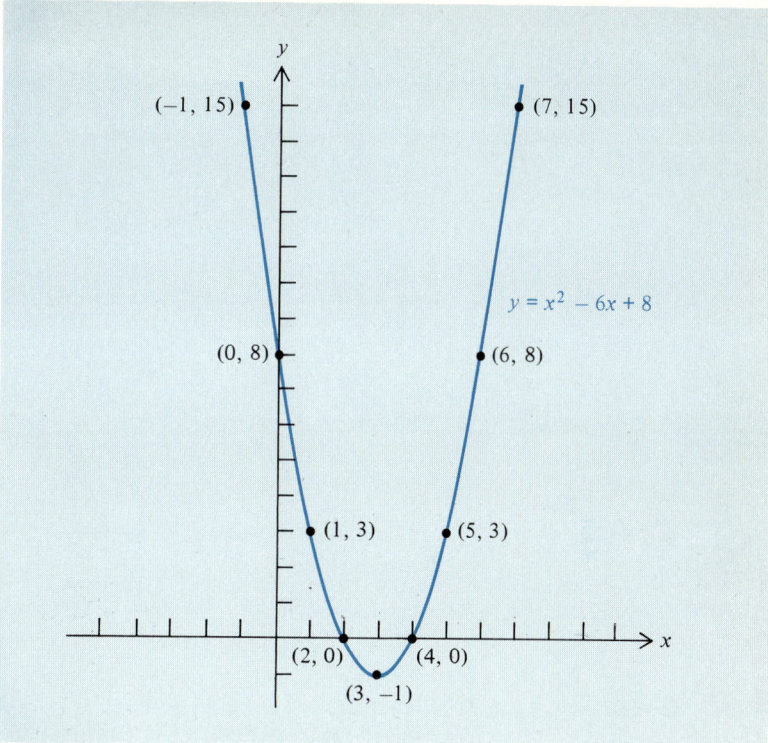

Figure 2.4

In graphing a function it is often important to determine the point(s) at which the graph crosses the coordinate axes. Such points are called *intercepts*. The x coordinate of a point at which a graph crosses the x axis is called an x *intercept*, and the y coordinate of a point at which a graph crosses the y axis is called a y *intercept*. For the graph of $f(x) = x^2 - 6x + 8$ in Figure 2.4, there are two x intercepts (2 and 4) and one y intercept (8). To find the x intercept(s) for a graph, set $y = 0$ in the equation and solve for x. Likewise, to find the y intercept(s), set $x = 0$ and solve for y. The following example will demonstrate the computation of intercepts.

intercepts
x intercept
y intercept

EXAMPLE 6

We shall determine the intercepts for the graph of $g(x) = 2x + 4$ and then graph this function.

Since we must graph $y = g(x)$, we plot ordered pairs that satisfy the equation $y = 2x + 4$. To find the x intercept, we set $y = 0$ and solve for x; this produces

$$0 = 2x + 4$$
$$-4 = 2x$$
$$-2 = x$$

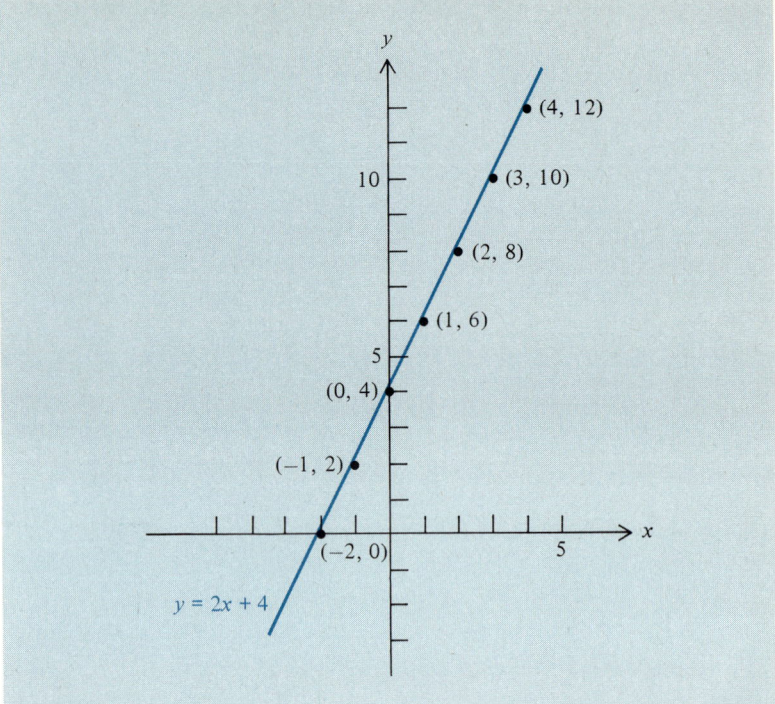

Figure 2.5

So this graph has only one x intercept, which is -2. Similarly, by setting $x = 0$ and solving for y, we obtain the y intercept

$$y = 2(0) + 4 = 4$$

Thus 4 is the only y intercept for this graph.

In addition to the intercepts $(-2, 0)$ and $(0, 4)$ determined above, the following table of values lists the coordinates of five other points on the graph of $y = 2x + 4$.

x	-1	1	2	3	4
y	2	6	8	10	12

By plotting these ordered pairs and connecting them with a smooth curve, we obtain the graph in Figure 2.5.

The technique for graphing that we have discussed cannot ensure us that our graphs are accurate. For example, although the points plotted in Example 6 suggest that the graph of $y = 2x + 4$ is the straight line shown in Figure 2.5, it is conceivable that the graph could actually be as in Figure 2.6. Thus we can only expect to obtain a reasonable approximation to the actual graph by merely plotting points. (We shall

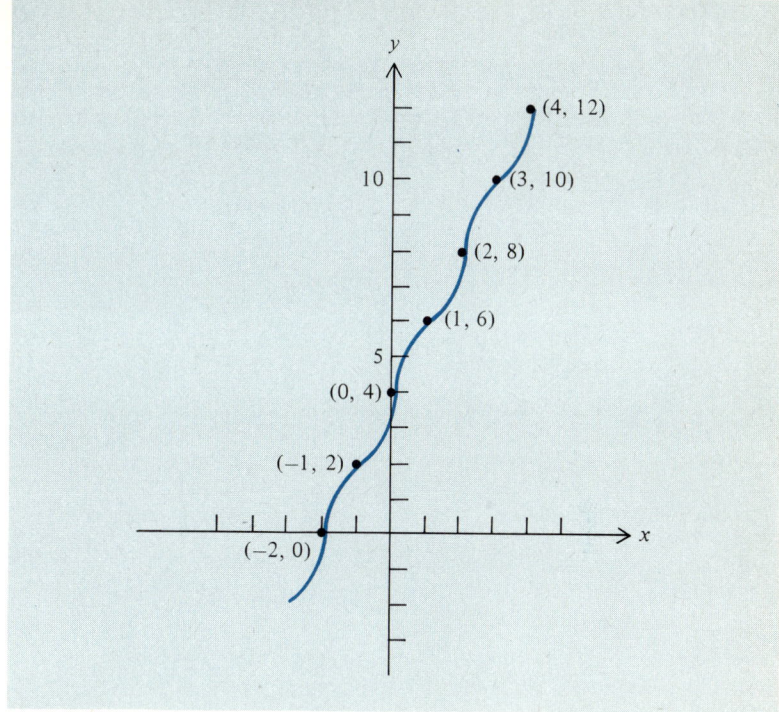

Figure 2.6

see in the next section, however, that the graph of $y = 2x + 4$ is actually a straight line.)

We conclude this section by discussing a mathematical model that uses the graph of a cost function as a means of minimizing inventory cost.

APPLICATION 1

Wholesale and retail stores purchase their merchandise from manufacturers or suppliers and then fill their customers' orders from their inventory. To obtain a model for inventory cost as a function of the size of an order purchased from a manufacturer or supplier, we make two simplifying assumptions:

1. The manufacturer or supplier fills an inventory order instantaneously; that is, there is no time lag between the placing of an order and its delivery.

2. Sales from inventory occur at a uniform rate.

Let

x denote the number of units of a particular item to be purchased from the manufacturer or supplier

14   Chapter 2   Linear Functions

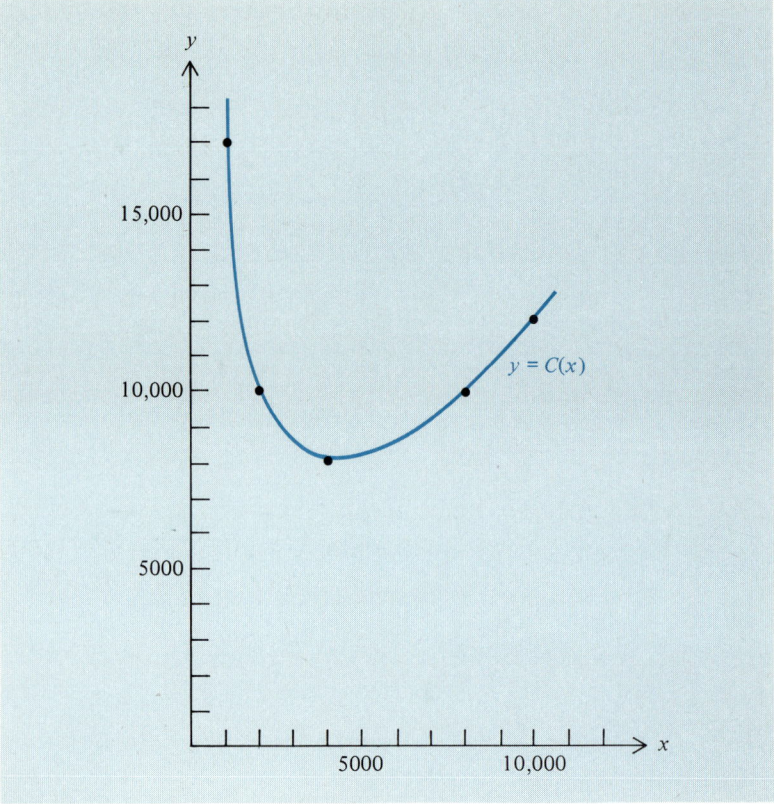

Figure 2.7

$C(x)$ denote the total inventory cost during some period of time

d denote the fixed demand for the item during this period

i denote the cost of storing one unit of inventory during this period

r denote the cost of placing an order with the manufacturer or supplier

Because of the first assumption we suppose that an order from the manufacturer or supplier is not placed until all the inventory for the item is gone. Thus inventory for this item varies uniformly between x units and 0 units, at which time a new order restores the inventory level to x units and the same pattern is repeated. Consequently the average number of units of this item in inventory during the period under consideration is $\frac{1}{2}x$, and so $\frac{1}{2}xi$ is the total cost of storing inventory during the period. Furthermore, the number of orders to be placed during the period is d/x, and thus the total cost of all orders placed during the period is dr/x. Therefore the total inventory cost during the period is given by

$$C(x) = \frac{1}{2}xi + \frac{dr}{x} \qquad (x > 0) \tag{2.1}$$

To illustrate (2.1), suppose that a retail book store anticipates that a certain book will sell 20,000 copies during a two-year period. If it expects the cost of storing 1 book for two years to be $2 and the cost of ordering to be $800 per order, then the total inventory cost (in dollars) for the two-year period will be

$$C(x) = \frac{1}{2}x(2) + \frac{20{,}000(800)}{x} = x + \frac{16{,}000{,}000}{x}$$

The graph of this function is shown in Figure 2.7. Notice that the minimum inventory cost seems to occur when $x = 4000$; in other words, the inventory cost will be a minimum when approximately 4000 books are ordered in each order. This minimum cost is approximately $C(4000) = \$8000$.

Exercises

1. If $v = g(u)$, identify the independent variable and the dependent variable.
2. If $q = h(p)$, identify the independent variable and the dependent variable.

In Exercises 3–10, compute $f(-3)$ for the given function f.

3. $f(x) = 5 - 2x^2$
4. $f(x) = 3x + 4$
5. $f(t) = 5 - 4t$
6. $f(t) = t^2 - 6$
7. $f(r) = \sqrt{r^2 + 7}$
8. $f(r) = r^3$
9. $f(s) = \dfrac{2s - 1}{s + 4}$
10. $f(s) = \dfrac{6s - 5}{2s + 1}$

In Exercises 11–18, compute the indicated value of $f(x) = \sqrt{x + 5}$.

11. $f(-5)$
12. $f(-4)$
13. $f(0)$
14. $f(3)$
15. $f(4)$
16. $f(-1)$
17. $f(7)$
18. $f(11)$

In Exercises 19–30, compute the indicated values of $f(x) = 12x - 48$.

19. $f(a)$
20. $f(\frac{1}{3}a)$
21. $f(\frac{1}{6}a)$
22. $f(2a)$
23. $f(a - 2)$
24. $f(a + 3)$
25. $f(2a - 1)$
26. $f(3a - \frac{1}{2})$
27. $f(\frac{1}{2}a + 4)$
28. $f(-2a - 1)$
29. $f(-\frac{1}{2}a + 6)$
30. $f(\frac{1}{4}a + 5)$

Compute $g(2, -1)$ for each of the functions in Exercises 31–38.

31. $g(x, y) = 3x + 5y$
32. $g(x, y) = 4x - 3y$
33. $g(r, s) = rs$
34. $g(r, s) = rs^2$
35. $g(p, q) = 5q - 1$
36. $g(p, q) = 4p + 3$
37. $g(x, y) = 2xy - 4x + 3y + 8$
38. $g(x, y) = x^2 - 4xy + y - 6$

In Exercises 39–46, compute the indicated values of $g(x, y) = 2x - 3y^2 - 1$.

39. $g(3, 0)$ **40.** $g(1, -1)$ **41.** $g(5, 2)$
42. $g(0, 4)$ **43.** $g(-4, -2)$ **44.** $g(0, 0)$
45. $g(3, 1)$ **46.** $g(-2, 2)$

In Exercises 47–58, plot the given point on a rectangular coordinate system.

47. $(4, -2)$ **48.** $(2, 3)$ **49.** $(0, -6)$
50. $(-5, 2)$ **51.** $(-7, -3)$ **52.** $(-4, 0)$
53. $(8, 1)$ **54.** $(2, -5)$ **55.** $(5, 0)$
56. $(-1, -6)$ **57.** $(-2, 6)$ **58.** $(0, 3)$

In Exercises 59–66, determine all the intercepts for the graph of the given function. Label each intercept an x intercept or a y intercept.

59. $f(x) = 5x - 30$ **60.** $g(x) = -4x - 8$
61. $g(x) = x^2 - 4$ **62.** $h(x) = x^2 + 1$
63. $h(x) = 4$ **64.** $f(x) = (x - 1)^3$
65. $r(x) = \sqrt{x^2 + 1}$ **66.** $p(x) = 1/x$

Graph the functions given in Exercises 67–78.

67. $f(x) = 8 - 2x$ **68.** $g(x) = 3x - 4$
69. $h(x) = x^2 + 2x$ **70.** $f(x) = x^2 + 3$
71. $g(x) = \sqrt{x}$ $(x \geq 0)$ **72.** $h(x) = 1/x$ $(x \neq 0)$
73. $f(x) = x^3$ **74.** $f(x) = 4 - x^2$
75. $g(x) = -2x^2 + 7$ **76.** $h(x) = 2x + 1/x$ $(x \neq 0)$
77. $h(x) = \dfrac{1}{x - 3}$ $(x \neq 3)$ **78.** $g(x) = \dfrac{1}{x^2 + 1}$

In Exercises 79–82, graph Equation (2.1) under the given conditions. Estimate from the graph the order size that minimizes the total inventory cost.

79. $i = 6, d = 500, r = 15$ **80.** $i = 5, d = 405, r = 5000$
81. $i = 2, d = 1600, r = 900$ **82.** $i = 8, d = 2000, r = 80$

2.2 Linear Functions and the Straight Line

Among the simplest, yet the most important, functions are those of the form

$$f(x) = mx + b$$

linear functions

Such functions are called *linear functions* because their graphs are straight lines.

EXAMPLE 7

If \$10 is borrowed at an interest rate of $1\frac{1}{2}\%$ simple interest per month, then the amount $A(t)$ to be repaid after t months is [2]

---

[2] We shall see how this formula is obtained in Section 10.3.

2.2 Linear Functions and the Straight Line   17

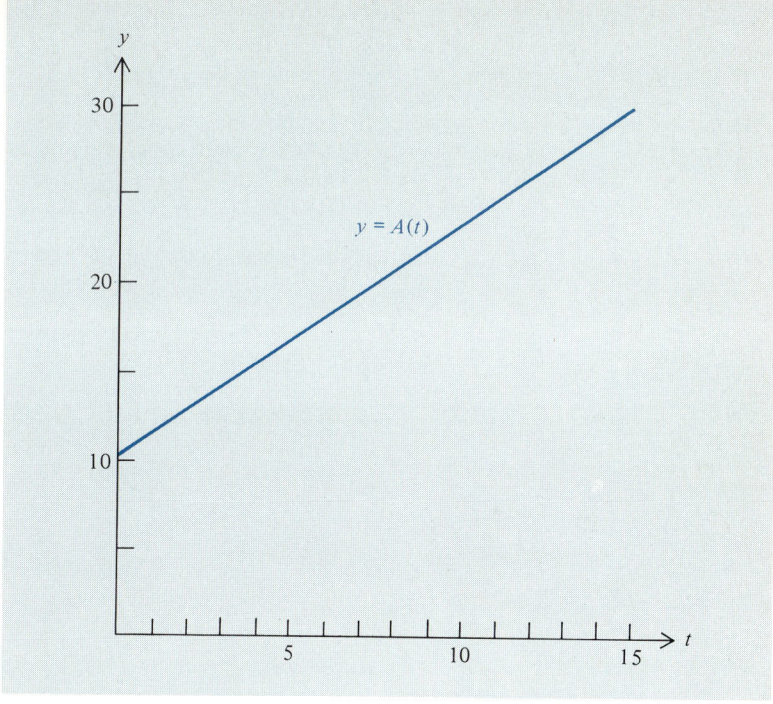

Figure 2.8

$$A(t) = 1.50t + 10 \quad \text{dollars}$$

Thus $A(t)$ is a linear function of t. The graph of this function for $t \geq 0$ is shown in Figure 2.8.

Rather than studying linear functions directly, let us consider the more general subject of the straight line. The graph of any equation of the form $ax + by = c$, where a, b, and c are constants and a and b are not both zero, is a (straight) line, and conversely any (straight) line can be described by an equation of this form. For this reason the equation

$$ax + by = c \quad (a \neq 0 \text{ or } b \neq 0) \tag{2.2}$$

general form of the equation of a line is called the *general form* of the equation of a line.

EXAMPLE 8

The graphs of the equations $2x - 3y = 12$ and $3x + 4y = 24$ are both lines, since each equation is of the form (2.2). Consequently the graph of each equation can be drawn if two points on each graph are known. These graphs are shown in Figures 2.9 and 2.10.

18   Chapter 2   Linear Functions

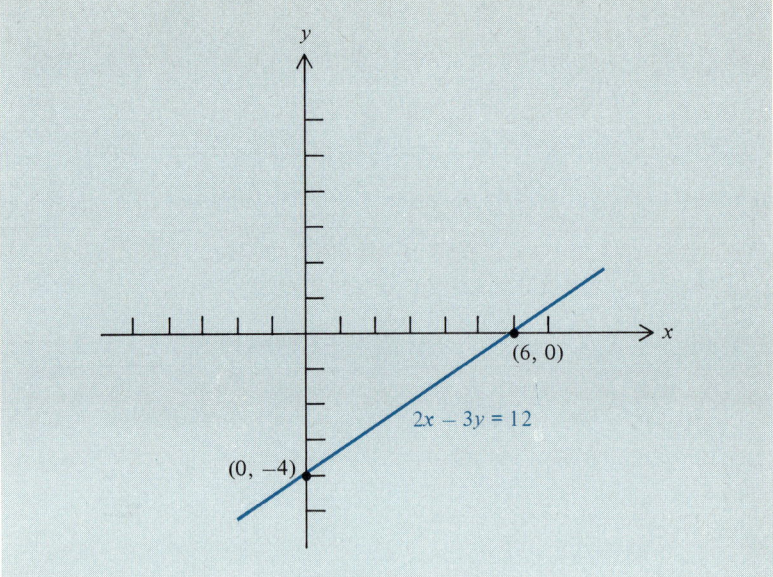

Figure 2.9

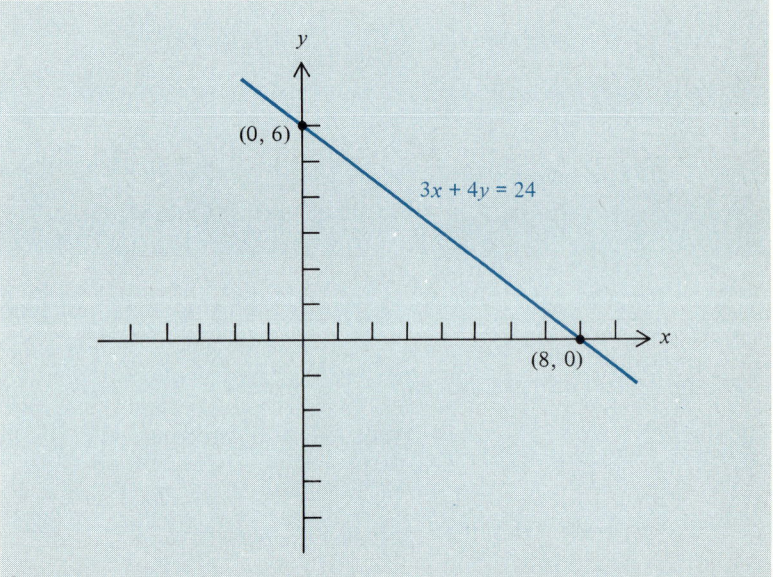

Figure 2.10

If $a = 0$ in (2.2), then the equation of the line simplifies to the form $y = k$. The graph of any such equation is a horizontal line (see Figure 2.11); conversely, the equation of any horizontal line is of the form $y = k$ for some constant k.

Likewise, if $b = 0$ in (2.2), then the equation of the line reduces to the form $x = k$. The graph of such an equation is a vertical line (see

2.2 Linear Functions and the Straight Line 19

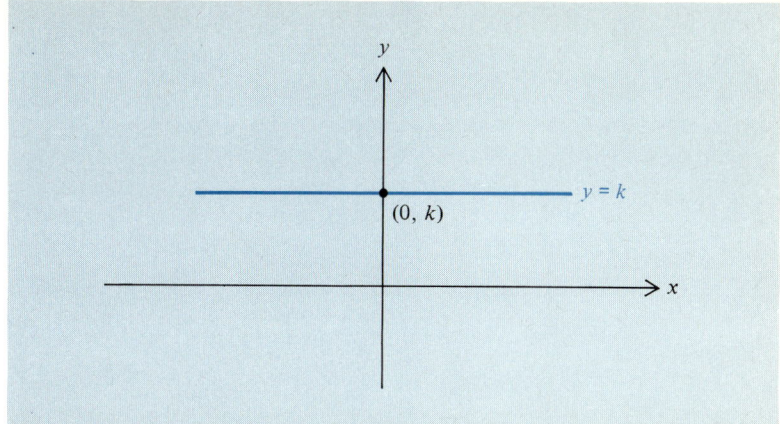

Figure 2.11

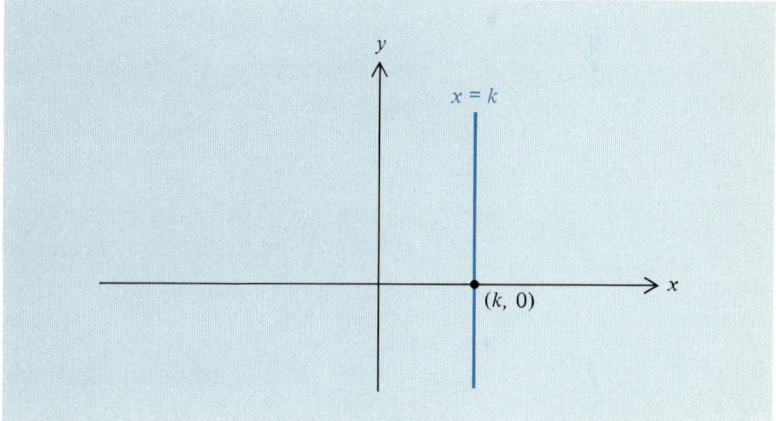

Figure 2.12

Figure 2.12); conversely, the equation of any vertical line is of the form $x = k$ for some k.

EXAMPLE 9

The equations of the horizontal and vertical lines through the point $(2, -3)$ are $y = -3$ and $x = 2$, respectively. These lines are shown in Figure 2.13.

If, as in Example 8, $a \neq 0$ and $b \neq 0$ in (2.2), then the line is neither horizontal nor vertical. For such a line it is important to have a measure of the angle between the line and the positive x axis. One such measure is the slope of the line. If (x_1, y_1) and (x_2, y_2) are two points on a non-vertical line, the number

$$\frac{y_2 - y_1}{x_2 - x_1} \tag{2.3}$$

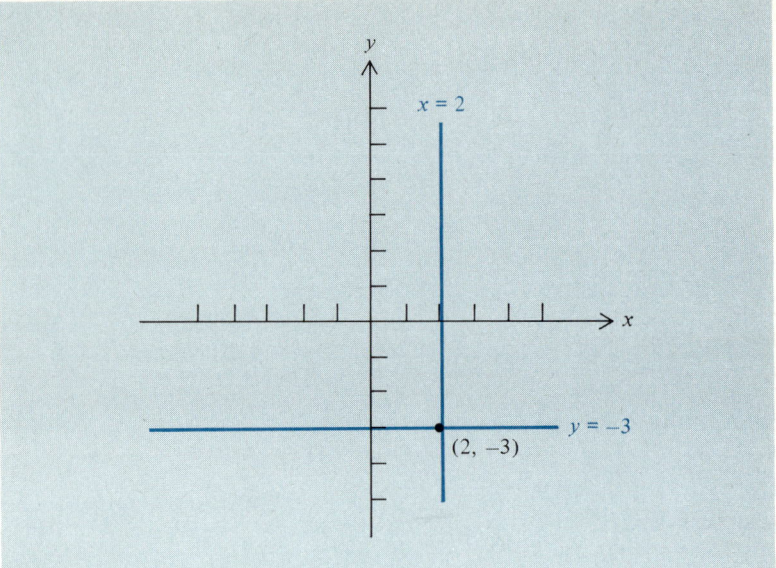

Figure 2.13

slope   is called the *slope* of the line. Notice that the slope of a vertical line is undefined and that the slope of a horizontal line is 0.

EXAMPLE 10

The slope of the line through the points $(3, -2)$ and $(-2, 8)$ is

$$\frac{8 - (-2)}{-2 - 3} = \frac{10}{-5} = -2$$

This value was computed by taking $(x_1, y_1) = (3, -2)$ and $(x_2, y_2) = (-2, 8)$ in (2.3). Which point is chosen as (x_1, y_1) is unimportant, however; for if we had taken $(x_1, y_1) = (-2, 8)$ and $(x_2, y_2) = (3, -2)$, then (2.3) would have again given the slope as

$$\frac{-2 - 8}{3 - (-2)} = \frac{-10}{5} = -2$$

In Figure 2.14 we can see the geometric significance of the slope of a line. The slope equals the vertical change $y_2 - y_1$ divided by the horizontal change $x_2 - x_1$. Hence the slope measures the rate of vertical change in the line per unit of horizontal change. In other words, the slope measures the rate at which the line is rising or falling. Thus a line with slope 3 increases three units vertically for each unit of increase horizontally. A line with a positive slope rises from left to right, whereas one with a negative slope falls from left to right. Lines through the origin with various slopes m are shown in Figure 2.15.

2.2 Linear Functions and the Straight Line   21

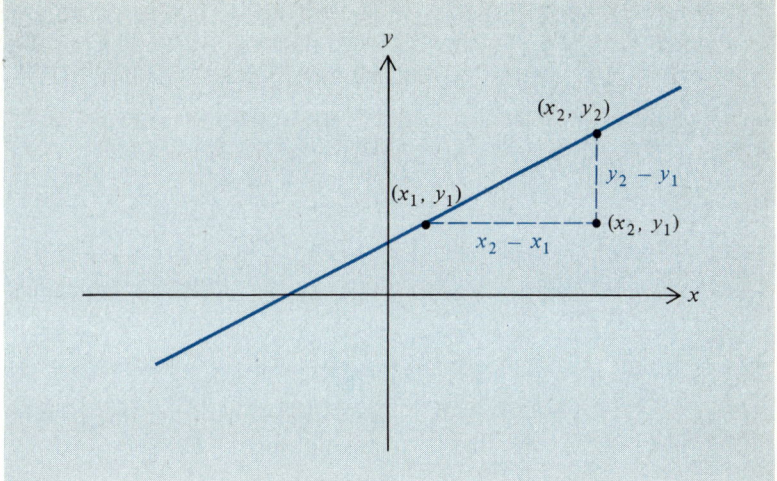

Figure 2.14

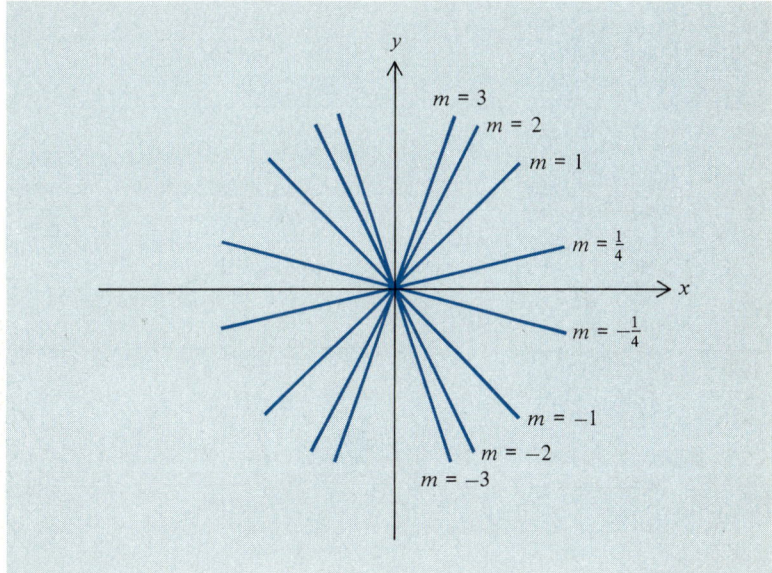

Figure 2.15

Since the slope of a line is a numerical measure of its slant, it is not surprising that lines having the same slope have the same slant. This fact may be stated as follows.

⋕ THEOREM 2.1

Parallel lines have the same slope, and two lines with the same slope are parallel.

We are now able to describe the equation of a line passing through a known point (x_1, y_1) and having a given slope m. For if (x, y) denotes an arbitrary point on the line, then

$$m = \frac{y - y_1}{x - x_1}$$

or

$$y - y_1 = m(x - x_1) \tag{2.4}$$

point-slope form of the equation of a line

This equation is called the *point-slope form* of the equation of a line.

EXAMPLE 11

The equation of the line passing through the point $(3, -1)$ and having slope -2 is

$$y - (-1) = -2(x - 3)$$

or

$$y = -2x + 5$$

EXAMPLE 12

The equation of the line passing through two given points can be found using the point-slope form. Suppose, for instance, that $(3, 4)$ and $(5, 16)$ are two points on the line. Then the slope of the line is

$$\frac{16 - 4}{5 - 3} = \frac{12}{2} = 6$$

Hence the equation of the line is

$$y - 4 = 6(x - 3)$$

or

$$y = 6x - 14$$

EXAMPLE 13

In [1][3] Brown describes an experiment with rats trained to run through a narrow passage in a cage in order to receive food in a goal box. The rats were then placed in harnesses attached to a spring scale and placed at distances of 30 and 170 centimeters from the goal box. The pull of the rats toward the goal box was measured, and the following data were obtained:

Distance from the goal box (centimeters)	30	170
Mean strength of pull (grams)	56.5	40.9

[3] Numbers in brackets direct the reader to the References at the end of each chapter.

Brown assumed that the strength of pull P was a linear function of the distance d of the rat from the goal box. The equation of the line through the points (30, 56.5) and (170, 40.9) can be computed as above to be

$$y - 56.5 = \frac{-15.6}{140}(x - 30)$$

So

$$y \approx -0.11x + 59.84$$

Thus the relationship between P and d can be approximated by the linear function

$$P = -0.11d + 59.84$$

In Examples 11 and 12 we simplified the equations of the lines to the form

$$y = mx + b \tag{2.5}$$

slope-intercept form of the equation of a line

This equation is called the *slope-intercept form* of the equation of a line. The reason for this name is that in (2.5) m is the slope of the line and b is its y intercept. Thus, to find the slope of a line or its y intercept when its equation is known, simply write the equation in the slope-intercept form; the slope will then be the coefficient of x, and the y intercept will be the constant term.

EXAMPLE 14

To find the equation of the line passing through the point $(-2, -4)$ and parallel to the line with equation $6x - 2y = 5$, we must first determine the slope of the desired line. From Theorem 2.1 we know that this slope is the same as that of the line with equation $6x - 2y = 5$. Rewriting this equation in the slope-intercept form $y = 3x - \frac{5}{2}$, we see that this line has slope 3 (and y intercept $-\frac{5}{2}$). Therefore the desired line passes through $(-2, -4)$ and has slope 3. Using the point-slope form of the equation of a line, we see that the equation of the line is

$$y - (-4) = 3[x - (-2)]$$

or

$$y = 3x + 2$$

Exercises

In Exercises, 1–8, which of the given equations graph as lines?

1. $3x - 4y = 6$
2. $x = 7$
3. $4x^2 + 9y^2 = 36$
4. $y = 2x^2 - 3$

5. $y = -5$
6. $y = \sqrt{7x - 5}$
7. $x = -3y - 8$
8. $y = 4x + 2$

In Exercises 9–16, graph the given equation.

9. $3x - 4y = 24$
10. $y = 5$
11. $y = 5x - 6$
12. $5x + 2y = -20$
13. $x = -7$
14. $y = -3x + 8$
15. $y = -4x$
16. $24x - 36y = 96$

In Exercises 17–28, write the equations of the horizontal and vertical lines passing through the given points.

17. $(-3, 0)$
18. $(6, 1)$
19. $(-8, -3)$
20. $(0, -5)$
21. $(7, 5)$
22. $(7, 0)$
23. $(4, -2)$
24. $(-1, -3)$
25. $(-2, 6)$
26. $(3, -5)$
27. $(0, 4)$
28. $(-7, 1)$

Determine the slope of the line passing through each of the pairs of points in Exercises 29–36.

29. $(3, -2)$ and $(5, -8)$
30. $(5, 1)$ and $(-4, -2)$
31. $(5, 2)$ and $(1, 12)$
32. $(-1, -8)$ and $(3, 12)$
33. $(2, 7)$ and $(-1, -5)$
34. $(7, 2)$ and $(4, 8)$
35. $(-7, -1)$ and $(5, 2)$
36. $(2, -8)$ and $(12, -6)$

In Exercises 37–44, write the equation of the line passing through the given point and having the given slope m.

37. $(-5, 3)$ and $m = -2$
38. $(4, 7)$ and $m = 5$
39. $(6, -1)$ and $m = 3$
40. $(-2, -5)$ and $m = -1$
41. $(8, 2)$ and $m = -4$
42. $(1, -3)$ and $m = -2$
43. $(-4, -5)$ and $m = 1$
44. $(-2, 6)$ and $m = 3$

In Exercises 45–52, write the equation of the line passing through each of the given pairs of points.

45. $(3, 1)$ and $(5, 5)$
46. $(-4, -2)$ and $(2, 10)$
47. $(4, 6)$ and $(-8, -2)$
48. $(1, 5)$ and $(4, 3)$
49. $(-4, -2)$ and $(6, 8)$
50. $(7, -2)$ and $(3, -1)$
51. $(5, -1)$ and $(3, -9)$
52. $(2, 6)$ and $(-2, -10)$

In Exercises 53–60, find the slope and y intercept of the lines having the given equation.

53. $y = 4 - 6x$
54. $y = 3x + 8$
55. $y = 7$
56. $2x - 4y = 5$
57. $3x + 2y = -4$
58. $x = -3$
59. $5x - 3y = 8$
60. $x + 3y = 7$

In Exercises 61–68, find the equation of the line through the given point and parallel to the line having the given equation.

61. $(3, -1)$ and $y = 4x + 2$
62. $(-3, 5)$ and $y = 3 - 2x$
63. $(-2, 5)$ and $y = 1 - 6x$
64. $(4, -2)$ and $y = 5x - 3$
65. $(2, 5)$ and $x = -6$
66. $(2, 3)$ and $3x - 2y = 6$
67. $(-1, -4)$ and $2x + 5y = 4$
68. $(-3, -7)$ and $y = 8$

Two lines are perpendicular if either one line is horizontal and the other is vertical or the product of the slopes of the two lines is -1. For Exercises 69–76, find the equation of the line through the given point and perpendicular to the line whose equation is given in Exercises 61–68.

77. A car can be rented from one company for $15.00 per day and $0.20 per mile and from a second company for $20.00 per day and $0.10 per mile. Which option is less expensive for a one-day rental if 80 miles are to be driven?

2.3 Market Equilibrium and Break-Even Analysis

In this section we discuss two important situations in which linear functions commonly occur—in analyzing the effect of supply and demand on price and in determining the level of production needed for revenues to equal costs. Although these two applications arise in different contexts (the first in economics and the second in business), both involve the same mathematical process, that of finding the point at which the graphs of two functions intersect.

Supply, Demand, and Market Prices

At the heart of the private enterprise system is an interaction among supply, demand, and market price. For each product or service available, price adjusts according to changes in the supply or demand for the item, and changes in price similarly influence the supply and demand. As the price of an item increases, the demand for the item normally decreases; hence demand is usually a decreasing function of price. On the other hand, as the price of an item increases, suppliers are willing to provide more of the item; thus supply is usually an increasing function of price.

Suppose that at a selling price p the supply of a product or service is $S(p)$ and the demand for the product or service is $D(p)$. Then the graphs of the functions $q = S(p)$ and $q = D(p)$ will have the general appearance of those shown in Figure 2.16.[4]

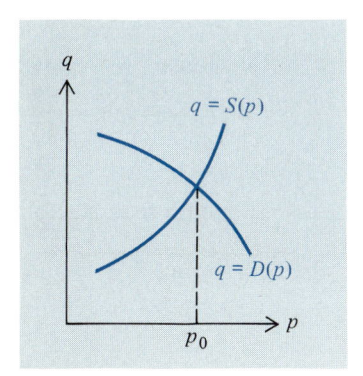

Figure 2.16

equilibrium price

In Figure 2.16 there is only one value at which price will be stable; this is the value p_0, called the *equilibrium price*, at which the supply and demand are equal. At prices greater than p_0, supply exceeds demand; hence suppliers will have to lower the selling price in order to find buyers. Similarly, at prices less than p_0, demand exceeds supply; so in this case buyers will have to offer higher prices in order to find suppliers. Thus the market price for the item will eventually reach its equilibrium value. When this occurs, the price will remain unchanged

---

[4] In Figure 2.16 we have followed standard mathematical practice and graphed the independent variable (price) along the horizontal axis and the dependent variable (quantity) along the vertical axis. Economists usually reverse this procedure and graph price along the vertical axis and quantity along the horizontal axis.

equilibrium supply
equilibrium demand

(unless there is a change in the supply or demand function), and the quantities bought and sold will likewise remain constant at the value $S(p_0) = D(p_0)$, called the *equilibrium supply* or *equilibrium demand*.

This theory of market equilibrium does not depend on any properties of the functions $q = S(p)$ and $q = D(p)$ other than that S and D are increasing and decreasing, respectively. Often, however, supply and demand can be approximated well by linear functions, and we assume in the example below and in the exercises in this section that both supply and demand are linear functions of price.

EXAMPLE 15

During a certain month the manufacturer of a certain kitchen utensil estimates that the demand for his product at price p (in dollars) will be given by

$$D(p) = 1200 - 150p$$

For this period the manufacturer is willing to supply $S(p)$ units of the utensil at a price of $3.00 or more per unit according to the function

$$S(p) = 300p - 600$$

To determine the equilibrium price for this utensil, we equate $S(p)$ and $D(p)$ and solve for p. Thus

$$300p - 600 = 1200 - 150p$$
$$450p = 1800$$
$$p = 4.00$$

So the equilibrium price is $4.00, and the equilibrium supply and equilibrium demand are

$$S(4.00) = 300(4.00) - 600 = 1200 - 600 = 600$$

Therefore the manufacturer can expect to sell 600 units of the utensil at a cost of $4.00 per unit during the month. (See Figure 2.17.)

Let us now consider how the imposition of a tax affects the equilibrium price. We assume that suppliers adjust their supply function to take the tax into account in the selling price. Thus only a portion of the selling price becomes revenue to the supplier; the remainder of the selling price pays the tax. For example, if a 5% sales tax is imposed on an item sold for $21 (tax included), then the supplier will receive only $20 in revenue and the government will receive $1 for the tax. In this context the number of units supplied is based on the revenue received per unit rather than on the selling price. Hence the supplier must make a downward adjustment in the supply curve to take the

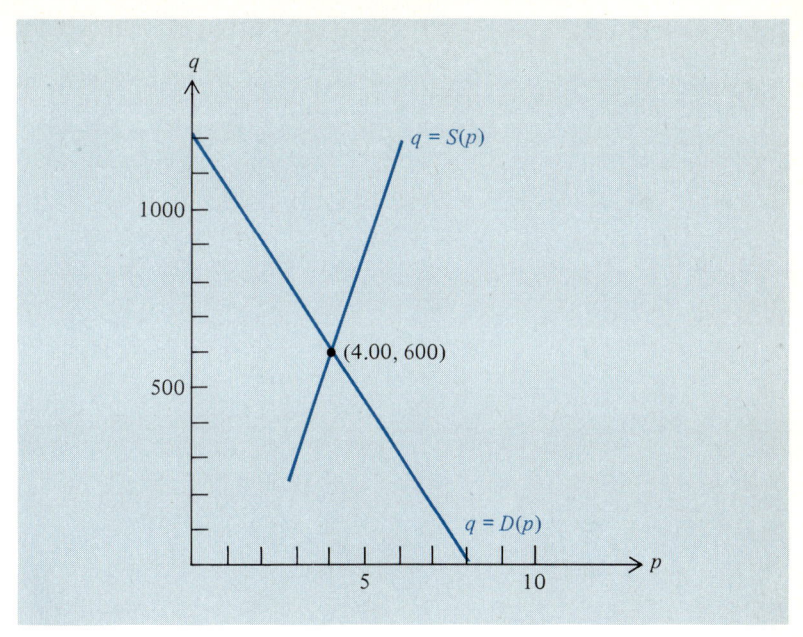

Figure 2.17

tax into account. The nature of this adjustment depends upon the type of tax levied.

Suppose that a sales tax is imposed at a rate r and that the selling price of each unit (including the tax) is p. Then u, the amount of revenue per unit received by the supplier, satisfies

$$p = u + ru = (1 + r)u$$

and so

$$u = \frac{1}{1+r} p$$

Since the supply function in this context is a function of u, the supply function before the tax is levied, $q = S(p)$, must be replaced by the new supply function $S_1(p) = S[(1/1 + r)p]$. This change will decrease the slope of the original supply function and will result in an increased equilibrium price and a decreased equilibrium demand.

EXAMPLE 16

Suppose that a 20% sales tax is imposed on the kitchen utensil in Example 15. Then the demand function will remain $D(p) = 1200 - 150p$, but the new supply function $S_1(p)$ will be

$$S_1(p) = S\left(\frac{1}{1.20} p\right) = 300\left(\frac{1}{1.20} p\right) - 600 = 250p - 600$$

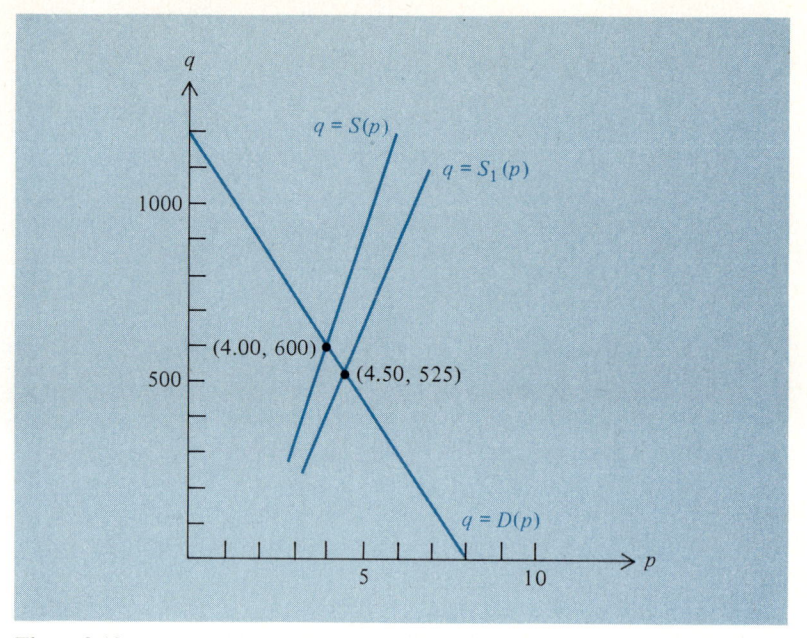

Figure 2.18

Equating $S_1(p)$ and $D(p)$ allows us to find the equilibrium price as before:

$$250p - 600 = 1200 - 150p$$
$$400p = 1800$$
$$p = 4.50$$

So after the tax is imposed, the equilibrium price will be $4.50 and the equilibrium supply will be $S_1(4.50) = 525$. (See Figure 2.18.)

stamp tax

Although a sales tax is the most common form of tax imposed on an item, another form of tax called a *stamp tax* is occasionally used. Unlike a sales tax, the amount of which varies according to the selling price of an item, a stamp tax assesses a fixed amount of tax on each item irrespective of its selling price. The most familiar example of a stamp tax is the tax on gasoline, in which case a fixed amount (ranging from $0.05 to $0.11 per gallon depending on location) is assessed on each gallon of gasoline regardless of the selling price. As with a sales tax, the supply function before the tax $S(p)$ must be modified because of the tax. But in this context the new supply function will be $S(p - t)$, where t is the fixed amount of the stamp tax.

EXAMPLE 17

Suppose that a $0.60 stamp tax is imposed on the kitchen utensil in Example 15. Then the demand function will remain $D(p) =$

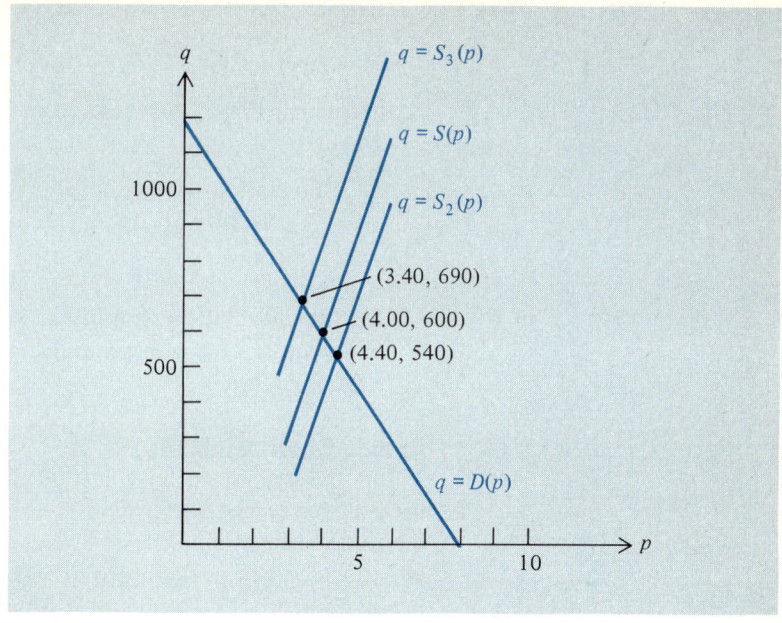

Figure 2.19

1200 − 150p, but the new supply function $S_2(p)$ will be

$$S_2(p) = S(p - 0.60) = 300(p - 0.60) - 600 = 300p - 780$$

By equating $S_2(p)$ and $D(p)$, we can find the new equilibrium price:

$$300p - 780 = 1200 - 150p$$
$$450p = 1980$$
$$p = 4.40$$

Thus after the stamp tax is imposed, the equilibrium price is $4.40 and the equilibrium supply is $S_2(4.40) = 540$. (See Figure 2.19.)

A government subsidy for the production of each unit of a particular item may be regarded as a negative stamp tax. For example, if the government provides a $1.00 subsidy for the production of each unit of an item, then the supply function for the item will be changed from $S(p)$ to $S(p + 1.00)$, just as though a stamp tax of $t = -\$1.00$ had been levied. The effect of a subsidy, of course, is to decrease the equilibrium price and increase the equilibrium demand.

EXAMPLE 18

Suppose that the government grants a $0.90 subsidy on each of the kitchen utensils in Example 15. Then the demand function will remain $D(p) = 1200 - 150p$, but the new supply function $S_3(p)$

will be

$$S_3(p) = S(p + 0.90) = 300(p + 0.90) - 600 = 300p - 330$$

As usual, the equilibrium price is found by equating $S_3(p)$ and $D(p)$:

$$300p - 330 = 1200 - 150p$$
$$450p = 1530$$
$$p = 3.40$$

So the effect of the subsidy is to lower the equilibrium price to $3.40 and increase the equilibrium supply to $S_3(3.40) = 690$. (See Figure 2.19.)

Break-Even Analysis

In theory, as we have just seen, the supply and demand for a product (or service) determine its market price. In practice, however, the demand function is rarely known, and prices are set in other ways, two of which will be described in Section 2.4. Suppose that a company produces a product it sells at a price of $6 per unit. Then the total revenue in dollars received from the sale of x units of the product is given by the function

$$R(x) = 6x$$

which is obviously linear.[5]

Costs, however, are usually related to the number of units produced in a more complicated manner. Nevertheless, for many purposes it is possible to approximate the total production cost $C(x)$ with a linear function of x, the number of units produced. For such a function

$$C(x) = mx + b$$

fixed cost

the value of b is independent of the level of production. Thus b equals the *fixed cost* of production, which reflects such expenses as insurance, depreciation, and supervisory personnel. On the other hand, the value of the term mx depends on the level of production. Hence mx equals

variable cost

the *variable cost* of production, which reflects such expenses as raw materials and labor involved directly with the manufacture of the

variable cost per unit

product. In this case the value of m represents the *variable cost per unit*, the cost of manufacturing each additional unit of the product.

EXAMPLE 19

A manufacturer has found the total cost of producing 300 units of a certain product is $4600 and that the total cost of producing 600 units of this product is $7000. Determine the total cost $C(x)$

---

[5] Theoretically, linear revenue functions occur only in the case of constant demand. For many purposes, however, approximating the revenue function by a linear function is appropriate. See, for example, [3].

2.3 Market Equilibrium and Break-Even Analysis

of producing x units of this product assuming that $C(x)$ is a linear function of x.

Since $C(x)$ is a linear function, the graph of $y = C(x)$ is a line passing through the points (300, 4600) and (600, 7000). The equation of this line can be found (as in Example 12) by computing the slope and using the point-slope form of the equation of a line. Since the slope of the line is

$$m = \frac{7000 - 4600}{600 - 300} = \frac{2400}{300} = 8$$

the equation of the line is

$$y - 4600 = 8(x - 300)$$

or

$$y = 8x + 2200$$

Thus the total cost of producing x units of this product is given by

$$C(x) = 8x + 2200 \quad \text{dollars}$$

So for this product the fixed cost is $2200 and the variable cost per unit is $8.

break-even quantity

Because of the presence of a fixed cost, for low levels of production the total cost of production will exceed the revenue generated from this production. In the case of linear revenue and cost functions, however, whenever the selling price is greater than the variable cost per unit, a point will be reached at which the total revenue will exceed the total cost for all higher levels of production. The level of production at which the total revenue and total cost are equal is called the *break-even quantity*. At levels of production below the break-even quantity, total costs exceed total revenues, and so the manufacturer is operating at a loss; on the other hand, at levels of production above the break-even quantity, total revenues exceed total costs, and so the company is operating at a profit.

EXAMPLE 20

A manufacturer produces a product for sale at a price of $5 per unit. For this product the manufacturer's fixed cost is $1600 and her variable cost per unit is $3. Determine

(a) The revenue, cost, and profit functions
(b) The break-even quantity
(c) The level of production required to earn a profit of $3000

(a) Since the selling price of the product is $5 per unit, the total revenue $R(x)$ (in dollars) at a production level of x units is

$$R(x) = 5x$$

Moreover, the total cost $C(x)$ (in dollars) at a production level of x units is

$$C(x) = 3x + 1600$$

the sum of fixed cost ($1600) and variable cost ($3x$ dollars). Finally, the total profit $P(x)$ (in dollars) at a production level of x units is the difference between the total revenue and the total cost at this level of production. Hence

$$P(x) = R(x) - C(x) = 5x - (3x + 1600) = 2x - 1600$$

(b) To find the break-even quantity, we must determine the value of x at which total revenue equals total cost. Thus we equate $R(x)$ and $C(x)$ and solve for x:

$$R(x) = C(x)$$
$$5x = 3x + 1600$$
$$2x = 1600$$
$$x = 800$$

Therefore the break-even quantity is 800 units.

(c) In order to earn a profit of $3000, we must have $P(x) = 3000$. This equation can be solved for x to find the level of production required:

$$P(x) = 3000$$
$$2x - 1600 = 3000$$
$$2x = 4600$$
$$x = 2300$$

So the production (and sale) of 2300 units will yield a profit of $3000.

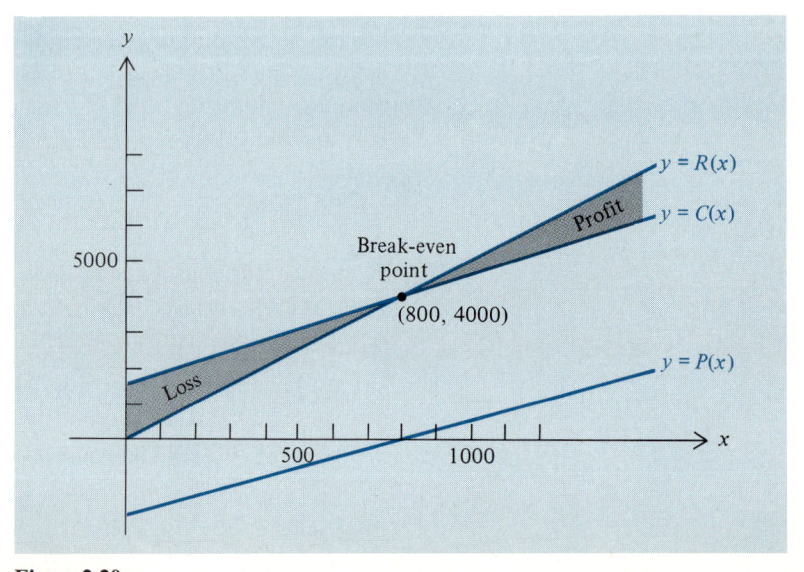

Figure 2.20

The total cost and total revenue functions in Example 20 are shown in Figure 2.20. Such a diagram is called a *break-even chart*. The point at which the graphs of $y = R(x)$ and $y = C(x)$ intersect is called the *break-even point*, and the first coordinate of this point is the break-even quantity.

break-even chart

break-even point

In Figure 2.20 the graph of the profit function in Example 20 is shown also. Notice that the break-even quantity is the x intercept of the graph of the profit function.

Exercises

In Exercises 1–8, find the equilibrium price and demand (supply) for the following demand and supply functions $D(p)$ and $S(p)$, respectively.

1. $D(p) = 4500 - 500p$, $S(p) = 250p$
2. $D(p) = 7000 - 200p$, $S(p) = 300p$
3. $D(p) = 1200 - 60p$, $S(p) = 100p$
4. $D(p) = 9900 - 400p$, $S(p) = 800p$
5. $D(p) = 1500 - 100p$, $S(p) = 400p - 2000$, for $p \geq 6.00$
6. $D(p) = 15{,}300 - 450p$, $S(p) = 300p - 2700$, for $p \geq 12.00$
7. $D(p) = 5040 - 280p$, $S(p) = 220p - 1660$, for $p \geq 8.00$
8. $D(p) = 19{,}000 - 7600p$, $S(p) = 2400p - 1800$, for $p \geq 1.00$

In Exercises 9–16, determine how the equilibrium price and demand (supply) in Exercises 1–8 change if the government grants a subsidy or imposes a tax as indicated below.

9. Subsidy of $3.00 per unit
10. Tax of $0.50 per unit
11. Tax of $0.80 per unit
12. Subsidy of $1.875 per unit
13. Tax of $0.50 per unit
14. Subsidy of $2.00 per unit
15. Subsidy of $5.00 per unit
16. Tax of $0.50 per unit

In Exercises 17–20, use the given demand and supply functions $D(p)$ and $S(p)$ to compute the equilibrium price and demand (supply) before and after the imposition of a sales tax of r.

17. $D(p) = 2400 - 280p$, $S(p) = 220p$, $r = 10\%$
18. $D(p) = 2520 - 200p$, $S(p) = 520p$, $r = 4\%$
19. $D(p) = 1800 - 120p$, $S(p) = 630p$, $r = 5\%$
20. $D(p) = 88{,}800 - 48p$, $S(p) = 102p$, $r = 2\%$

21. (a) A manufacturer has found that the demand for one of his products is 1600 units when the price per unit is $8 and is 1000 units when the price per unit is $10. If the manufacturer is willing to supply $S(p) = 200p - 1200$ units at any price p exceeding $7 per unit, determine the equilibrium price and supply if demand is a linear function of p.
    (b) How are the equilibrium price and supply in part (a) changed if the demand for the product is only 800 units (instead of 1000 units) when the price per unit is $10?

22. (a) A manufacturer is willing to supply 800 units of a product at a price per unit of $6 and 1200 units at a price per unit of $7. The manufacturer has found that the demand for the product is 7100 units at a

price of $6 per unit and 6800 units at a price of $7 per unit. If the supply and demand functions are both linear, determine the equilibrium price and demand.
(b) How are the equilibrium price and demand in part (a) changed if the manufacturer is only willing to supply 700 units (instead of 800 units) when the price is $6 per unit?

Determine $R(x)$, the revenue received from the sale of x units of an item, and $C(x)$, the total cost of producing x units of an item, under the conditions given in Exercises 23–30.

23. Selling price, $7; fixed cost, $830; variable cost per unit, $4.
24. Selling price, $14; fixed cost, $1560; variable cost per unit, $11.
25. Selling price, $8; fixed cost, $1250; variable cost per unit, $6.
26. Selling price, $6; fixed cost, $240; variable cost per unit, $5.
27. Selling price, $9.50; fixed cost, $1600; variable cost per unit, $7.80.
28. Selling price, $4.75; fixed cost, $950; variable cost per unit, $3.25.
29. Selling price, $5.80; fixed cost, $1125; variable cost per unit, $4.00.
30. Selling price, $7.50; fixed cost, $880; variable cost per unit, $6.20.

Determine the fixed cost and the variable cost per unit for a linear cost function under the conditions given in Exercises 31–38.

31. The cost of producing 0 items is $2100, and the cost of producing 100 items is $2800.
32. The cost of producing 100 items is $2100, and the cost of producing 400 items is $3900.
33. The cost of producing 200 items is $3800, and the cost of producing 600 items is $5000.
34. The cost of producing 150 items is $3700, and the cost of producing 500 items is $6500.
35. The cost of producing 50 items is $1950, and the cost of producing 250 items is $2950.
36. The cost of producing 100 items is $4000, and the cost of producing 300 items is $7200.
37. The cost of producing 300 items is $6300, and the cost of producing 600 items is $9900.
38. The cost of producing 100 items is $3300, and the cost of producing 600 items is $10,800.

In Exercises 39–46, determine the break-even quantity and construct a break-even chart for the given revenue and cost functions $R(x)$ and $C(x)$.

39. $R(x) = 6x$, $C(x) = 2x + 3600$
40. $R(x) = 8x$, $C(x) = 5x + 4200$
41. $R(x) = 7x$, $C(x) = 3x + 4800$
42. $R(x) = 15x$, $C(x) = 7x + 6000$
43. $R(x) = 12x$, $C(x) = 10x + 3200$
44. $R(x) = 6x$, $C(x) = 3x + 3900$
45. $R(x) = 20x$, $C(x) = 11x + 5400$
46. $R(x) = 12x$, $C(x) = 7x + 5500$

47. A manufacturer produces a product for sale at a price of $12 per unit. For this product the fixed cost is $4400 and the variable cost per unit is $8. Determine
   (a) The revenue, cost, and profit functions
   (b) The break-even quantity

(c) The level of production required to earn a profit of $3600
(d) The break-even quantity if the variable cost per unit is $10 (instead of $8)

48. A manufacturer produces a product for sale at a price of $13 per unit. For this product the fixed cost is $4650 and the variable cost per unit is $10. Determine
   (a) The revenue, cost, and profit functions
   (b) The break-even quantity
   (c) The level of production required to earn a profit of $1950
   (d) The break-even quantity if the fixed cost is $4200 (instead of $4650)

49. A manufacturer produces a product for sale at a price of $4.50 per unit. For this product the fixed cost is $1800.00 and the variable cost per unit is $3.00. Determine
   (a) The revenue, cost, and profit functions
   (b) The break-even quantity
   (c) The level of production required to earn a profit of $4200.
   (d) The break-even quantity if the price is $5.00 (instead of $4.50)

50. A manufacturer produces a product for sale at a price of $7 per unit. For this product the fixed cost is $2100 and the variable cost per unit is $5. Determine
   (a) The revenue, cost, and profit functions
   (b) The break-even quantity
   (c) The level of production required to earn a profit of $1800
   (d) The break-even quantity if the variable cost per unit is $4 (instead of $5)

51. The owners of a country club can manage the club for fixed costs of $15,000 and variable costs of $40 per member. The owners can also hire a management firm to run the club at fixed costs of $21,000 and variable costs of $35 per member.
   (a) If the club has 1000 members, which option allows the club to be run more economically?
   (b) If the club has 1500 members, which option allows the club to be run more economically?
   (c) At what level of membership do the two options cost the same amount?

*2.4 Further Applications of Linear Functions

In this section we present several additional business and economic applications involving linear functions. The simple economic model in Section 2.3 for establishing the market price of an item requires that the supply and demand functions for the item be known. In practice, these functions are never known with certainty, and con-

---

* A section number preceded by an asterisk indicates that the section may be omitted without loss of continuity.

sequently other methods for determining the price of an item are used. We began by examining two cost-oriented methods of pricing.

Markup Pricing

Retail outlets purchase goods from manufacturers or suppliers and sell them to consumers. In order to pay expenses and earn a profit, the retailer must price his merchandise above the cost at which it was purchased. This difference between the retailer's selling price and his cost is called a *markup*. For the year 1965, typical department store markup rates were 28% for cameras, 34% for books, 41% for dresses, and 46% for costume jewelry. Such pricing policies make selling price a linear function of cost.

markup

EXAMPLE 21

Suppose that a gift shop normally determines the selling price of its items by adding a 38% markup to its cost. Then the selling price $S(c)$ of an item costing c is given by

$$S(c) = c + 0.38c = 1.38c$$

a linear function. Hence an item costing $3.50 would be priced at

$$S(\$3.50) = 1.38(\$3.50) = \$4.83$$

Target Pricing

In target pricing, manufacturers price their products so as to achieve a specified target rate of return on their total costs. Target pricing policies are frequently used by public utilities, but such policies are most often associated with General Motors, which has stated that its automobile prices are established so that the average rate of return on its investment will be between 15 and 20%.

To use target pricing, a manufacturer must make an estimate of the expected sales volume and the total cost at that level of production. Suppose that the expected sales volume is q and the total production cost for q units is c. If the company desires a net return of r percent, then the revenue received for selling q units must be

$$c + rc = c(1 + r)$$

To ensure this rate of return, the manufacturer will then choose his total revenue function to be a linear function passing through the points

$$(0, 0) \quad \text{and} \quad (q, c(1 + r))$$

The slope of this revenue function will be the price at which one unit must be sold to achieve the desired rate of return.

EXAMPLE 22

A company would like to use target pricing to ensure a return of 15% based on sales of 100,000 items. If the total cost of producing 100,000 items is $2,000,000, then the revenue required from the sale of 100,000 units must be $2,300,000 in order to have a 15% return. Hence the revenue function will be a linear function such that its graph passes through the points

$$(0, 0) \quad \text{and} \quad (100{,}000,\ 2{,}300{,}000)$$

Thus the total revenue function will be

$$R(x) = 23x \quad \text{dollars}$$

So the price per unit should be set at $23.

Linear Depreciation

Businesses acquire fixed assets such as land and equipment for use in revenue-producing operations. Because fixed assets other than land have limited lifetimes, there is an expense that results from the acquisition and use of assets in producing revenue. Such an expense is called a *depreciation expense* and must be taken into account when measuring the earnings of a business.

depreciation expense

linear method of depreciation

There are several common methods for estimating depreciation, the simplest of which is called the *linear* (or *straight-line*) *method*. This method is one of the permissible ways of computing depreciation for tax purposes, but it is rarely used for this purpose by large businesses because other methods are available that have the effect of postponing the payment of taxes. The linear method, however, is often used in the preparation of financial statements.

With the linear method, the total amount to be depreciated is allocated equally throughout the life of the asset. Suppose, for instance, that a particular item has been purchased at a cost C. If the item is expected to have a useful life of n years and a salvage (or scrap) value S, then the net cost of the item (which is the total amount to be depreciated) is $C - S$. Hence the amount D to be depreciated each year is

$$D = \frac{C - S}{n} \tag{2.6}$$

book value

The cost of purchase minus the accumulated depreciation is called the *book value* of the item.

EXAMPLE 23

Use the linear method of depreciation to find the book value after 5 years for an item purchased at a cost of $32,000 that is expected to have a useful life of 12 years and a salvage value of $2000.

The amount to be depreciated each year is

$$D = \frac{C - S}{n} = \frac{\$32{,}000 - \$2000}{12} = \$2500$$

Thus after 5 years, the accumulated depreciation is

$$5(\$2500) = \$12{,}500$$

So the book value of the item after 5 years will be

$$\$32{,}000 - \$12{,}500 = \$19{,}500$$

Financial Leverage

Often a firm is faced with the problem of determining how to finance new investment proposals, that is, determining how to allocate its capital so as to minimize the cost of financing new ventures. Firms can usually obtain funds at a fixed cost by issuing shares of common stock, issuing shares of preferred stock, or borrowing at a fixed rate of interest. *Favorable financial leverage* is said to have been obtained if the assets purchased with these funds contribute more to the firm's earnings than the fixed cost of raising the funds. Whether or not financial leverage is favorable is determined by the effect of the use of the funds on the earnings per share of the firm.

In analyzing financial leverage to determine the best method for obtaining funds, we must examine the way in which the various financing options influence the relationship between the firm's earnings before interest and taxes (EBIT) and earnings per share (EPS) of common stock. To illustrate the ideas involved, we consider a company having a capitalization of $20 million from 500,000 shares of common stock at $40 per share and a 50% federal income tax rate. Suppose that the company wishes to raise an additional $4 million in capital by one of the following methods:

1. Issuing 100,000 additional shares of common stock at a price of $40 per share
2. Issuing preferred stock with an 8% dividend
3. Borrowing at 10% annual interest

Table 2.1 shows the calculation of EPS for each of the three options when EBIT is $3 million.[6]

Using the information in Table 2.1, we can now construct an *indifference chart* similar to the break-even charts in Section 2.3. An indifference chart is constructed by plotting EBIT along the horizontal axis and EPS along the vertical axis. For each of the three options the graph of EPS as a function of EBIT will be a line. Hence

---

[6] The assumption that EBIT is $3 million is completely arbitrary. We are interested here in the ratio of EPS to EBIT, and this ratio will not change even if a different value of EBIT is chosen.

2.4 Further Applications of Linear Functions

Table 2.1 *Calculation of Earnings per Share*

	Option 1	Option 2	Option 3
EBIT	$3,000,000	$3,000,000	$3,000,000
Interest on borrowed money	—	—	−400,000
Earnings before taxes	3,000,000	3,000,000	2,600,000
Federal income tax	−1,500,000	−1,500,000	−1,300,000
Earnings after taxes	1,500,000	1,500,000	1,300,000
Dividend on preferred stock	—	−320,000	—
Earnings available to common stockholders	1,500,000	1,180,000	1,300,000
Number of outstanding shares of common stock	600,000	500,000	500,000
EPS	2.50	2.36	2.60

we need only two points to determine each graph. For each option, one of these points is provided by Table 2.1: (3, 2.50) for the first option, (3, 2.36) for the second option, and (3, 2.60) for the third option. The second point on each graph can be found by determining EBIT required to pay the annual fixed costs for each option; these values will be the horizontal intercepts of each graph. For the first option there are no fixed costs, and so the point (0, 0) lies on its graph. For the second option there must be EBIT of $640,000 (the total dividend on the preferred stock divided by $1 - r$, where r is the tax rate) to pay the $320,000 dividend, and so the point (0.64, 0) lies on its graph. For the third option there must be EBIT of $400,000 to pay the interest on the borrowed money, and so the point (0.4, 0) lies on its graph. Therefore the indifference chart for these three options is as shown in Figure 2.21.

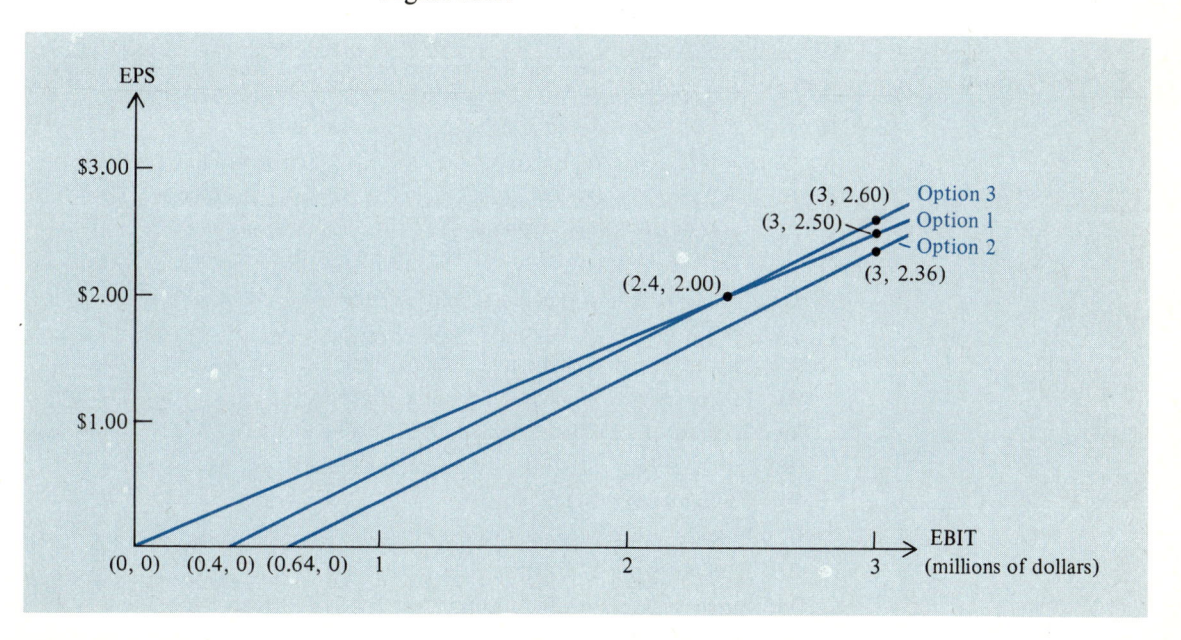

Figure 2.21

In Figure 2.21 we see that the EPS resulting from the first option is higher than those of the other options when EBIT is less than $2.4 million, but that the EPS resulting from the third option is higher than those of the other options when EBIT is greater than $2.4 million. Thus we see that, if the firm's EBIT is less than $2.4 million, the additional capital should be raised using the first option, whereas if EBIT exceeds $2.4 million, the additional capital should be raised using the third option. The value of EBIT at which the EPS is the same for the first and third options (namely, $2.4 million) is called the *EPS indifference point* between these two options.

EPS indifference point

It is interesting to note that in Figure 2.21 the graphs for the second and third options are parallel lines. As a result, the third option always produces a higher EPS than the second option. In general, the indifference chart for a preferred stock option and a borrowing option will consist of two parallel lines with slope $(1 - r)/s$, where r is the tax rate and s is the number of shares of stock outstanding. Which of the two options results in the higher earnings per share will depend on the preferred stock dividend rate, the interest rate at which money is borrowed, and the tax rate.

Exercises

In Exercises 1–8, determine the selling price $S(c)$ of an item costing c dollars if a retail store determines its selling price by using each of the following markups.

1. 42%
2. 36%
3. 30%
4. 34%
5. 45%
6. 41%
7. 27%
8. 31%

In Exercises 9–16, determine the revenue $R(x)$ derived from the sale of x units of a product if the manufacturer uses target pricing to ensure a return of r when q units are produced at production costs of c dollars.

9. $r = 0.20$, $q = 1200$, $c = 7500$
10. $r = 0.10$, $q = 1100$, $c = 3000$
11. $r = 0.15$, $q = 4600$, $c = 20{,}000$
12. $r = 0.25$, $q = 1600$, $c = 8000$
13. $r = 0.30$, $q = 800$, $c = 2000$
14. $r = 0.20$, $q = 900$, $c = 4500$
15. $r = 0.18$, $q = 6000$, $c = 30{,}000$
16. $r = 0.12$, $q = 2240$, $c = 9000$

Use the linear method of depreciation to determine the book value after 4 years for an asset satisfying the conditions given in Exercises 17–24.

17. Purchase price, $3800; salvage value, $200; life, 12 years.
18. Purchase price, $6500; salvage value, $500; life, 15 years.
19. Purchase price, $8000; salvage value, $800; life, 6 years.
20. Purchase price, $19,500; salvage value, $300; life, 8 years.
21. Purchase price, $4000; salvage value, $0; life, 5 years.
22. Purchase price, $16,000; salvage value, $1000; life, 6 years.
23. Purchase price, $18,000; salvage value, $2000; life, 10 years.
24. Purchase price, $6500; salvage value, $200; life, 9 years.
25. In the financial leverage example described on page 38, suppose that the income tax rate is changed from 50 to 20% and the interest rate is changed from 10 to $11\tfrac{1}{4}$%.

(a) In this case what is the EPS indifference point?
(b) Which of the three options for raising capital is preferable if EBIT equals $2 million?
(c) Which of the three options for raising capital is preferable if EBIT equals $3 million?

26. A company with a capitalization of $800,000 from 40,000 shares of common stock wants to raise an additional $200,000. If the company's tax rate is 50%, calculate the EPS based on an EBIT of $100,000 (as in Table 2.1) for the following three options.
    (i) Issuing 10,000 additional shares of common stock at $20 per share
    (ii) Issuing preferred stock with a 6% dividend
    (iii) Borrowing at 8% annual interest

27. (a) Using the data in Exercise 26 determine the EPS indifference point between options (i) and (iii).
    (b) Construct an indifference chart for the three options.
    (c) Which of the options is preferable if EBIT equals $50,000?
    (d) Which of the options is preferable if EBIT equals $90,000?

28. A company with a capitalization of $8 million from 200,000 shares of common stock wants to raise an additional $2 million using one of the following methods:
    (i) Issuing 50,000 additional shares of common stock at $40 per share
    (ii) Issuing preferred stock with a 10% dividend
    (iii) Borrowing at 12% annual interest

    Construct an indifference chart for the three options if the company's tax rate is 50% and determine
    (a) The EPS indifference point between options (i) and (iii)
    (b) Which of the options is preferable if EBIT equals $1 million
    (c) Which of the options is preferable if EBIT equals $1.8 million

29. A company with a capitalization of $40 million from 800,000 shares of common stock wants to raise an additional $10 million using one of the following methods:
    (i) Issuing 200,000 additional shares of common stock at $50 per share
    (ii) Issuing preferred stock with an 8% dividend
    (iii) Borrowing at 11% annual interest

    Construct an indifference chart for the three options if the company's tax rate is 20% and determine
    (a) The EPS indifference point between options (i) and (ii)
    (b) Which of the options is preferable if EBIT equals $2 million
    (c) Which of the options is preferable if EBIT equals $6 million

30. A company with a capitalization of $1.8 million from 90,000 shares of common stock wants to raise an additional $0.2 million using one of the following methods:
    (i) Issuing 10,000 additional shares of common stock at $20 per share
    (ii) Issuing preferred stock with a 9% dividend
    (iii) Borrowing at 11% annual interest

    Construct an indifference chart for the three options if the company's tax rate is 10% and determine
    (a) The EPS indifference point between options (i) and (ii)
    (b) Which of the options is preferable if EBIT equals $0.15 million
    (c) Which of the options is preferable if EBIT equals $0.35 million

31. Compute the equations of the three lines in Figure 2.21 and verify that (2.40, 2.00) is the EPS indifference point between the first and third options.

Chapter Review

New Terms

book value (p. 37)
break-even chart (p. 32)
break-even point (p. 32)
break-even quantity (p. 31)
coordinates (p. 9)
dependent variable (p. 7)
depreciation expense (p. 37)
earnings-per-share indifference point (p. 40)
equilibrium demand (p. 26)
equilibrium price (p. 25)
equilibrium supply (p. 26)
favorable financial leverage (p. 38)
fixed cost (p. 30)
function (p. 6)
general form of the equation of a line (p. 17)
graph of a function (p. 8)
independent variable (p. 7)
indifference chart (p. 38)

intercept(s) (p. 11)
linear function (p. 16)
linear method of depreciation (p. 37)
markup (p. 36)
point-slope form of the equation of a line (p. 22)
rectangular coordinate system (p. 8)
slope of a line (p. 20)
slope-intercept form of the equation of a line (p. 23)
stamp tax (p. 28)
variable cost (p. 30)
variable cost per unit (p. 30)
x axis (p. 8)
x coordinate (p. 9)
x intercept (p. 11)
y axis (p. 8)
y coordinate (p. 9)
y intercept (p. 11)

Review Exercises

1. Label the following statements true or false.
   (a) To find the x intercept(s) of an equation involving the variables x and y, set $x = 0$ and solve for y.
   (b) If $s = g(t)$, then s is the independent variable and t is the dependent variable.
   (c) To graph a function $f(x)$ means to graph the equation $y = f(x)$.
   (d) The graph of any equation of the form $ax + by = c$, where a, b, and c are constants and a and b are not both zero, is a line.
   (e) The graph of any equation of the form $x = c$, where c is a constant, is a horizontal line.
   (f) Two parallel lines must have the same slope.
   (g) The line with equation $y = mx + b$ has slope b and y intercept m.
   (h) The equilibrium price is the price at which supply and demand are equal.
   (i) If a tax is levied on a previously untaxed item, then the equilibrium price will increase and the equilibrium supply will decrease.
   (j) If $C(x) = mx + b$ represents the total cost of producing x items, then the fixed cost of production is b and the variable cost is m.
   (k) The break-even quantity is the level of production at which revenue equals cost.

2. Determine all the intercepts of each of the following functions.
   (a) $f(x) = \frac{1}{2}x - 4$
   (b) $g(x) = 7$
   (c) $h(x) = \sqrt{x + 3}$
   (d) $F(x) = 3x$
   (e) $G(x) = 2x^2 - 8$
   (f) $H(x) = -x^2 - 2x + 3$

3. For the functions $f(x) = 3x - 2$ and $g(x) = 2x^2 + 1$, compute
   (a) $f(5)$
   (b) $g(-4)$
   (c) $g(a)$
   (d) $f(a)$
   (e) $f(2a + 4)$
   (f) $g(2a + 3)$
   (g) $g(3a - 1)$
   (h) $f(\frac{1}{3}a - 5)$

4. Graph the following functions.
   (a) $f(x) = 400 - x^2$
   (b) $f(x) = 4x - 3$
   (c) $f(x) = 3$
   (d) $f(x) = \sqrt{2x}$

5. Determine the slope of the line passing through the following pairs of points.
   (a) $(9, 2)$ and $(1, -1)$
   (b) $(4, -3)$ and $(-5, -3)$
   (c) $(-4, -3)$ and $(1, 7)$
   (d) $(-6, 2)$ and $(4, -6)$

6. Write the equation of the line passing through the given point and having the given slope m.
   (a) $(5, -3)$ and $m = 4$
   (b) $(-1, 8)$ and $m = -2$
   (c) $(0, 6)$ and $m = -3$
   (d) $(-2, -3)$ and $m = 5$

7. Write the equation of the line passing through each of the following pairs of points.
   (a) $(-2, 8)$ and $(-2, -5)$
   (b) $(5, -3)$ and $(2, 9)$
   (c) $(-3, -7)$ and $(2, 8)$
   (d) $(-3, 7)$ and $(8, 7)$

8. Find the equilibrium price and equilibrium demand (supply) for the following demand and supply functions $D(p)$ and $S(p)$, respectively.
   (a) $D(p) = 2520 - 30p$, $S(p) = 42p$
   (b) $D(p) = 2800 - 200p$, $S(p) = 300p$
   (c) $D(p) = 3600 - 180p$, $S(p) = 120p$
   (d) $D(p) = 10{,}260 - 270p$, $S(p) = 330p$

9. Find the new equilibrium price and equilibrium demand for the corresponding parts of Exercise 8 under the following conditions.
   (a) A sales tax of 5% is levied.
   (b) A stamp tax of $0.40 per unit is assessed.
   (c) A subsidy of $0.50 per unit is granted.
   (d) A sales tax of 10% is imposed.

10. Determine the fixed cost and the variable cost per unit for a linear cost function for which the cost of producing 200 items is $3600 and the cost of producing 500 items is $5400.

11. Determine the break-even quantity and construct a break-even chart for the following revenue and cost functions $R(x)$ and $C(x)$, respectively.
    (a) $R(x) = 8x$, $C(x) = 5x + 2700$
    (b) $R(x) = 11x$, $C(x) = 7x + 4800$
    (c) $R(x) = 15x$, $C(x) = 10x + 5650$
    (d) $R(x) = 18x$, $C(x) = 12x + 5700$

12. A manufacturer produces a product for sale at a price of $10 per unit. For this product the fixed cost is $6000 and the variable cost per unit is $6.
    (a) Determine the revenue, cost, and profit functions.
    (b) Construct a break-even chart.
    (c) Compute the break-even quantity.
    (d) Determine the level of production required to earn a profit of $3000.

*13. An asset purchased for $12,500 is expected to have a salvage value of $500 and a life of 15 years.
   (a) Determine the amount to be depreciated each year using the linear method of depreciation.
   (b) Calculate the book value of the asset after 9 years.

*14. A company with capitalization of $400,000 from 20,000 shares of common stock wants to raise an additional $100,000 using one of the following methods:
   (i) Issuing 5000 additional shares of common stock at $20 per share
   (ii) Issuing preferred stock with an 8% dividend
   (iii) Borrowing at 10% annual interest

   Construct an indifference chart for the three options if the company's tax rate is 50%, and determine
   (a) The EPS indifference point between options (i) and (iii)
   (b) Which of the options is preferable if EBIT equals $30,000
   (c) Which of the options is preferable if EBIT equals $80,000

References

1. Brown, Judson S., "Gradients of Approach and Avoidance Responses and Their Relation to Level of Motivation," *J. Comp. Physiol. Psychol.*, vol. 41, no. 6 (December 1948), pp. 450–465.
2. Daus, Paul H. and William M. Whyburn, *Introduction to Mathematical Analysis*. Reading, Mass.: Addison-Wesley, 1958.
3. Hartl, Robert J., "The Linear Total Revenue Curve in Cost-Volume-Profit Analysis," *Manage. Account.* (New York), vol. 41, no. 9 (March 1975), pp. 49–52.
4. Kotler, Philip, *Marketing Management*, 3rd ed. Englewood Cliffs, N.J.: Prentice-Hall, 1976, pp. 256–257.
5. Van Horne, James C., *Financial Management and Policy*, 4th ed. Englewood Cliffs, N.J.: Prentice-Hall, 1977, Chapters 9, 10, and 27.

* Exercises denoted by an asterisk require familiarity with material in optional sections.

3

Matrices and Systems of Linear Equations

The first use of matrices is generally attributed to the English mathematician Arthur Cayley in 1858. The widespread use of matrices is much more recent, however. In fact, the development of high-speed computers capable of doing matrix calculations is the primary reason for the present use of matrices in business and the social sciences.

Matrices are closely related to systems of linear equations, a topic that has numerous applications. In this chapter we introduce matrices and the fundamental matrix operations and then apply matrices to the solution of systems of linear equations. Applications of these ideas to business and social science are presented in Sections 3.4 and 3.7.

3.1 Matrices

In recent years there has been a significant increase in the use of numerical data in agriculture, business, the life sciences, and the social sciences. Such data are usually categorized in two or more different ways and can be conveniently represented in tabular form. For example, data on the nutritional value of certain foods might be classified according to the type of food and the quantity of certain nutrients possessed. Such information might then be presented as in Table 3.1.

46 Chapter 3 Matrices and Systems of Linear Equations

Table 3.1 *Nutritional Value of 100 Grams of Selected Foods*

Food	Protein (grams)	Fat (grams)	Carbohydrates (grams)	Vitamin A (international units)	Thiamine (milligrams)	Riboflavin (milligrams)	Niacin (milligrams)
Mashed potatoes with milk	2.1	0.7	13.0	20	0.08	0.05	1.0
Cooked spinach	3.0	0.3	3.6	8,100	0.07	0.14	0.5
Raw carrots	1.1	0.2	9.7	11,000	0.06	0.05	0.6
Cooked lima beans	7.6	0.5	19.8	280	0.18	0.10	1.3
Solid tuna (canned in oil)	24.2	20.5	0.0	90	0.04	0.09	10.1
Steamed crab	17.3	1.9	0.5	2,170	0.16	0.08	2.8
Roasted chicken (light meat without skin)	23.4	1.9	0.0	60	0.05	0.09	10.7
Cooked beef rib (choice grade)	19.9	39.4	0.0	80	0.05	0.15	3.6
Cooked spareribs	19.7	42.5	0.0	0	0.40	0.19	3.2

Source: Bernice K. Watt and Annabel L. Merrill, *Composition of Foods, Agriculture Handbook Number 8*. Washington, D.C.: Consumer and Food Economics Research Division, United States Department of Agriculture, 1963.

When the row and column headings in Table 3.1 are removed, we are left with the rectangular array of numbers:

$$\begin{pmatrix} 2.1 & 0.7 & 13.0 & 20 & 0.08 & 0.05 & 1.0 \\ 3.0 & 0.3 & 3.6 & 8{,}100 & 0.07 & 0.14 & 0.5 \\ 1.1 & 0.2 & 9.7 & 11{,}000 & 0.06 & 0.05 & 0.6 \\ 7.6 & 0.5 & 19.8 & 280 & 0.18 & 0.10 & 1.3 \\ 24.2 & 20.5 & 0.0 & 90 & 0.04 & 0.09 & 10.1 \\ 17.3 & 1.9 & 0.5 & 2{,}170 & 0.16 & 0.08 & 2.8 \\ 23.4 & 1.9 & 0.0 & 60 & 0.05 & 0.09 & 10.7 \\ 19.9 & 39.4 & 0.0 & 80 & 0.05 & 0.15 & 3.6 \\ 19.7 & 42.5 & 0.0 & 0 & 0.40 & 0.19 & 3.2 \end{pmatrix} \qquad (3.1)$$

In general, any rectangular array of numbers having the form

$$\begin{pmatrix} a_{11} & a_{12} & \cdots & a_{1j} & \cdots & a_{1n} \\ a_{21} & a_{22} & \cdots & a_{2j} & \cdots & a_{2n} \\ \vdots & \vdots & & \vdots & & \vdots \\ a_{i1} & a_{i2} & \cdots & a_{ij} & \cdots & a_{in} \\ \vdots & \vdots & & \vdots & & \vdots \\ a_{m1} & a_{m2} & \cdots & a_{mj} & \cdots & a_{mn} \end{pmatrix} \qquad (3.2)$$

matrix
entries

is called a *matrix*, and the numbers a_{ij} ($i = 1, 2, \ldots, m$ and $j = 1, 2, \ldots, n$) are called the *entries* of the matrix. Throughout this book we denote matrices by capital italic letters. It will often be convenient to denote the matrix A of (3.2) by writing $A = (a_{ij})$, where $i = 1, 2, \ldots, m$ and $j = 1, 2,$

..., n. The entries

$$a_{i1} \quad a_{i2} \quad \cdots \quad a_{ij} \quad \cdots \quad a_{in}$$

ith row form the *ith row* of the matrix, and the entries

$$\begin{matrix} a_{ij} \\ a_{2j} \\ \vdots \\ a_{ij} \\ \vdots \\ a_{mj} \end{matrix}$$

jth column compose the *jth column* of the matrix. Observe that in (3.2) the sub-scripts of an entry designate its location; for instance, a_{ij} is the entry in
i, j entry of a matrix row i and column j. We refer to this entry as the i,j *entry* of A. The entries a_{11}, a_{22}, a_{33}, and so forth, for which the row number and column number are the same form the *diagonal* (also called the *main* or *principal*
diagonal *diagonal*) of the matrix. The diagonals of the matrices below are denoted in italics.

$$\begin{pmatrix} 3 & 4 & -2 \\ 1 & -1 & 2 \end{pmatrix} \quad \begin{pmatrix} 2 & 0 & -1 \\ 1 & -3 & 2 \\ -4 & 5 & 1 \end{pmatrix} \quad \text{and} \quad \begin{pmatrix} 1 & 2 & 0 \\ 0 & -5 & 3 \\ 3 & -1 & 2 \\ -2 & 4 & 1 \end{pmatrix}$$

size of a matrix The *size* of a matrix is determined by the number of rows and columns it contains; a matrix such as (3.2) having m rows and n columns
$m \times n$ matrix is called an $m \times n$ (read "m by n") matrix. Notice that the number of rows is listed first in the size and the number of columns is listed second. For example, the matrices

$$\begin{pmatrix} 2 & -1 & 3 \\ 4 & 0 & 5 \end{pmatrix} \quad \begin{pmatrix} 1 \\ -3 \\ 2 \\ 0 \end{pmatrix} \quad (1 \quad 7) \quad \begin{pmatrix} -2 & 1 & 3 \\ 4 & 0 & 1 \\ -2 & -1 & -5 \\ 3 & 6 & 0 \end{pmatrix}$$

and

$$\begin{pmatrix} 1 & -1 & 2 \\ 4 & 1 & 1 \\ 0 & -3 & 2 \end{pmatrix} \tag{3.3}$$

are of sizes 2×3, 4×1, 1×2, 4×3, and 3×3, respectively. Matrices containing only one row or only one column are usually called *row*
row and column vectors *vectors* and *column vectors*, respectively. In addition, a matrix having
square matrix the same number of rows as columns is said to be *square*. Thus of the

matrices in (3.3) the second is a column vector, the third is a row vector, and the fifth is square.

EXAMPLE 1

In 1972 there were 10,750 hotels, 27,739 motels, and 2348 motor hotels in the United States. The total number of rooms each type of business had available was 755,000 for the hotels, 1,034,000 for the motels, and 206,000 for the motor hotels.[1] This information can be recorded as the 2 × 3 matrix

$$\begin{array}{c} \text{Hotels} \quad \text{Motels} \quad \text{Motor hotels} \\ \begin{array}{c} \text{Businesses} \\ \text{Rooms} \end{array} \begin{pmatrix} 10{,}750 & 27{,}739 & 2{,}348 \\ 755{,}000 & 1{,}034{,}000 & 206{,}000 \end{pmatrix} \end{array}$$

or as the 3 × 2 matrix

$$\begin{array}{c} \text{Businesses} \quad \text{Rooms} \\ \begin{array}{c} \text{Hotels} \\ \text{Motels} \\ \text{Motor hotels} \end{array} \begin{pmatrix} 10{,}750 & 755{,}000 \\ 27{,}739 & 1{,}034{,}000 \\ 2{,}348 & 206{,}000 \end{pmatrix} \end{array}$$

equality of matrices

Although the two matrices in Example 1 convey the same information, they are not equal. Matrices A and B are *equal* if they have the same size and their corresponding entries are equal; the equality of A and B is denoted by writing $A = B$. On the other hand, if the matrices A and B are not equal, then we write $A \neq B$. Thus the matrices

$$X = \begin{pmatrix} 3 & -2 \\ a & b \end{pmatrix} \quad \text{and} \quad Y = \begin{pmatrix} c & d \\ 1 & 4 \end{pmatrix}$$

are equal only when $a = 1$, $b = 4$, $c = 3$, and $d = -2$.

EXAMPLE 2

Neither of the following pairs of matrices is equal:

(a) $\begin{pmatrix} 1 & 2 \\ 3 & 4 \\ 0 & 0 \end{pmatrix}$ and $\begin{pmatrix} 1 & 2 \\ 3 & 4 \end{pmatrix}$

because the matrices do not have the same size;

(b) $\begin{pmatrix} 1 & 2 \\ 3 & 4 \end{pmatrix}$ and $\begin{pmatrix} 1 & 3 \\ 2 & 4 \end{pmatrix}$

because the 1, 2 entries are not equal.

---

[1] *Source: Statistical Abstract of the United States, 1976.* Washington, D.C.: U.S. Department of Commerce, Bureau of the Census.

Sometimes only a portion of the data contained in a matrix is needed for a particular problem. For instance, if we were interested only in the vitamin content of vegetables, we could form a 4 × 4 matrix from the first four rows and the last four columns of Table 3.1 instead of the 9 × 7 matrix (3.1). A smaller matrix obtained by deleting one or more submatrix   of the rows or columns of a matrix M is called a *submatrix* of M. It is customary also to regard every matrix as a submatrix of itself.

EXAMPLE 3

The 2 × 3 matrix

$$\begin{pmatrix} 1 & 2 & 3 \\ 4 & 5 & 6 \end{pmatrix}$$

has 21 different submatrices, some of which are

$$\begin{pmatrix} 1 & 2 & 3 \\ 4 & 5 & 6 \end{pmatrix} \quad \begin{pmatrix} 1 & 2 \\ 4 & 5 \end{pmatrix} \quad \begin{pmatrix} 1 \\ 4 \end{pmatrix} \quad (1 \ \ 2 \ \ 3) \quad (1 \ \ 2)$$

and (1)

In certain types of problems (such as those concerned with statistical samples), it is desirable to group some rows or some columns of a matrix into submatrices. These groupings are usually denoted by drawing dashed lines through the matrix. For example, if the foods in Table 3.1 are grouped into vegetables, seafoods, poultry, and meats, and the nutrients are grouped as nonvitamins and vitamins, then (3.1) is blocks   subdivided into eight submatrices called *blocks*.

	Nonvitamin content	Vitamin content
Vegetables	2.1 0.7 13.0 3.0 0.3 3.6 1.1 0.2 9.7 7.6 0.5 19.8	20 0.08 0.05 1.0 8,100 0.07 0.14 0.5 11,000 0.06 0.05 0.6 280 0.18 0.10 1.3
Seafood	24.2 20.5 0.0 17.3 1.9 0.5	90 0.04 0.09 10.1 2,170 0.16 0.08 2.8
Poultry	23.4 1.9 0.0	60 0.05 0.09 10.7
Meats	19.9 39.4 0.0 19.7 42.5 0.0	80 0.05 0.15 3.6 0 0.40 0.19 3.2

At this point we have said that tabular data may be represented by a matrix, but we have given no reasons for representing the data in this form. We shall see in the next two sections, however, that several types of calculations with data can be greatly simplified when they are presented in matrix form.

Exercises

In Exercises 1–10 give the size of each matrix. Which matrices are square?

1. $\begin{pmatrix} 1 & 4 & 0 & 5 \\ -3 & 2 & 1 & -1 \\ 2 & -5 & -3 & 6 \end{pmatrix}$

2. $\begin{pmatrix} 9 \\ -3 \\ 5 \end{pmatrix}$

3. $\begin{pmatrix} 3 & -2 & 5 \\ 7 & 6 & -4 \end{pmatrix}$

4. $\begin{pmatrix} -4 & 1 \\ 3 & 0 \end{pmatrix}$

5. $\begin{pmatrix} 5 & -2 & 1 & 2 \\ 4 & 0 & 6 & 1 \\ -2 & 3 & -5 & 2 \\ 3 & 4 & -4 & 3 \\ -1 & 2 & 3 & 4 \end{pmatrix}$

6. $\begin{pmatrix} 4 & -2 & 3 \\ 5 & -1 & 2 \\ 0 & 6 & 0 \end{pmatrix}$

7. $\begin{pmatrix} 4 & -5 \\ -2 & 4 \\ 3 & 0 \end{pmatrix}$

8. $\begin{pmatrix} 1 & -1 & 9 & -3 \\ 2 & -4 & -5 & 6 \end{pmatrix}$

9. $\begin{pmatrix} 3 & 5 \\ -2 & 1 \end{pmatrix}$

10. $(-3 \quad 2 \quad 0 \quad -5 \quad 6)$

For Exercises 11–20 identify the entries of each matrix in Exercises 1–10 that lie on the diagonal.

In Exercises 21 and 22 solve for x, y, and z.

21. $\begin{pmatrix} 3 & -2 & y \\ 0 & x & 5 \end{pmatrix} = \begin{pmatrix} z & -2 & 4 \\ 0 & 3 & 5 \end{pmatrix}$

22. $\begin{pmatrix} 2 & x & 3 \\ -4 & 5 & 2 \\ 3 & 0 & y \end{pmatrix} = \begin{pmatrix} 2 & -1 & 3 \\ -4 & 5 & 2 \\ 3 & z & -2 \end{pmatrix}$

23. How many entries are there in an $m \times n$ matrix?
24. Write out the matrix $B = (b_{ij})$, where $i = 1, 2, 3, 4$ and $j = 1, 2, 3$.
25. Write out the matrix $A = (a_{ij})$, where $i = 1, 2, \ldots, 5$ and $j = 1, 2, \ldots, 5$, if $a_{ij} = 2i + j$.

In Exercises 26–29 list all the submatrices of the given matrices.

26. $\begin{pmatrix} 2 & 1 \\ 0 & -3 \\ 1 & -2 \end{pmatrix}$

27. $\begin{pmatrix} 1 & -1 \\ 3 & 2 \end{pmatrix}$

28. $\begin{pmatrix} 5 \\ -3 \\ 2 \end{pmatrix}$

29. $\begin{pmatrix} 3 & -4 & 2 \\ 1 & 5 & -1 \end{pmatrix}$

In Exercises 30–33 use Table 3.1 to write each of the following matrices.

30. A 2×3 matrix describing the protein, fat, and carbohydrate content of certain meats
31. A 4×4 matrix describing the vitamin content of certain vegetables
32. A 4×2 matrix describing the vitamin content of two seafoods

33. A 3 × 4 matrix describing the protein, fat, and carbohydrate content of certain vegetables

3.2 Matrix Addition and Scalar Multiplication

In this section we shall define several operations that can be performed with matrices. Before discussing these operations, however, let us consider the following data. Matrix A below lists the estimated number of million tons of various types of pollutants emitted into the air of the United States from different sources during the year 1970.[2] Matrix B lists similar information for the year 1971.[2]

	Transportation	Stationary fuel combustion	Industrial processes	Solid waste disposal	Miscellaneous	
Carbon monoxide	82.3	1.1	11.8	5.5	6.6	
Sulfur oxides	0.7	27.0	6.4	0.1	0.1	
Hydrocarbons	14.7	1.6	2.9	1.4	11.5	$= A$
Particulates	1.2	8.3	15.7	1.1	1.2	
Nitrogen oxides	9.3	10.1	0.6	0.3	0.1	

	Transportation	Stationary fuel combustion	Industrial processes	Solid waste disposal	Miscellaneous	
Carbon monoxide	77.5	1.0	11.4	3.8	4.9	
Sulfur oxides	1.0	26.3	5.1	0.1	0.1	
Hydrocarbons	14.7	0.3	5.6	1.0	4.7	$= B$
Particulates	1.0	6.5	13.5	0.7	4.9	
Nitrogen oxides	11.2	10.2	0.2	0.2	0.2	

If we wished to know the total amount of sulfur oxides emitted from industrial processes during both years, we would add together 6.4 and 5.1, the 2, 3 entries of A and B. Likewise, adding each pair of corresponding entries in A and B will give the total emission of each of the pollutants from each of the sources during the two-year period 1970–1971. The resulting matrix

	Transportation	Stationary fuel combustion	Industrial processes	Solid waste disposal	Miscellaneous
Carbon monoxide	159.8	2.1	23.2	9.3	11.5
Sulfur oxides	1.7	53.3	11.5	0.2	0.2
Hydrocarbons	29.4	1.9	8.5	2.4	16.2
Particulates	2.2	14.8	29.2	1.8	6.1
Nitrogen oxides	20.5	20.3	0.8	0.5	0.3

is called the sum of A and B.

---

[2] *Source: Statistical Abstract of the United States, 1974.* Washington, D.C.: U.S. Department of Commerce, Bureau of the Census.

sum of matrices   In general the *sum* of two $m \times n$ matrices P and Q is the $m \times n$ matrix denoted $P + Q$ in which the entries are the sum of the corresponding entries of P and Q. That is, the i, j entry of $P + Q$ is the sum of the i, j entry of P and the i, j entry of Q. Observe that only matrices of the same size can be added.

EXAMPLE 4

If

$$P = \begin{pmatrix} 1 & 4 \\ -3 & 1 \\ 2 & -5 \end{pmatrix} \quad \text{and} \quad Q = \begin{pmatrix} 6 & -2 \\ -1 & 5 \\ 3 & 0 \end{pmatrix}$$

then

$$P + Q = \begin{pmatrix} 1 + 6 & 4 + (-2) \\ (-3) + (-1) & 1 + 5 \\ 2 + 3 & (-5) + 0 \end{pmatrix} = \begin{pmatrix} 7 & 2 \\ -4 & 6 \\ 5 & -5 \end{pmatrix}$$

Consider again the data on air pollution contained in matrix B above. If the Environmental Protection Agency embarked upon a program for restricting each type and source of pollution to no more than 80% of the amount emitted in 1971, then the maximum possible amount of hydrocarbons that could be emitted by transportation would be 80% of 14.7, or $0.8(14.7) = 11.76$ million tons. Likewise, by multiplying each entry of B by 0.8 we would obtain the maximum possible emissions for each type of pollutant and each source. The resulting matrix

	Transportation	Stationary fuel combustion	Industrial processes	Solid waste disposal	Miscellaneous
Carbon monoxide	62.00	0.80	9.12	3.04	3.92
Sulfur oxides	0.80	21.04	4.08	0.08	0.08
Hydrocarbons	11.76	0.24	4.48	0.80	3.76
Particulates	0.80	5.20	10.80	0.56	3.92
Nitrogen oxides	8.96	8.16	0.16	0.16	0.16

is called the scalar product of B and 0.8.

scalar product   The *scalar product* of a number k and an $m \times n$ matrix P is the $m \times n$ matrix denoted kP obtained by multiplying each entry of P by **scalar** k. (The number k is called a *scalar* in this context to distinguish it from a matrix.)

EXAMPLE 5

If

$$P = \begin{pmatrix} 1 & -2 & 4 \\ -1 & 3 & 2 \end{pmatrix} \text{ and } Q = \begin{pmatrix} -2 & 0 \\ 5 & 2 \\ 1 & -3 \end{pmatrix}$$

then

$$4P = \begin{pmatrix} 4(1) & 4(-2) & 4(4) \\ 4(-1) & 4(3) & 4(2) \end{pmatrix} = \begin{pmatrix} 4 & -8 & 16 \\ -4 & 12 & 8 \end{pmatrix}$$

and

$$-5Q = \begin{pmatrix} (-5)(-2) & (-5)(0) \\ (-5)(5) & (-5)(2) \\ (-5)(1) & (-5)(-3) \end{pmatrix} = \begin{pmatrix} 10 & 0 \\ -25 & -10 \\ -5 & 15 \end{pmatrix}$$

Suppose now that we wished to know the change in the amount of particulates due to fuel combustion in 1971 as compared to 1970. In this case we subtract 8.3 (the 4, 2 entry of A) from 6.5 (the 4, 2 entry of B). Likewise, by subtracting each entry of A from the corresponding entry of B we obtain the difference between the amount of each pollutant contributed by each source in 1971 and in 1970. The resulting matrix

	Transportation	Stationary fuel combustion	Industrial processes	Solid waste disposal	Miscellaneous
Carbon monoxide	−4.8	−0.1	−0.4	−1.7	−1.7
Sulfur oxides	0.3	−0.7	−1.3	0.0	0.0
Hydrocarbons	0.0	−1.3	2.7	−0.4	−6.8
Particulates	−0.2	−1.8	−2.2	−0.4	3.7
Nitrogen oxides	1.9	0.1	−0.4	−0.1	0.1

is called the difference of B and A. Here, of course, negative entries signify a decrease in emissions and positive entries signify an increase in emissions from 1970 to 1971.

difference of matrices   In general the *difference* $P - Q$ of two $m \times n$ matrices is the $m \times n$ matrix formed by subtracting each entry of Q from the corresponding entry of P. It is easily seen that the difference $P - Q$ equals $P + (-1)Q$, where $(-1)Q$ denotes the scalar product of Q and -1.

EXAMPLE 6

If

$$P = \begin{pmatrix} 5 & -2 & 4 \\ -1 & 0 & 2 \end{pmatrix} \text{ and } Q = \begin{pmatrix} 4 & -5 & 0 \\ 2 & -2 & -3 \end{pmatrix}$$

then
$$P - Q = \begin{pmatrix} 5-4 & -2-(-5) & 4-0 \\ -1-2 & 0-(-2) & 2-(-3) \end{pmatrix}$$
$$= \begin{pmatrix} 1 & 3 & 4 \\ -3 & 2 & 5 \end{pmatrix}$$

zero matrix   For any matrix A the difference $A - A$ is a matrix in which all the entries are zero. Such a matrix is called a *zero matrix* and denoted by *0*. Obviously there are zero matrices of every size; some examples of zero matrices are

$$\begin{pmatrix} 0 \\ 0 \\ 0 \end{pmatrix} \quad (0 \ 0 \ 0 \ 0) \quad \begin{pmatrix} 0 & 0 \\ 0 & 0 \\ 0 & 0 \end{pmatrix} \quad \text{and} \quad \begin{pmatrix} 0 & 0 & 0 & 0 \\ 0 & 0 & 0 & 0 \\ 0 & 0 & 0 & 0 \end{pmatrix}$$

The operations of matrix addition and scalar multiplication defined in this section possess many of the properties of addition and multiplication of real numbers. The following theorem lists some of these properties.

THEOREM 3.1

Let A, B, and C be any $m \times n$ matrices and c and k be any scalars. Then the following results are true:

(a) $A + B = B + A$ (commutative property of matrix addition)

(b) $(A + B) + C = A + (B + C)$ (associative property of matrix addition)

(c) $A + 0 = A$

(d) $(ck)A = c(kA)$

(e) $c(A + B) = cA + cB$

(f) $(c + k)A = cA + kA$

The following example illustrates parts (d) and (e) of this theorem.

EXAMPLE 7

Let

$$A = \begin{pmatrix} 3 & 4 & -2 \\ -1 & 0 & 5 \end{pmatrix} \quad B = \begin{pmatrix} 0 & -2 & 6 \\ 6 & 1 & -5 \end{pmatrix}$$

$c = 2$, and $k = -3$. The computations below illustrate the corresponding parts of Theorem 3.1.

(d) $(ck)A = (-6)A = \begin{pmatrix} -18 & -24 & 12 \\ 6 & 0 & -30 \end{pmatrix}$

$c(kA) = 2(-3A) = 2\begin{pmatrix} -9 & -12 & 6 \\ 3 & 0 & -15 \end{pmatrix}$

$= \begin{pmatrix} -18 & -24 & 12 \\ 6 & 0 & -30 \end{pmatrix}$

(e) $c(A + B) = 2\begin{pmatrix} 3 & 2 & 4 \\ 5 & 1 & 0 \end{pmatrix} = \begin{pmatrix} 6 & 4 & 8 \\ 10 & 2 & 0 \end{pmatrix}$

$cA + cB = 2\begin{pmatrix} 3 & 4 & -2 \\ -1 & 0 & 5 \end{pmatrix} + 2\begin{pmatrix} 0 & -2 & 6 \\ 6 & 1 & -5 \end{pmatrix}$

$= \begin{pmatrix} 6 & 8 & -4 \\ -2 & 0 & 10 \end{pmatrix} + \begin{pmatrix} 0 & -4 & 12 \\ 12 & 2 & -10 \end{pmatrix}$

$= \begin{pmatrix} 6 & 4 & 8 \\ 10 & 2 & 0 \end{pmatrix}$

Exercises

In Exercises 1–4 compute $2A$, $(-3)B$, $A + B$, $A - B$, and $4A - 2B$ for each of the given pairs of matrices A and B.

1. $A = \begin{pmatrix} 3 & -2 \\ 1 & 1 \end{pmatrix}$, $B = \begin{pmatrix} -2 & 5 \\ 0 & 3 \end{pmatrix}$

2. $A = \begin{pmatrix} -2 & 0 & 1 \\ 1 & 3 & 0 \end{pmatrix}$, $B = \begin{pmatrix} 6 & 3 & -2 \\ 2 & -4 & 1 \end{pmatrix}$

3. $A = \begin{pmatrix} -4 & 1 \\ 2 & 3 \\ 0 & -1 \end{pmatrix}$, $B = \begin{pmatrix} 2 & -4 \\ 1 & -2 \\ 3 & -1 \end{pmatrix}$

4. $A = \begin{pmatrix} 1 & -2 & 3 \\ 2 & 0 & -1 \\ -1 & 4 & 2 \end{pmatrix}$, $B = \begin{pmatrix} 0 & 3 & -2 \\ 1 & -4 & 3 \\ -1 & 1 & 2 \end{pmatrix}$

In Exercises 5–8 compute $5A$, $(-1)B$, $A + B$, $A - B$, and $3A + 2B$ for each of the given pairs of matrices A and B.

5. $A = \begin{pmatrix} -2 & 1 \\ 0 & 3 \end{pmatrix}$, $B = \begin{pmatrix} 5 & 0 \\ 2 & -1 \end{pmatrix}$

6. $A = \begin{pmatrix} 3 & -2 & 2 \\ -1 & 4 & 0 \end{pmatrix}$, $B = \begin{pmatrix} 0 & 5 & 4 \\ 4 & 1 & -3 \end{pmatrix}$

7. $A = \begin{pmatrix} 1 & 0 \\ -2 & 3 \\ 0 & -1 \end{pmatrix}$, $B = \begin{pmatrix} -2 & 1 \\ 5 & 2 \\ -4 & -3 \end{pmatrix}$

56　Chapter 3　Matrices and Systems of Linear Equations

8. $$A = \begin{pmatrix} 7 & -3 & 6 \\ -2 & 9 & 2 \\ 4 & -5 & 3 \end{pmatrix}, B = \begin{pmatrix} 6 & 8 & -4 \\ 7 & 5 & -3 \\ 5 & -6 & 8 \end{pmatrix}$$

9. Write the 3×5 zero matrix.

10. Write the 4×2 zero matrix.

11. Verify parts (d) and (e) of Theorem 3.1 for

$$A = \begin{pmatrix} 2 & -3 & 1 \\ -2 & 4 & 0 \end{pmatrix}, B = \begin{pmatrix} -3 & 7 & -2 \\ 5 & 0 & -1 \end{pmatrix}, c = 4, k = 2$$

12. Verify parts (d) and (e) of Theorem 3.1 for

$$A = \begin{pmatrix} -3 & 1 \\ 1 & -2 \\ 2 & 4 \end{pmatrix}, B = \begin{pmatrix} 2 & -5 \\ 1 & 0 \\ 3 & -1 \end{pmatrix}, c = -3, k = 5$$

13. Which parts of Theorem 3.1 are true if $+$ is replaced by $-$?
    Hint: Test each equation with any three matrices of the same size.

14. (a) In 1972 there were 741 tornadoes in the United States, resulting in 27 deaths. The same year there were 3 hurricanes reaching the coast of the United States and causing 121 deaths.[3] Record this information as a 2×2 matrix A.
    (b) In 1973, 1108 tornadoes caused 87 deaths, and 1 hurricane caused 5 deaths. In 1974, 949 tornadoes caused 361 deaths and 1 hurricane caused 1 death.[3] Record this information in two 2×2 matrices B and C.
    (c) Compute $A + B + C$ and interpret the result.

15. (a) In 1973 the number of motor vehicle registrations in Washington, D.C., was 261,000. In Illinois, Maryland, New York, and Wisconsin the corresponding figures were 5,952,000, 2,259,000, 7,319,000, and 2,472,000, respectively. In the same year there were 335,000 drivers licensed in Washington, D.C., 6,124,000 in Illinois, 2,218,000 in Maryland, 8,546,000 in New York, and 2,594,000 in Wisconsin.[3] Record these data as a 2×5 matrix A.
    (b) In 1974 Washington, D.C., had 263,000 motor vehicle registrations and 332,000 licensed drivers; Illinois had 6,174,000 registrations and 6,300,000 licensed drivers; Maryland had 2,346,000 registrations and 2,359,000 licensed drivers; New York had 7,458,000 registrations and 8,731,000 licensed drivers, and Wisconsin had 2,578,000 registrations and 2,664,000 licensed drivers.[3] Record this information as a 2×5 matrix B.
    (c) Compute $B - A$ and interpret the result.

16. Table 3.2 contains information about the number of thousands of active proprietorships, partnerships, and corporations for four industries during 1972 and 1973.

---

[3] *Source: Statistical Abstract of the United States, 1976.* Washington, D.C.: U.S. Department of Commerce, Bureau of the Census.

Table 3.2 *Thousands of Active Proprietorships, Partnerships, and Corporations in Four Industries*

	1972			1973		
Industry	Proprie-torships	Partner-ships	Corpor-ations	Proprie-torships	Partner-ships	Corpor-ations
Agriculture, forestry, and fisheries	3206	114	43	3415	124	47
Construction	805	61	154	857	66	176
Manufacturing	203	30	203	210	30	209
Wholesale and retail trade	2173	196	568	2164	199	582

Source: Statistical Abstract of the United States, 1976. Washington, D.C.: U.S. Department of Commerce, Bureau of the Census.

Record this information in two 4×3 matrices, A for 1972 and B for 1973. Compute $B - A$ and interpret the result.

3.3 Matrix Multiplication

In Section 3.2 we discussed scalar multiplication, the product of a matrix and a real number. In this section we define a different type of multiplication, the product of two matrices.

To help in formulating a definition of matrix multiplication, let us consider the following example. During its end-of-month inventory, the Sporting Chance, a retail sporting goods store, determined that its inventory of tennis racquets was as indicated in matrix A below.

$$\begin{array}{c} \\ \text{Downtown store} \\ \text{Suburban store} \end{array} \begin{pmatrix} \text{Metal} & \text{Graphite} & \text{Wood} \\ 20 & 12 & 48 \\ 18 & 28 & 32 \end{pmatrix} = A$$

Racquets can be sold either unstrung or strung with nylon. Prices (in dollars) for each type of racquet are given in matrix B.

$$\begin{array}{c} \\ \text{Metal} \\ \text{Graphite} \\ \text{Wood} \end{array} \begin{pmatrix} \text{Unstrung} & \text{Strung} \\ 50 & 60 \\ 55 & 65 \\ 20 & 30 \end{pmatrix} = B$$

To find the total retail value of the unstrung racquets in the downtown store, we multiply the number of racquets of each type in the downtown store times the corresponding price and add the three products. This gives

$$20(\$50) + 12(\$55) + 48(\$20) = \$1000 + \$660 + \$960 = \$2620$$

If these racquets were strung, then their value would be

$$20(\$60) + 12(\$65) + 48(\$30) = \$1200 + \$780 + \$1440 = \$3420$$

Likewise the retail value of the racquets in the suburban store is

$$18(\$50) + 28(\$55) + 32(\$20) = \$900 + \$1540 + \$640 = \$3080$$

if unstrung and

$$18(\$60) + 28(\$65) + 32(\$30) = \$1080 + \$1820 + \$960 = \$3860$$

if strung. Let us record these values as the matrix

$$\begin{array}{c} \text{Downtown store} \\ \text{Suburban store} \end{array} \begin{pmatrix} \text{Unstrung} & \text{Strung} \\ 2620 & 3420 \\ 3080 & 3860 \end{pmatrix} = C$$

This matrix is called the product of A and B. Notice that the entry of C in row i, column j was formed by summing the products of corresponding entries of row i of A and column j of B, that is,

$$C = AB = \begin{pmatrix} 20 & 12 & 48 \\ 18 & 28 & 32 \end{pmatrix} \begin{pmatrix} 50 & 60 \\ 55 & 65 \\ 20 & 30 \end{pmatrix}$$

$$= \begin{pmatrix} 20(50) + 12(55) + 48(20) & 20(60) + 12(65) + 48(30) \\ 18(50) + 28(55) + 32(20) & 18(60) + 28(65) + 32(30) \end{pmatrix}$$

(The colored screens indicate the numbers involved in computation of the 2, 1 entry of C.) Observe also that the product of the 2×3 matrix A and the 3×2 matrix B is a 2×2 matrix.

product of matrices   In general the *product* of an $m \times n$ matrix P and an $n \times p$ matrix Q is an $m \times p$ matrix denoted PQ. The entry of PQ in row i, column j, is formed by summing the n products of each entry of row i of P and the corresponding entry of row j of Q. Note that the size of the product matrix can be found easily from the symbolic relationship

$$\begin{array}{cc} P & Q \\ m \times n & n \times p \end{array}$$

Must be equal

Size of product is $m \times p$

EXAMPLE 8

The product of the 3×4 matrix A and the 4×2 matrix B, where

$$A = \begin{pmatrix} 3 & 0 & -1 & 1 \\ -1 & 2 & 1 & 4 \\ -3 & 1 & -2 & 0 \end{pmatrix} \quad \text{and} \quad B = \begin{pmatrix} 2 & 1 \\ -1 & 3 \\ 0 & 4 \\ 1 & -2 \end{pmatrix}$$

is the 3 × 2 matrix

$$AB = \begin{pmatrix} 3(2) + 0(-1) + (-1)(0) + 1(1) & 3(1) + 0(3) + (-1)(4) + 1(-2) \\ (-1)(2) + 2(-1) + 1(0) + 4(1) & (-1)(1) + 2(3) + 1(4) + 4(-2) \\ (-3)(2) + 1(-1) + (-2)(0) + 0(1) & (-3)(1) + 1(3) + (-2)(4) + 0(-2) \end{pmatrix}$$

$$= \begin{pmatrix} 7 & -3 \\ 0 & 1 \\ -7 & -8 \end{pmatrix}$$

Observe that the product BA is not defined in this case.

EXAMPLE 9

In Section 3.2 we worked with matrices in which the entries represented the amounts of five types of air pollutants emitted from five different sources. Of the pollutants due to transportation, most are emitted by road vehicles. The entries of matrix A below are the average proportions of transportation pollutants due to road vehicles for the years 1970 and 1971.[4]

$$A = \begin{pmatrix} \text{Carbon} & \text{Sulfur} & \text{Hydro-} & & \text{Nitrogen} \\ \text{monoxide} & \text{oxides} & \text{carbons} & \text{Particulates} & \text{oxides} \\ 0.843 & 0.353 & 0.830 & 0.727 & 0.737 \end{pmatrix}$$

The matrix

$$\begin{matrix} & 1970 & 1971 \\ \text{Carbon monoxide} \\ \text{Sulfur oxides} \\ \text{Hydrocarbons} \\ \text{Particulates} \\ \text{Nitrogen oxides} \end{matrix} \begin{pmatrix} 82.3 & 77.5 \\ 0.7 & 1.0 \\ 14.7 & 14.7 \\ 1.2 & 1.0 \\ 9.3 & 11.2 \end{pmatrix} = B$$

gives the number of million tons of each pollutant emitted by transportation in 1970 and 1971. So the entries of the product matrix

$$\begin{matrix} & 1970 & 1971 \end{matrix}$$
$$AB \approx \begin{pmatrix} 89.6 & 86.9 \end{pmatrix}$$

give the total amount (in millions of tons) of all five pollutants due to road vehicles for each year.

We have seen that, for any matrix A, the zero matrix 0 of the same size has the property that $A + 0 = A$. Thus zero matrices behave with respect to matrix addition as the number 0 behaves with respect to addition of real numbers. We now define a class of matrices that behave

---

[4] *Source: Statistical Abstract of the United States, 1974.* Washington, D.C.: U.S. Department of Commerce, Bureau of the Census.

identity matrix

with respect to matrix multiplication as the number 1 behaves with respect to multiplication of real numbers. The $n \times n$ matrix having 1s on the diagonal and 0s elsewhere is called the $n \times n$ *identity matrix* and is denoted by I_n or I. For instance,

$$I_2 = \begin{pmatrix} 1 & 0 \\ 0 & 1 \end{pmatrix} \quad I_3 = \begin{pmatrix} 1 & 0 & 0 \\ 0 & 1 & 0 \\ 0 & 0 & 1 \end{pmatrix} \quad \text{and} \quad I_4 = \begin{pmatrix} 1 & 0 & 0 & 0 \\ 0 & 1 & 0 & 0 \\ 0 & 0 & 1 & 0 \\ 0 & 0 & 0 & 1 \end{pmatrix}$$

The reader may verify that, if

$$A = \begin{pmatrix} 1 & 2 & -5 \\ -3 & 0 & 4 \end{pmatrix}$$

then

$$I_2 A = \begin{pmatrix} 1 & 0 \\ 0 & 1 \end{pmatrix} \begin{pmatrix} 1 & 2 & -5 \\ -3 & 0 & 4 \end{pmatrix} = \begin{pmatrix} 1 & 2 & -5 \\ -3 & 0 & 4 \end{pmatrix} = A$$

and

$$A I_3 = \begin{pmatrix} 1 & 2 & -5 \\ -3 & 0 & 4 \end{pmatrix} \begin{pmatrix} 1 & 0 & 0 \\ 0 & 1 & 0 \\ 0 & 0 & 1 \end{pmatrix} = \begin{pmatrix} 1 & 2 & -5 \\ -3 & 0 & 4 \end{pmatrix} = A$$

If M is a square matrix, then the matrix product MM is defined. In fact, MM is a square matrix of the same size as M, and so the product $M(MM)$ is defined. Likewise for any positive integer k the product of k factors of M is defined, and this product is denoted M^k. For example, if

$$M = \begin{pmatrix} 1 & 2 \\ -1 & 1 \end{pmatrix}$$

then

$$M^2 = \begin{pmatrix} 1 & 2 \\ -1 & 1 \end{pmatrix} \begin{pmatrix} 1 & 2 \\ -1 & 1 \end{pmatrix} = \begin{pmatrix} -1 & 4 \\ -2 & -1 \end{pmatrix}$$

and

$$M^3 = M(M^2) = \begin{pmatrix} 1 & 2 \\ -1 & 1 \end{pmatrix} \begin{pmatrix} -1 & 4 \\ -2 & -1 \end{pmatrix} = \begin{pmatrix} -5 & 2 \\ -1 & -5 \end{pmatrix}$$

APPLICATION 1

The discipline of demography studies populations in order to predict their future structure. In [4] Stone demonstrates how such predictions can be made if we know the number of females of different ages at a certain time, the number of these women who survive during a given time interval beginning at that time, and the

3.3 Matrix Multiplication

Table 3.3 *Population Data for Females Aged 0–44 in 1940 and 1955*

	Number of females in 1940	Number of surviving females in 1955	Number of surviving daughters born from 1940 to 1955 (classified by the mother's age)
0–14	14,459	16,428	4,651
15–29	15,264	14,258	10,403
30–44	11,346	14,837	1,374

number of female offspring born during this time interval. For example, Stone uses the data in Table 3.3 based on the 1940 U.S. census.

Notice that of the 14,459 women aged 0–14 in 1940, 14,258 survived until 1955 (hence were aged 15–29). Similarly, of the 15,264 women aged 15–29 in 1940, 14,837 survived until 1955 (and thus were aged 30–44). So the ratios

$$14{,}258/14{,}459 \quad \text{and} \quad 14{,}837/15{,}264$$

represent the proportion of women aged 0–14 and 15–29 in 1940 who were aged 15–29 and 30–44 in 1955.

In addition, the ratios

$$4651/14{,}459 \quad 10{,}403/15{,}264 \quad \text{and} \quad 1374/11{,}346$$

indicate the proportions of women in each 1940 age group who gave birth (during the years 1940–1955) to daughters surviving until 1955. (These daughters were necessarily aged 0–14 in 1955.)

These ratios are then incorporated into a matrix

$$\begin{array}{cc}
 & \begin{array}{ccc} \text{1940 ages} & & \\ 0\text{--}14 & 15\text{--}29 & 30\text{--}44 \end{array} \\
\begin{array}{c} \text{1955 ages} \\ \begin{array}{c} 0\text{--}14 \\ 15\text{--}29 \\ 30\text{--}44 \end{array} \end{array} &
\begin{pmatrix} 4651/14{,}459 & 10{,}403/15{,}264 & 1374/11{,}346 \\ 14{,}258/14{,}459 & 0 & 0 \\ 0 & 14{,}837/15{,}264 & 0 \end{pmatrix} = M
\end{array}$$

The entries of M may be thought of as the relative frequencies with which each 1940 age group contributed to each 1955 age group. When M is multiplied by the column vector

$$P = \begin{pmatrix} 14{,}459 \\ 15{,}264 \\ 11{,}346 \end{pmatrix}$$

in which the entries are the number of females in each 1940 age group, the product

$$MP \approx \begin{pmatrix} 0.31267 & 0.68154 & 0.12110 \\ 0.98610 & 0 & 0 \\ 0 & 0.97203 & 0 \end{pmatrix} \begin{pmatrix} 14{,}459 \\ 15{,}264 \\ 11{,}346 \end{pmatrix} \approx \begin{pmatrix} 16{,}428 \\ 14{,}258 \\ 14{,}837 \end{pmatrix}$$

gives the number of females expected in each 1955 age group. Thus we expect 16,428 females aged 0–14, 14,258 females aged 15–29, and 14,837 females aged 30–44 in 1955.

The matrices M^2, M^3, and so forth, may be used to obtain similar information about the population at later times. For example, if we assume that the trend during the years 1940–1955 continued during another 15-year period (until 1970), then the entries of

$$\text{1970 ages} \begin{array}{c} \\ 0\text{--}14 \\ 15\text{--}29 \\ 30\text{--}44 \end{array} \overset{\begin{array}{ccc} \text{1940 ages} \\ 0\text{--}14 & 15\text{--}29 & 30\text{--}44 \end{array}}{\begin{pmatrix} 0.77554 & 0.33694 & 0.03895 \\ 0.31720 & 0.67207 & 0.11942 \\ 0.95852 & 0 & 0 \end{pmatrix}} \approx M^2$$

represent the relative frequencies with which each 1940 age group contributed to each 1970 age group. Likewise the entries of

$$\text{1985 ages} \begin{array}{c} \\ 0\text{--}14 \\ 15\text{--}29 \\ 30\text{--}44 \end{array} \overset{\begin{array}{ccc} \text{1940 ages} \\ 0\text{--}14 & 15\text{--}29 & 30\text{--}44 \end{array}}{\begin{pmatrix} 0.58173 & 0.56643 & 0.09392 \\ 0.76476 & 0.33226 & 0.03841 \\ 0.30833 & 0.65327 & 0.11608 \end{pmatrix}} \approx M^3$$

represent the relative frequencies with which each 1940 age group will contribute to each 1985 age group if the trend during the years 1940–1955 continues for three 15-year periods (until 1985). Hence the entries of

$$M^2 P \approx \begin{pmatrix} 16{,}799 \\ 16{,}200 \\ 13{,}859 \end{pmatrix} \quad \text{and} \quad M^3 P \approx \begin{pmatrix} 18{,}123 \\ 16{,}565 \\ 15{,}747 \end{pmatrix}$$

give the numbers of females in each age group in 1970 and 1985, respectively.

In Example 8 the matrix product AB was computed. Notice that in this example the product BA is not defined because B has two columns and A has three rows. Thus the order in which matrices are multiplied is of great importance. In fact, even if both AB and BA are defined, the products need not be equal. For instance,

$$\begin{pmatrix} 1 & -2 \\ 2 & 3 \end{pmatrix} \begin{pmatrix} -1 & 4 \\ 5 & 1 \end{pmatrix} = \begin{pmatrix} -11 & 2 \\ 13 & 11 \end{pmatrix}$$

but

$$\begin{pmatrix} -1 & 4 \\ 5 & 1 \end{pmatrix} \begin{pmatrix} 1 & -2 \\ 2 & 3 \end{pmatrix} = \begin{pmatrix} 7 & 14 \\ 7 & -7 \end{pmatrix}$$

3.3 Matrix Multiplication

Many of the other properties of multiplication of real numbers, however, are possessed by matrix multiplication, as the following theorem shows.

THEOREM 3.2

Let A be an $m \times n$ matrix, B and D be $n \times p$ matrices, C be a $p \times q$ matrix, and k be a scalar. Then

(a) $(AB)C = A(BC)$ (associative property of matrix multiplication)
(b) $A(B + D) = AB + AD$ and $(B + D)C = BC + DC$ (distributive properties)
(c) $AI_n = A$ and $I_m A = A$
(d) $(kA)B = k(AB)$ and $A(kB) = k(AB)$

The following example illustrates parts (a) and (b) of Theorem 3.2.

EXAMPLE 10

Let

$$A = \begin{pmatrix} 3 & 1 & 0 \\ -1 & 2 & 1 \end{pmatrix} \qquad B = \begin{pmatrix} -2 & 4 & 1 & 0 \\ 1 & -1 & 0 & 2 \\ 3 & 2 & -2 & 1 \end{pmatrix}$$

$$D = \begin{pmatrix} 1 & 0 & 2 & -4 \\ -2 & 1 & 0 & 3 \\ 1 & -3 & 1 & 0 \end{pmatrix} \quad \text{and} \quad C = \begin{pmatrix} 1 & -1 \\ -3 & 2 \\ 0 & 4 \\ 2 & 1 \end{pmatrix}$$

The computations below demonstrate the corresponding parts of Theorem 3.2.

(a)
$$(AB)C = \left[\begin{pmatrix} 3 & 1 & 0 \\ -1 & 2 & 1 \end{pmatrix} \begin{pmatrix} -2 & 4 & 1 & 0 \\ 1 & -1 & 0 & 2 \\ 3 & 2 & -2 & 1 \end{pmatrix} \right] C$$

$$= \begin{pmatrix} -5 & 11 & 3 & 2 \\ 7 & -4 & -3 & 5 \end{pmatrix} \begin{pmatrix} 1 & -1 \\ -3 & 2 \\ 0 & 4 \\ 2 & 1 \end{pmatrix}$$

$$= \begin{pmatrix} -34 & 41 \\ 29 & -22 \end{pmatrix}$$

$$A(BC) = A\left[\begin{pmatrix} -2 & 4 & 1 & 0 \\ 1 & -1 & 0 & 2 \\ 3 & 2 & -2 & 1 \end{pmatrix} \begin{pmatrix} 1 & -1 \\ -3 & 2 \\ 0 & 4 \\ 2 & 1 \end{pmatrix}\right]$$

$$= \begin{pmatrix} 3 & 1 & 0 \\ -1 & 2 & 1 \end{pmatrix} \begin{pmatrix} -14 & 14 \\ 8 & -1 \\ -1 & -6 \end{pmatrix} = \begin{pmatrix} -34 & 41 \\ 29 & -22 \end{pmatrix}$$

(b)
$$A(B + D) = A\left[\begin{pmatrix} -2 & 4 & 1 & 0 \\ 1 & -1 & 0 & 2 \\ 3 & 2 & -2 & 1 \end{pmatrix} + \begin{pmatrix} 1 & 0 & 2 & -4 \\ -2 & 1 & 0 & 3 \\ 1 & -3 & 1 & 0 \end{pmatrix}\right]$$

$$= \begin{pmatrix} 3 & 1 & 0 \\ -1 & 2 & 1 \end{pmatrix} \begin{pmatrix} -1 & 4 & 3 & -4 \\ -1 & 0 & 0 & 5 \\ 4 & -1 & -1 & 1 \end{pmatrix}$$

$$= \begin{pmatrix} -4 & 12 & 9 & -7 \\ 3 & -5 & -4 & 15 \end{pmatrix}$$

$$AB + AD = \begin{pmatrix} 3 & 1 & 0 \\ -1 & 2 & 1 \end{pmatrix} \begin{pmatrix} -2 & 4 & 1 & 0 \\ 1 & -1 & 0 & 2 \\ 3 & 2 & -2 & 1 \end{pmatrix}$$

$$+ \begin{pmatrix} 3 & 1 & 0 \\ -1 & 2 & 1 \end{pmatrix} \begin{pmatrix} 1 & 0 & 2 & -4 \\ -2 & 1 & 0 & 3 \\ 1 & -3 & 1 & 0 \end{pmatrix}$$

$$= \begin{pmatrix} -5 & 11 & 3 & 2 \\ 7 & -4 & -3 & 5 \end{pmatrix} + \begin{pmatrix} 1 & 1 & 6 & -9 \\ -4 & -1 & -1 & 10 \end{pmatrix}$$

$$= \begin{pmatrix} -4 & 12 & 9 & -7 \\ 3 & -5 & -4 & 15 \end{pmatrix}$$

$$(B + D)C = \left[\begin{pmatrix} -2 & 4 & 1 & 0 \\ 1 & -1 & 0 & 2 \\ 3 & 2 & -2 & 1 \end{pmatrix}\right.$$

$$\left.+ \begin{pmatrix} 1 & 0 & 2 & -4 \\ -2 & 1 & 0 & 3 \\ 1 & -3 & 1 & 0 \end{pmatrix}\right]C$$

$$= \begin{pmatrix} -1 & 4 & 3 & -4 \\ -1 & 0 & 0 & 5 \\ 4 & -1 & -1 & 1 \end{pmatrix} \begin{pmatrix} 1 & -1 \\ -3 & 2 \\ 0 & 4 \\ 2 & 1 \end{pmatrix}$$

$$= \begin{pmatrix} -21 & 17 \\ 9 & 6 \\ 9 & -9 \end{pmatrix}$$

$$BC + DC = \begin{pmatrix} -2 & 4 & 1 & 0 \\ 1 & -1 & 0 & 2 \\ 3 & 2 & -2 & 1 \end{pmatrix} \begin{pmatrix} 1 & -1 \\ -3 & 2 \\ 0 & 4 \\ 2 & 1 \end{pmatrix}$$

$$+ \begin{pmatrix} 1 & 0 & 2 & -4 \\ -2 & 1 & 0 & 3 \\ 1 & -3 & 1 & 0 \end{pmatrix} \begin{pmatrix} 1 & -1 \\ -3 & 2 \\ 0 & 4 \\ 2 & 1 \end{pmatrix}$$

$$= \begin{pmatrix} -14 & 14 \\ 8 & -1 \\ -1 & -6 \end{pmatrix} + \begin{pmatrix} -7 & 3 \\ 1 & 7 \\ 10 & -3 \end{pmatrix} = \begin{pmatrix} -21 & 17 \\ 9 & 6 \\ 9 & -9 \end{pmatrix}$$

Exercises

In Exercises 1–6 which of the given pairs of matrices can be multiplied in the order indicated? If the product is defined, what is its size?

1. $\begin{pmatrix} 2 & 1 \\ 0 & -3 \end{pmatrix} \begin{pmatrix} 4 & -3 \\ 1 & 1 \end{pmatrix}$

2. $\begin{pmatrix} 4 & -2 \\ 0 & -1 \\ 1 & 2 \end{pmatrix} \begin{pmatrix} 1 & -4 \\ -1 & 1 \end{pmatrix}$

3. $\begin{pmatrix} 8 & -4 & 6 \\ 5 & -3 & 7 \\ -6 & 8 & 5 \end{pmatrix} \begin{pmatrix} -1 & 4 & 0 \\ 3 & -2 & 1 \end{pmatrix}$

4. $\begin{pmatrix} 5 & 2 \\ -4 & -3 \end{pmatrix} \begin{pmatrix} -3 & 1 & 2 \\ 1 & -2 & 4 \end{pmatrix}$

5. $\begin{pmatrix} 1 & -2 \\ 2 & 5 \\ -4 & -3 \end{pmatrix} \begin{pmatrix} 1 & -4 & 0 & 5 \\ -3 & 2 & 1 & -1 \end{pmatrix}$

6. $\begin{pmatrix} -3 & 4 & 0 & 5 \\ 1 & -2 & -1 & -3 \\ 2 & 3 & 1 & -2 \end{pmatrix} \begin{pmatrix} 1 \\ -1 \\ 2 \\ 1 \end{pmatrix}$

In Exercises 7–12 compute each matrix product.

7. $\begin{pmatrix} 2 & -2 & 0 \\ -1 & 3 & 1 \end{pmatrix} \begin{pmatrix} -3 & 2 & 1 \\ 4 & -1 & 2 \\ 1 & -1 & -1 \end{pmatrix}$

8. $\begin{pmatrix} 2 & 0 & 1 \\ 0 & 3 & 2 \\ -1 & 1 & 0 \end{pmatrix} \begin{pmatrix} -1 & 2 & 3 \\ 2 & -1 & 2 \\ 1 & -1 & 1 \end{pmatrix}$

9. $\begin{pmatrix} -2 & 3 & 1 \\ 1 & 0 & 2 \end{pmatrix} \begin{pmatrix} -2 & 1 \\ -1 & 3 \\ 4 & -1 \\ 2 & 0 \end{pmatrix}$

10. $\begin{pmatrix} 2 & -1 \\ -1 & 4 \\ 2 & 2 \end{pmatrix} \begin{pmatrix} 3 \\ -2 \end{pmatrix}$

11. $\begin{pmatrix} 1 & -4 & 3 \\ -1 & 1 & 2 \end{pmatrix} \begin{pmatrix} 2 & -2 \\ -3 & 4 \\ 0 & 1 \end{pmatrix}$

12. $\begin{pmatrix} 2 & -1 & 3 \\ 1 & 2 & -1 \\ -1 & 1 & 1 \end{pmatrix} \begin{pmatrix} -3 & -4 & 2 \\ 4 & -2 & -3 \\ -2 & 3 & 5 \end{pmatrix}$

In Exercise 13–16 compute A^2 and A^3 for each of the given matrices A.

13. $\begin{pmatrix} 2 & -1 \\ 1 & 3 \end{pmatrix}$

14. $\begin{pmatrix} 2 & 0 \\ 0 & -3 \end{pmatrix}$

15. $\begin{pmatrix} 1 & 2 & -1 \\ 0 & -3 & 1 \\ 0 & 0 & 2 \end{pmatrix}$

16. $\begin{pmatrix} 1 & 0 & -1 \\ 0 & -1 & 1 \\ 1 & 1 & 0 \end{pmatrix}$

17. Write I_2, I_5, and $2I_3$.

18. Verify each part of Theorem 3.2 for

$$A = \begin{pmatrix} 2 & -1 \\ 0 & 1 \end{pmatrix}, B = \begin{pmatrix} 1 & 3 & -1 \\ 2 & 0 & 1 \end{pmatrix}, D = \begin{pmatrix} -1 & 2 & 0 \\ 3 & 1 & -1 \end{pmatrix},$$

$$C = \begin{pmatrix} 3 & -1 & 2 \\ 0 & 1 & -1 \\ 1 & 2 & 2 \end{pmatrix}, k = 4$$

19. Verify each part of Theorem 3.2 for

$$A = \begin{pmatrix} 4 & -1 & 1 \\ 2 & 3 & -1 \end{pmatrix}, B = \begin{pmatrix} -1 & 1 & 2 \\ 1 & 0 & 1 \\ 0 & 2 & 1 \end{pmatrix}, D = \begin{pmatrix} 2 & -1 & 3 \\ 1 & 1 & 1 \\ -1 & 4 & 0 \end{pmatrix}$$

$$C = \begin{pmatrix} 1 & 2 \\ 0 & -1 \\ 2 & 1 \end{pmatrix}, k = -2$$

20. Most of the pollutants due to stationary fuel combustion are emitted by electrical utilities. Matrix A below gives the average proportion of the stationary fuel combustion pollutants caused by electrical utilities for the period 1970–1971, and matrix B gives the amounts (in millions of tons) of each pollutant emitted by stationary fuel combustion in 1970 and 1971.[5]

	Carbon monoxide	Sulfur oxides	Hydrocarbons	Particulates	Nitrogen oxides
$A =$	(0.190	0.752	0.105	0.568	0.537)

	1970	1971
Carbon monoxide	1.1	1.0
Sulfur oxides	27.0	26.3
Hydrocarbons	1.6	0.3	$= B$
Particulates	8.3	6.5
Nitrogen oxides	10.1	10.2

Compute the product AB and interpret its meaning.

21. A factory produces two alloys, A and B, from three raw materials (iron, copper, and zinc). Matrix P below gives the number of units of each raw material used in producing one ton of each alloy.

---

[5] *Source: Statistical Abstract of the United States, 1974.* Washington, D.C.: U.S. Department of Commerce, Bureau of the Census.

$$\begin{array}{c} \\ \text{Iron} \\ \text{Copper} \\ \text{Zinc} \end{array} \begin{array}{c} \text{A} \quad \text{B} \\ \begin{pmatrix} 3 & 4 \\ 1 & 2 \\ 2 & 1 \end{pmatrix} = P \end{array}$$

In preparing the raw materials for use the factory uses three forms of energy (electricity, natural gas, and oil). Matrix Q gives the number of units of each form of energy required to process one unit of each raw material.

$$\begin{array}{c} \\ \text{Electricity (kilowatt-hours)} \\ \text{Natural gas (British thermal units)} \\ \text{Oil (gallons)} \end{array} \begin{array}{c} \text{Iron} \quad \text{Copper} \quad \text{Zinc} \\ \begin{pmatrix} 2 & 1 & 1 \\ 1 & 0 & 1 \\ 1 & 1 & 0 \end{pmatrix} = Q \end{array}$$

Use matrix multiplication to determine the number of units of each form of energy required to produce one ton of each alloy.

22. A grocery store with three locations sells its own brand of four food items. Matrix A below contains the number of units of each of these items sold at each store on a given day. Matrix B below contains the price and profit (in dollars) for each of these items. Use matrix multiplication to determine the total revenue and total profit at each location for these four items on the day in question.

$$\begin{array}{c} \\ \text{Location 1} \\ \text{Location 2} \\ \text{Location 3} \end{array} \begin{array}{c} \text{Peas} \quad \text{Beans} \quad \text{Applesauce} \quad \text{Milk} \\ \begin{pmatrix} 9 & 8 & 12 & 20 \\ 7 & 10 & 8 & 30 \\ 6 & 6 & 14 & 30 \end{pmatrix} = A \end{array}$$

$$\begin{array}{c} \\ \text{Peas (16-ounce can)} \\ \text{Beans (16-ounce can)} \\ \text{Applesauce (24-ounce jar)} \\ \text{Milk ($\frac{1}{2}$ gallon)} \end{array} \begin{array}{c} \text{Price} \quad \text{Profit} \\ \begin{pmatrix} 0.30 & 0.04 \\ 0.35 & 0.06 \\ 0.50 & 0.05 \\ 0.80 & 0.10 \end{pmatrix} = B \end{array}$$

23. The Sporting Chance is having a sale on men's tennis apparel. During the sale all tennis shirts are priced at $8, all shorts are $15, and all shoes are $20. To take advantage of the low prices, Tom bought 3 shirts, 1 pair of shorts, and 1 pair of shoes, and Steve bought 2 shirts, 2 pairs of shorts, and 2 pairs of shoes. Use matrix multiplication to determine the amount of money spent by Tom and Steve.

24. A bakery has received special orders for 6 loaves of bread, 2 cakes, 8 dozen Danish pastries, and 4 pies on Friday, and 8 loaves of bread, 4 cakes, 9 dozen pastries, and 7 pies on Saturday. Each loaf of bread requires 4 cups of flour and $\frac{1}{4}$ cup of shortening; each cake requires 6 eggs, 2 cups of flour, 2 cups of milk, 1 cup of shortening, and 3 cups of sugar; a dozen pastries requires 2 eggs, 4 cups of flour, 1 cup of milk, $\frac{1}{2}$ cup of shortening, and 4 cups of sugar; and each pie requires 1 cup of flour, $\frac{1}{2}$ cup of shortening, and 1 cup of sugar. Use matrix multiplication to determine the amounts of each ingredient required to fill each day's special orders.

25. In 1974 in the United States there were 25.7 million people aged 18–24, 29.3 million aged 25–34, 22.4 million aged 35–44, 43.0 million aged 45–64, and 21.0 million aged 65 or above. Of those aged 18–24, 23.7% voted in the national election and 76.3% did not; of those aged 25–34, 37.0% voted and 63.0% did not; of those aged 35–44, 49.1% voted and 50.9% did not; of those aged 45–64, 56.9% voted and 43.1% did not; and of those aged 65 or above, 51.4% voted and 48.6% did not.[6] Use matrix multiplication to determine the number of voters and nonvoters in 1974.

26. In 1972 manufacturing corporations earned $0.043 profit per dollar of sales, and the corresponding figure for 1973 was $0.047. In 1972 manufacturers of durable goods had sales of $435.8 billion, and manufacturers of nondurable goods had sales of $413.7 billion. For 1973 the corresponding figures were $527.3 billion for durable goods and $489.9 billion for nondurable goods.[7] Use matrix multiplication to determine the total profits for manufacturers of durable goods and for manufacturers of nondurable goods during the two-year period 1972–1973.

*3.4 Incidence Matrices

Although we have used matrices in the preceding sections only to record quantitative data, they can also be useful in work with certain types of qualitative data. In this section we shall consider a special type of matrix that has been used in the study of communication networks and sociological relations.

Suppose that we have a relation defined for a set of n persons (or objects). This relation can be completely described with an $n \times n$ matrix $A = (a_{ij})$ by defining $a_{ij} = 1$ if person i stands in the given relationship to person j and $a_{ij} = 0$ otherwise. Any square matrix such as this in which the entries consist entirely of zeros and ones is called an *incidence matrix*. For convenience we also require that the diagonal entries of every incidence matrix be zero, that is, that no person is related to himself or herself.

incidence matrix

For the sake of illustration, let us assume that we have four people with communication devices and that the only transmissions possible are those indicated in Table 3.4.

Table 3.4 *Possible Transmissions*

Sender	Possible receivers
1	2, 4
2	3, 4
3	1, 4
4	2

---

[6] *Source: Statistical Abstract of the United States, 1976.* Washington, D.C.: U.S. Department of Commerce, Bureau of the Census.

[7] *Source: Statistical Abstract of the United States, 1975.* Washington, D.C.: U.S. Department of Commerce, Bureau of the Census.

In this case the relation "can send to" is described by the incidence matrix

$$A = \begin{pmatrix} 0 & 1 & 0 & 1 \\ 0 & 0 & 1 & 1 \\ 1 & 0 & 0 & 1 \\ 0 & 1 & 0 & 0 \end{pmatrix}$$

Let us consider the significance of the entries of

$$A^2 = \begin{pmatrix} 0 & 1 & 1 & 1 \\ 1 & 1 & 0 & 1 \\ 0 & 2 & 0 & 1 \\ 0 & 0 & 1 & 1 \end{pmatrix}$$

Since the i, j entry of A^2 can be nonzero only if some entry in row i of A and the corresponding entry in column j are both 1s, it is not difficult to see that the i, j entry of A^2 represents the number of two-stage transmissions that can be sent from person i to person j. By a *two-stage transmission* from i to j we mean a transmission sent from i to j through one intermediate sender. For example, the 1, 3 entry of A^2 signifies that there is one two-stage transmission from person 1 to person 3, namely, sending from person 1 to person 2 and then from person 2 to person 3. Likewise the 3, 2 entry of A^2 signifies that there are two different two-stage transmissions from person 3 to person 2—one via person 1 and another via person 4.

Similarly it may be shown that the i, j entry of A^m represents the number of different m-stage transmissions from person i to person j. However, not all these transmissions are efficient; that is, a transmission from i to j to i to k is counted as a three-stage transmission even though the same communication could have occurred directly from i to k. With these inefficient communications included, it is easy to see that the i, j entry of

$$A + A^2 + \cdots + A^m$$

represents the number of different transmissions from person i to person j that are possible in m stages or less. Analogous interpretations may be given to the entries of A^m and $A + A^2 + \cdots + A^m$ for any incidence matrix A.

clique   Let us again return to the general situation of an arbitrary relation for a set of n persons. By a *clique* we mean any maximal collection (that is, one that cannot be enlarged) of three or more persons with the property that each person in the clique is related to every other person in the clique.

EXAMPLE 11

Consider a relation for a group of five persons for which the associated incidence matrix is

$$A = \begin{pmatrix} 0 & 1 & 0 & 1 & 1 \\ 0 & 0 & 1 & 1 & 1 \\ 1 & 1 & 0 & 1 & 1 \\ 1 & 1 & 1 & 0 & 1 \\ 1 & 1 & 1 & 0 & 0 \end{pmatrix}$$

Persons 2, 3, and 4 form a clique because each is related to the other two and no larger set has this property. Specifically person 1 cannot be included with persons, 2, 3, and 4 to form a larger set because he is not related to person 3, and person 5 cannot be included because she is not related to person 4. The reader should verify that persons 2, 3, and 5 also form a clique.

When the number of individuals in the group is large, it is quite difficult to determine cliques by inspection. Fortunately, there is an easy method for detecting membership in a clique that utilizes matrix multiplication. In order to determine which persons belong to cliques, we form from the incidence matrix of the relation a new matrix $B = (b_{ij})$ as follows: If $A = (a_{ij})$, where $i = 1, 2, \ldots, n$ and $j = 1, 2, \ldots, n$, is the incidence matrix, then we define b_{ij} for $i = 1, 2, \ldots, n$ and $j = 1, 2, \ldots, n$ to be

$$\begin{cases} 1 & \text{if } a_{ij} = 1 \text{ and } a_{ji} = 1 \\ 0 & \text{otherwise} \end{cases}$$

Then person i belongs to a clique precisely when the i, i entry of B^3 (that is, the ith diagonal entry) is nonzero.

EXAMPLE 12

For the incidence matrix A in Example 11 the matrix B is

$$B = \begin{pmatrix} 0 & 0 & 0 & 1 & 1 \\ 0 & 0 & 1 & 1 & 1 \\ 0 & 1 & 0 & 1 & 1 \\ 1 & 1 & 1 & 0 & 0 \\ 1 & 1 & 1 & 0 & 0 \end{pmatrix}$$

Thus

$$B^2 = \begin{pmatrix} 2 & 2 & 2 & 0 & 0 \\ 2 & 3 & 2 & 1 & 1 \\ 2 & 2 & 3 & 1 & 1 \\ 0 & 1 & 1 & 3 & 3 \\ 0 & 1 & 1 & 3 & 3 \end{pmatrix} \quad \text{and} \quad B^3 = \begin{pmatrix} 0 & 2 & 2 & 6 & 6 \\ 2 & 4 & 5 & 7 & 7 \\ 2 & 5 & 4 & 7 & 7 \\ 6 & 7 & 7 & 2 & 2 \\ 6 & 7 & 7 & 2 & 2 \end{pmatrix}$$

Since the first diagonal entry of B^3 is zero, person 1 belongs to no cliques. But the second, third, fourth, and fifth diagonal entries of B^3 are nonzero, and thus persons 2, 3, 4, and 5 all belong to at least one clique.

Under certain circumstances it is possible to deduce the number of cliques to which person i belongs from the value of the ith diagonal entry of B^3. The interested reader should refer to [1].

In large business organizations certain individuals are required to communicate while performing their jobs and others are not. In this situation it is appropriate to assume that if person i communicates with person j, then person j will also communicate with person i. Hence if $A = (a_{ij})$, where $i = 1, 2, \ldots, n$ and $j = 1, 2, \ldots, n$, is the incidence matrix describing this communication relation, then $a_{ij} = 1$ if and only if $a_{ji} = 1$. We assume further that every individual in the organization can communicate with every other individual in a finite number of stages.

liaison person

A member of this organization is called a *liaison person* if his or her removal from the relation makes it impossible for some individuals to communicate. Liaison persons play crucial roles in ensuring that the organization operates smoothly; an inefficient liaison person can easily become a "bottleneck" who obstructs communication throughout the organization.

It is easy to see that in an organization containing n people, two persons who can communicate must be able to communicate in at most $n - 1$ stages. Thus the assumption that every pair of individuals in the organization can communicate in a finite number of stages implies that the matrix

$$A + A^2 + \cdots + A^{n-1}$$

has no zero entries. Likewise *person i will be a liaison person precisely when the matrix*

$$B + B^2 + \cdots + B^{n-2}$$

where B is obtained by deleting row i and column i from A, has at least one zero entry.

EXAMPLE 13

Let

$$A = \begin{pmatrix} 0 & 1 & 1 & 0 & 0 & 0 \\ 1 & 0 & 1 & 1 & 0 & 0 \\ 1 & 1 & 0 & 1 & 0 & 0 \\ 0 & 1 & 1 & 0 & 1 & 1 \\ 0 & 0 & 0 & 1 & 0 & 1 \\ 0 & 0 & 0 & 1 & 1 & 0 \end{pmatrix}$$

be the incidence matrix describing the communication network of a six-person business organization. The reader should verify that $A + A^2 + \cdots + A^5$ contains no zero entries. To check if person 2 is a liaison person, we form the matrix

$$B = \begin{pmatrix} 0 & 1 & 0 & 0 & 0 \\ 1 & 0 & 1 & 0 & 0 \\ 0 & 1 & 0 & 1 & 1 \\ 0 & 0 & 1 & 0 & 1 \\ 0 & 0 & 1 & 1 & 0 \end{pmatrix}$$

by deleting the second row and second column from A. Computing

$$B + B^2 + B^3 + B^4 = \begin{pmatrix} 0 & 1 & 0 & 0 & 0 \\ 1 & 0 & 1 & 0 & 0 \\ 0 & 1 & 0 & 1 & 1 \\ 0 & 0 & 1 & 0 & 1 \\ 0 & 0 & 1 & 1 & 0 \end{pmatrix} + \begin{pmatrix} 1 & 0 & 1 & 0 & 0 \\ 0 & 2 & 0 & 1 & 1 \\ 1 & 0 & 3 & 1 & 1 \\ 0 & 1 & 1 & 2 & 1 \\ 0 & 1 & 1 & 1 & 2 \end{pmatrix}$$

$$+ \begin{pmatrix} 0 & 2 & 0 & 1 & 1 \\ 2 & 0 & 4 & 1 & 1 \\ 0 & 4 & 2 & 4 & 4 \\ 1 & 1 & 4 & 2 & 3 \\ 1 & 1 & 4 & 3 & 2 \end{pmatrix} + \begin{pmatrix} 2 & 0 & 4 & 1 & 1 \\ 0 & 6 & 2 & 5 & 5 \\ 4 & 2 & 12 & 6 & 6 \\ 1 & 5 & 6 & 7 & 6 \\ 1 & 5 & 6 & 6 & 7 \end{pmatrix}$$

$$= \begin{pmatrix} 3 & 3 & 5 & 2 & 2 \\ 3 & 8 & 7 & 7 & 7 \\ 5 & 7 & 17 & 12 & 12 \\ 2 & 7 & 12 & 11 & 11 \\ 2 & 7 & 12 & 11 & 11 \end{pmatrix}$$

we see that person 2 is not a liaison person since $B + B^2 + B^3 + B^4$ has no zero entries. On the other hand, person 4 is a liaison person, for if we delete the fourth row and fourth column from A we obtain

$$C = \begin{pmatrix} 0 & 1 & 1 & 0 & 0 \\ 1 & 0 & 1 & 0 & 0 \\ 1 & 1 & 0 & 0 & 0 \\ 0 & 0 & 0 & 0 & 1 \\ 0 & 0 & 0 & 1 & 0 \end{pmatrix}$$

and $C + C^2 + C^3 + C^4$ is easily seen to contain zero entries (see Exercise 33).

Another common type of sociological relation is the dominance relation. In this type of relation it is impossible for two persons to dominate each other. Thus if $A = (a_{ij})$ is the incidence matrix of a dominance relation, then it is impossible for both $a_{ij} = 1$ and $a_{ji} = 1$. We assume also that, for any two individuals i and j, either i dominates j or j dominates i. This assumption combined with the previous observation implies that for all i and j, $a_{ij} = 1$ if and only if $a_{ji} = 0$. An example of this type of relation is the pecking order among a flock of chickens.

In this situation a surprising result can be proved: *There must be at least one person who dominates all the others in either one or two stages; that is, some row of $A + A^2$ contains positive entries in every position except on the diagonal. In fact, any person who dominates the greatest number of people in one stage must dominate all the others in at most two stages.* Likewise there must be at least one person who is dominated by all the others in either one or two stages; that is, some column of $A + A^2$ contains positive entries in every position except on the diagonal. Moreover, any person who is dominated by the greatest number of people in one stage must have this property.

APPLICATION 2

S. Sidney Ulmer [5] made use of these ideas to study the influence among justices of the Michigan Supreme Court from 1958 to 1960. By determining the number of times one judge supported an opinion written by another, Ulmer was able to determine a dominance relation among the eight justices. The incidence matrix A corresponding to this dominance relation is as follows:

	Black	Carr	Dethmers	Edwards	Kavanagh	Kelly	Smith	Voelker
Black	0	0	0	0	0	0	0	0
Carr	1	0	1	1	0	1	1	0
Dethmers	1	0	0	1	0	1	1	1
Edwards	1	0	0	0	0	1	0	0
Kavanagh	1	1	1	1	0	1	1	0
Kelly	1	0	0	0	0	0	0	0
Smith	1	0	0	1	0	1	0	0
Voelker	1	1	0	1	1	1	1	0

Since Kavanagh and Voelker each dominate the greatest number of persons in one stage (six), the result stated above guarantees that each of them dominates the other seven justices in at most two stages. To verify this conclusion note that rows 5 and 8 of $A + A^2$ contain nonzero entries in every position except on the diagonal.

$$A + A^2 = \begin{pmatrix} 0 & 0 & 0 & 0 & 0 & 0 & 0 & 0 \\ 5 & 0 & 1 & 3 & 0 & 4 & 2 & 1 \\ 5 & 1 & 0 & 3 & 1 & 4 & 2 & 1 \\ 2 & 0 & 0 & 0 & 0 & 1 & 0 & 0 \\ 6 & 1 & 2 & 4 & 0 & 5 & 3 & 1 \\ 1 & 0 & 0 & 0 & 0 & 0 & 0 & 0 \\ 3 & 0 & 0 & 1 & 0 & 2 & 0 & 0 \\ 6 & 2 & 2 & 4 & 1 & 5 & 3 & 0 \end{pmatrix}$$

Observe that in this case Justice Dethmers also dominates all the others in at most two stages, and Justice Black, who is dominated in one stage by all the others, is the only judge dominated by all his colleagues in two stages.

Exercises

1. Of the six children living in a certain neighborhood, John likes to play with Curtis, George, and Mary; Linda likes to play with Mary and Lisa; Curtis likes to play with George, John, and Linda; Mary likes to play with Linda, Lisa, and George; George likes to play with Curtis and John; and Lisa likes to play with Linda, Mary, and John. Write the incidence matrix describing these children's preferences for playmates.

For each of the incidence matrices in Exercises 2–4 determine the number of two-stage and three-stage transmissions from person 1 to person 3.

2. $\begin{pmatrix} 0 & 1 & 1 \\ 0 & 0 & 1 \\ 0 & 1 & 0 \end{pmatrix}$

3. $\begin{pmatrix} 0 & 1 & 0 & 0 \\ 1 & 0 & 1 & 1 \\ 1 & 1 & 0 & 0 \\ 1 & 0 & 1 & 0 \end{pmatrix}$

4. $\begin{pmatrix} 0 & 1 & 0 & 1 \\ 1 & 0 & 0 & 1 \\ 1 & 0 & 1 & 0 \\ 0 & 1 & 1 & 0 \end{pmatrix}$

If the incidence matrices in Exercises 5–9 represent the possibility of sending a message from one person to another, is it possible for each person to send a message to every other person? If so, what is the minimum number of stages required?

5. $\begin{pmatrix} 0 & 1 & 0 \\ 0 & 0 & 1 \\ 1 & 0 & 0 \end{pmatrix}$

6. $\begin{pmatrix} 0 & 1 & 1 \\ 0 & 0 & 1 \\ 0 & 1 & 0 \end{pmatrix}$

7. $\begin{pmatrix} 0 & 1 & 0 & 0 \\ 1 & 0 & 0 & 0 \\ 0 & 0 & 0 & 1 \\ 0 & 0 & 1 & 0 \end{pmatrix}$

8. $\begin{pmatrix} 0 & 0 & 1 & 0 \\ 1 & 0 & 0 & 0 \\ 0 & 0 & 0 & 1 \\ 0 & 1 & 0 & 0 \end{pmatrix}$

9. $\begin{pmatrix} 0 & 1 & 0 & 0 \\ 0 & 0 & 1 & 0 \\ 1 & 0 & 0 & 0 \\ 1 & 0 & 1 & 0 \end{pmatrix}$

10. A civic organization has established a telephone chain to communicate with its officers. One round of calls consists of Smith calling Jones and Taylor, Taylor calling Johnson and White, White calling Johnson and Clark, Clark calling Smith and Taylor, or Johnson calling Jones and Smith. (Jones refuses to call anyone.) If Johnson makes the first call, how many

rounds of calls are necessary before everyone is called? What if White makes the first call?

In the relations having the incidence matrices given in Exercises 11–14, determine which persons belong to at least one clique.

11. $\begin{pmatrix} 0 & 1 & 1 & 1 \\ 1 & 0 & 0 & 1 \\ 0 & 1 & 0 & 1 \\ 1 & 1 & 1 & 0 \end{pmatrix}$
12. $\begin{pmatrix} 0 & 1 & 1 & 0 \\ 1 & 0 & 1 & 1 \\ 0 & 1 & 0 & 1 \\ 0 & 1 & 1 & 0 \end{pmatrix}$

13. $\begin{pmatrix} 0 & 0 & 1 & 1 & 1 \\ 1 & 0 & 1 & 1 & 1 \\ 1 & 1 & 0 & 1 & 1 \\ 0 & 1 & 1 & 0 & 1 \\ 0 & 1 & 1 & 1 & 0 \end{pmatrix}$
14. $\begin{pmatrix} 0 & 1 & 1 & 1 & 1 \\ 1 & 0 & 1 & 1 & 1 \\ 1 & 1 & 0 & 1 & 1 \\ 1 & 0 & 1 & 0 & 1 \\ 1 & 1 & 0 & 1 & 0 \end{pmatrix}$

15. For six doctors in a certain city, the following facts were found:

   Anderson makes referrals to Brown, Carter, Dooley, and Evans.
   Brown makes referrals to Anderson, Carter, Dooley, and Fisher.
   Carter makes referrals to Anderson, Brown, Dooley, and Evans.
   Dooley makes referrals to Brown, Carter, Evans, and Fisher.
   Evans makes referrals to Anderson, Brown, Dooley, and Fisher.
   Fisher makes referrals to each of the other five doctors.

   Prepare an incidence matrix (a_{ij}) for this relation in which $a_{ij} = 1$ if doctor i makes referrals to doctor j and $a_{ij} = 0$ otherwise. Then determine which doctors belong to at least one clique.

16. Suppose that:

   Denmark has foreign investments in England, France, Germany, and Italy.
   England has foreign investments in Denmark, France, Germany, and Italy.
   France has foreign investments in Denmark, England, Germany, and Italy.
   Germany has foreign investments in Denmark, England, France, Holland, and Italy.
   Holland has foreign investments in Denmark, France, and Italy.
   Italy has foreign investments in Denmark, England, Germany, and Holland.

   Prepare an incidence matrix (a_{ij}) for this relation in which $a_{ij} = 1$ if country i has foreign investments in country j and $a_{ij} = 0$ otherwise. Then determine which countries belong to at least one clique.

Determine the liaison persons (if any) in the communication relations described by the incidence matrices in Exercises 17–20.

17. $\begin{pmatrix} 0 & 1 & 0 & 1 & 0 \\ 1 & 0 & 0 & 1 & 0 \\ 0 & 0 & 0 & 1 & 1 \\ 1 & 1 & 1 & 0 & 1 \\ 0 & 0 & 1 & 1 & 0 \end{pmatrix}$
18. $\begin{pmatrix} 0 & 1 & 0 & 0 & 1 \\ 1 & 0 & 1 & 1 & 1 \\ 0 & 1 & 0 & 1 & 0 \\ 0 & 1 & 1 & 0 & 1 \\ 1 & 1 & 0 & 1 & 0 \end{pmatrix}$

19. $\begin{pmatrix} 0 & 1 & 1 & 0 & 1 \\ 1 & 0 & 0 & 1 & 1 \\ 1 & 0 & 0 & 1 & 0 \\ 0 & 1 & 1 & 0 & 1 \\ 1 & 1 & 0 & 1 & 0 \end{pmatrix}$ 20. $\begin{pmatrix} 0 & 1 & 0 & 1 & 0 \\ 1 & 0 & 1 & 0 & 0 \\ 0 & 1 & 0 & 0 & 1 \\ 1 & 0 & 0 & 0 & 1 \\ 0 & 0 & 1 & 1 & 0 \end{pmatrix}$

21. Suppose that the following pairs of countries maintain diplomatic relations: Austria and Belgium, Austria and Denmark, Belgium and Czechoslovakia, Belgium and Denmark, Czechoslovakia and Denmark, and Czechoslovakia and Estonia. Prepare an incidence matrix for the relationship "maintains diplomatic relations" and verify that this relationship is a communication relation for these five countries. Then determine all the liaison countries.

22. Among a group of former college classmates, the following pairs have continued to correspond: Alice and Carol, Alice and Denise, Barbara and Carol, Barbara and Elaine, and Carol and Elaine. Prepare an incidence matrix for the relationship "corresponds" and verify that this is a communication relation. Then determine all the liaison persons.

Show that each of the incidence matrices in Exercises 23–28 is the matrix of a dominance relation. Predict without computation which persons will dominate all the others in at most two stages and which persons will be dominated by all the others in at most two stages. Then compute if there are any others with these properties.

23. $\begin{pmatrix} 0 & 1 & 0 \\ 0 & 0 & 0 \\ 1 & 1 & 0 \end{pmatrix}$ 24. $\begin{pmatrix} 0 & 0 & 1 \\ 1 & 0 & 0 \\ 0 & 1 & 0 \end{pmatrix}$ 25. $\begin{pmatrix} 0 & 0 & 0 & 1 \\ 1 & 0 & 1 & 1 \\ 1 & 0 & 0 & 0 \\ 0 & 0 & 1 & 0 \end{pmatrix}$

26. $\begin{pmatrix} 0 & 0 & 1 & 0 \\ 1 & 0 & 1 & 0 \\ 0 & 0 & 0 & 1 \\ 1 & 1 & 0 & 0 \end{pmatrix}$ 27. $\begin{pmatrix} 0 & 0 & 1 & 1 \\ 1 & 0 & 0 & 1 \\ 0 & 1 & 0 & 1 \\ 0 & 0 & 0 & 0 \end{pmatrix}$ 28. $\begin{pmatrix} 0 & 1 & 1 & 0 \\ 0 & 0 & 1 & 0 \\ 0 & 0 & 0 & 0 \\ 1 & 1 & 1 & 0 \end{pmatrix}$

29. In Application 2 determine the dominance relation among the three Republican justices (Carr, Dethmers, and Kelly). Who dominates the others in two stages?

30. In Application 2 determine the dominance relation among the five Democratic justices (Black, Edwards, Kavanagh, Smith, and Voelker). Who dominates the others in two stages?

31. During the year 1977:[8]

> Canada had a trade surplus with Italy, Japan, and the United States.
> France had a trade surplus with Canada.
> Italy had a trade surplus with France, Japan, and the United States.
> Japan had a trade surplus with France and the United States.
> The United States had a trade surplus with France.

Prepare an incidence matrix $A = (a_{ij})$ for this relationship in which $a_{ij} = 1$ if country i had a trade surplus with country j and $a_{ij} = 0$ other-

[8] *Source: Yearbook of International Trade Statistics 1977*, vol. 1. New York: United Nations Publishing Service, 1978.

wise. Show that A is the incidence matrix for a dominance relation, and predict without computation which country or countries will dominate all the others in at most two stages and which will be dominated by all the others in at most two stages. Then determine if there are any other countries with these properties by examining $A + A^2$.

32. Each of the five high school football teams in a particular city plays against the other four teams. Last season's results were as follows:

> Central beat Southern and Western.
> Northern beat Central, Eastern, and Western.
> Southern beat Northern and Western.
> Eastern beat Central and Southern.
> Western beat Eastern.

Prepare an incidence matrix $A = (a_{ij})$ for this relationship in which $a_{ij} = 1$ if team i beat team j and $a_{ij} = 0$ otherwise. Show that A is the incidence matrix for a dominance relation and predict without computation which team(s) will dominate all the others in at most two stages and which team(s) will be dominated by all the others in at most two stages. Then determine if there are any other teams with these properties by computing $A + A^2$.

33. In checking if person 4 was a liaison person in Example 13 we obtained a matrix C. If C is subdivided as

$$C = \begin{pmatrix} 0 & 1 & 1 & | & 0 & 0 \\ 1 & 0 & 1 & | & 0 & 0 \\ 1 & 1 & 0 & | & 0 & 0 \\ \hline 0 & 0 & 0 & | & 0 & 1 \\ 0 & 0 & 0 & | & 1 & 0 \end{pmatrix}$$

show that in the same subdivisions of C^2, C^3, and C^4 the lower left and upper right blocks have no nonzero entries.

3.5 Systems of Two Linear Equations in Two Unknowns

As we shall see in Section 3.7, many applications of mathematics involve systems of linear equations. In this section we shall consider the simplest case of such a system—a system of two linear equations in two unknowns. The general case will be considered in Section 3.6.

Recall that a linear equation in two unknowns x and y has the form

$$ax + by = p$$

system of two linear equations in two unknowns

where a, b, and p are constants. By a *system of two linear equations in two unknowns* we mean a pair of such equations

$$\begin{aligned} ax + by &= p \\ cx + dy &= q \end{aligned} \qquad (3.4)$$

where a, b, c, d, p, and q are constants.

solution

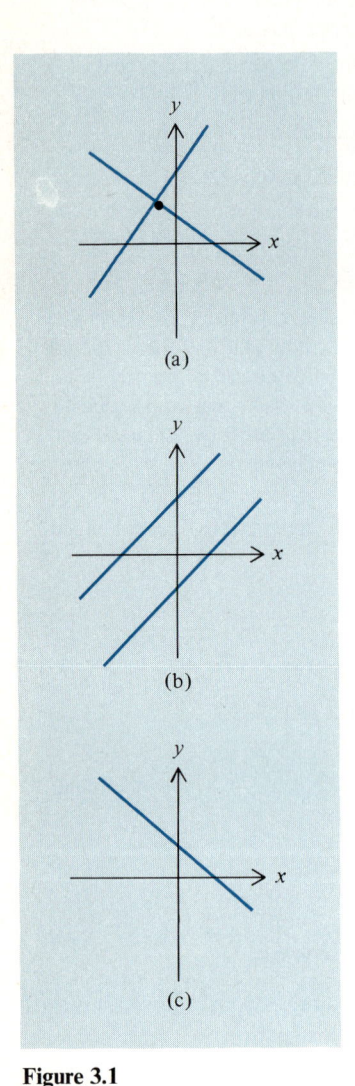

A *solution* of (3.4) is an ordered pair (s, t) such that each equation in the system is satisfied when s and t are substituted for x and y, respectively. Thus $(3, -2)$ is a solution of the system

$$x + 2y = -1$$
$$2x - y = 8$$

since both equations are satisfied when x is replaced by 3 and y is replaced by -2. On the other hand, $(1, -1)$ is not a solution of this system even though replacing x by 1 and y by -1 satisfies the first equation in the system.

We saw in Section 2.3 that the graph of every linear equation in two unknowns is a line. Geometrically, a solution of (3.4) represents a point that lies on the graph of both equations in the system. Thus there are only three possibilities for the collection of all solutions to a system of two linear equations in two unknowns:

1. There is a unique solution. This case occurs when the graphs of the equations in the system are a pair of intersecting lines. [See Figure 3.1(a).]
2. There is no solution. This situation occurs when the graphs of the equations in the system are a pair of parallel lines. [See Figure 3.1(b).]
3. There are infinitely many solutions. This is the case when the graphs of the equations in the system are lines that coincide. [See Figure 3.1(c).]

EXAMPLE 14

By graphing the equations in the systems

(a) $2x - y = 7$ (b) $x + 3y = 9$ (c) $x - 2y = 4$
    $x + y = 5$ $2x + 6y = -6$ $3x - 6y = 12$

we obtain the graphs shown in Figure 3.2. Thus we see that system (a) has a unique solution, system (b) has no solutions, and system (c) has infinitely many solutions.

For the remainder of this section, we restrict our attention to systems having unique solutions. The other possibilities will be considered in Section 3.6.

There are two principal methods for solving systems of linear equations. In the *method of substitution*, one of the equations is solved for one unknown in terms of the other and the resulting expression is substituted into the remaining equation. This substitution yields an equation involving only one variable, and hence it can be solved easily.

Figure 3.1

method of substitution

EXAMPLE 15

We shall solve the system

$$3x + 2y = 11$$
$$2x - y = 5$$

3.5 Systems of Two Linear Equations in Two Unknowns   79

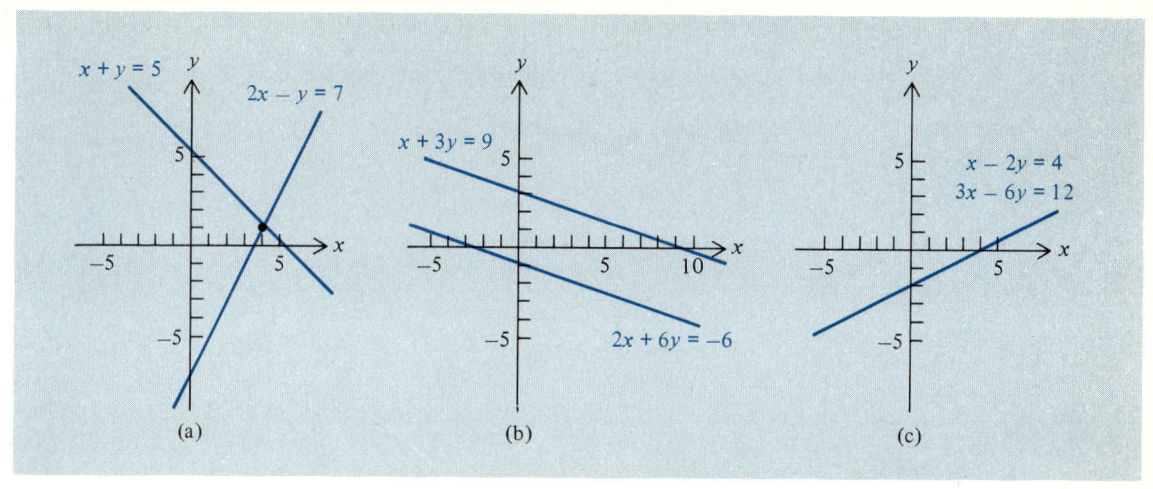

(a)   (b)   (c)

Figure 3.2

by substitution. Since the unknown y occurs with a coefficient of -1 in the second equation, it is easy to solve the second equation for y in terms of x. This yields

$$y = 2x - 5$$

When this expression is substituted into the first equation, the resulting equation can be solved for x as follows.

$$\begin{aligned} 3x + 2y &= 11 \\ 3x + 2(2x - 5) &= 11 \\ 3x + 4x - 10 &= 11 \\ 7x &= 21 \\ x &= 3 \end{aligned}$$

Once the value of x is known, we can calculate y from the equation that expresses y in terms of x:

$$y = 2x - 5 = 2(3) - 5 = 6 - 5 = 1$$

Thus (3, 1) is the unique solution of the original system.

Although the method of substitution works well for systems of two equations in two unknowns, it is usually inconvenient to use with larger systems. The *method of elimination*, on the other hand, is easily adapted to larger systems.

In the method of elimination, the original system is replaced by a system that has the same solutions but is easier to solve. The essence of the method is to replace the original system by one in which each equation contains only a single unknown (that is, to "eliminate" one of the unknowns from each equation). There are three operations

method of elimination

Chapter 3 Matrices and Systems of Linear Equations

that can be used to simplify the system:

1. Interchange the order of the equations.
2. Multiply (or divide) an equation by a nonzero number.[9]
3. Add (or subtract) a multiple of one equation to (or from) another.

EXAMPLE 16

We shall solve the system

$$\frac{1}{5}x - \frac{1}{2}y = \frac{-2}{5}$$

$$\frac{1}{8}x - \frac{1}{6}y = \frac{1}{3}$$

by the method of elimination. Before attempting to eliminate one of the unknowns, we can multiply each equation by a suitable number in order to remove the fractions. If we multiply the first equation by 10 and the second by 24, we will obtain

$$2x - 5y = -4$$
$$3x - 4y = 8$$

Now multiplying the first equation by 3 and the second equation by 2 allows us to eliminate x easily. The result of these operations is

$$6x - 15y = -12$$
$$6x - 8y = 16$$

If we now subtract the first equation from the second, we will eliminate x from the second equation:

$$6x - 15y = -12$$
$$7y = 28$$

It is now easy to solve for y by dividing the second equation by 7; this operation yields

$$6x - 15y = -12$$
$$y = 4$$

Thus by adding 15 times the second equation to the first, we can eliminate y from the first equation. The result of this operation is the system

$$6x = 48$$
$$y = 4$$

---

[9] To multiply (or divide) an equation by a number means to multiply (or divide) both sides of the equation by that number.

So dividing the first equation by 6 produces

$$x \quad = 8$$
$$y = 4$$

a system in which the solution is explicit. As we shall see, this latter system has the same solutions as the original system. Thus we can conclude that the unique solution of the original system is (8, 4).

One other remark is appropriate. It is always wise to check solutions by substituting into the original equations. Since

$$3(3) + 2(1) = 11 \quad \text{and} \quad 2(3) - 1 = 5$$

we see, for example, that (3, 1) satisfies both the original equations in Example 15. The reader should verify similarly that (8, 4) satisfies both the original equations in Example 16.

Notice in Example 16 that the important information in each system of equations is the coefficients of the unknowns and the constants on the right sides of the equations. Thus we can abbreviate a system of equations by writing only these numbers; the resulting matrix is called the "augmented matrix" of the system.

EXAMPLE 17

The augmented matrix of the system of linear equations

$$2x - y = 8$$
$$x + 2y = -1$$

is

$$\begin{pmatrix} 2 & -1 & | & 8 \\ 1 & 2 & | & -1 \end{pmatrix}$$

The dashed line in the matrix separates the coefficients of the unknowns from the constants on the right side of the equations.

The operations on page 80 that can be used to simplify a system of equations correspond to the following operations on the rows of the augmented matrix.

1. Interchange any two rows of the matrix.
2. Multiply (or divide) any row by a nonzero number.
3. Add (or subtract) a multiple of one row to (or from) another.

elementary row operations

These three operations are called *elementary row operations*. Their usefulness in solving systems of linear equations is a consequence of the following result.

THEOREM 3.3

If an elementary row operation is performed on the augmented matrix of a system of linear equations, the resulting matrix is the augmented matrix of a system that has the same solution(s) as the original system.

To illustrate the use of these operations, we shall solve the system of equations in Example 17. For the sake of comparison we shall also solve the system by operating on the equations as in Example 16.

System · **Augmented Matrix**

$$2x - y = 8$$
$$x + 2y = -1$$

$$\begin{pmatrix} 2 & -1 & | & 8 \\ 1 & 2 & | & -1 \end{pmatrix}$$

Interchange the first and second equations. · Interchange the first and second rows.

$$x + 2y = -1$$
$$2x - y = 8$$

$$\begin{pmatrix} 1 & 2 & | & -1 \\ 2 & -1 & | & 8 \end{pmatrix}$$

Add -2 times the first equation to the second. · Add -2 times the first row to the second.

$$x + 2y = -1$$
$$-5y = 10$$

$$\begin{pmatrix} 1 & 2 & | & -1 \\ 0 & -5 & | & 10 \end{pmatrix}$$

Divide the second equation by -5. · Divide the second row by -5.

$$x + 2y = -1$$
$$y = -2$$

$$\begin{pmatrix} 1 & 2 & | & -1 \\ 0 & 1 & | & -2 \end{pmatrix}$$

Add -2 times the second equation to the first. · Add -2 times the second row to the first.

$$x = 3$$
$$y = -2$$

$$\begin{pmatrix} 1 & 0 & | & 3 \\ 0 & 1 & | & -2 \end{pmatrix}$$

The unique solution of the given system is therefore $(3, -2)$.

EXAMPLE 18

A craftsman designs and manufactures clocks of two different sizes. Each small clock requires 3 hours of manufacturing time and parts costing $50, whereas each large clock requires 6 hours of manufacturing time and parts costing $80. How many clocks of each size should the craftsman make during a three-week period in order to use exactly 120 hours of manufacturing time and $1800 for parts?

In order to answer this question, let x and y denote the number of small and large clocks to be made. The information in the preceding paragraph can then be represented in the following tabular form.

	Small clock	Large clock	Amount available
Number made	x	y	—
Manufacturing time (hours)	3	6	120
Cost of parts (dollars)	50	80	1800

From this table it is easy to see that the system of linear equations describing this problem is

$$3x + 6y = 120 \quad \text{(manufacturing time restriction)}$$
$$50x + 80y = 1800 \quad \text{(cost restriction)}$$

The augmented matrix of this system is

$$\begin{pmatrix} 3 & 6 & | & 120 \\ 50 & 80 & | & 1800 \end{pmatrix}$$

We shall solve this system by using elementary row operations to simplify the augmented matrix. First, to reduce the size of the numbers involved, let us divide the first row by 3 and the second row by 10. The result of these operations is

$$\begin{pmatrix} 1 & 2 & | & 40 \\ 5 & 8 & | & 180 \end{pmatrix}$$

Adding -5 times the first row to the second row produces

$$\begin{pmatrix} 1 & 2 & | & 40 \\ 0 & -2 & | & -20 \end{pmatrix}$$

Dividing the second row by -2 yields

$$\begin{pmatrix} 1 & 2 & | & 40 \\ 0 & 1 & | & 10 \end{pmatrix}$$

Finally, by adding -2 times the second row to the first row, we obtain

$$\begin{pmatrix} 1 & 0 & | & 20 \\ 0 & 1 & | & 10 \end{pmatrix}$$

So $x = 20$ and $y = 10$; that is, the craftsman should make 20 small clocks and 10 large clocks during the three-week period.

In the next section the process of simplifying the augmented matrix will be used to obtain a procedure for solving any system of linear equations.

Exercises

In Exercises 1–10, solve the given systems by the method of substitution.

1. $2x + y = 9$
   $3x - y = 6$

2. $x - 2y = 6$
   $x + 5y = -8$

3. $x + 4y = -9$
   $2x - 3y = 4$

4. $2x + y = 10$
   $3x - 4y = 4$

5. $4x - 3y = -2$
   $2x + y = -6$

6. $2x + 3y = 9$
   $x + 2y = 2$

7. $2x - 3y = 3$
   $5x + 2y = 36$

8. $3x + 2y = -16$
   $2x - 7y = 6$

9. $2x + 5y = 10$
   $6x + 2y = -9$

10. $2x - 4y = 7$
    $5x + 3y = -2$

In Exercises 11–20, solve the given systems by simplifying the augmented matrix.

11. $x - 2y = -6$
    $x + 3y = 4$

12. $3x + y = 15$
    $2x - y = 5$

13. $3x - y = -3$
    $2x + 5y = -2$

14. $x - 5y = 5$
    $2x - 7y = 4$

15. $2x + 7y = 6$
    $3x + 5y = -2$

16. $3x - 2y = -21$
    $5x + 7y = -4$

17. $\frac{1}{5}x - \frac{1}{3}y = \frac{1}{3}$
    $\frac{1}{4}x - \frac{3}{8}y = \frac{1}{2}$

18. $\frac{1}{4}x - \frac{1}{6}y = \frac{1}{2}$
    $\frac{1}{10}x + \frac{1}{4}y = \frac{1}{5}$

19. $\frac{1}{6}x - \frac{1}{4}y = \frac{2}{3}$
    $\frac{1}{2}x - \frac{1}{5}y = \frac{9}{10}$

20. $\frac{1}{10}x + \frac{1}{30}y = \frac{1}{3}$
    $\frac{1}{5}x - \frac{1}{2}y = -\frac{8}{5}$

21. During the summer months a grocery store has found that, when the price of a head of lettuce does not exceed $0.90, the demand for lettuce is described by the equation $q = 180 - 200p$, where q denotes the quantity and p denotes the price. In addition, farmers are willing to supply heads of lettuce according to the equation $q = 150p - 30$ whenever the price per head exceeds $0.20. Determine the price at which supply equals demand.

22. A salesperson is considering two job offers. The first job pays a weekly salary of $200 plus a 6% commission on gross sales, and the second job pays a 10% commission on gross sales. For what amount of gross sales will these two jobs pay the same weekly salary?

23. A $10,000 inheritance was invested in government bonds and mutual funds. After one year the total return was $810. If the government bonds yielded a 9% return and the mutual funds yielded a 6% return, how much money was invested in each way?

24. A piggy bank contains 90 coins, each of which is either a nickel or a dime. If the value of the coins is $7.40, how many coins of each type are there?

25. A drug company must complete the manufacturing of aspirin and sleeping pills by filling and labeling bottles. Each lot of aspirin requires $1\frac{1}{2}$ hours on the filling machine and 1 hour on the labeling machine, whereas each lot of sleeping pills requires 1 hour on the filling machine and $\frac{3}{4}$ hour on the labeling machine. If the company wishes to operate the filling machine for 20 hours and the labeling machine for 14 hours, how many lots of each product can be bottled and labeled?

26. Laboratory animals being used in an experiment are to be fed a diet containing exactly 12 grams of protein and 4.6 grams of fat. Two foods are available from which to prepare the diet. The first food contains 20% protein and 12% fat, and the second food contains 30% protein and 8% fat. How many grams of each food should be mixed in order to provide the precise amounts of protein and fat required in this diet?

27. A boating enthusiast would like to canoe and sail a combined total of 30 times next summer. When this person canoes, he spends 3 hours canoeing, and when he sails, he spends 8 hours sailing. If he expects to have 120 hours to spend canoeing and sailing, how many times will he canoe and how many times will he sail?

28. An athlete is planning a daily 15-minute exercise program consisting of push-ups and sit-ups. She can do 10 push-ups per minute and 20 sit-ups per minute. If she would like to perform a total of 200 exercises, how many of each exercise should she do?

3.6 Gaussian Elimination

In Section 3.5 we saw how the elementary row operations could be used to solve a system of two linear equations in two unknowns. In this section we shall generalize this process to obtain a procedure that can be used to solve any system of linear equations.

system of linear equations

By a *system of m linear equations in n unknowns* we mean a set of equations of the form[10]

$$
\begin{aligned}
a_{11}x_1 + a_{12}x_2 + \cdots + a_{1n}x_n &= b_1 \\
a_{21}x_1 + a_{22}x_2 + \cdots + a_{2n}x_n &= b_2 \\
&\vdots \\
a_{m1}x_1 + a_{m2}x_2 + \cdots + a_{mn}x_n &= b_m
\end{aligned}
\tag{3.5}
$$

solution of a system of equations

where the coefficients a_{ij} and the constants b_i are known. A *solution* of (3.5) is an n-tuple $(c_1, c_2, \ldots, c_n)$ that satisfies every equation in the system when c_1 is substituted for x_1, c_2 is substituted for x_2, and so forth.

EXAMPLE 19

We shall see later in this section that the system of three linear equations in three unknowns

$$
\begin{aligned}
x - y + 2z &= 7 \\
-x - 9y + 8z &= 13 \\
2x + 3y - z &= 4
\end{aligned}
$$

has infinitely many solutions. The reader should verify that both $(2, 1, 3)$ and $(3, 0, 2)$ are solutions but that $(3, -2, 1)$ and $(1, 1, 1)$ are not.

---

[10] When the number of unknowns is four or less, we usually denote the unknowns by x, y, z, and w rather than by x_1, x_2, x_3, and x_4.

As in Section 3.5, the matrix

$$\begin{pmatrix} a_{11} & a_{12} & \cdots & a_{1n} & | & b_1 \\ a_{21} & a_{22} & \cdots & a_{2n} & | & b_2 \\ \vdots & \vdots & & \vdots & | & \vdots \\ a_{m1} & a_{m2} & \cdots & a_{mn} & | & b_m \end{pmatrix}$$

augmented matrix

row echelon form

consisting of the coefficients of the unknowns and the constants in (3.5) is called the *augmented matrix* of the system. Later in this section we shall describe a procedure that will enable us to transform the augmented matrix of a system of linear equations into a simple form called the *row echelon form* from which the solution(s) of the system can be easily found. First, however, we shall discuss how to obtain the solution(s) from an augmented matrix in this form.

Let us begin with a simple example. The matrix

$$\begin{pmatrix} 1 & 0 & -2 & | & 6 \\ 0 & 1 & 3 & | & 5 \end{pmatrix} \tag{3.6}$$

is the augmented matrix of the system

$$\begin{aligned} x \quad - 2z &= 6 \\ y + 3z &= 5 \end{aligned} \tag{3.7}$$

leading variable

We refer to the first unknown with a nonzero coefficient in some equation of a given system as a *leading variable*. In (3.7), for instance, x and y are the leading variables. Because of the simple form of the augmented matrix (3.6), it is easy to solve for every leading variable in (3.7) in terms of the remaining unknown z. Solving for x and y in (3.7), we obtain

$$\begin{aligned} x &= 6 + 2z \\ y &= 5 - 3z \end{aligned} \tag{3.8}$$

parameter

The variable z in (3.8) is called a *parameter*. For any choice of the parameter, we obtain values for x and y so that (x, y, z) is a solution of (3.7). If $z = 0$, for example, we obtain $x = 6$ and $y = 5$ in (3.8); thus $(x, y, z) = (6, 5, 0)$ is a solution of (3.7). Likewise if $z = 1$ in (3.8), then $x = 8$ and $y = 2$; so $(8, 2, 1)$ is another solution of (3.7). In general, if we assign an arbitrary value r to the parameter z in (3.8), we will obtain a solution of (3.7) having the form

$$(x, y, z) = (6 + 2r, 5 - 3r, r)$$

EXAMPLE 20

We shall determine the solutions of the system

$$\begin{aligned} x_1 \quad - 2x_3 \quad\quad - 4x_5 &= 7 \\ x_2 + 3x_3 \quad\quad + 2x_5 &= -5 \\ x_4 - 3x_5 &= 2 \end{aligned}$$

by expressing the leading variables in terms of the other unknowns. Since x_1, x_2, and x_4 are the leading variables in this system, we have

$$x_1 = 7 + 2x_3 + 4x_5$$
$$x_2 = -5 - 3x_3 - 2x_5$$
$$x_4 = 2 + 3x_5$$

If we assign the arbitrary values r and s to the parameters x_3 and x_5, we see that any 5-tuple of the form

$$(x_1, x_2, x_3, x_4, x_5) = (7 + 2r + 4s, -5 - 3r - 2s, r, 2 + 3s, s)$$

is a solution of the given system.

EXAMPLE 21

The augmented matrix

$$\begin{pmatrix} 1 & 0 & 0 & | & 2 \\ 0 & 1 & 0 & | & 3 \\ 0 & 0 & 1 & | & 4 \\ 0 & 0 & 0 & | & 0 \end{pmatrix}$$

corresponds to the system

$$x = 2$$
$$ y = 3$$
$$ z = 4$$

in which every unknown is a leading variable. This system has the unique solution $(x, y, z) = (2, 3, 4)$.

Gaussian elimination

The following procedure, called *Gaussian elimination* after the great German mathematician Karl Gauss (1777–1855), can be used to transform the augmented matrix of a system of linear equations into its row echelon form.

Step 1: Find the leftmost column of the matrix that contains a nonzero entry. This column is called the *pivot column*.

pivot column

Step 2: Interchange rows, if necessary, so that there is a nonzero entry a at the top of the pivot column. (In order to simplify subsequent calculations, it is desirable to make $a = 1$ or $a = -1$ if possible.)

Step 3: Divide the top row of the matrix by a.

Step 4: Make all the entries of the pivot column beneath the top entry become zero by adding suitable multiples of the top row of the matrix to the rows below.

Step 5: Cover the top row of the matrix. If there are no uncovered rows remaining, or if none of the uncovered rows contains a nonzero entry, go to step 6. Otherwise repeat steps 1–5 on the uncovered *submatrix* that remains.

Step 6: Uncover all the covered rows. Beginning with the last nonzero row and working upward, add appropriate multiples of each row to the preceding rows so that all the entries above the first nonzero number in each row become zero.

To illustrate this procedure, we shall solve the system of equations in Example 19, for which the augmented matrix is

$$\begin{pmatrix} 1 & -1 & 2 & | & 7 \\ -1 & -9 & 8 & | & 13 \\ 2 & 3 & -1 & | & 4 \end{pmatrix}$$

Since the first column contains a nonzero entry, it is the pivot column. In this case the entry at the top of the pivot column is 1, so no row interchanges are required in step 2. Moreover, in step 3 we divide the top row by 1, so no changes occur in the matrix during step 3. In step 4 we must make the 2, 1 entry and the 3, 1 entry become zero. Thus we add row 1 to row 2 and add -2 times row 1 to row 3; these operations yield

$$\begin{pmatrix} 1 & -1 & 2 & | & 7 \\ 0 & -10 & 10 & | & 20 \\ 0 & 5 & -5 & | & -10 \end{pmatrix}$$

In step 5 we cover the top row as shown below.

$$\begin{pmatrix} 1 & -1 & 2 & | & 7 \\ 0 & -10 & 10 & | & 20 \\ 0 & 5 & -5 & | & -10 \end{pmatrix}$$

Because nonzero entries remain in the uncovered rows, we must repeat steps 1–5 on the uncovered submatrix.

Since the second column is the leftmost column containing a nonzero entry in the uncovered submatrix, it is the new pivot column. Again no row interchanges are needed because the entry at the top of the pivot column (in the uncovered submatrix) is -10. Next we divide the top row of the submatrix by -10 to obtain

$$\begin{pmatrix} 1 & -1 & 2 & | & 7 \\ 0 & 1 & -1 & | & -2 \\ 0 & 5 & -5 & | & -10 \end{pmatrix}$$

Then we add -5 times row 1 of the submatrix to row 2; this operation yields

$$\begin{pmatrix} 1 & -1 & 2 & | & 7 \\ 0 & 1 & -1 & | & -2 \\ 0 & 0 & 0 & | & 0 \end{pmatrix}$$

In step 5 we cover the top row of the uncovered submatrix while continuing to cover any rows covered previously. When this step is completed, we have

$$\begin{pmatrix} 1 & -1 & 2 & | & 7 \\ 0 & 1 & -1 & | & -2 \\ 0 & 0 & 0 & | & 0 \end{pmatrix}$$

Because there are no nonzero entries in the only uncovered row, we proceed to step 6.

In step 6 we begin with row 2 of the matrix

$$\begin{pmatrix} 1 & -1 & 2 & | & 7 \\ 0 & 1 & -1 & | & -2 \\ 0 & 0 & 0 & | & 0 \end{pmatrix}$$

We wish to make zero all the entries above the first nonzero number in this row; that is, we must make the $1, 2$ entry become zero. Thus we add row 2 to row 1 to obtain

$$\begin{pmatrix} 1 & 0 & 1 & | & 5 \\ 0 & 1 & -1 & | & -2 \\ 0 & 0 & 0 & | & 0 \end{pmatrix}$$

Since all the entries are zero above the first nonzero number in each row, step 6 is complete. The system of equations corresponding to the matrix above is

$$\begin{aligned} x + z &= 5 \\ y - z &= -2 \end{aligned}$$

and this system can be solved by the method described previously. The solutions of this system are of the form

$$(x, y, z) = (5 - r, -2 + r, r)$$

EXAMPLE 22

We shall use the method of Gaussian elimination to solve the system

$$\begin{aligned} x_1 + 2x_2 + 3x_3 + x_4 + 2x_5 &= 6 \\ 3x_1 + 6x_2 + 7x_3 + 6x_4 + 3x_5 &= 21 \\ 2x_1 + 4x_2 + 5x_3 + 3x_4 &= 10 \\ x_1 + 2x_2 + 4x_3 - x_4 + x_5 &= 1 \end{aligned}$$

The augmented matrix of this system is

$$\begin{pmatrix} 1 & 2 & 3 & 1 & 2 & | & 6 \\ 3 & 6 & 7 & 6 & 3 & | & 21 \\ 2 & 4 & 5 & 3 & 0 & | & 10 \\ 1 & 2 & 4 & -1 & 1 & | & 1 \end{pmatrix}$$

Since the 1,1 entry of this matrix is 1, we can begin with step 3 of the procedure. Accordingly we add -3 times row 1 to row 2, -2 times row 1 to row 3, and -1 times row 1 to row 4; these operations yield

$$\begin{pmatrix} 1 & 2 & 3 & 1 & 2 & | & 6 \\ 0 & 0 & -2 & 3 & -3 & | & 3 \\ 0 & 0 & -1 & 1 & -4 & | & -2 \\ 0 & 0 & 1 & -2 & -1 & | & -5 \end{pmatrix}$$

The third column is the next pivot column. In order to simplify subsequent calculations, we interchange rows 2 and 4 to obtain

$$\begin{pmatrix} 1 & 2 & 3 & 1 & 2 & | & 6 \\ 0 & 0 & 1 & -2 & -1 & | & -5 \\ 0 & 0 & -1 & 1 & -4 & | & -2 \\ 0 & 0 & -2 & 3 & -3 & | & 3 \end{pmatrix}$$

Next we add row 2 to row 3 and twice row 2 to row 4; the result of these operations is

$$\begin{pmatrix} 1 & 2 & 3 & 1 & 2 & | & 6 \\ 0 & 0 & 1 & -2 & -1 & | & -5 \\ 0 & 0 & 0 & -1 & -5 & | & -7 \\ 0 & 0 & 0 & -1 & -5 & | & -7 \end{pmatrix}$$

The fourth column is the next pivot column. Dividing row 3 by -1 produces

$$\begin{pmatrix} 1 & 2 & 3 & 1 & 2 & | & 6 \\ 0 & 0 & 1 & -2 & -1 & | & -5 \\ 0 & 0 & 0 & 1 & 5 & | & 7 \\ 0 & 0 & 0 & -1 & -5 & | & -7 \end{pmatrix}$$

Then we add row 3 to row 4 to obtain

$$\begin{pmatrix} 1 & 2 & 3 & 1 & 2 & | & 6 \\ 0 & 0 & 1 & -2 & -1 & | & -5 \\ 0 & 0 & 0 & 1 & 5 & | & 7 \\ 0 & 0 & 0 & 0 & 0 & | & 0 \end{pmatrix}$$

We are now ready to begin step 6. First we must make the entries above the first nonzero number in row 3 (that is, the 1,4 entry and the 2,4 entry) become zero. Thus we add -1 times row 3 to row 1 and 2 times row 3 to row 2; these operations yield

$$\begin{pmatrix} 1 & 2 & 3 & 0 & -3 & | & -1 \\ 0 & 0 & 1 & 0 & 9 & | & 9 \\ 0 & 0 & 0 & 1 & 5 & | & 7 \\ 0 & 0 & 0 & 0 & 0 & | & 0 \end{pmatrix}$$

All that remains is to make the entry above the first nonzero number in row 2 (the 1, 3 entry) become zero. We therefore add -3 times row 2 to row 1 to obtain

$$\begin{pmatrix} 1 & 2 & 0 & 0 & -30 & | & -28 \\ 0 & 0 & 1 & 0 & 9 & | & 9 \\ 0 & 0 & 0 & 1 & 5 & | & 7 \\ 0 & 0 & 0 & 0 & 0 & | & 0 \end{pmatrix}$$

The matrix above is in row echelon form. The corresponding system of linear equations is

$$\begin{aligned} x_1 + 2x_2   - 30x_5 &= -28 \\ x_3 + 9x_5 &= 9 \\ x_4 + 5x_5 &= 7 \end{aligned}$$

So the solutions of the original system have the form

$$(x_1, x_2, x_3, x_4, x_5) = (-28 - 2r + 30s, r, 9 - 9s, 7 - 5s, s)$$

In previous examples we have considered only systems of equations that have solutions. The system

$$\begin{aligned} x + 2y - z &= 1 \\ 2x + 5y - z &= 4 \\ 3x + 4y - 5z &= 6 \end{aligned} \tag{3.9}$$

has no solutions. Let us attempt to solve this system by Gaussian elimination. Since the augmented matrix of (3.9) is

$$\begin{pmatrix} 1 & 2 & -1 & | & 1 \\ 2 & 5 & -1 & | & 4 \\ 3 & 4 & -5 & | & 6 \end{pmatrix}$$

We can begin by adding -2 times row 1 to row 2 and -3 times row 1 to row 3. These operations yield

$$\begin{pmatrix} 1 & 2 & -1 & | & 1 \\ 0 & 1 & 1 & | & 2 \\ 0 & -2 & -2 & | & 3 \end{pmatrix}$$

When we next add 2 times row 2 to row 3, we obtain

$$\begin{pmatrix} 1 & 2 & -1 & | & 1 \\ 0 & 1 & 1 & | & 2 \\ 0 & 0 & 0 & | & 7 \end{pmatrix}$$

The system of linear equations corresponding to the augmented matrix above is

$$\begin{aligned} x + 2y - z &= 1 \\ 0x + y + z &= 2 \\ 0x + 0y + 0z &= 7 \end{aligned}$$

Clearly there are no values of x, y, and z that will satisfy the third equation; so this system has no solutions. But Theorem 3.3 then implies that (3.9) also has no solutions.

The situation illustrated above is true in general. *A system of linear equations has no solutions if at some stage of Gaussian elimination a matrix is obtained having a row of the form*

$$0 \quad 0 \quad \cdots \quad 0 \mid k$$

where k is any nonzero number.

Exercises

In Exercises 1–10 solve the given systems by writing the leading variables in terms of the remaining unknowns.

1. $x_1 - 2x_2 + 6x_3 + 4x_5 = 7$
   $x_4 + 3x_5 = 9$

2. $x_1 + 3x_2 + 5x_5 = 4$
   $x_3 + 2x_4 - x_5 = 6$

3. $x_1 - 2x_2 = 28$
   $x_3 = -1$
   $x_4 = -5$

4. $x_1 + 8x_3 - 3x_5 = 4$
   $x_2 - 2x_3 + 5x_5 = 7$
   $x_4 + 2x_5 = 6$

5. $x_1 + 7x_3 - 5x_5 = 8$
   $x_2 - 4x_3 + 3x_5 = -3$
   $x_4 + 2x_5 = 6$

6. $x_1 + 5x_2 + 2x_4 - x_6 = 7$
   $x_3 - 3x_4 = 9$
   $x_5 + 4x_6 = 3$

7. $x_1 - 2x_3 = -1$
   $x_2 + 3x_3 = 2$
   $x_4 = 5$
   $x_5 = 4$

8. $x_1 + 3x_2 + 2x_5 = 7$
   $x_3 - x_5 = -6$
   $x_4 - 2x_5 = 5$
   $x_6 = 8$

9. $x_1 + 2x_4 - x_6 = 4$
   $x_2 + 5x_6 = -3$
   $x_3 + 4x_4 - 2x_6 = 6$
   $x_5 + 3x_6 = -2$

10. $x_1 + 3x_3 - x_6 = 2$
    $x_2 - 4x_3 + 2x_6 = 1$
    $x_4 + 5x_6 = 4$
    $x_5 - 2x_6 = -3$

Solve the systems of equations in Exercises 11–28 using Gaussian elimination.

11. $2x + 2y + 7z = 2$
    $x + 2y + 3z = 3$
    $4x + 2y + 14z = 2$

12. $2x + y - 3z = -11$
    $x + 2y + z = 4$
    $2x + 5y + 4z = 15$

13. $x + 2y - z = 3$
    $2x + 5y + z = 7$
    $2x + 3y - 5z = 2$

14. $2x - 3y + z = 3$
    $3x - 5y - z = 6$
    $x - y + 2z = 1$

15. $x + 2y - z = -1$
    $2x + 2y + z = 1$
    $3x + 5y - 2z = -1$

16. $x - 3y + z = 2$
    $2x - 7y = 3$
    $x - y + 10z = 3$

17. $x + 2y + 2w = 6$
    $3x + 5y - z + 6w = 17$
    $2x + 4y + z + 2w = 12$
    $2x - 7z + 11w = 7$

18. $x - y + 2z + 3w = -7$
    $2x - y + 6z + 6w = -2$
    $-2x + y - 4z - 3w = 0$
    $3x - 2y + 9z + 10w = -5$

19. $x_1 - 4x_2 - x_3 + x_4 = 3$
    $2x_1 - 8x_2 + x_3 - 4x_4 = 9$
    $-x_1 + 4x_2 - 2x_3 + 5x_4 = -6$

20. $x_1 + 2x_2 - x_3 + 3x_4 = 2$
    $2x_1 + 4x_2 - x_3 + 6x_4 = 5$
    $x_2 + 2x_4 = 3$

21. $x_1 - x_2 - 2x_3 + x_4 = 2$
    $-2x_1 + 2x_2 + x_3 + x_4 = 5$
    $-x_1 + x_2 + x_3 + x_4 = -1$

22. $2x_1 - 2x_2 - x_3 + 6x_4 - 2x_5 = 3$
    $x_1 - x_2 + x_3 + 2x_4 - x_5 = 2$
    $4x_1 - 4x_2 + 5x_3 + 7x_4 - x_5 = 6$

23. $x_1 - 2x_2 + x_3 - x_4 = 3$
    $2x_1 - x_2 + x_4 = 7$
    $3x_1 - 5x_2 + 2x_3 - 2x_4 = 5$
    $7x_1 - 4x_2 + x_3 + 3x_4 = 3$

24. $x_1 - 2x_2 - x_3 = 1$
    $2x_1 - 3x_2 + x_3 = 6$
    $3x_1 - 5x_2 = 7$
    $x_1 + 5x_3 = 9$

25. $3x_1 - x_2 + x_3 - x_4 + 2x_5 = 5$
    $x_1 - x_2 - x_3 - 2x_4 - x_5 = 2$
    $5x_1 - 2x_2 + x_3 - 3x_4 + 3x_5 = 10$
    $2x_1 - x_2 - 2x_4 + x_5 = 5$

26. $2x_1 - 2x_2 + x_3 - x_4 = -4$
    $x_1 - 2x_2 + 3x_3 + x_4 + 2x_5 = 2$
    $-x_1 + x_2 - x_3 + 2x_4 + 3x_5 = 1$
    $3x_1 - 4x_2 + 2x_3 + 6x_4 + 14x_5 = 3$

27. $3x_1 - x_2 + 2x_3 + 4x_4 + x_5 = 2$
    $x_1 - x_2 + 2x_3 + 3x_4 + x_5 = -1$
    $2x_1 - 3x_2 + 6x_3 + 9x_4 + 4x_5 = -5$
    $7x_1 - 2x_2 + 4x_3 + 8x_4 + x_5 = 6$

28. $2x_1 + 3x_3 - 4x_5 = 5$
    $3x_1 - 4x_2 + 8x_3 + 3x_4 = 8$
    $x_1 - x_2 + 2x_3 + x_4 - x_5 = 2$
    $-2x_1 + 5x_2 - 9x_3 - 3x_4 - 5x_5 = -8$

29. Three herbicides are available that contain the chemicals A, B, and C. One gallon of the first herbicide contains 1 unit of chemical A, 1 unit of chemical C, and none of chemical B; one gallon of the second herbicide contains none of chemical A, 2 units of chemical B, and 1 unit of chemical C; and one gallon of the third herbicide contains 1 unit of chemical A, 1 unit of chemical B, and none of chemical C. To control a certain crop disease, a farmer wants to apply 11 units of chemical A, 12 units of chemical B, and 14 units of chemical C per acre. How many gallons of each herbicide should be used per acre?

30. A piggy bank contains 90 coins, each of which is a penny, nickel, or dime. If the total value of the coins is $3.30 and the value of the nickels equals the value of the other two coins, how many coins are there of each type?

31. An investor asked her investment counselor to invest $18,000 for her in a mutual fund, in stocks, and in a speculative land development. She asked only that the counselor invest 5 times as much in the mutual fund and stocks combined as in land. One year later she learned that her $18,000 investment had yielded a $580 return and that the mutual fund had yielded a 5% return, the stocks had yielded a 3% return, and the land had lost 1%. How much money had been invested in each way?

32. At his next party, a host intends to serve a punch made from fruit juice, wine, and brandy. The alcoholic content of the ingredients is 0% for the fruit juice, 12% for the wine, and 40% for the brandy. If the host's recipe calls for twice as much wine as brandy, how much of each ingredient should he use in order to make 200 fluid ounces of punch containing 15.2% alcohol?

33. A merchant mixed peanuts costing $0.60 per pound, cashews costing $1.50 per pound, and almonds costing $2.00 per pound. Twice as many pounds of cashews as almonds were used, and 40 pounds of a mixture were obtained that cost $1.28 per pound. How much of each ingredient was used?

34. Three dairies, A, B, and C, provide all the milk for the 2480 households in a certain city. A survey in June showed that 80% of the households using

dairy A planned to use dairy A in July, 10% of the households using dairy B planned to use dairy A in July, and 20% of the households using dairy C planned to use dairy A in July. Likewise 60% of the households using dairy B in June planned to use dairy B in July, 10% of those using dairy A in June planned to use dairy B in July, and 10% of those using dairy C in June planned to use dairy B in July. When these data were analyzed, it was found that each dairy would serve exactly the same number of households in the city during July that it served during June. How many households in the city used each dairy in June?

35. A 200-acre farm is used to grow corn and soybeans. For the coming year the owner estimates yields of 100 bushels per acre for corn and 50 bushels per acre for soybeans and selling prices of $2.30 per bushel for corn and $5.00 per bushel for soybeans. The owner wishes to use all of her 550 tons of available fertilizer on the land where the corn and soybeans are planted and intends to apply 4 tons of fertilizer per acre of corn and 3 tons of fertilizer per acre of soybeans. In addition, some land may be left fallow, in which case a federal price support program will pay $85 per acre to the owner. To receive an equitable return on her investment for land and equipment while remaining in a desirable tax bracket, the owner desires a net return of $42,000 for her farm. How many acres should be planted with corn, how many acres should be planted with soybeans, and how many acres should lie fallow to meet these conditions?

36. In a certain city there are two high schools. Eastern High School has 1400 white students and 1200 black students, and Western High School has 1600 white students and 800 black students. In order to achieve a racial balance in the two schools some of the students attending Eastern are going to be bused to Western, and some of those now attending Western will be bused to Eastern. The city's school board has suggested the following guidelines:

   (i) The total number of students to be bused should be 20% of the total population of the two schools.
   (ii) The total number of white students who are bused should equal the total number of black students who are bused.
   (iii) The proportion of white to black students who are bused from Western to Eastern should equal the present proportion of white students to black students at Western.
   (iv) The percentage of black students at Western after the busing plan is implemented should equal the percentage of black students in both schools.

   [Observe that condition (iv) ensures that the proportion of black students to white students is the same in both schools.] Determine the number of black students and the number of white students now attending each school who should be bused to the other school.

*3.7 Some Applications of Systems of Linear Equations

In this section three applications of systems of linear equations will be presented. The first of these is a mathematical model for allocating service charges in accounting, the second is a mathematical model due to Wassily Leontief[11] that may be used to describe various economic phenomena, and the third is a technique for analyzing traffic flow through a road network.

A Model for Allocating Service Charges

Manufacturing firms typically are composed of two types of departments having entirely different functions. Service departments such as data processing and shipping provide services to other departments within the firm, whereas production departments produce commodities for sale outside the firm. Before the commodities made by the production departments can be priced for sale, the firm must know the total cost for each production department. These costs consist not only of direct costs such as salaries and material costs but also of indirect costs such as charges for services provided by the service departments. Standard accounting procedures require that the direct costs of the service departments be charged to the production departments in accordance with the amount of service used.

We now consider a mathematical model for allocating the charges of service departments to production departments. To illustrate this technique, let us consider a firm consisting of three service departments (maintenance, shipping and receiving, and data processing) and two production departments (small appliances and large appliances). Suppose that the direct costs per month for each department (in the order listed) are $1000, $800, $1200, $2000, and $3000 and that the proportions of services used by each department have been determined to be as in Table 3.5.

Notice that, since all the services are used internally by the five departments, the sum of each column of Table 3.5 is 1. If $x_1, x_2, x_3, x_4,$ and x_5 are the total costs of the five departments, then the total, direct, and indirect costs for each department are as in Table 3.6.

Since the total cost of each department is the sum of the direct and indirect costs for that department, we have the following system of equations

$$\begin{aligned} x_1 &= 1000 + 0.3x_1 + 0.3x_2 + 0.2x_3 \\ x_2 &= 800 + 0.3x_1 + 0.3x_2 + 0.2x_3 \\ x_3 &= 1200 + 0.1x_1 + 0.1x_2 + 0.4x_3 \\ x_4 &= 2000 + 0.1x_1 + 0.1x_2 + 0.1x_3 \\ x_5 &= 3000 + 0.2x_1 + 0.2x_2 + 0.1x_3 \end{aligned} \qquad (3.10)$$

Notice that x_4 and x_5 appear only in the last two equations. Hence we can easily solve for x_4 and x_5 in (3.10) once the values of $x_1, x_2,$ and x_3 are known. But these values can be found by solving the first three equations in (3.10). Rewriting these equations with all the variables on

---

[11] Leontief was the 1973 recipient of the Nobel prize for Economics. See *Newsweek*, vol. 82, no. 18 (October 29, 1973), p. 94.

Table 3.5 *Proportion of Services Used*

	Provider of service		
User of services	Maintenance	Shipping and receiving	Data processing
Maintenance	0.3	0.3	0.2
Shipping and receiving	0.3	0.3	0.2
Data processing	0.1	0.1	0.4
Small appliances	0.1	0.1	0.1
Large appliances	0.2	0.2	0.1

Table 3.6 *Department Costs*

Department		Total cost	Direct cost (dollars)	Indirect costs from Maintenance	Shipping and receiving	Data processing
Maintenance	x_1		1000	$0.3x_1$	$0.3x_2$	$0.2x_3$
Shipping and receiving	x_2		800	$0.3x_1$	$0.3x_2$	$0.2x_3$
Data processing	x_3		1200	$0.1x_1$	$0.1x_2$	$0.4x_3$
Small appliances	x_4		2000	$0.1x_1$	$0.1x_2$	$0.1x_3$
Large appliances	x_5		3000	$0.2x_1$	$0.2x_2$	$0.1x_3$

the left side gives the system

$$0.7x_1 - 0.3x_2 - 0.2x_3 = 1000$$
$$-0.3x_1 + 0.7x_2 - 0.2x_3 = 800$$
$$-0.1x_1 - 0.1x_2 + 0.6x_3 = 1200$$

The solution of this system can be easily determined by Gaussian elimination to be $x_1 = \$4000$, $x_2 = \$3800$, and $x_3 = \$3300$. Thus from (3.10) we obtain $x_4 = \$3110$ and $x_5 = \$4890$.

Let us reinterpret the data in Table 3.6 in view of the calculations above. We see from Table 3.6 that the indirect costs for the small-appliance department are

$$0.1x_1 + 0.1x_2 + 0.1x_3 = \$400 + \$380 + \$330 = \$1110$$

and for the large-appliance department are

$$0.2x_1 + 0.2x_2 + 0.1x_3 = \$800 + \$760 + \$330 = \$1890$$

Observe that the sum of these indirect costs ($\$1110 + \$1890 = \$3000$) equals the direct costs of the three service departments ($\$1000 + \$800 + \$1200$). Thus we have allocated the direct costs of the service departments to the production departments in such a way that each department is charged according to the amount of services it receives. Moreover, the total cost of the two production departments ($x_4 + x_5 = \$3110 + \$4890 = \$8000$) equals the sum of the direct costs of all five departments ($\$1000 + \$800 + \$1200 + \$2000 + \$3000$) in accordance with standard accounting procedures.

3.7 Some Applications of Systems of Linear Equations

The Leontief Input-Output Model

Input-output models can be used to describe two types of production-consumption situations in which everything produced is consumed. The *open input-output model* can be used to describe an economy in which some of the production is consumed externally, whereas the *closed input-output model* can be used to describe an economy in which everything produced is consumed internally. Although Leontief identified as many as 42 different segments of the United States economy in [2], for simplicity we restrict our attention to hypothetical economies consisting of only two or three segments.

Consider a simple society composed of three types of people (or industries): farmers who grow all the food, tailors who make all the clothing, and carpenters who build all the housing. Each of these groups will consume food, clothing, and housing. Suppose that production of 1 unit of food requires 0.30 unit of food, 0.10 unit of clothing, and 0.30 unit of housing; that production of 1 unit of clothing requires 0.20 unit of food, 0.40 unit of clothing, and 0.20 unit of housing; and that production of 1 unit of housing requires 0.30 unit of food, 0.10 unit of clothing, and 0.30 unit of housing. This pattern of consumption can be described by the 3×3 input-output matrix

$$\text{Inputs} \begin{array}{c} \\ \text{Food} \\ \text{Clothing} \\ \text{Housing} \end{array} \overset{\displaystyle \overset{\text{Outputs}}{\text{Food \quad Clothing \quad Housing}}}{\begin{pmatrix} 0.30 & 0.20 & 0.30 \\ 0.10 & 0.40 & 0.10 \\ 0.30 & 0.20 & 0.30 \end{pmatrix}} = A$$

Observe that the rows represent the *inputs* and the columns represent the *outputs* of the production process.

More generally, an open economy consisting of n industries can be described by an $n \times n$ input-output matrix $A = (a_{ij})$ in which a_{ij} represents the amount of the product produced by industry i that is needed to produce one unit of output by industry j. Let

$$X = \begin{pmatrix} x_1 \\ x_2 \\ \vdots \\ x_n \end{pmatrix} \quad \text{and} \quad D = \begin{pmatrix} d_1 \\ d_2 \\ \vdots \\ d_n \end{pmatrix}$$

be vectors in which x_i represents the number of units produced by the ith industry and d_i represents the number of units of external demand for the product produced by the ith industry. Then the entries of AX represent the number of units of the product produced by each industry that is consumed during the production process. Hence

$$X - AX = (I_n - A)X$$

is the number of units produced by each industry not consumed internally. Since we are assuming that everything not consumed internally must be consumed externally, it follows that

$$(I_n - A)X = D$$

Returning to our example, let us suppose that there is an external demand for 30 units of food, 20 units of clothing, and 10 units of housing. Then

$$D = \begin{pmatrix} 30 \\ 20 \\ 10 \end{pmatrix}$$

In order to determine what level of gross production X is needed to meet the external demand D, we must solve the system $(I - A)X = D$. Thus we have

$$\left[\begin{pmatrix} 1 & 0 & 0 \\ 0 & 1 & 0 \\ 0 & 0 & 1 \end{pmatrix} - \begin{pmatrix} 0.30 & 0.20 & 0.30 \\ 0.10 & 0.40 & 0.10 \\ 0.30 & 0.20 & 0.30 \end{pmatrix} \right] \begin{pmatrix} x_1 \\ x_2 \\ x_3 \end{pmatrix} = \begin{pmatrix} 30 \\ 20 \\ 10 \end{pmatrix}$$

or

$$\begin{pmatrix} 0.70 & -0.20 & -0.30 \\ -0.10 & 0.60 & -0.10 \\ -0.30 & -0.20 & 0.70 \end{pmatrix} \begin{pmatrix} x_1 \\ x_2 \\ x_3 \end{pmatrix} = \begin{pmatrix} 30 \\ 20 \\ 10 \end{pmatrix}$$

This matrix equation is equivalent to the system of linear equations

$$0.70x_1 - 0.20x_2 - 0.30x_3 = 30$$
$$-0.10x_1 + 0.60x_2 - 0.10x_3 = 20$$
$$-0.30x_1 - 0.20x_2 + 0.70x_3 = 10$$

and can be solved as in Section 3.6 to obtain $x_1 = 90$, $x_2 = 60$, and $x_3 = 70$. Thus a gross production of 90 units of food, 60 units of clothing, and 70 units of housing is necessary to supply 30 units of food, 20 units of clothing, and 10 units of housing for external consumption.

In the closed input-output model, everything produced by the economy is consumed internally; so it is no longer of interest to determine the level of production necessary to satisfy an external demand. Instead, it is important to know how the total income of the economy should be divided among the basic industries in order to maintain an equilibrium between income and consumption.

As in the open model, a closed economy consisting of n industries can be described by an $n \times n$ input-output matrix $A = (a_{ij})$. In this case, however, a_{ij} represents the proportion of the goods produced by industry j that is consumed by industry i. If

$$X = \begin{pmatrix} x_1 \\ x_2 \\ \vdots \\ x_n \end{pmatrix}$$

is a column vector in which x_i represents the total income of industry i, then the ith entry of the vector AX represents the value of all the goods consumed by the ith industry. Since equilibrium will be maintained in the economy if an industry's income equals the value of the goods it consumes, the condition ensuring equilibrium is $X = AX$, or equivalently,

$$(I_n - A)X = 0$$

where 0 denotes the zero column vector.

Suppose, for instance, that in the simple society of farmers, tailors, and carpenters the farmers consume 40% of the food, 20% of the clothing, and 20% of the housing; the tailors consume 10% of the food, 70% of the clothing, and 20% of the housing; and the carpenters consume 50% of the food, 10% of the clothing, and 60% of the housing. Then the input-output matrix for this society is

$$\text{Consumers} \begin{array}{c} \\ \text{Food} \\ \text{Clothing} \\ \text{Housing} \end{array} \overset{\overset{\text{Producers}}{\text{Food} \quad \text{Clothing} \quad \text{Housing}}}{\begin{pmatrix} 0.40 & 0.20 & 0.20 \\ 0.10 & 0.70 & 0.20 \\ 0.50 & 0.10 & 0.60 \end{pmatrix}} = A$$

Notice that each of the columns of A sums to 1, indicative of the fact that everything produced is consumed internally.

For this economy the matrix equation $(I - A)X = 0$ is equivalent to the following system of linear equations.

$$\begin{aligned} 0.60x_1 - 0.20x_2 - 0.20x_3 &= 0 \\ -0.10x_1 + 0.30x_2 - 0.20x_3 &= 0 \\ -0.50x_1 - 0.10x_2 + 0.40x_3 &= 0 \end{aligned} \qquad (3.11)$$

This system can be shown to have infinitely many solutions of the form $(\frac{5}{8}r, \frac{7}{8}r, r)$. If we let t denote the total income of the economy, then

$$t = x_1 + x_2 + x_3 = \tfrac{5}{8}r + \tfrac{7}{8}r + r = \tfrac{5}{2}r$$

Thus $r = \tfrac{2}{5}t$, and so

$$x_1 = \tfrac{5}{8}r = \tfrac{1}{4}t \qquad x_2 = \tfrac{7}{8}r = \tfrac{7}{20}t \quad \text{and} \quad x_3 = r = \tfrac{2}{5}t$$

Thus the farmers earn $\tfrac{1}{4}$ of the total income of the economy, the tailors earn $\tfrac{7}{20}$ of the total income of the economy, and the carpenters earn $\tfrac{2}{5}$ of the total income of the economy.

Traffic Flow Through a Road Network

Network analysis has been used for many years in physics and engineering to study the flow of current through electric circuits. More recently, this subject has proved useful in other fields as well. The next application involves a technique for analyzing traffic flow through a road network.

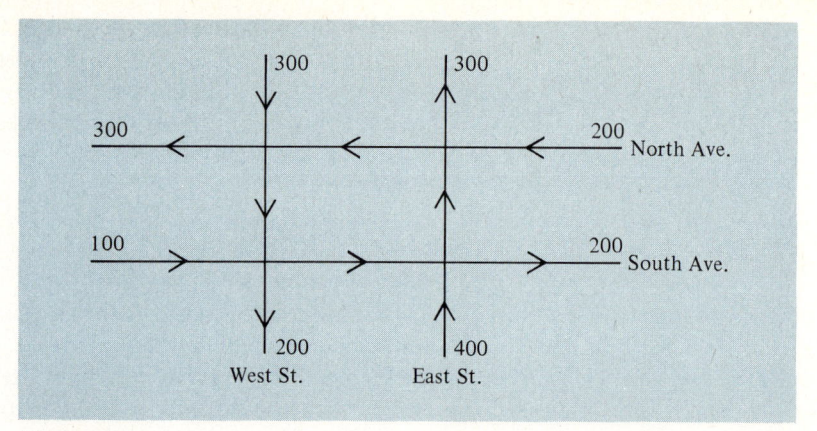

Figure 3.3

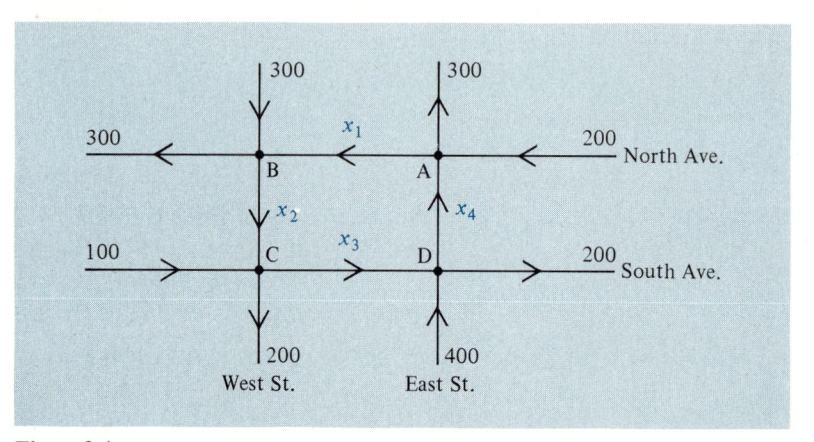

Figure 3.4

Figure 3.3 shows the number of vehicles per hour using certain portions of four one-way streets during rush hour. Suppose that the city would like to know the minimum number of cars that must travel East Street between South Avenue and North Avenue in order to avoid congestion. This information would be needed, for example, if construction along East Street closed one or more lanes to traffic.

To describe the pattern of traffic flow, let x_1, x_2, x_3, and x_4 be the number of vehicles per hour using the portions of the roads indicated in Figure 3.4 during rush hour. We assume that, at each of the intersections labeled A, B, C, and D in Figure 3.4, the number of cars entering the intersection equals the number of cars leaving the intersection. This assumption leads to the following system of linear equations:

Intersection A	$x_4 + 200 = x_1 + 300$
Intersection B	$x_1 + 300 = x_2 + 300$
Intersection C	$x_2 + 100 = x_3 + 200$
Intersection D	$x_3 + 400 = x_4 + 200$

When this system is solved by Gaussian elimination, the row echelon form of the augmented matrix is

$$\begin{pmatrix} 1 & 0 & 0 & -1 & | & -100 \\ 0 & 1 & 0 & -1 & | & -100 \\ 0 & 0 & 1 & -1 & | & -200 \\ 0 & 0 & 0 & 0 & | & 0 \end{pmatrix}$$

Hence

$$x_1 = x_4 - 100$$
$$x_2 = x_4 - 100$$
$$x_3 = x_4 - 200$$

In the context of this problem it is clear that all the variables must be nonnegative. For this to be the case x_4 must therefore be at least 200. That is, at least 200 vehicles per hour must use East Street between South Avenue and North Avenue to avoid congestion.

Exercises

1. A manufacturing firm that produces desk calculators and typewriters has three service departments—data processing, maintenance, and payroll. Table 3.7 gives the direct cost of each department and the proportion of services used by each department. Determine the total costs for each department.

Table 3.7 *Direct Costs and Proportion of Services Used*

User of services	Direct cost (dollars)	Provider of service		
		Data processing	Maintenance	Payroll
Data processing	3000	0.3	0.1	0.3
Maintenance	4000	0.2	0.4	0.2
Payroll	1500	0.1	0.2	0.1
Calculators	6000	0.2	0.2	0.2
Typewriters	7000	0.2	0.1	0.2

2. A firm manufactures laboratory equipment and culture media, which it supplies to hospitals. Its three service departments (data processing,

Table 3.8 *Direct Costs and Proportion of Services Used*

User of services	Direct cost (dollars)	Provider of service		
		Data processing	Research and development	Electronics
Data processing	4,000	0.4	0	0.2
Research and development	10,000	0.1	0.8	0.1
Electronics	3,000	0.2	0	0.1
Equipment	12,000	0.1	0.1	0.5
Media	15,000	0.2	0.1	0.1

research and development, and electronics) provide services to the five departments as indicated in Table 3.8. Using the direct costs in Table 3.8, determine the total costs for each department.

3. A men's clothing factory manufactures trousers, jackets, and suits. These three production departments use services from the accounts receivable, data processing, and maintenance departments as indicated in Table 3.9. Determine the total costs for each department.

Table 3.9 *Direct Costs and Proportion of Services Used*

		Provider of service		
User of services	Direct cost (dollars)	Accounts receivable	Data processing	Maintenance
Accounts receivable	22,000	0.1	0.2	0.1
Data processing	40,000	0.2	0.1	0.3
Maintenance	2,000	0.1	0.2	0.1
Trousers	20,000	0.2	0.2	0.1
Jackets	20,000	0.2	0.1	0.1
Suits	30,000	0.2	0.2	0.3

4. A certain simple society produces housing, clothing, and food. Production of 1 unit of housing or 1 unit of clothing requires 0.2 unit of housing, 0.2 unit of clothing, and 0.1 unit of food. Production of 1 unit of food requires 0.4 unit of housing, 0.4 unit of clothing, and 0.2 unit of food. What gross production is necessary to meet an external demand for 10 units of housing, 10 units of clothing, and 20 units of food?

5. Suppose that a small country produces three forms of energy—electricity, natural gas, and oil. Production of 1 unit of electricity requires 0.4 unit of electricity, 0.2 unit of natural gas, and 0.1 unit of oil. Production of 1 unit of natural gas requires 0.1 unit of electricity, 0.1 unit of natural gas, and 0.05 unit of oil. Finally, production of 1 unit of oil requires 0.4 unit of natural gas and 0.2 unit of oil. What gross production is required to meet an external demand for 400 units of electricity, 200 units of natural gas, and 300 units of oil?

6. A small country produces three forms of energy—electricity, oil, and coal. Production of 1 unit of electricity requires 0.2 unit of electricity, 0.2 unit of oil, and 0.1 unit of coal. Production of 1 unit of oil requires 0.4 unit of electricity, 0.4 unit of oil, and 0.2 unit of coal. Finally, production of 1 unit of coal requires 0.1 unit of electricity, 0.1 unit of oil, and 0.3 unit of coal. What gross production is necessary to meet an external demand for 100 units of electricity, 200 units of oil, and 100 units of coal?

7. Suppose that a simple economy produces transportation, food, and oil. Production of 1 unit of transportation or 1 unit of food requires 0.1 unit of oil, and 0.1 unit of coal. Production of 1 unit of oil requires 0.4 of 1 unit of oil requires 0.3 unit of transportation, 0.25 unit of food, and 0.3 unit of oil. What gross production is necessary to meet an external demand for 40 units of transportation, 60 units of food, and 80 units of oil?

Consider a simple closed economy which produces only food and housing. In Exercises 8–11 determine the proportion of the economy's total income earned by each industry under the given conditions.

8. The food industry consumes 90% of the food and 20% of the housing, and the housing industry consumes 10% of the food and 80% of the housing.

9. The food industry consumes 60% of the food and 40% of the housing, and the housing industry consumes 40% of the food and 60% of the housing.

10. The food industry consumes 80% of the food and 30% of the housing, and the housing industry consumes 20% of the food and 70% of the housing.

11. The food industry consumes 90% of the food and 30% of the housing, and the housing industry consumes 10% of the food and 70% of the housing.

A simple closed economy produces only food, oil, and transportation. In Exercises 12–15 determine the proportion of the economy's total income earned by each industry under the given conditions.

12. The food industry consumes 80% of the food and 10% of the transportation; the oil industry consumes 10% of the food, 90% of the oil, and 20% of the transportation; and the transportation industry consumes 10% of the food, 10% of the oil, and 70% of the transportation.

13. The food industry consumes 60% of the food, 10% of the oil, and 60% of the transportation; the oil industry consumes 30% of the food, 80% of the oil, and 30% of the transportation; and the transportation industry consumes 10% of the food, 10% of the oil, and 10% of the transportation.

14. The food industry consumes 80% of the food, 20% of the oil, and 40% of the transportation; the oil industry consumes 10% of the food, 50% of the oil, and 30% of the transportation; and the transportation industry consumes 10% of the food, 30% of the oil, and 40% of the transportation.

15. The food industry consumes 70% of the food, 30% of the oil, and 30% of the transportation; the oil industry consumes 20% of the food, 70% of the oil, and 20% of the transportation; and the transportation industry consumes 10% of the food and 50% of the transportation.

16. Figure 3.5 shows the number of vehicles per hour using certain portions of five one-way streets during rush hour. The city would like to repave East Street between North Avenue and South Avenue. Determine the

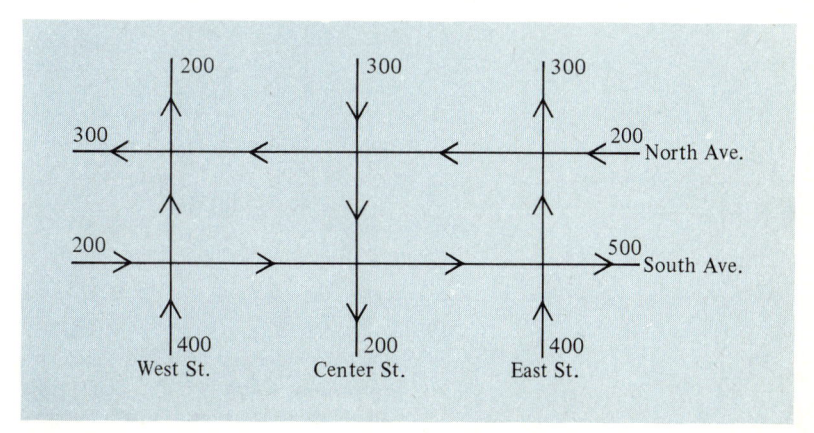

Figure 3.5

104 Chapter 3 Matrices and Systems of Linear Equations

minimum number of vehicles per hour that must use this portion of East Street in order to avoid congestion.

17. Figure 3.6 shows the number of vehicles per hour using certain portions of five one-way streets during rush hour. Determine the minimum number of vehicles per hour that must use Third Avenue between Washington Street and Adams Street to avoid congestion.

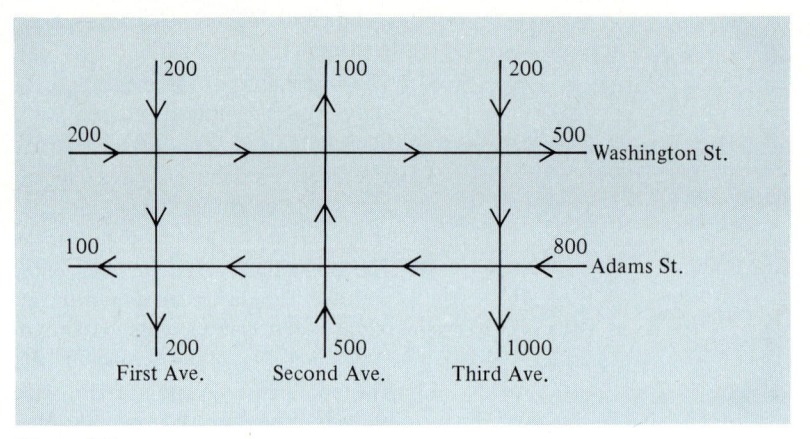

Figure 3.6

18. Figure 3.7 shows the number of vehicles per hour using certain portions of five one-way streets during rush hour. Determine the minimum number of vehicles per hour that must use Pine Street between Jefferson Avenue and Monroe Avenue in order to avoid congestion.

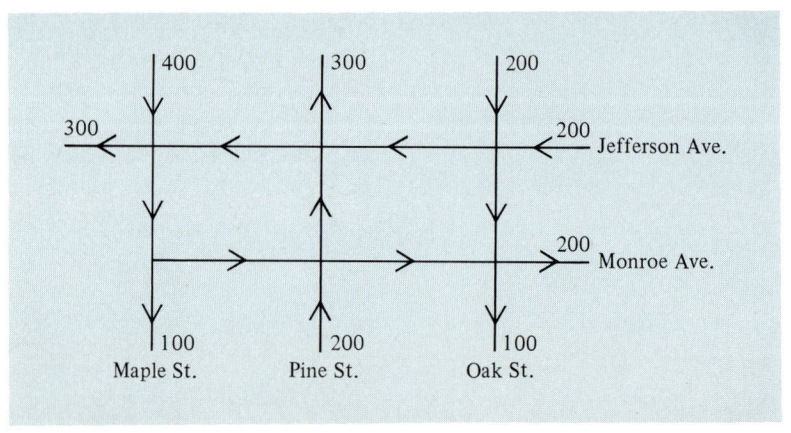

Figure 3.7

19. An investor wishes to invest $60,000 in four stocks, A, B, C, and D. Stocks A and B are blue-chip stocks selling for $80 and $60 per share, respectively, whereas C and D are speculative stocks selling for $20 and $40 per share, respectively. The investor has decided to invest four times as much money in the blue-chip stocks as in the speculative stocks and

wants a total return of $1125. Presently stock A returns $1.50 per share, B returns $1.20 per share, C returns $0.30 per share, and D returns $0.75 per share. If the stocks are available only in multiples of 100 shares, what purchase options are available to the investor?

20. An investor wishes to invest $18,000 in four stocks, A, B, C, and D. Stocks A and B are blue-chip stocks selling for $40 and $30 per share, respectively, whereas C and D are speculative stocks selling for $20 and $10 per share, respectively. The investor has decided to invest twice as much money in the blue-chip stocks as in the speculative stocks and wants a total return of $920. Presently stock A returns $2.00 per share, B returns $1.60 per share, C returns $0.80 per share, and D returns $0.60 per share. If the stocks are available only in multiples of 100 shares, what purchase options are available to the investor?

3.8 The Inverse of a Matrix

Throughout the first three sections of this chapter we observed many similarities between the addition, subtraction, and multiplication of matrices and the addition, subtraction, and multiplication of real numbers. In this section we shall discuss the matrix analog of the division of real numbers.

First, recall that division by a nonzero real number c is the same as multiplication by the reciprocal of c, the number that when multiplied by c equals 1. The reciprocal of c is denoted by either $1/c$ or c^{-1}. Thus, for example, $8 \div 2 = 8 \cdot \frac{1}{2}$. The inverse of a matrix is the matrix analog of the reciprocal of a real number, but unlike real numbers every nonzero matrix does not have an inverse. If, for a given $n \times n$ matrix P, there exists an $n \times n$ matrix Q such that $PQ = QP = I_n$, then Q is called the *inverse* of P. If the inverse of P exists, it is denoted by P^{-1}.

inverse of a matrix

The following facts about inverses should be noted:

1. Only square matrices can have inverses. However, not every square matrix has an inverse.
2. If a matrix has an inverse, then the inverse is unique; that is, no matrix can have more than one inverse.
3. To determine if a particular $n \times n$ matrix Q is the inverse of an $n \times n$ matrix P, it is sufficient to verify that either $PQ = I_n$ or $QP = I_n$. For in this setting both of the conditions $PQ = I_n$ and $QP = I_n$ will be satisfied if either one is satisfied.

EXAMPLE 23

Let
$$Q = \begin{pmatrix} 7 & -13 & -5 \\ -4 & 8 & 3 \\ -2 & 8 & 1 \end{pmatrix} \quad \text{and} \quad P = \begin{pmatrix} 1 & 2 & -1 \\ 2 & 3 & 1 \\ -4 & -5 & -4 \end{pmatrix}$$

Since

$$PQ = \begin{pmatrix} 1 & 2 & -1 \\ 2 & 3 & 1 \\ -4 & -5 & -4 \end{pmatrix} \begin{pmatrix} 7 & -13 & -5 \\ -4 & 8 & 3 \\ -2 & 3 & 1 \end{pmatrix} = \begin{pmatrix} 1 & 0 & 0 \\ 0 & 1 & 0 \\ 0 & 0 & 1 \end{pmatrix} = I_3$$

it follows from remark 3 above that Q is the inverse of P (that is, $Q = P^{-1}$).

On the other hand, it is easy to see that the 2×2 matrix

$$M = \begin{pmatrix} 1 & 0 \\ 0 & 0 \end{pmatrix}$$

has no inverse; for no matter what 2×2 matrix N is chosen, the second row of MN contains only zero entries (hence $MN \neq I_2$).

Observe that the system of m linear equations in n unknowns

$$\begin{aligned}
a_{11}x_1 + a_{12}x_2 + \cdots + a_{1n}x_n &= b_1 \\
a_{21}x_1 + a_{22}x_2 + \cdots + a_{2n}x_n &= b_2 \\
&\vdots \\
a_{m1}x_1 + a_{m2}x_2 + \cdots + a_{mn}x_n &= b_m
\end{aligned} \qquad (3.12)$$

can be expressed as a single matrix equation $AX = B$, where

$$A = \begin{pmatrix} a_{11} & a_{12} & \cdots & a_{1n} \\ a_{21} & a_{22} & \cdots & a_{2n} \\ \vdots & \vdots & & \vdots \\ a_{m1} & a_{m2} & \cdots & a_{mn} \end{pmatrix} \quad X = \begin{pmatrix} x_1 \\ x_2 \\ \vdots \\ x_n \end{pmatrix} \quad \text{and} \quad B = \begin{pmatrix} b_1 \\ b_2 \\ \vdots \\ b_m \end{pmatrix}$$

When solving the linear equation $ax = b$, where a and b are real numbers and $a \neq 0$, we multiply both sides of the equation by the reciprocal of a to obtain

$$\begin{aligned}
a^{-1}(ax) &= a^{-1}b \\
(a^{-1}a)x &= a^{-1}b \\
1 \cdot x &= a^{-1}b \\
x &= a^{-1}b
\end{aligned}$$

Likewise, if the coefficient matrix of (3.12) has an inverse, then by multiplying both sides of the equation on the left[12] by A^{-1} we can express the solution of the matrix equation $AX = B$ in the form $X = A^{-1}B$.

Since only square matrices have inverses, this representation is not possible unless the number of equations, m, and the number of unknowns, n, in (3.12) are the same.

---

[12] Recall that the order in which matrices are multiplied is of great importance.

EXAMPLE 24

The system of three linear equations in three unknowns

$$\begin{aligned} x + y - 3z &= -2 \\ -3x - 4y + 11z &= 5 \\ x + 3y - 8z &= -4 \end{aligned} \qquad (3.13)$$

can be written in the matrix form $AX = B$, where

$$A = \begin{pmatrix} 1 & 1 & 3 \\ -3 & -4 & 11 \\ 1 & 3 & -8 \end{pmatrix} \quad X = \begin{pmatrix} x \\ y \\ z \end{pmatrix} \quad \text{and} \quad B = \begin{pmatrix} -2 \\ 5 \\ -4 \end{pmatrix}$$

The inverse of A is the matrix

$$A^{-1} = \begin{pmatrix} -1 & -1 & -1 \\ -13 & -5 & -2 \\ -5 & -2 & -1 \end{pmatrix}$$

(The reader should verify that $AA^{-1} = I$.) Thus

$$X = A^{-1}B = \begin{pmatrix} -1 & -1 & -1 \\ -13 & -5 & -2 \\ -5 & -2 & -1 \end{pmatrix} \begin{pmatrix} -2 \\ 5 \\ -4 \end{pmatrix} = \begin{pmatrix} 1 \\ 9 \\ 4 \end{pmatrix}$$

So the solution of the given system is $(x, y, z) = (1, 9, 4)$.

The following procedure can be used to find the inverse of any $n \times n$ matrix A or to determine that A has no inverse. First, adjoin to A a copy of the identity matrix I_n. The resulting $n \times 2n$ matrix will be denoted by $(A|I_n)$. Then perform elementary row operations on $(A|I_n)$ to transform it into the form $(I_n|B)$. If a matrix of the form $(I_n|B)$ is obtained, then $B = A^{-1}$; but if such a matrix cannot be obtained, then A has no inverse.

To illustrate this procedure, let us find the inverse of the matrix

$$A = \begin{pmatrix} -3 & 8 & -6 \\ 1 & -2 & 1 \\ 2 & -5 & 4 \end{pmatrix}$$

Since A is a 3×3 matrix, we adjoin a copy of I_3 to A to obtain the 3×6 matrix

$$(A|I_3) = \begin{pmatrix} -3 & 8 & -6 & | & 1 & 0 & 0 \\ 1 & -2 & 1 & | & 0 & 1 & 0 \\ 2 & -5 & 4 & | & 0 & 0 & 1 \end{pmatrix}$$

which will be changed into the form

$$(I_3|B) = \begin{pmatrix} 1 & 0 & 0 & - & - & - \\ 0 & 1 & 0 & - & - & - \\ 0 & 0 & 1 & - & - & - \end{pmatrix}$$

by elementary row operations. In making this change, each column will be transformed into the desired form beginning with the first column. First, we interchange rows 1 and 2 of $(A|I_3)$ so that the 1,1 entry will be 1; this gives

$$\begin{pmatrix} 1 & -2 & 1 & 0 & 1 & 0 \\ -3 & 8 & -6 & 1 & 0 & 0 \\ 2 & -5 & 4 & 0 & 0 & 1 \end{pmatrix}$$

Adding 3 times row 1 to row 2 and -2 times row 1 to row 3 produces

$$\begin{pmatrix} 1 & -2 & 1 & 0 & 1 & 0 \\ 0 & 2 & -3 & 1 & 3 & 0 \\ 0 & -1 & 2 & 0 & -2 & 1 \end{pmatrix}$$

a matrix in which the first column has the desired form. Next we must transform the second column of the matrix above into the second column of I_3. Rather than dividing the second row by 2 to make the 2, 2 entry a 1, subsequent calculations will be easier if the second and third rows are interchanged and the new second row is multiplied by -1. These operations yield

$$\begin{pmatrix} 1 & -2 & 1 & 0 & 1 & 0 \\ 0 & 1 & -2 & 0 & 2 & -1 \\ 0 & 2 & -3 & 1 & 3 & 0 \end{pmatrix}$$

Now adding 2 times row 2 to row 1 and -2 times row 2 to row 3 produces

$$\begin{pmatrix} 1 & 0 & -3 & 0 & 5 & -2 \\ 0 & 1 & -2 & 0 & 2 & -1 \\ 0 & 0 & 1 & 1 & -1 & 2 \end{pmatrix}$$

All that remains is to transform the third column of the matrix above into the proper form. To do this, we add 3 times row 3 to row 1 and 2 times row 3 to row 2. The resulting matrix is

$$\begin{pmatrix} 1 & 0 & 0 & 3 & 2 & 4 \\ 0 & 1 & 0 & 2 & 0 & 3 \\ 0 & 0 & 1 & 1 & -1 & 2 \end{pmatrix}$$

which has the desired form $(I_3|B)$. Thus

$$A^{-1} = B = \begin{pmatrix} 3 & 2 & 4 \\ 2 & 0 & 3 \\ 1 & -1 & 2 \end{pmatrix}$$

3.8 The Inverse of a Matrix 109

We leave it to the reader to verify that $AA^{-1} = I$.

Let us now attempt to find an inverse of

$$M = \begin{pmatrix} 1 & -4 & 3 \\ 3 & -11 & 8 \\ 1 & -6 & 5 \end{pmatrix}$$

by transforming

$$(M|I_3) = \begin{pmatrix} 1 & -4 & 3 & | & 1 & 0 & 0 \\ 3 & -11 & 8 & | & 0 & 1 & 0 \\ 1 & -6 & 5 & | & 0 & 0 & 1 \end{pmatrix}$$

into the form $(I_3|B)$ using elementary row operations. To obtain zeros in the necessary positions in the first column, we must add -3 times row 1 to row 2 and -1 times row 1 to row 3. These operations yield

$$\begin{pmatrix} 1 & -4 & 3 & | & 1 & 0 & 0 \\ 0 & 1 & -1 & | & -3 & 1 & 0 \\ 0 & -2 & 2 & | & -1 & 0 & 1 \end{pmatrix}$$

in which the first column has the desired form. Now add 4 times row 2 to row 1 and 2 times row 2 to row 3 to obtain

$$\begin{pmatrix} 1 & 0 & -1 & | & -11 & 4 & 0 \\ 0 & 1 & -1 & | & -3 & 1 & 0 \\ 0 & 0 & 0 & | & -7 & 2 & 1 \end{pmatrix}$$

It is clear that the third row of this matrix can never be put into the form

$$0 \quad 0 \quad 1 \quad - \quad - \quad -$$

by using elementary row operations because the first three entries of the row are zeros. Thus the matrix M has no inverse. This example illustrates the following principle: *If P is an $n \times n$ matrix for which some sequence of elementary row operations performed on $(P|I_n)$ produces a matrix in which the first n entries of some row (that is, all the entries to the left of the slash) are zeros, then P has no inverse.*

Although we have seen that the solution of a system of linear equations $AX = B$ can be conveniently expressed in the form $X = A^{-1}B$ when the inverse of the coefficient matrix exists, it is unwise to compute A^{-1} in order to solve the system in this way. To see why this is so, consider system (3.13) in Example 24. If we were to compute A^{-1}, we would have to transform the matrix

$$(A|I_3) = \begin{pmatrix} 1 & 1 & -3 & | & 1 & 0 & 0 \\ -3 & -4 & 11 & | & 0 & 1 & 0 \\ 1 & 3 & -8 & | & 0 & 0 & 1 \end{pmatrix}$$

into the form $(I_3|B)$ by elementary row operations. This process amounts to using Gaussian elimination to solve three systems simultaneously:

$$\begin{array}{ccc} x + y - 3z = 1 & x + y - 3z = 0 & x + y - 3z = 0 \\ -3x - 4y + 11z = 0 & -3x - 4y + 11z = 1 & -3x - 4y + 11z = 0 \\ x + 3y - 8z = 0 & x + 3y - 8z = 0 & x + 3y - 8z = 1 \end{array}$$

In each of these systems A occurs as the coefficient matrix and one of the three columns of I_3 occurs as the right-side constants. (In fact, the three columns of A^{-1} are the respective solutions of these systems.) And clearly it makes no sense to solve three systems of equations in order to find the solution of the single system (3.13).

In Section 8.3 we shall consider an important application of the inverse of a matrix. Another use occurs in cryptography, the writing or deciphering of coded messages. A sophisticated type of code that is extremely difficult to break makes use of an extremely large matrix to encode a message. The receiver of the message is then able to decode the message using the inverse of the original matrix.

To illustrate the basic ideas, let us encode the message

THE ENEMY IS NEAR

using the matrix

$$A = \begin{pmatrix} 1 & 2 & 1 \\ 2 & 3 & 1 \\ -2 & 0 & 1 \end{pmatrix}$$

Both the sender and receiver of the message must know the matrix A and a prearranged correspondence between the letters of the alphabet and the positive integers. For simplicity we associate each letter with its position in the alphabet; thus A is associated with 1, B with 2, and so forth. In addition, a blank between words is denoted by – and is associated with the integer 27. The letters in the message to be coded therefore correspond to numbers in the following way:

T H E - E N E M Y - I S - N E A R
20 8 5 27 5 14 5 13 25 27 9 19 27 14 5 1 18

Since matrix A is 3×3, the sender will divide the above numbers into 3×1 column vectors as shown below.

$$\begin{pmatrix} 20 \\ 8 \\ 5 \end{pmatrix} \begin{pmatrix} 27 \\ 5 \\ 14 \end{pmatrix} \begin{pmatrix} 5 \\ 13 \\ 25 \end{pmatrix} \begin{pmatrix} 27 \\ 9 \\ 19 \end{pmatrix} \begin{pmatrix} 27 \\ 14 \\ 5 \end{pmatrix} \text{ and } \begin{pmatrix} 1 \\ 18 \\ 27 \end{pmatrix}$$

(Notice that it was necessary to add one blank to the end of the message in order to complete the last column vector.) The message is then encoded by multiplying the matrix A by each of these column vectors to obtain

$$\begin{pmatrix} 1 & 2 & 1 \\ 2 & 3 & 1 \\ -2 & 0 & 1 \end{pmatrix} \begin{pmatrix} 20 \\ 8 \\ 5 \end{pmatrix} = \begin{pmatrix} 41 \\ 69 \\ -35 \end{pmatrix}$$

$$\begin{pmatrix} 1 & 2 & 1 \\ 2 & 3 & 1 \\ -2 & 0 & 1 \end{pmatrix} \begin{pmatrix} 27 \\ 5 \\ 14 \end{pmatrix} = \begin{pmatrix} 51 \\ 83 \\ -40 \end{pmatrix}$$

and so forth. The entries of the resulting product matrices are then transmitted to the receiver as the coded message

41, 69, -35, 51, 83, -40, ...

In order for the receiver of the message to decode it, he or she must group the numbers into the column vectors

$$\begin{pmatrix} 41 \\ 69 \\ -35 \end{pmatrix} \quad \begin{pmatrix} 51 \\ 83 \\ -40 \end{pmatrix} \quad \text{etc.}$$

and multiply A^{-1} by each of these column vectors to obtain the column vectors used by the sender. From these vectors the original message can be easily read.

Exercises

In Exercises 1–8 verify that the given matrices are inverses of each other.

1. $\begin{pmatrix} 4 & 3 \\ 3 & 2 \end{pmatrix}$ and $\begin{pmatrix} -2 & 3 \\ 3 & -4 \end{pmatrix}$

2. $\begin{pmatrix} 3 & 2 \\ 7 & 5 \end{pmatrix}$ and $\begin{pmatrix} 5 & -2 \\ -7 & 3 \end{pmatrix}$

3. $\begin{pmatrix} 4 & 7 \\ 3 & 5 \end{pmatrix}$ and $\begin{pmatrix} -5 & 7 \\ 3 & -4 \end{pmatrix}$

4. $\begin{pmatrix} 7 & 3 \\ 9 & 4 \end{pmatrix}$ and $\begin{pmatrix} 4 & -3 \\ -9 & 7 \end{pmatrix}$

5. $\begin{pmatrix} 1 & -1 & 0 \\ -1 & 0 & 1 \\ -7 & 3 & 3 \end{pmatrix}$ and $\begin{pmatrix} -3 & 3 & -1 \\ -4 & 3 & -1 \\ -3 & 4 & -1 \end{pmatrix}$

6. $\begin{pmatrix} 1 & 1 & 1 \\ 0 & 2 & -1 \\ 2 & 3 & -1 \end{pmatrix}$ and $\begin{pmatrix} -0.2 & -0.8 & 0.6 \\ 0.4 & 0.6 & -0.2 \\ 0.8 & 0.2 & -0.4 \end{pmatrix}$

7. $\begin{pmatrix} 1 & 0 & 1 \\ 4 & 4 & 3 \\ -4 & -3 & -3 \end{pmatrix}$ and $\begin{pmatrix} -3 & -3 & -4 \\ 0 & 1 & 1 \\ 4 & 3 & 4 \end{pmatrix}$

8. $\begin{pmatrix} 0 & 1 & 2 \\ 1 & 1 & 7 \\ 2 & 4 & 17 \end{pmatrix}$ and $\begin{pmatrix} -11 & -9 & 5 \\ -3 & -4 & 2 \\ 2 & 2 & -1 \end{pmatrix}$

Chapter 3 Matrices and Systems of Linear Equations

In Exercises 9–22 compute the inverses of the following matrices or determine that no inverse exists.

9. $\begin{pmatrix} 1 & 3 \\ -2 & -7 \end{pmatrix}$
10. $\begin{pmatrix} 4 & -7 \\ -1 & 2 \end{pmatrix}$

11. $\begin{pmatrix} 1 & 5 \\ -2 & -10 \end{pmatrix}$
12. $\begin{pmatrix} 2 & 1 \\ 1 & -1 \end{pmatrix}$

13. $\begin{pmatrix} 2 & -3 \\ 4 & -5 \end{pmatrix}$
14. $\begin{pmatrix} 2 & 3 \\ 6 & 9 \end{pmatrix}$

15. $\begin{pmatrix} 1 & 2 & -1 \\ -2 & -2 & -1 \\ 3 & 5 & -2 \end{pmatrix}$
16. $\begin{pmatrix} 1 & 1 & -3 \\ 1 & 2 & 1 \\ 2 & 4 & 1 \end{pmatrix}$

17. $\begin{pmatrix} 1 & -1 & 1 \\ 2 & -1 & 3 \\ 1 & 1 & 3 \end{pmatrix}$
18. $\begin{pmatrix} 5 & 3 & -3 \\ 2 & 1 & -2 \\ -1 & 0 & 2 \end{pmatrix}$

19. $\begin{pmatrix} 2 & 1 & -1 \\ 2 & -4 & 8 \\ -1 & 1 & -2 \end{pmatrix}$
20. $\begin{pmatrix} 3 & -4 & 2 \\ -1 & 2 & -1 \\ 4 & -2 & 1 \end{pmatrix}$

21. $\begin{pmatrix} 2 & -1 & -1 & 1 \\ 1 & -1 & -1 & 1 \\ 2 & -1 & -2 & 2 \\ 1 & 1 & 0 & -1 \end{pmatrix}$
22. $\begin{pmatrix} 2 & -1 & 1 & 0 \\ 0 & 1 & 0 & 2 \\ 1 & 0 & 0 & 1 \\ 1 & 0 & 1 & 0 \end{pmatrix}$

Each of the following systems of linear equations has as its coefficient matrix one of the matrices in Exercises 9–22. Use the inverse matrices computed above to solve these systems.

23. $\begin{aligned} x + 3y &= -1 \\ -2x - 7y &= 4 \end{aligned}$
24. $\begin{aligned} 4x - 7y &= -1 \\ -x + 2y &= 1 \end{aligned}$

25. $\begin{aligned} 2x - 3y &= 5 \\ 4x - 5y &= 3 \end{aligned}$
26. $\begin{aligned} x + y - 3z &= 5 \\ x + 2y + z &= 0 \\ 2x + 4y + z &= 2 \end{aligned}$

27. $\begin{aligned} x + 2y - z &= 0 \\ -2x - 2y - z &= -1 \\ 3x + 5y - 2z &= 2 \end{aligned}$
28. $\begin{aligned} 5x + 3y - 3z &= 0 \\ 2x + y - 2z &= 1 \\ -x + 2z &= -4 \end{aligned}$

29. $\begin{aligned} 2x + y - z &= 1 \\ 2x - 4y + 8z &= 12 \\ -x + y - 2z &= -4 \end{aligned}$
30. $\begin{aligned} 2x - y + z &= 4 \\ y + 2w &= -4 \\ x + w &= 2 \\ x + z &= 1 \end{aligned}$

In Exercises 31–34 use the correspondence below to encode or decode the given message.

A B C D E F G H I J K L M
↕ ↕ ↕ ↕ ↕ ↕ ↕ ↕ ↕ ↕ ↕ ↕ ↕
1 2 3 4 5 6 7 8 9 10 11 12 13

N O P Q R S T U V W X Y Z -
↕ ↕ ↕ ↕ ↕ ↕ ↕ ↕ ↕ ↕ ↕ ↕ ↕ ↕
14 15 16 17 18 19 20 21 22 23 24 25 26 27

31. Encode the message THE QUEEN IS DEAD using the matrix

$$\begin{pmatrix} 1 & 2 \\ 2 & 3 \end{pmatrix}$$

32. Encode the message DO NOT SURRENDER using the matrix

$$\begin{pmatrix} 1 & 2 & 1 \\ 2 & 3 & 1 \\ -2 & 0 & 1 \end{pmatrix}$$

33. Decode the message

    41, 62, 22, 43, 25, 39, 29, 57, 74, 121, 44, 73, 43, 72

    that was encoded using the matrix in Exercise 31.

34. Decode the message

    35, 49, −6, 71, 106, −7, 79, 125, −32, 76, 111, −15

    that was encoded using the matrix in Exercise 32.

Chapter Review

New Terms

augmented matrix (p. 86)
block (p. 49)
clique (p. 69)
closed input-output model (p. 97)
column (p. 47)
column vector (p. 47)
diagonal (p. 47)
difference of matrices (p. 53)
elementary row operations (p. 81)
entry of a matrix (p. 46)
equality of matrices (p. 48)
Gaussian elimination (p. 87)
identity matrix (p. 60)
incidence matrix (p. 68)
input-output matrix (p. 97)
inverse matrix (p. 105)
leading variable (p. 86)
liaison person (p. 71)
matrix (p. 46)

method of elimination (p. 79)
method of substitution (p. 78)
open input-output model (p. 97)
parameter (p. 86)
pivot column (p. 87)
product of matrices (p. 58)
row (p. 47)
row echelon form (p. 86)
row vector (p. 47)
scalar (p. 52)
scalar product (p. 52)
size of a matrix (p. 47)
solution of a system of linear
 equations (p. 85)
square matrix (p. 47)
submatrix (p. 49)
sum of matrices (p. 52)
system of linear equations (p. 85)
zero matrix (p. 54)

Review Exercises

1. Label the following statements true or false.
   (a) An $m \times n$ matrix has n rows and m columns.
   (b) The diagonal of a matrix consists of those entries a_{ij} for which $i = j$.
   (c) Only matrices of the same size may be added or subtracted.
   (d) Only matrices of the same size may be multiplied.
   (e) The product of an $m \times n$ matrix and an $n \times p$ matrix is an $m \times p$ matrix.

(f) Every entry of an identity matrix is zero.
(g) If A and B are arbitrary $n \times n$ matrices, then $AB = BA$.
*(h) Every incidence matrix is square and has only zeros and ones as entries.
*(i) If three persons are such that each is related to the other two, then these three persons form a clique.
*(j) If A is an $n \times n$ matrix describing a business communication network, and if B is the matrix obtained by deleting row i and column i from A, then person i is a liaison person precisely when B^{n-2} contains a zero entry.
*(k) In a dominance relation there must be one or more persons who dominate all the others in two stages.
(l) Every system of linear equations has at least one solution.
(m) No system of linear equations can have more than one solution.
*(n) In the closed input-output model the sum of the entries of each column of the input-output matrix is one.
(o) Every square matrix has an inverse.
(p) Some matrices have more than one inverse.
(q) If A is an $n \times n$ matrix and elementary row operations are used to transform $(A|I_n)$ to $(I_n|B)$, then $B = A^{-1}$.

2. For the matrices

$$A = \begin{pmatrix} 1 & 4 & -3 \\ -2 & -1 & 5 \end{pmatrix} \quad \text{and} \quad B = \begin{pmatrix} -2 & 0 & 2 \\ 3 & 1 & -1 \end{pmatrix}$$

compute each of the following.

(a) $A + B$
(b) $A - B$
(c) $-3B$
(d) $3A - 4B$

3. Compute each of the following matrix products.

(a) $\begin{pmatrix} 2 & -1 \\ 1 & 3 \end{pmatrix} \begin{pmatrix} -3 & 2 \\ 0 & 4 \end{pmatrix}$
(b) $\begin{pmatrix} -1 & 4 \\ 2 & 1 \end{pmatrix} \begin{pmatrix} 3 & -2 & 1 \\ -1 & 3 & 4 \end{pmatrix}$

(c) $\begin{pmatrix} 1 & 2 \\ 3 & -1 \\ 0 & 4 \end{pmatrix} \begin{pmatrix} 2 & 4 \\ -3 & 1 \end{pmatrix}$
(d) $\begin{pmatrix} 2 & -1 & 3 \\ -1 & 4 & 0 \\ 1 & 2 & 1 \end{pmatrix} \begin{pmatrix} -3 & 4 \\ 5 & -2 \\ 1 & 1 \end{pmatrix}$

*4. Among six ham radio operators Harry can transmit to Lisa, Bruce, and George; George can transmit to Bruce and Joan; Joan can transmit to Lisa, Harry, and Nancy; Lisa can transmit to Harry, Bruce, and Nancy; Nancy can transmit to Joan, George, and Lisa; and Bruce can transmit to Lisa, Harry, and Joan.

(a) Write the incidence matrix that describes the possible transmissions among these six people.
(b) Determine any cliques in this relation.

*5. Among the officers of an organization Mary influences Jim, Tom, and Linda; Barbara influences Mary and Jim; Sam influences Mary, Barbara, and Jim; Jim influences Linda and Tom; Tom influences Barbara and Sam; and Linda influences Barbara, Sam, and Tom. Which of the six can influence each of the others through at most one intermediary?

6. Solve each of the following systems of linear equations.
   (a) $x + 2y - 4z = 9$
       $2x + y\ \ \ \ \ \ = 5$
       $x + y - 2z = 6$
   (b) $2x + y - 12z = 2$
       $-x + y + 3z = 2$
       $2x - y - 9z = -3$
   (c) $3x - 4y - 5z\ \ \ \ \ \ = 2$
       $2x - 5y + 2z - w = -1$
       $x - 2y\ \ \ \ \ \ + w = 3$
       $2x - 10y + 14z + 2w = 4$
   (d) $2x - 4y + 3z + 7w = 19$
       $3x + y + 7z + 6w = 22$
       $x - y + 2z + 3w = 9$
       $2x + 4y + 10z + 4w = 16$

*7. A manufacturing firm that produces prepared foods has three service departments (maintenance, data processing, and personnel) and two production departments (frozen food and canned food). Table 3.10 gives the direct cost of each department and the proportion of services used by each department. Determine the total cost of each department.

Table 3.10 *Direct Costs and Proportion of Services Used*

		Provider of service		
User of services	Direct cost (dollars)	Maintenance	Data processing	Personnel
Maintenance	900	0.2	0.1	0.1
Data processing	2100	0.2	0.3	0.1
Personnel	1500	0.2	0.2	0.1
Frozen food	6000	0.2	0.2	0.4
Canned food	5000	0.2	0.2	0.3

*8. A certain simple society produces wool, electricity, and food. Production of 1 unit of wool requires 0.2 unit of wool, 0.1 unit of electricity, and 0.1 unit of food; production of 1 unit of electricity requires 0.3 unit of electricity, 0.1 unit of food, and no wool; and production of 1 unit of food requires 0.2 unit of wool, 0.1 unit of electricity, and 0.1 unit of food. What gross production is necessary to meet an external demand for 14 units of wool, 11 units of electricity, and 5 units of food?

9. Solve each of the following systems of linear equations.
   (a) $x_1 - 3x_2 + 2x_3 - 2x_4 - x_5 = 2$
       $2x_1 - 6x_2 + 2x_3 + x_4 + x_5 = 3$
       $3x_1 - 9x_2 + 7x_3 - 9x_4 + 2x_5 = 5$
   (b) $4x_1 - 5x_2 - 2x_3 + 5x_4 + 8x_5 = 3$
       $x_1 - 2x_2 + x_3\ \ \ \ \ \ + 2x_5 = 1$
       $2x_1 - 3x_2\ \ \ \ \ \ + 2x_4 + 3x_5 = 0$
   (c) $3x_1 + 2x_2 + 3x_3 - 6x_4 + 15x_5 - 3x_6 = 9$
       $x_1\ \ \ \ \ \ + 3x_3 - x_4 + 4x_5 - 2x_6 = 3$
       $2x_1 + 4x_2 - 6x_3 - 8x_4 + 13x_5 + 4x_6 = 10$
       $2x_1 - x_2 + 9x_3\ \ \ \ \ \ + 6x_5 - 5x_6 = 7$
   (d) $2x_1 - 2x_2 + 6x_3 + x_4 - 3x_5\ \ \ \ \ \ = 13$
       $3x_1 - 3x_2 + 7x_3 + 7x_4 - x_5 - 5x_6 = 8$
       $x_1 - x_2 + 2x_3 + 3x_4\ \ \ \ \ \ - 2x_6 = 2$
       $-2x_1 + 2x_2 - 2x_3 - 13x_4 - 5x_5 + 12x_6 = 6$

10. Compute the inverses of the following matrices or determine that no inverse exists.

(a) $\begin{pmatrix} 1 & -2 & 1 \\ 0 & 4 & -3 \\ 2 & -5 & 3 \end{pmatrix}$
(b) $\begin{pmatrix} 2 & 3 & 1 \\ 1 & 2 & -1 \\ 1 & 0 & 4 \end{pmatrix}$
(c) $\begin{pmatrix} 2 & 0 & -6 \\ 1 & -1 & 2 \\ 3 & -2 & 1 \end{pmatrix}$
(d) $\begin{pmatrix} 2 & -2 & -6 \\ 1 & -4 & 0 \\ -2 & 6 & 3 \end{pmatrix}$

References

1. Johnston, John B., G. Baley Price, and Fred S. Van Vleck, *Linear Equations and Matrices*. Reading, Mass.: Addison-Wesley, 1966.
2. Leontief, Wassily W., "Input-Output Economics," *Sci. Am.*, vol. 185, no. 4 (October 1951), pp. 15–21.
3. Leontief, Wassily W., *The Structure of American Economy, 1919–1935*. New York: Oxford University Press, 1951.
4. Stone, Richard, "Mathematics in the Social Sciences," *Sci. Am.*, vol. 211, no. 3 (September 1964), pp. 168–182.
5. Ulmer, S. Sidney, "Leadership in the Michigan Supreme Court," in *Judicial Decision-Making*, Glendon Schubert, ed. New York: Free Press, 1963.

4
Linear Programming

Practical problems that involve mathematics often require determining the maximum or minimum value of a variable quantity subject to one or more restrictions. A businessperson, for example, may wish to maximize the profit obtained from the sale of products that can be made from limited amounts of raw materials, or a dietician may wish to minimize the cost of a special diet that must satisfy certain specific nutritional requirements.

linear programming problems

In this chapter we discuss a class of problems called *linear programming problems* that require maximizing or minimizing a linear function subject to restrictions that can be expressed as linear inequalities. We begin by considering simple linear programming problems in which only two variables are present. Such problems can be solved graphically, and Sections 4.1–4.3 are devoted to this technique. In Sections 4.4–4.6 we discuss an important algebraic method for solving linear programming problems involving any number of variables. This procedure, called the *simplex method*, was developed by George Dantzig in 1947 to solve problems of supply allocation for the U.S. Air Force. Since that time, the simplex method has made possible the solution of linear programming problems involving hundreds of inequalities and variables, thus contributing to the widespread use of linear programming to solve problems in many disciplines.

4.1 Systems of Linear Inequalities

In Section 2.3 we saw that the graph of any equation of the form $ax + by = c$, where $a \neq 0$ or $b \neq 0$, is a line. We now consider the

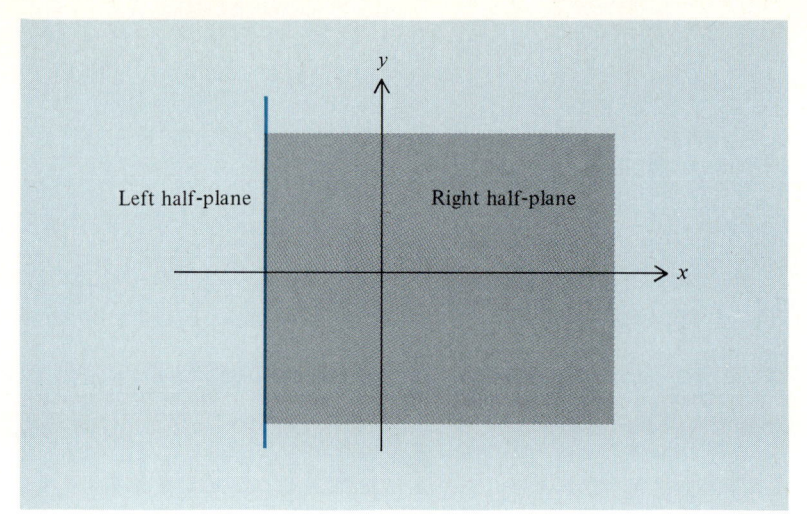

Figure 4.1

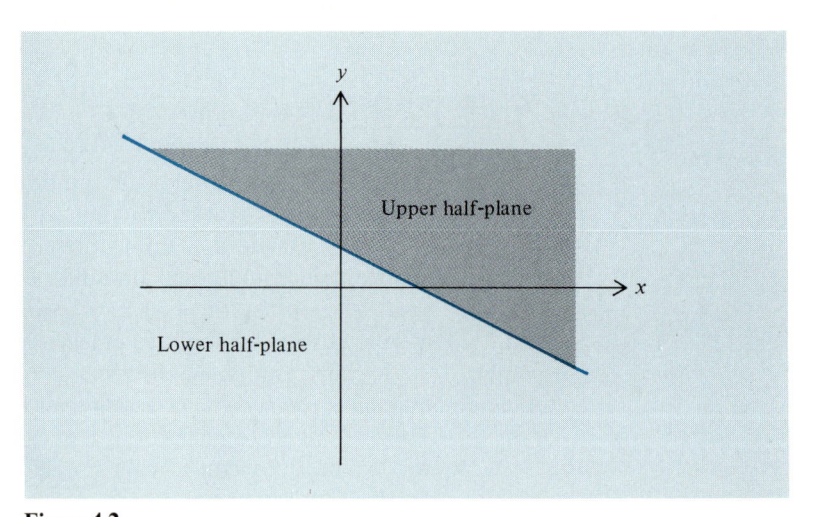

Figure 4.2

linear inequalities

related *linear inequalities*

$$ax + by < c \quad \text{and} \quad ax + by > c$$

half-plane

right and left half-planes
upper and lower half-planes

Any line divides the plane into two parts called *half-planes* which consist of all the points lying on the same side of the line. For a vertical line we speak of the *right* and *left* half-planes (as shown in Figure 4.1), and for nonvertical lines we speak of the *upper* and *lower* half-planes (as shown in Fig 4.2).

Let us compare the graphs of the linear inequalities

$$y > 2x - 6 \quad \text{and} \quad y < 2x - 6$$

with that of the linear equation $y = 2x - 6$. The graph of $y = 2x - 6$

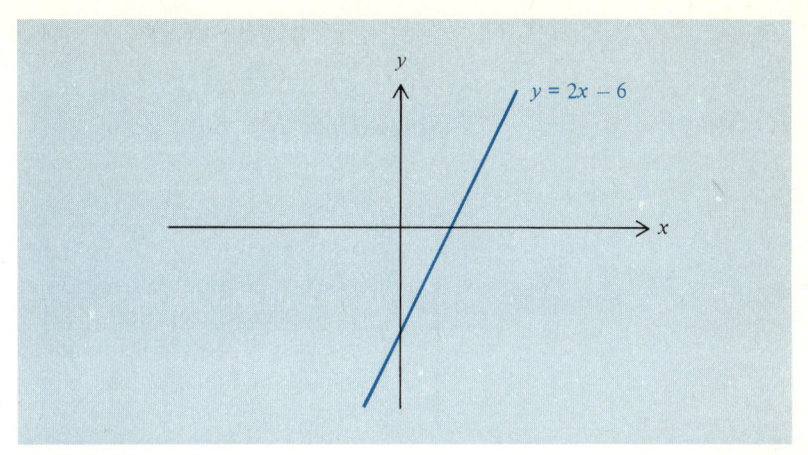

Figure 4.3

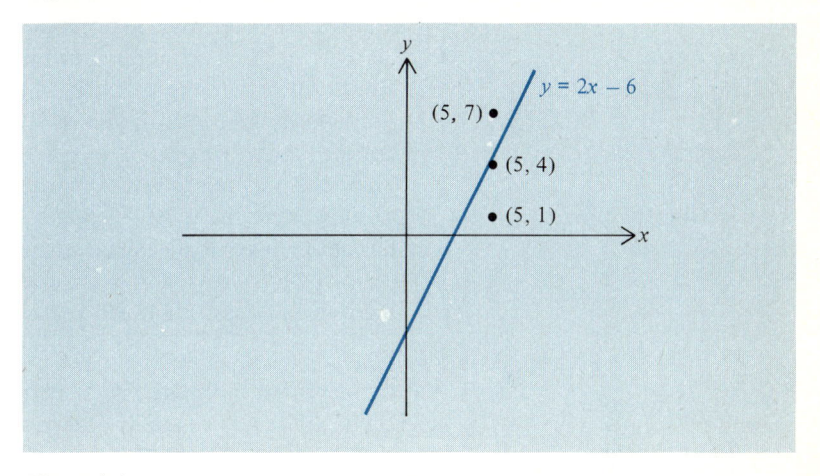

Figure 4.4

is the line shown in Figure 4.3. For any value of x there is exactly one value of y, namely, $2x - 6$, for which the ordered pair (x, y) lies on this line. Now for any greater value of y, the point (x, y) will lie above the line, and for any smaller value of y, the point (x, y) will lie below the line. (See Figure 4.4.) Thus the graph of the inequality $y > 2x - 6$ is the upper half-plane in Figure 4.3, and the graph of the inequality $y < 2x - 6$ is the lower half-plane in Figure 4.3.

More generally, the following result is true.

THEOREM 4.1

Each of the linear inequalities

$$ax + by > c \quad \text{and} \quad ax + by < c$$

where $a \neq 0$ or $b \neq 0$, has as its graph one of the two half-planes determined by the line with equation $ax + by = c$.

Notice that Theorem 4.1 does not state which of the two inequalities describes the upper half-plane and which describes the lower half-plane. The following example shows how to determine which inequality corresponds to each half-plane.

EXAMPLE 1

The set of points satisfying the inequality $3x + 4y < 24$ is one of the half-planes determined by the line with equation $3x + 4y = 24$. Consequently, to graph the inequality $3x + 4y < 24$, we begin by graphing the equation $3x + 4y = 24$. The resulting line is shown in Figure 4.5.

We must now determine whether the upper or lower half-plane in Figure 4.5 corresponds to the given inequality. For this purpose it is sufficient to test any point not lying on the line with equation $3x + 4y = 24$ to see if its coordinates satisfy the given inequality. For convenience the point $(0, 0)$ is usually used as the test point. Substituting the coordinates $x = 0$ and $y = 0$ of the test point into the inequality, we obtain $3(0) + 4(0) < 24$, or equivalently, $0 < 24$. Since the inequality $0 < 24$ is true, we conclude that the test point $(0, 0)$ satisfies the given inequality. But in this case the test point lies in the lower half-plane determined by the line; hence the graph of $3x + 4y < 24$ is this lower half-plane. Therefore the graph of $3x + 4y < 24$ is the shaded region in Figure 4.6.

Observe that in Figure 4.6 the equation $3x + 4y = 24$ was graphed as a dashed line. A dashed line is used when the points on the line are not part of the shaded region (i.e., the inequality has a $>$ or $<$ sign), and a solid line is used when the points on the line are included in the shaded region (i.e., the inequality has a $\geq$ or $\leq$ sign).

The procedure for graphing the linear inequalities $ax + by < c$, $ax + by > c$, $ax + by \leq c$, and $ax + by \geq c$ can be summarized as follows:

1. Graph the equation $ax + by = c$ as a dashed line if equality is not permitted in the given inequality and as a solid line if equality is permitted.
2. Select a test point not lying on the line graphed in step 1. [If possible, the choice of $(0, 0)$ will simplify computations.] Substitute the coordinates of the test point into the original inequality and determine whether the resulting inequality is true or false. If it is true, then the half-plane containing the test point will satisfy the given inequality; otherwise, the half-plane not containing the test point will satisfy the given inequality.

4.1 Systems of Linear Inequalities 121

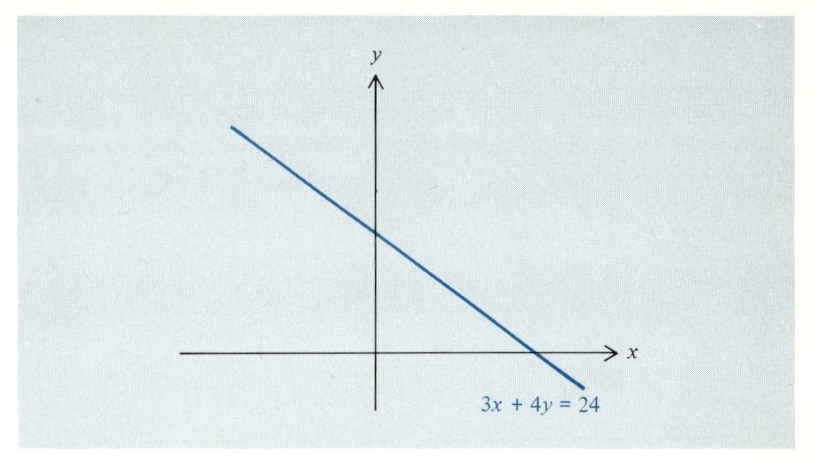

Figure 4.5

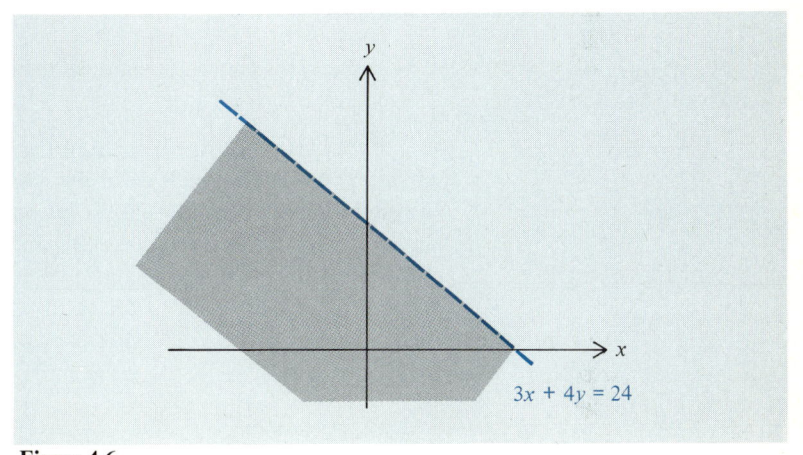

Figure 4.6

EXAMPLE 2

We shall graph the inequality $3x - y \geq 0$. As before, we begin by graphing the line with equation $3x - y = 0$; this line is shown in Figure 4.7. We must now determine which half-plane corresponds to the points satisfying $3x - y > 0$. Since the point $(0, 0)$ lies on the line $3x - y = 0$, we cannot choose $(0, 0)$ as our test point. Instead, we select any point not on the line, say $(0, 1)$. Substituting $x = 0$ and $y = 1$ into the given inequality produces the false statement $3(0) - 1 \geq 0$; so $(0, 1)$ does not satisfy the given inequality. Since the test point $(0, 1)$ lies in the upper half-plane determined by $3x - y = 0$, we see that the graph of $3x - y > 0$ must be the lower half-plane. In this case the points on the line $3x - y = 0$ are to be included in the region; so the set of points satisfying $3x - y \geq 0$

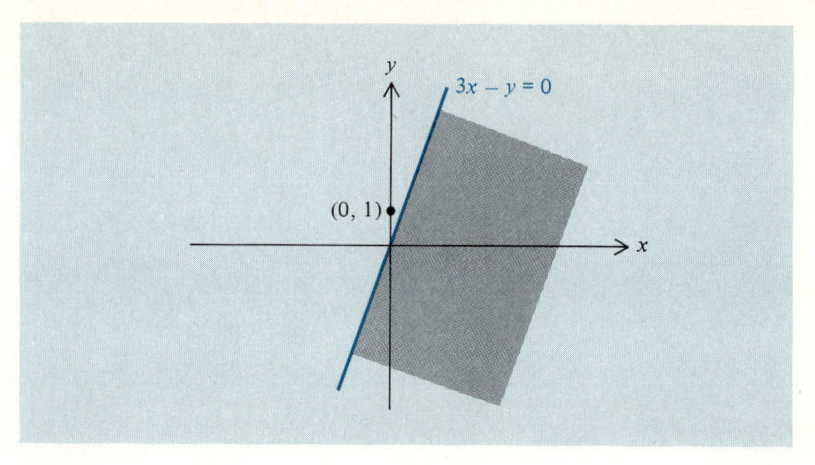

Figure 4.7

consists of the points on the line $y - 3x = 0$ or in its lower half-plane. This region is shaded in Figure 4.7.

By a system of linear inequalities involving x and y we mean two or more linear inequalities in the variables x and y. As was true for a system of linear equations, a solution of a system of linear inequalities involving x and y is an ordered pair of real numbers (a, b) such that the substitution of $x = a$ and $y = b$ satisfies *every* inequality in the system. The collection of all solutions of a system of inequalities is called the *set of feasible solutions* or the *feasible set* for the system.

feasible set

EXAMPLE 3

The ordered pair $(4, 6)$ is a solution of the system of linear inequalities

$$3x - y \geq 5$$
$$x - y \leq 1$$
$$x + y \leq 15$$

since each inequality is satisfied when $x = 4$ and $y = 6$. Other solutions of this system are $(3, 4)$, $(6, 9)$, and $(5, 4)$. On the other hand, the ordered pair $(6, 4)$ is not a solution of this system because the second inequality is not satisfied if $x = 6$ and $y = 4$.

Since the restrictions in a linear programming problem form a system of linear inequalities, it will be necessary to be able to graph the set of feasible solutions for any system of linear inequalities in x and y. But, because a solution to the system is nothing more than an

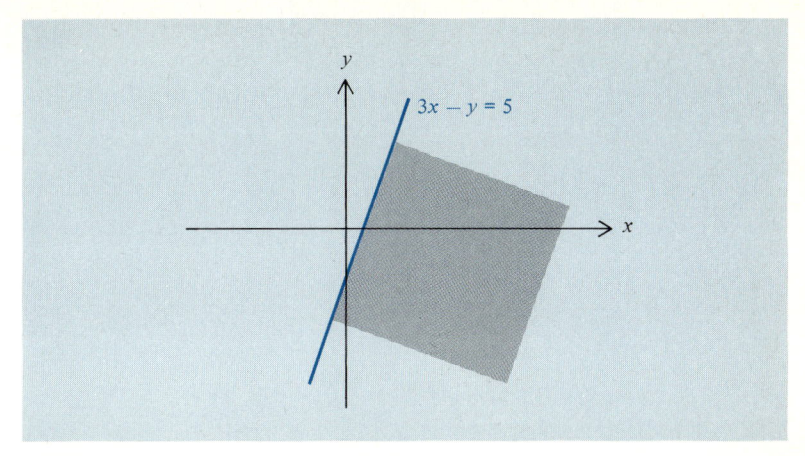

Figure 4.8

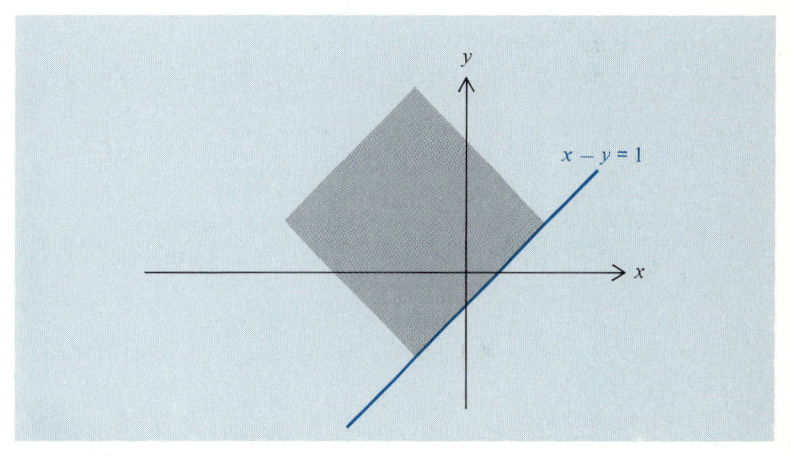

Figure 4.9

ordered pair satisfying each inequality in the system, the graph of the feasible set is merely the region common to the graphs of all the inequalities in the system.

EXAMPLE 4

The graphs of the three inequalities in Example 3 are shown in Figures 4.8–4.10.

These three graphs are shown together in Figure 4.11. The arrows on each line designate the half-plane that satisfies the corresponding inequality. The region common to the graphs of all three inequalities is the graph of the feasible set for the given system; this region is shaded in Figure 4.11.

124 Chapter 4 Linear Programming

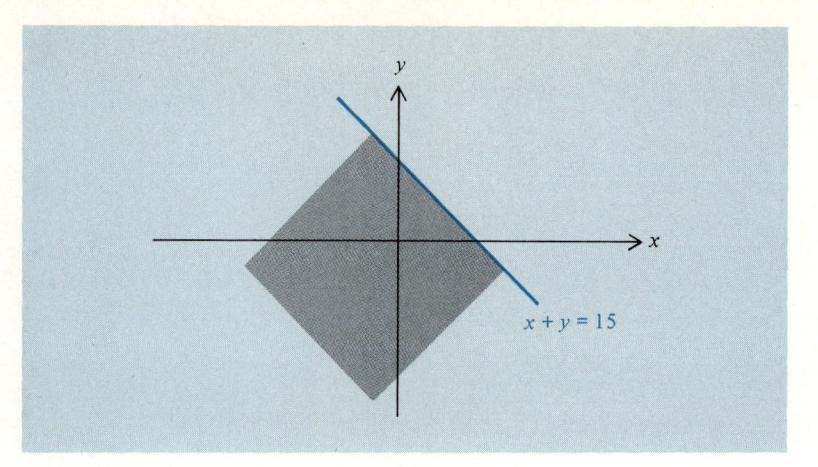

Figure 4.10

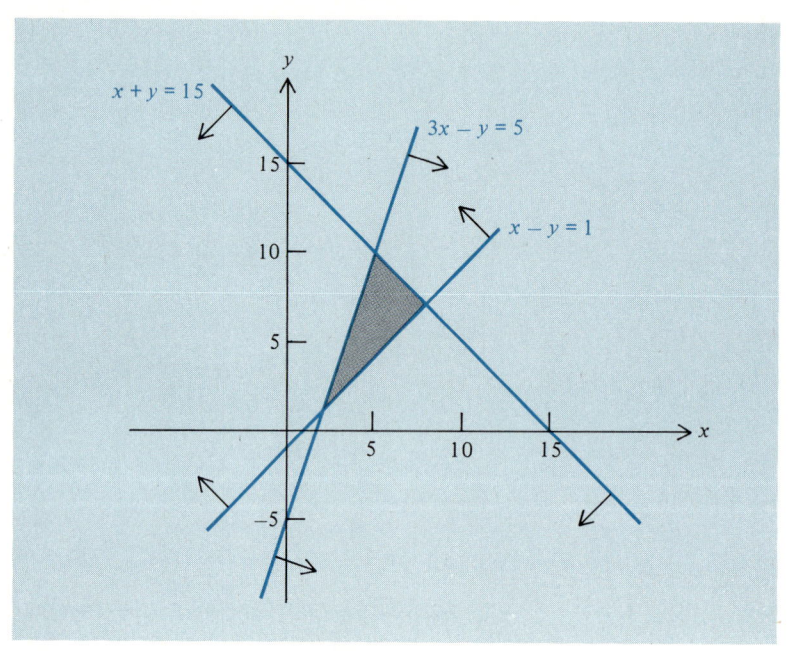

Figure 4.11

EXAMPLE 5

To graph the set of feasible solutions for the system of linear inequalities

$$x + 2y \geq 8$$
$$2x + y \geq 12$$
$$x - 2y \leq 0$$
$$x \geq 0$$
$$y \geq 0$$

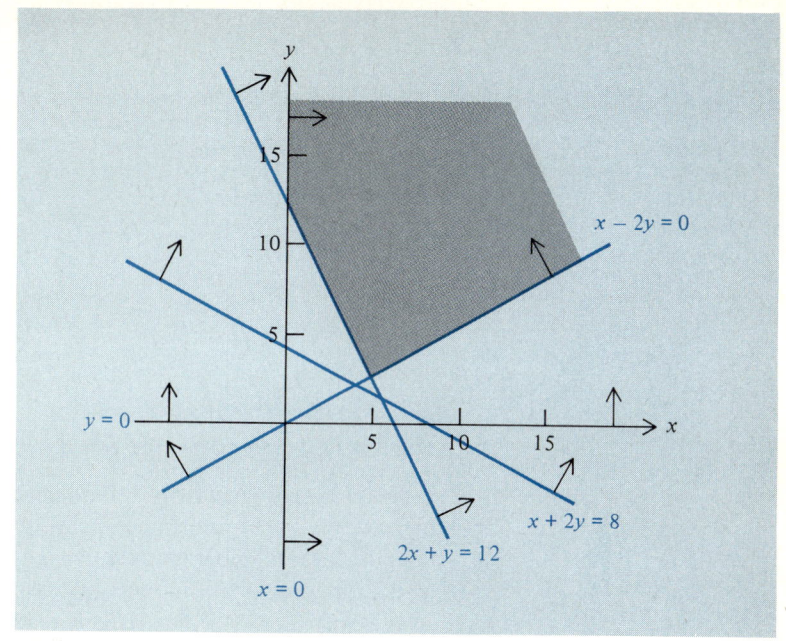

Figure 4.12

we must first graph each of the inequalities in the system. These graphs are indicated by the arrows in Figure 4.12. Then the region common to all the inequalities is the graph of the feasible set of the given system. This region is shaded in Figure 4.12.

Exercises

Graph the linear inequalities in Exercises 1–10.

1. $2x - 5y > 20$
2. $3x + 5y \leq 30$
3. $x \geq 7$
4. $y \leq 20$
5. $3x + 4y \leq 24$
6. $12x + 15y \geq 120$
7. $y < -5$
8. $x > 10$
9. $7x + 5y \geq 140$
10. $3x - y < 18$

Graph the set of feasible solutions for the systems of linear inequalities in Exercises 11–25.

11. $x \geq -5$
    $x \leq 8$
    $y \geq -2$
    $y \leq 6$

12. $x \geq 0$
    $x < 7$
    $y > -5$
    $y \leq -1$

13. $x + y \geq 10$
    $x + 4y < 16$

14. $2x + 3y \geq 36$
    $4x + y > 32$

15. $x + y \leq 150$
    $x + 2y \leq 200$
    $x \geq 30$
    $y \geq 20$

16. $y - x \leq 6$
    $y < 2x$
    $x < 9$
    $y \geq -4$

17. $2x + y \geq 4$
    $4y - x < 52$
    $2x - y < 8$

18. $2x + 3y \leq 30$
    $x - 3y < 6$
    $4x - 3y \leq 6$

19. $x + 3y \leq 15$
    $2x + y \leq 20$
    $x \geq 0$
    $y \geq 0$

20. $x + y \leq 12$
    $2x + y \leq 18$
    $x \geq 0$
    $y \geq 0$

21. $x + 3y \geq 24$
    $2x + y \geq 18$
    $x \geq 0$
    $y \geq 0$

22. $x + 4y \geq 32$
    $7x + 2y \geq 42$
    $x \geq 0$
    $y \geq 0$

23. $5x + 3y \leq 60$
    $3x + y \geq 24$
    $x \geq 0$
    $y \geq 2$

24. $2x + y \geq 18$
    $2x + 3y \geq 42$
    $x \leq 2y$
    $x \geq 0$
    $y \geq 0$

25. $x + y \leq 20$
    $3x + y \leq 24$
    $y \geq x$
    $x \geq 3$
    $y \geq 0$

4.2 Mathematical Models Involving Systems of Linear Inequalities

We have already mentioned that linear programming problems require maximizing or minimizing a linear function subject to restrictions that take the form of linear inequalities. Thus linear programming problems lead to mathematical models involving systems of linear inequalities. In this section we are primarily concerned with creating mathematical models (formulations) of linear programming problems. However, we shall also learn to compute the coordinates of certain important points in the set of feasible solutions for the system of inequalities in the model. These skills will be used in Section 4.3 to solve linear programming problems involving only two variables.

EXAMPLE 6

Having stopped production of an unprofitable item, a manufacturer has additional production capacity that can be used for the manufacture of two new products. Both these products require time on a lathe and a milling machine: Each unit of the first product requires 1 hour on a lathe and 3 hours on a milling machine, whereas each unit of the second product requires 2 hours on a lathe and 2 hours on a milling machine. Because of the current production schedule for other products, a lathe is available for at most 14 hours per week and a milling machine is available for at most 18 hours per week. The manufacturer expects to be able to sell as many units of either new product as can be produced, and the anticipated profit is $20 per unit for the first product and $30 per unit for the second. Under these conditions, how many units of each new product should be made in order to earn a maximum profit?

In order to formulate a mathematical model for this problem, notice that the unknowns are the number of units of the first product and the number of units of the second product to be made. Let x and y, respectively, denote these two quantities. As in Section 3.5, it is helpful to summarize the given information in the following tabular form:

	First product	Second product	Available time
Quantity produced	x	y	—
Time on a lathe (hours per unit)	1	2	14
Time on a milling machine (hours per unit)	3	2	18

It is now easy to see that the time restrictions are as follows:

$x + 2y \leq 14$ (lathe restriction)

$3x + 2y \leq 18$ (milling machine restriction)

In addition, there are two implicit restrictions in this problem: the quantity of each product to be made cannot be negative.[1] Hence we have two additional restrictions

$x \geq 0$ and $y \geq 0$

Thus the restrictions for this problem can be stated mathematically as the following system of linear inequalities:

$$x + 2y \leq 14$$
$$3x + 2y \leq 18$$
$$x \geq 0$$
$$y \geq 0$$

constraints

The inequalities in this system are called the *constraints* for the linear programming problem. The set of feasible solutions for the constraints can be graphed as in Section 4.1; the resulting diagram is shown in Figure 4.13.

Finally, let us note that, since the manufacturer expects to earn a $20 profit on each unit of the first product and a $30 profit on each unit of the second product, the total profit from x units of the first product and y units of the second product is $20x + 30y$. So the total profit (in dollars) is given by the function

$$P(x, y) = 20x + 30y$$

a linear function of two variables. To solve the stated problem, we must find an ordered pair (x, y) in the set of feasible solutions at which $P(x, y)$ assumes its maximum value. We shall see how to find such an ordered pair in Section 4.3.

---

[1] In this example it is more realistic to require that x and y be nonnegative integers. Such a restriction leads to a special type of linear programming problem called an *integer programming problem*. Because integer programming problems require special techniques beyond the scope of this book, we always assume that the variables in a linear programming problem are not restricted to integer values.

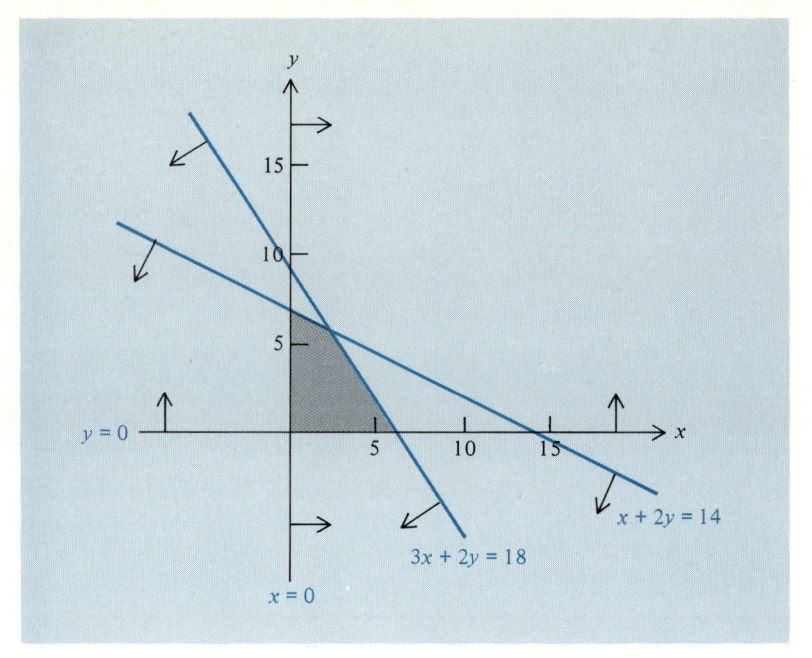

Figure 4.13

EXAMPLE 7

The owner of a house with a 10-acre lot would like to fertilize his lawn. He has determined that he will need fertilizer containing at least 320 pounds of nitrogen, at least 48 pounds of phosphoric acid, and at least 24 pounds of potash. Two brands of lawn fertilizer, Fastgro and Greengro, are available at prices of $40 and $50 per bag, respectively. Each bag of Fastgro will provide 25 pounds of nitrogen, 3 pounds of phosphoric acid, and 1 pound of potash, whereas each bag of Greengro will provide 20 pounds of nitrogen, 4 pounds of phosphoric acid, and 4 pounds of potash. Under these conditions how many bags of each brand of fertilizer should be bought in order to fertilize the lawn at the minimum cost?

Let x and y denote the number of bags of Fastgro and Greengro, respectively, to be bought. Observe that the given data can be recorded in the following tabular form:

	Fastgro	Greengro	Required amount
Number of bags bought	x	y	—
Nitrogen content (pounds per bag)	25	20	320
Phosphoric acid content (pounds per bag)	3	4	48
Potash content (pounds per bag)	1	4	24

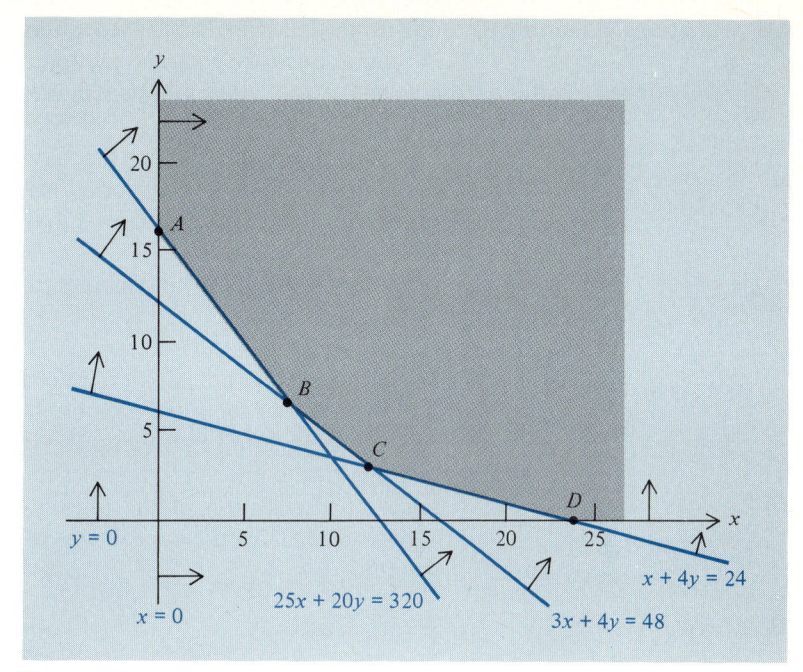

4.2 Mathematical Models Involving Systems of Linear Inequalities 129

Figure 4.14

Thus the constraints for this problem are

$$25x + 20y \geq 320 \quad \text{(nitrogen restriction)}$$
$$3x + 4y \geq 48 \quad \text{(phosphoric acid restriction)}$$
$$x + 4y \geq 24 \quad \text{(potash restriction)}$$
$$x \geq 0$$
$$y \geq 0$$

and the set of feasible solutions is as shown in Figure 4.14.

In this problem, we would like to minimize the total cost of the fertilizer, which is given (in dollars) by

$$C(x, y) = 40x + 50y$$

objective function

Let us consider the common aspects of Examples 6 and 7. In each case we want to determine an ordered pair (x, y) that maximizes or minimizes a linear function called the *objective function*. (In Example 6 the objective function is $P(x, y) = 20x + 30y$, and in Example 7 it is $C(x, y) = 40x + 50y$.) The ordered pairs to be considered are those in the set of feasible solutions for the constraints of the problem.

Notice that the graph of the set of feasible solutions for Example 6 (shown in Figure 4.13) differs from that in Example 7 (shown in Figure

bounded feasible set

unbounded feasible set

vertex

4.14) in the following way: The feasible set in Example 6 is *bounded* (that is, its graph can be enclosed in a circle), whereas that in Example 7 is *unbounded* (that is, its graph cannot be enclosed in a circle). Nevertheless, the boundary of each graph is formed by parts of lines. Any point in the set of feasible solutions that lies on two different lines forming the boundary is called a *vertex* (or *corner point*) of the set of feasible solutions. We shall see in Section 4.3 that the vertices of the set of feasible solutions play a special role in the solution of a linear programming problem. Consequently, it is important to be able to determine the coordinates of each vertex.

In Figure 4.14 the four vertices have been labeled A, B, C, and D. Since each vertex is the point of intersection of two of the lines forming the boundary of the set of feasible solutions, the coordinates of each vertex can be found by solving the system of linear equations corresponding to the lines that intersect there. For example, vertex C is the point of intersection of the lines with equations $3x + 4y = 48$ and $x + 4y = 24$. Thus the coordinates of vertex C are the solution of the system

$$3x + 4y = 48$$
$$x + 4y = 24$$

which is easily seen to be $(12, 3)$. So the coordinates of vertex C are $(12, 3)$. Likewise the coordinates of vertices A, B, and D can be found to be $(0, 16)$, $(8, 6)$, and $(24, 0)$, respectively.

EXAMPLE 8

A candy store sells two mixtures of peanuts and cashews. Each pound of the regular mixture contains 12 ounces of peanuts and 4 ounces of cashews and yields a $0.50 profit, and each pound of the deluxe mixture contains 8 ounces of peanuts and 8 ounces of cashews and yields a $0.70 profit. If the store has 240 ounces of peanuts and 160 ounces of cashews available, how much of each type of mixture should be made in order to obtain a maximum profit?

We shall write the constraints and the objective function, graph the set of feasible solutions, and find the coordinates of each vertex. Let x and y denote the number of pounds of the regular and deluxe mixtures to be made, respectively. The tabular form of the given data is as follows.

	Regular	Deluxe	Amount available
Number of pounds of mixture	x	y	—
Peanut content (ounces per pound)	12	8	240
Cashew content (ounces per pound)	4	8	160

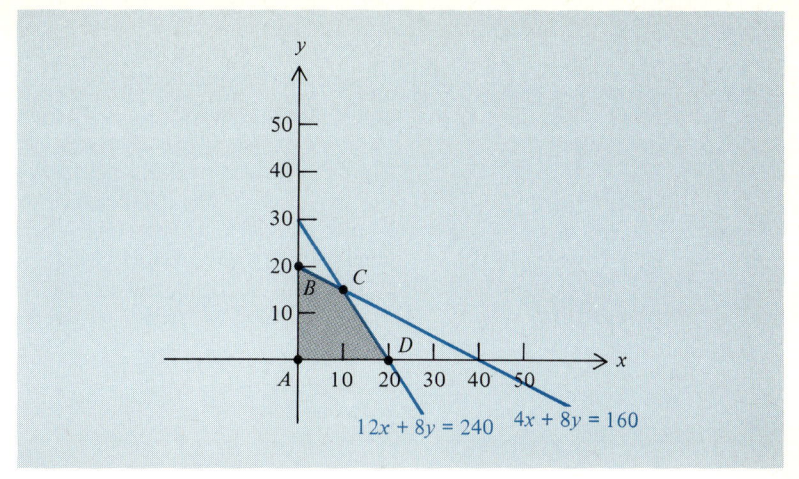

Figure 4.15

The constraints for this problem are

$$12x + 8y \leq 240$$
$$4x + 8y \leq 160$$
$$x \geq 0$$
$$y \geq 0$$

The set of feasible solutions for these constraints is graphed in Figure 4.15, and the four vertices are labeled A, B, C, and D. Since vertices A, B, and D lie on the coordinate axes, it is easy to compute their coordinates; they are $(0,0)$, $(0,20)$, and $(20,0)$, respectively. Vertex C is the point of intersection of the lines $12x + 8y = 240$ and $4x + 8y = 160$, and so its coordinates are $(10, 15)$.

Finally, the objective function for this problem is

$$P(x, y) = 0.50x + 0.70y$$

Exercises

For each of the following problems, write the constraints and the objective function, graph the set of feasible solutions, and find the coordinates of each vertex. Do not attempt to solve the problems.

1. For an experiment on animal behavior a psychologist must train rats and mice to run two mazes. The amount of time each rat and each mouse is given in the mazes is shown below.

	Time per rat (minutes)	Time per mouse (minutes)	Available time (minutes)
Maze A	12	8	240
Maze B	10	15	300

Under these conditions what is the maximum number of animals that can be used in this experiment, and what combination of rats and mice will produce this maximum?

2. A manufacturer makes two sizes of glass vases. The taller ones, being more sturdy than the shorter ones, are less expensive to ship but more expensive to produce. If the production and shipping costs for each type of vase are as given in the table below, and if the manufacturer earns a $4 profit on the taller vases and a $3 profit on the shorter vases, what combination of vases will yield the maximum profit? What is this profit?

	Taller vase	Shorter vase	Maximum available
Production cost	$10	$4	$6000
Shipping cost	$1	$2	$ 800

3. Using two foods, a hospital dietician must prepare a special meal that contains required amounts of vitamin A and calcium. The amount of vitamin A and calcium supplied by one ounce of each food and the required amounts are shown in the table below.

	Units per ounce		Amount
	Food 1	Food 2	
Vitamin A	800 international units	300 international units	6000 international units
Calcium	50 milligrams	150 milligrams	900 milligrams

If each ounce of food 1 contains 200 calories and each ounce of food 2 contains 150 calories, what combination of the foods will supply the required amounts of vitamin A and calcium with the fewest calories? What is the minimum number of calories?

4. A homeowner wants to mix two lawn fertilizers, Nourish and Greenup, to obtain a mixture of nitrogen and phosphoric acid for use on her lawn. The amounts of each chemical provided by the two fertilizers are given in the following table:

	Pounds per bag		Minimum needed (pounds)
	Nourish	Greenup	
Nitrogen	$2\frac{1}{4}$	$1\frac{1}{2}$	36
Phosphoric acid	$\frac{1}{4}$	$\frac{1}{2}$	7

If each bag of Nourish costs $5 and each bag of Greenup costs $6, what combination of the two fertilizers will provide the necessary amounts of nitrogen and phosphoric acid at the least cost?

5. A certain manufacturing process requires at least 5 tons of coal per day. The manufacturer can use Illinois coal costing $40 per ton or low-sulfur western coal costing $60 per ton. Each ton of Illinois coal burned emits 8 units of sulfur oxides, whereas each ton of western coal burned emits 3 units of sulfur oxides. If the Environmental Protection Agency permits

the manufacturer to emit no more than 24 units of sulfur oxides per day, what combination of the two types of coal should be used to minimize the daily cost of coal?

6. An investor has $48,000 to invest in municipal bonds. The expected return on bonds with an Aa rating is 6%, and the expected return on bonds with a Ba rating is 10%. For reasons of security the amount that the investor spends for bonds with a Ba rating must not exceed three times the amount spent for bonds with an Aa rating. Under these conditions what combination of bonds will yield the maximum expected return? What is the maximum expected return?

7. The manufacture of products A and B requires time on three machines. Each unit of product A requires 1 minute on the first machine, 2 minutes on the second machine, and no time on the third machine, whereas each unit of product B requires 1 minute on each of the three machines. During a particular production period the first machine is available for at most 4000 minutes, the second machine is available for at most 6000 minutes, and the third machine is available for at most 3000 minutes. If each unit of product A earns a $0.70 profit and each unit of product B earns a $0.75 profit, how should production be scheduled during this period in order to earn a maximum profit? What is this profit?

8. A wholesale distributor of art reproductions manufactures two kinds of wooden frames which are given away with the paintings. It takes 20 minutes to cut, 10 minutes to assemble, and 10 minutes to finish a plain frame, and it takes 10 minutes to cut, 20 minutes to assemble, and 60 minutes to finish a more ornate frame. The cost of manufacturing one plain frame is $7.50, and the cost of manufacturing one ornate frame is $14.00. If a certain production run includes at least 8 hours of cutting, at least 10 hours of assembling, and at least 18 hours of finishing, how many frames of each style should be made to minimize the manufacturing cost? What is the minimum cost?

9. Parts A and B are to be manufactured and stored in a warehouse with a capacity of 36,000 square feet. Part A requires 4 square feet of space per unit, and part B requires 3 square feet of space per unit. Manufacturing each unit of A requires 4 hours, and manufacturing each unit of B requires 5 hours. In addition, each unit of A requires 2 hours for painting, and each unit of B requires 5 hours for painting. A total of 40,000 hours is available for manufacturing the parts, and 30,000 hours are available for painting the parts. If each unit of part A earns a $5 profit and each unit of part B earns a $4 profit, how many units of each part should be made for a maximum profit?

10. A pound of food A costing $1 contains 2 ounces of nutrient I and 4 ounces of nutrient II, whereas a pound of food B costing $2 contains 3 ounces of nutrient I and 1 ounce of nutrient II. A mixture of foods A and B is to be made that weighs no more than 40 pounds yet contains at least 90 ounces of nutrient I and at least 80 ounces of nutrient II. How should this mixture be made so that its cost is a minimum?

11. A university wants to purchase at least 12, but not more than 15, hours of additional computer time. The computer cooperative to which the university belongs will sell prime time at a cost of $500 per hour and evening time at a cost of $200 per hour. If the university wishes at least

one-third of the time purchased to be prime time, how many hours of each type should be purchased to minimize the cost? What is the minimum cost?

12. A lake is being stocked with two species of fish that feed on two types of food, F_1 and F_2, that grow in the lake at rates of 6000 and 2400 units per day, respectively. The first species of fish has an average weight of 1 pound and consumes an average of 6 units of F_1 and 2 units of F_2 per day. The second species of fish has an average weight of $2\frac{1}{2}$ pounds and consumes an average of 8 units of F_1 and 4 units of F_2 per day. If the number of fish of the first species is to be at least as large as the number of fish of the second species, how should the lake be stocked in order to support the maximum total weight of these two species of fish? What is the maximum weight?

13. A political candidate is seeking election to the state legislature from a district consisting of one large town and a surrounding rural area. During the next month she wants to distribute at least 3600 pieces of campaign literature throughout the district. She can distribute an average of 30 pieces of literature per hour in the town and an average of 20 pieces of literature in the rural area. Because the majority of the district's population lives in the town, the candidate wishes to spend at least $\frac{2}{3}$ of her total campaign time in the town but feels that she must spend at least 15 hours campaigning in the rural area. Under these conditions what is the least amount of time the candidate can spend campaigning, and how is this time divided between the town and the rural area?

14. Suppose in Exercise 12 that, instead of requiring the number of fish of the first species to be at least as large as the number of fish of the second species, it is required that the number of fish of the first species be at least twice as large as the number of fish of the second species. Show that under these conditions the constraint involving F_2 no longer affects the problem. (Such a constraint is called *nonbinding*.) What would be the solution to Exercise 12 under these conditions?

nonbinding constraint

15. A western Illinois farmer intends to plant corn and soybeans on his 200-acre farm. For this farm's soil (gumbo clay), each acre of corn will yield a profit of $220 and each acre of soybeans will yield a profit of $195. Production costs for each acre of corn are $110 and for each acre of soybeans are $85, and the farmer does not want his total production costs to exceed $18,700. If the farmer intends to plant at least 66 acres of soybeans and wants at least $\frac{1}{4}$ of the total acreage planted to be devoted to corn, how many acres of each crop should be planted in order to obtain a maximum profit? What is the maximum profit under these conditions?

4.3 Geometric Solution of Linear Programming Problems

In Section 4.2 we considered several linear programming problems involving only two variables. We saw that solving such problems requires finding an ordered pair (x, y) in the set of feasible solutions at which the objective function assumes its maximum or minimum value. Since there is usually an infinite number of points in the set of feasible

4.3 Geometric Solution of Linear Programming Problems 135

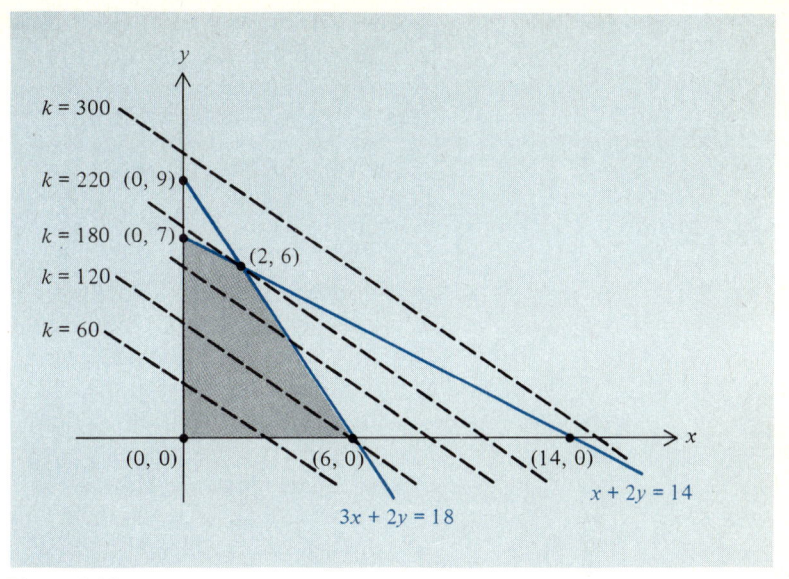

Figure 4.16

solutions, it is not possible to compute the value of the objective function at each point in order to determine where the maximum or minimum value occurs.

We shall now discuss a method for determining a point in the feasible set at which the objective function assumes its optimal value. To illustrate the ideas involved, let us consider the linear programming problem in Example 6 in Section 4.2. We have seen that this problem has the following mathematical formulation:

Maximize $P(x, y) = 20x + 30y$
Subject to $x + 2y \leq 14$
  $3x + 2y \leq 18$
  $x \geq 0, y \geq 0$

For any fixed value k, the graph of the equation $P(x, y) = k$ contains all the ordered pairs (x, y) that yield a profit of k dollars. Thus the graph of $P(x, y) = 180$, that is, $20x + 30y = 180$, contains all the ordered pairs that produce a profit of \$180; some of these pairs are $(9, 0)$, $(6, 2)$, $(3, 4)$, and $(0, 6)$. In Figure 4.16 the graph of $P(x, y) = k$ for certain values of k has been superimposed on the graph of the feasible set (from Figure 4.13). Notice that these graphs are parallel lines since the slope (which can be found by writing the equation in slope-intercept form) of any line of the form $20x + 30y = k$ is $-\frac{2}{3}$.

We wish to find a point (x, y) in the set of feasible solutions at which $P(x, y)$ assumes a maximum value. This value will be the largest value of k for which a line of the form $P(x, y) = k$ passes through a point in the feasible set. From Figure 4.16 it is clear that the largest such value is $k = 220$ and that the only point in the feasible set that lies on the line $P(x, y) = 220$ is the vertex $(2, 6)$. More generally, the following result is true.

THEOREM 4.2

For any linear programming problem

(a) If the set of feasible solutions is bounded, then the objective function will have both a maximum and minimum value in the set. Moreover, these values will occur at vertices of the feasible set.
(b) If the set of feasible solutions is unbounded, then the objective function may not have a maximum or minimum value in the set. However, if either of these exists, it will occur at a vertex of the feasible set.

The following pair of examples will illustrate how Theorem 4.2 can be used to solve linear programming problems.

EXAMPLE 9

In Example 8 in Section 4.2 we found that the graph of the set of feasible solutions for the problem

Maximize $\qquad P(x, y) = 0.50x + 0.70y$
Subject to $\qquad 12x + 8y \leq 240$
$\qquad\qquad\quad 4x + 8y \leq 160$
$\qquad\qquad\quad x \geq 0, y \geq 0$

is as shown in Figure 4.15. Since this feasible set is bounded, Theorem 4.2(a) guarantees that the objective function will have a maximum value on the set and that this value will occur at some vertex. We have seen that the coordinates of the four vertices are $(0, 0)$, $(0, 20)$, $(10, 15)$, and $(20, 0)$. Thus to determine the point in the feasible set at which the objective function has its maximum value, we need only determine the largest value of the objective function at a vertex, that is, the largest of the four values $P(0, 0)$, $P(0, 20)$, $P(10, 15)$, and $P(20, 0)$.

Vertex (x, y)	Value of the Objective Function $P(x, y) = 0.50x + 0.70y$	
(0, 0)	$0.50(0) + 0.70(0)\ \ = 0$	
(0, 20)	$0.50(0) + 0.70(20) = 14.00$	
(10, 15)	$0.50(10) + 0.70(15) = 15.50$	← Maximum
(20, 0)	$0.50(20) + 0.70(0)\ = 10.00$	

Therefore the maximum value of the objective function is 15.50, and it is obtained when $x = 10$ and $y = 15$. In the context of this problem we see that the candy store should make 10 pounds of the regular mixture and 15 pounds of the deluxe mixture in order to earn a maximum profit of \$15.50.

Although unimportant in this problem, notice also that the objective function has a minimum value of 0 in the feasible set and that this value occurs at the vertex $(0, 0)$.

EXAMPLE 10

In Example 7 in Section 4.2 we saw that the vertices of the set of feasible solutions for the problem

$$\begin{aligned}
\text{Minimize} \quad & C(x, y) = 40x + 50y \\
\text{Subject to} \quad & 25x + 20y \geq 320 \\
& 3x + 4y \geq 48 \\
& x + 4y \geq 24 \\
& x \geq 0, y \geq 0
\end{aligned}$$

are $(0, 16)$, $(8, 6)$, $(12, 3)$, and $(24, 0)$. We know from Theorem 4.2 that, if the objective function has a minimum value in the feasible set, then this value must occur at one of the vertices. Consequently, we must evaluate the objective function at these four points.

Vertex (x, y)	Value of the Objective Function $C(x, y) = 40x + 50y$
$(0, 16)$	$40(0) + 50(16) = 800$
$(8, 6)$	$40(8) + 50(6) = 620 \leftarrow$ Minimum
$(12, 3)$	$40(12) + 50(3) = 630$
$(24, 0)$	$40(24) + 50(0) = 960$

Thus the smallest value of the objective function at a vertex is 620, and it occurs at the vertex $(8, 6)$. In Figure 4.17 we have graphed the lines $C(x, y) = k$ for certain values of k. It is easy to see from this figure that 620 is indeed the minimum value of the objective function in the feasible set. So the solution of the given problem is obtained when $x = 8$ and $y = 6$; in other words, the homeowner should buy 8 bags of Fastgro and 6 bags of Greengro for a minimum cost of \$620.

Observe that in this problem the objective function has no maximum value in the feasible set, for if $k \geq 620$, the line $C(x, y) = k$ will always pass through points in the set of feasible solutions. Thus although 960 is the largest value of the objective function at a vertex of the set of feasible solutions, 960 is not the largest

138 Chapter 4 Linear Programming

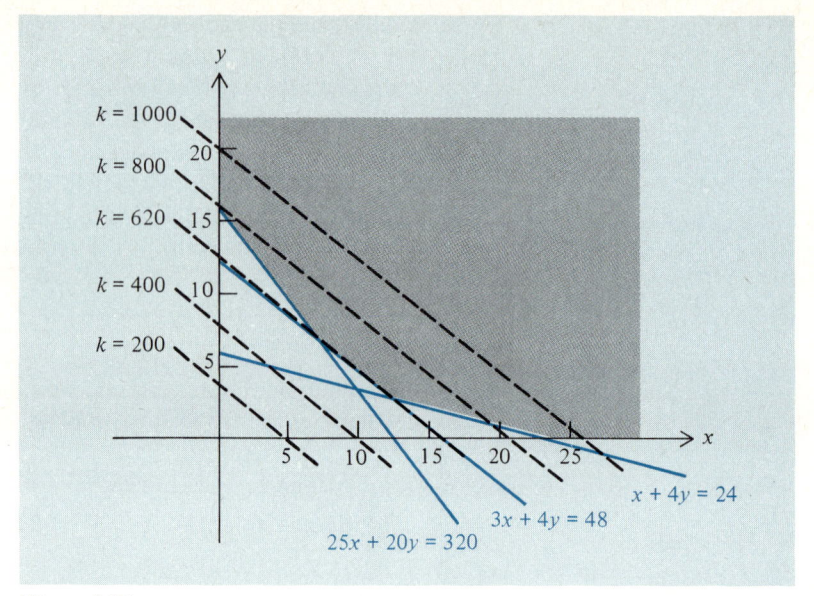

Figure 4.17

value of the objective function in the entire set. This illustrates Theorem 4.2(b): The maximum or minimum value of the objective function need not exist when the feasible set is unbounded.

Theorem 4.2 asserts that the maximum (or minimum) value of the objective function, if it exists, will always occur at a vertex of the set of feasible solutions. It is possible that this value can occur at more than one vertex, as the following example shows:

EXAMPLE 11

A monthly magazine is published in an eastern and western version which are identical except for certain pages of advertising. The publisher must print at least 30,000 copies of the eastern version and at least 20,000 copies of the western version because of existing subscriptions. Sales for the magazine indicate that the number of copies of the western version to be printed should not exceed twice the number of copies of the eastern edition and that the total number of copies of both editions should not exceed 120,000. Shipping charges to newsstands are $80 per 1000 copies for the eastern version and $60 per 1000 copies for the western version, and the publisher has at most $8400 available for shipping charges. If the publisher earns a profit of $200 for each 1000 of the eastern version and $150 for each 1000 of the western version, how many copies of each version should be printed in order to earn a maximum profit?

If x and y denote the number of thousand copies of the eastern and western versions to be printed, respectively, then the mathe-

4.3 Geometric Solution of Linear Programming Problems   139

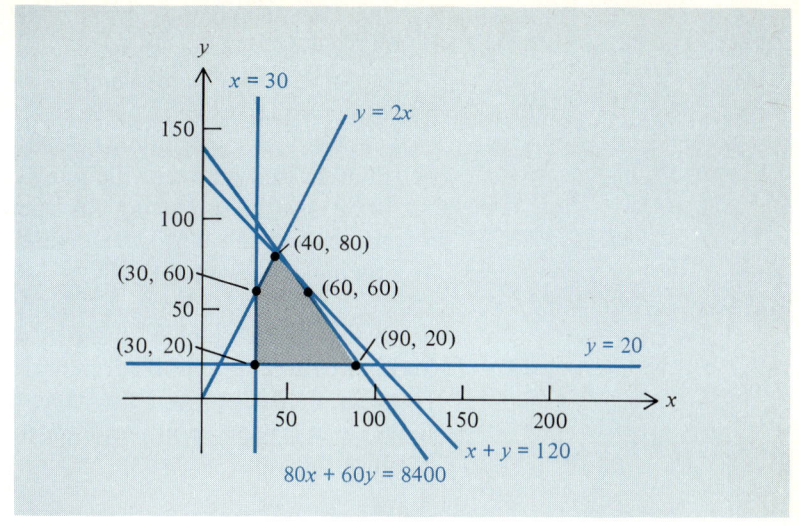

Figure 4.18

matical formulation of this problem is as follows:

Maximize $\quad P(x, y) = 200x + 150y$

Subject to
$$x \geq 30$$
$$y \geq 20$$
$$y \leq 2x$$
$$x + y \leq 120$$
$$80x + 60y \leq 8400$$
$$x \geq 0, y \geq 0$$

Using the techniques in Section 4.1, we obtain the graph in Figure 4.18 from these constraints.

Since the feasible set is bounded, Theorem 4.2 guarantees that the objective function will assume a maximum value at some vertex of the set.

Vertex (x, y)	Value of the Objective Function $200x + 150y$
(30, 20)	9,000
(30, 60)	15,000
(40, 80)	20,000
(60, 60)	21,000 ← Maximum
(90, 20)	21,000 ← Maximum

Thus the maximum value of 21,000 is assumed at two different vertices, (60, 60) and (90, 20). The reason for this occurrence is that the part of the boundary between these two vertices lies on the line of maximum profit, $P(x, y) = 21{,}000$. In this case the maximum value occurs not only at the vertices $(60, 60)$ and $(90, 20)$ but also at any point on the line segment joining these vertices. For example, the value of the objective function at the points $(72, 44)$, $(75, 40)$, and $(84, 28)$ is also 21,000. Hence there are multiple solutions to this problem; the publisher can earn a maximum profit of \$21,000 by producing any combination of the two versions of the magazine that corresponds to a point on the line segment joining $(60, 60)$ and $(90, 20)$.

Notice that Example 11 shows that there may be solutions to a linear programming problem that are not vertices of the feasible set. However, if the objective function has a maximum (or minimum) value in the set of feasible solutions, there must always be at least one vertex at which this value occurs.

Exercises

Solve the following linear programming problems geometrically.

1. Maximize $5x + 4y$
   Subject to $x + 2y \leq 150$
   $3x + 2y \leq 270$
   $x \geq 0, y \geq 0$

2. Maximize $8x + 10y$
   Subject to $x + 2y \leq 600$
   $16x + 9y \leq 7300$
   $x \geq 0, y \geq 0$

3. Maximize $7x + 4y$
   Subject to $x + y \leq 160$
   $3x + 2y \leq 360$
   $x \geq 0, y \geq 0$

4. Minimize $4x + 3y$
   Subject to $x + 2y \geq 320$
   $5x + 4y \geq 1000$
   $x \geq 0, y \geq 0$

5. Minimize $5x + 6y$
   Subject to $x + 4y \geq 300$
   $3x + 2y \geq 600$
   $x \geq 50, y \geq 0$

6. Minimize $8x + 5y$
   Subject to $x + y \geq 150$
   $5x + 3y \geq 600$
   $y \geq 30, x \geq 0$

7. Minimize $2x + 5y$
   Subject to $2x + y \geq 200$
   $3x + 4y \geq 720$
   $x \geq 0, y \geq 0$

8. Maximize $2x + 2y$
   Subject to $4x + 3y \leq 1200$
   $4x + 5y \leq 1600$
   $x \geq 3y$
   $x \geq 0, y \geq 0$

9. Maximize $5x + 8y$
   Subject to $3x + 4y \leq 252$
   $x + 2y \leq 90$
   $x \geq y$
   $x \geq 0, y \geq 0$

10. Minimize $2x + 3y$
    Subject to $x + y \leq 10$
    $2x + 4y \geq 28$
    $x \geq 3y$
    $x \geq 0, y \geq 0$

For Exercises 11–25, solve Exercises 1–15 in Section 4.2.

4.4 An Introduction to the Simplex Method

In Section 4.3 we discussed a geometric method for solving linear programming problems. Unfortunately, this method cannot be applied unless the set of feasible solutions can be graphed. Consequently it is useful primarily in solving linear programming problems involving only two variables.

4.4 An Introduction to the Simplex Method

In order to obtain a more general procedure for solving linear programming problems, we must obtain an algebraic (rather than a geometric) description of the vertices of the set of feasible solutions. In this section we obtain such a description of the vertices and use it to formulate a procedure for solving linear programming problems involving any number of variables. The key insight required for this description is that the constraints of a linear programming problem can be replaced by an equivalent system of linear equations. For the present we restrict our attention to inequalities in which an expression involving the variables is less than or equal to a *nonnegative* constant, that is, to inequalities of the form

$$a_1 x_1 + a_2 x_2 + \cdots + a_n x_n \leq b$$

where $b \geq 0$.

To illustrate the ideas involved, we shall consider the linear programming problem

Maximize $\quad P = 20x + 30y$

Subject to
$$x + 2y \leq 14$$
$$3x + 2y \leq 18 \quad\quad (4.1)$$
$$x \geq 0, y \geq 0$$

which was solved geometrically in Section 4.3. Let us introduce new variables that will "take up the slack" between the right and left sides of the first two inequalities in (4.1); inclusion of these new variables will then convert the inequalities into equations. These variables, called *slack variables*, are defined by

slack variables

$$r = 14 - (x + 2y) \quad \text{and} \quad s = 18 - (3x + 2y)$$

and represent the number of hours that the lathe and milling machine are unused. Since r and s equal the difference between the right and left sides of one of the inequalities in (4.1), it is clear that both r and s must be *nonnegative*. Thus we can rewrite (4.1) in the equivalent form:

Maximize $\quad P = 20x + 30y$

Subject to
$$x + 2y + r = 14$$
$$3x + 2y + s = 18 \quad\quad (4.2)$$
$$x \geq 0, y \geq 0, r \geq 0, s \geq 0$$

EXAMPLE 12

We shall rewrite the linear programming problem:

Maximize $\quad P = 6x + 4y$

Subject to
$$x + y \leq 100$$
$$2x + y \leq 180$$
$$x + 3y \leq 240$$
$$x \geq 0, y \geq 0$$

as a problem involving slack variables. Letting r, s, and t be the slack variables to be used in the first, second, and third inequalities, respectively, we can express the problem in the form

$$\begin{aligned}
\text{Maximize} \quad & P = 6x + 4y \\
\text{Subject to} \quad & x + y + r = 100 \\
& 2x + y + s = 180 \\
& x + 3y + t = 240 \\
& x \geq 0, y \geq 0, r \geq 0, s \geq 0, t \geq 0
\end{aligned} \qquad (4.3)$$

We are seeking an algebraic description of the vertices of the set of feasible solutions in a linear programming problem. Recall from Figure 4.16 that the vertices of the feasible set for (4.1) are $(0,0)$, $(0,7)$, $(2,6)$, and $(6,0)$. These vertices correspond to the following solutions (x, y, r, s) of the equations in (4.2):

$(0, 0, 14, 18) \qquad (0, 7, 0, 4) \qquad (2, 6, 0, 0) \quad \text{and} \quad (6, 0, 8, 0)$

Notice that in each of these 4-tuples two variables have the value zero. There are, however, two other solutions of the equations in (4.2) in which two of the variables equal zero: $(0, 9, -4, 0)$ and $(14, 0, 0, -24)$. But in these two solutions some variables have negative values; so they are not feasible solutions of (4.2) because the nonnegativity assumptions are violated. Observe that these solutions correspond to the points $(0, 9)$ and $(14, 0)$ in Figure 4.16 that do not lie in the set of feasible solutions.

More generally, if slack variables are introduced into a linear programming problem that contains n unknowns, the solutions of the resulting system of equations that correspond to the vertices of the set of feasible solutions for the original problem are the nonnegative solutions in which at least n of the variables equal zero. Such solutions are called *basic feasible solutions*. In a basic feasible solution variables having the value zero are called *nonbasic variables* and those having nonzero values are called *basic variables*. Thus the basic feasible solutions (x, y, r, s) of (4.2) are $(0, 0, 14, 18)$, $(0, 7, 0, 4)$, $(2, 6, 0, 0)$, and $(6, 0, 8, 0)$. For $(6, 0, 8, 0)$ the nonbasic variables are y and s, and the basic variables are x and r.

basic feasible solutions
nonbasic variables
basic variables

EXAMPLE 13

The basic feasible solutions of (4.3) can be found by systematically setting each pair of variables equal to zero and solving for the remaining three variables. This produces the following list of solutions (x, y, r, s, t):

$(0, 0, 100, 180, 240)$ $(100, 0, 0, -20, 140)$ $(80, 20, 0, 0, 100)$
$(0, 100, 0, 80, -60)$ $(90, 0, 10, 0, 150)$ $(30, 70, 0, 50, 0)$
$(0, 180, -80, 0, -300)$ $(240, 0, -140, -300, 0)$ $(60, 60, -20, 0, 0)$
$(0, 80, 20, 100, 0)$

4.4 An Introduction to the Simplex Method

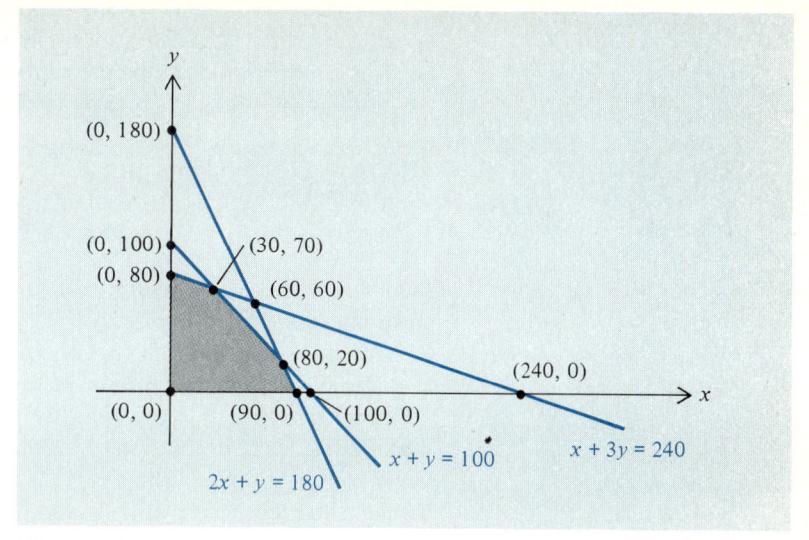

Figure 4.19

So the basic feasible solutions of (4.3), those solutions in which all the coordinates are nonnegative, are (0, 0, 100, 180, 240), (0, 80, 20, 100, 0), (90, 0, 10, 0, 150), (80, 20, 0, 0, 100), and (30, 70, 0, 50, 0).

Note the correspondence between the 10 solutions above and the ordered pairs marked in Figure 4.19, which shows the graph of the set of feasible solutions for the original problem.

Observe that the values of the basic variables in a basic feasible solution can be easily found if the associated system of equations is solved for the basic variables in terms of the nonbasic variables. Suppose, for instance, that x and r are the nonbasic variables in (4.2). By adding -1 times the first equation to the second, we obtain

$$x + 2y + r = 14$$
$$2x \quad - r + s = 4$$

This system can now be solved for the basic variables in terms of the nonbasic variables as follows:[2]

$$y = 7 - 0.5x - 0.5r$$
$$s = 4 - 2x + r$$

Assigning the value zero to the nonbasic variables x and r, we find that $y = 7$ and $s = 4$. Thus we have determined the values of the basic variables in the basic feasible solution having x and r as nonbasic variables.

Let us incorporate the ideas above into an algebraic procedure for solving (4.2). This procedure is the essence of the simplex method,

---

[2] Observe that this representation is the general solution of (4.2) in which the nonbasic variables are used as the parameters. By setting the parameters equal to zero, we obtain a particular solution of this system.

an efficient algorithm for solving linear programming problems. In Section 4.5 we shall describe the simplex method in much more detail.

Solving (4.2) requires finding a solution (x, y, r, s) to the system

$$\begin{aligned} x + 2y + r &= 14 \\ 3x + 2y \phantom{{}+r} + s &= 18 \\ -20x - 30y \phantom{{}+r+s} + P &= 0 \end{aligned} \quad (4.4)$$

such that P has a maximum value and the variables x, y, r, and s are all nonnegative.

We have already seen that the maximum value of P must occur at some basic feasible solution of the first two equations. Beginning with any basic feasible solution, we shall obtain a sequence of additional basic feasible solutions, stopping when one that maximizes the value of P is obtained. The simplest basic feasible solution with which to begin is the one in which x and y are the nonbasic variables and r and s are the basic variables. From (4.4) we obtain the values

$$x = 0, \ y = 0, \ r = 14, \ s = 18 \quad \text{and} \quad P = 0$$

Examining the objective function in (4.2), or equivalently, the third equation in (4.4), we see that the value of P can be increased by increasing the value of x or y. Since each unit increase in x increases P by $20 and each unit increase in y increases P by $30, let us choose to increase y. Notice that, as y is increased in (4.4), the values of r and s are decreased. Because the variables must be nonnegative, we cannot increase y by an amount that would make r or s negative. Considering the first two equations in (4.4) with $x = 0$, we see that

$$r = 14 - 2y \quad \text{and} \quad s = 18 - 2y$$

Thus y can be increased to $\frac{14}{2} = 7$ without making r negative and can be increased to $\frac{18}{2} = 9$ without making s negative. Because we want both $r \geq 0$ and $s \geq 0$, we let y equal 7, the smaller of the two numbers above. This choice ensures that neither r nor s will be negative.

By letting $y = 7$, we are making $r = 0$. Thus y, a nonbasic variable, becomes a basic variable, and r, a basic variable, becomes a nonbasic variable. So we are proceeding from the original basic feasible solution to the basic feasible solution in which y and s are the basic variables.

In order to compute the coordinates of this new basic feasible solution we must rewrite (4.4) in a form in which the basic variables are expressed in terms of the nonbasic variables. Specifically, we must write (4.4) so that y appears only in the first equation. To begin, multiply the first equation by 0.5 to make the coefficient of y equal 1. This operation produces

$$\begin{aligned} 0.5x + y + 0.5r &= 7 \\ 3x + 2y \phantom{{}+0.5r} + s &= 18 \\ -20x - 30y \phantom{{}+0.5r+s} + P &= 0 \end{aligned}$$

4.4 An Introduction to the Simplex Method

Now add -2 times the first equation to the second and 30 times the first equation to the third in the system above. These operations will eliminate y from the second and third equations:

$$\begin{aligned} 0.5x + y + 0.5r &= 7 \\ 2x - r + s &= 4 \\ -5x + 15r + P &= 210 \end{aligned} \qquad (4.5)$$

In this form the values of the basic variables y and s can easily be seen to be $y = 7$ and $s = 4$. Thus the new basic feasible solution is

$$x = 0,\ y = 7,\ r = 0,\ s = 4, \quad \text{and} \quad P = 210$$

Observe that the value of P has increased from 0 to 210 by this change in basic feasible solutions. To determine if P can be increased even more, rewrite the third equation in (4.5) as

$$P = 210 + 5x - 15r$$

It is clear from this equation that P can be increased further by allowing x to become positive.

As before, we cannot increase x by an amount that will make any basic variable negative. Considering the first two equations in (4.5) with $r = 0$, we see that

$$y = 7 - 0.5x \quad \text{and} \quad s = 4 - 2x$$

Since we want both y and s to be nonnegative, we let x be the smaller of the numbers $\frac{7}{0.5} = 14$ and $\frac{4}{2} = 2$. This choice will make $s = 0$, and so we have determined that the next basic feasible solution to consider will be the one in which x and y are the basic variables and r and s are the nonbasic variables.

To compute the coordinates of this new basic feasible solution, we proceed as above to transform (4.5) so that x occurs only in the second equation. First multiply the second equation by 0.5 so that the coefficient of x becomes 1:

$$\begin{aligned} 0.5x + y + 0.5r &= 7 \\ x - 0.5r + 0.5s &= 2 \\ -5x + 15r + P &= 210 \end{aligned}$$

Now eliminate x from the first and third equations above by adding -0.5 times the second equation to the first and 5 times the second equation to the third. The resulting system is

$$\begin{aligned} y + 0.75r - 0.25s &= 6 \\ x - 0.50r + 0.50s &= 2 \\ 12.50r + 2.50s + P &= 220 \end{aligned} \qquad (4.6)$$

and so the basic variables y and x are easily seen to equal 6 and 2, respectively. Therefore, we have the values

$$x = 2,\ y = 6,\ r = 0,\ s = 0, \quad \text{and} \quad P = 220$$

Again this change in basic feasible solutions has increased P (from 210 to 220). We must now determine if P can be increased even further. Rewriting the third equation in (4.6) as

$$P = 220 - 12.50r - 2.50s$$

we see that making r or s positive will not increase P. Hence we conclude that the basic feasible solution $x = 2$, $y = 6$, $r = 0$, $s = 0$ gives P its maximum value of 220. Notice that this basic feasible solution corresponds to the vertex $(2, 6)$ of the set of feasible solutions at which the maximum profit was previously found to occur.

In Section 4.5 we shall introduce a convenient means for storing the data and simplifying the computations required to solve a problem by this method. For now, simply observe that this procedure began with one basic feasible solution and then successively obtained others by replacing one of the basic variables with one of the nonbasic variables. At each new basic feasible solution the value of the objective function was greater than at the previous one, and the process was continued until a basic feasible solution was obtained for which it was impossible to increase the objective function further. This last basic feasible solution was the one at which the objective function assumed its maximum value.

Exercises

For each of the following linear programming problems, rewrite the constraints and the objective function as a system of linear equations by introducing slack variables.

1. Maximize $P = 6x + 4y$
   Subject to
   $x + 3y \le 200$
   $2x + 5y \le 500$
   $x \ge 0, y \ge 0$

2. Maximize $P = 3x + 5y$
   Subject to
   $4x + 3y \le 200$
   $x + y \le 60$
   $x \ge 0, y \ge 0$

3. Maximize $P = 3x + 8y$
   Subject to
   $2x + 4y \le 1200$
   $x + 3y \le 1000$
   $x \ge 0, y \ge 0$

4. Maximize $P = 4x + 3y$
   Subject to
   $2x + 3y \le 200$
   $2x + y \le 300$
   $x \ge 0, y \ge 0$

5. Maximize $P = 4.50x + 3.50y$
   Subject to
   $6x + 5y \le 600$
   $3x + 4y \le 240$
   $x \ge 0, y \ge 0$

6. Maximize $P = 2.50x + 0.90y$
   Subject to
   $5x + 2y \le 3000$
   $0.2x + 0.4y \le 160$
   $x \ge 0, y \ge 0$

7. Maximize $P = 5x + 12y$
   Subject to
   $3x + 4y \le 300$
   $x + 2y \le 120$
   $x \le 30$
   $x \ge 0, y \ge 0$

8. Maximize $P = 6x + 5y$
   Subject to
   $x + 4y \le 240$
   $2x + 3y \le 200$
   $3x + 5y \le 360$
   $x \ge 0, y \ge 0$

9. Maximize $P = 5x + 4y$
   Subject to $4x + 3y \leq 36{,}800$
   $4x + 5y \leq 40{,}000$
   $2x + 5y \leq 30{,}000$
   $x \geq 0, y \geq 0$

10. Maximize $P = 0.70x + 0.75y$
    Subject to $x + y \leq 3000$
    $2x + y \leq 5000$
    $y \leq 2000$
    $x \geq 0, y \geq 0$

4.5 The Simplex Method

The procedure described in Section 4.4 can be simplified considerably through the use of matrices. In this section we present a five-step process called the *simplex method* which can be used to solve any linear programming problem for which a basic feasible solution can be found to begin the process. As we have seen, finding a basic feasible solution is easy when the inequalities are all of the form

$$a_1 x_1 + a_2 x_2 + \cdots + a_n x_n \leq b$$

where $b \geq 0$, for in this case we can take the slack variables to be the basic variables. In this section we therefore continue to consider only inequalities of this type.

As in Section 4.4, we shall consider the problem

Maximize $P = 20x + 30y$
Subject to $x + 2y \leq 14$
$3x + 2y \leq 18$
$x \geq 0, y \geq 0$

We observed there that this problem was equivalent to that of finding a solution to

$$\begin{aligned} x + 2y + r &= 14 \\ 3x + 2y \phantom{{}+r} + s &= 18 \\ -20x - 30y \phantom{{}+r+s} + P &= 0 \end{aligned} \quad (4.7)$$

such that P has a maximum value and the variables x, y, r, and s are all nonnegative.

The method used in Section 4.4 to solve this problem began with the obvious basic feasible solution $x = 0, y = 0, r = 14, s = 18$ obtained by taking the slack variables r and s in (4.7) as the basic variables. For this choice, each of the first two equations in (4.7) contains only one basic variable, namely, r and s, respectively. The augmented matrix of (4.7) is called a *simplex tableau*. For convenience we separate the objective function from the constraints by a dashed line and label each row above the dashed line with the name of the only basic variable appearing in the corresponding equation. Thus the simplex tableau corresponding to (4.7) is

$$\begin{array}{c} \\ r \\ s \\ \end{array} \left(\begin{array}{ccccc|c} x & y & r & s & P & \\ 1 & 2 & 1 & 0 & 0 & 14 \\ 3 & 2 & 0 & 1 & 0 & 18 \\ \hline -20 & -30 & 0 & 0 & 1 & 0 \\ \end{array} \right) \qquad (4.8)$$

Note that the last entry of each of the first two rows is the value of the basic variable with which that row is labeled; that is, $r = 14$ and $s = 18$ for the current basic feasible solution. Also observe that the entry of the tableau in the last row and last column is the value of the objective function at this basic feasible solution.

We saw in Section 4.4 that, since the coefficient of some nonbasic variable was negative in the last equation in (4.7), the current basic feasible solution would not yield the maximum value of the objective function. More generally, we can state the following result.

THEOREM 4.3 *Test for maximality*

If every entry in the bottom row of a simplex tableau is nonnegative except possibly the last entry, then the maximum value of the objective function will occur at the basic feasible solution associated with that tableau; otherwise, the maximum value of the objective function (if it exists) will occur at some other basic feasible solution.

It follows from the test for maximality that the basic feasible solution $x = 0$, $y = 0$, $r = 14$, $s = 18$ associated with (4.8) does not yield the maximum value of the objective function. Consequently we must find a new basic feasible solution that will yield a larger value of the objective function. In Section 4.4 we saw that such a basic feasible solution could be obtained by replacing one of the basic variables with one of the nonbasic variables. Moreover, we saw that the variable having the most negative entry in the last row of the simplex tableau was the variable that yielded the largest increase per unit in the objective function. Accordingly we choose the new basic variable to be the variable having the most negative entry in the last row of the simplex tableau; the column containing this variable is called the *pivot column*.

pivot column

$$\begin{array}{c} \\ r \\ s \\ \end{array} \left(\begin{array}{ccccc|c} x & y & r & s & P & \\ 1 & 2 & 1 & 0 & 0 & 14 \\ 3 & 2 & 0 & 1 & 0 & 18 \\ \hline -20 & -30 & 0 & 0 & 1 & 0 \\ \end{array} \right)$$
$$\uparrow$$
$$\text{Pivot column}$$

Now we must determine which of the present basic variables should become the new nonbasic variable. In order to ensure that all the variables will be nonnegative, we saw in Section 4.4 that it was necessary to let the new nonbasic variable be the one corresponding to the smaller of the quotients $\frac{14}{2}$ and $\frac{18}{2}$ obtained by dividing each entry of the last column above the dashed line by the corresponding entry of the pivot column. The row in which the smallest nonnegative quotient occurs is called the *pivot row*.

pivot row

$$\begin{array}{c} \\ \text{Pivot row} \rightarrow r \\ s \\ \\ \end{array} \begin{array}{c} x \quad y \quad r \quad s \quad P \\ \left(\begin{array}{ccccc|c} 1 & ② & 1 & 0 & 0 & 14 \\ 3 & 2 & 0 & 1 & 0 & 18 \\ \hline -20 & -30 & 0 & 0 & 1 & 0 \end{array} \right) \\ \uparrow \\ \text{Pivot} \\ \text{column} \end{array} \quad \begin{array}{c} \text{Quotients} \\ \frac{14}{2} = 7 \\ \frac{18}{2} = 9 \\ \\ \end{array}$$

The entry lying in the pivot row and pivot column is called the *pivot element*. (The pivot element is circled in the tableau above.) We are now ready to perform the fundamental step in the simplex method, called a *pivot*. A pivot transforms one simplex tableau into another which is associated with a new basic feasible solution in which the variable corresponding to the pivot column replaces the variable corresponding to the pivot row as a basic variable. A pivot is acccomplished by using the elementary row operations of multiplying a row by a nonzero number and adding multiples of one row to another in order to change the pivot element to 1 and every other entry of the pivot column to 0.

pivot element

pivot

In the tableau above we must first multiply the first row by 0.5 in order to change the pivot element to 1; this operation produces

$$\left(\begin{array}{ccccc|c} 0.5 & ① & 0.5 & 0 & 0 & 7 \\ 3.0 & 2 & 0.0 & 1 & 0 & 18 \\ \hline -20.0 & -30 & 0.0 & 0 & 1 & 0 \end{array} \right)$$

Now add -2 times the first row to the second and 30 times the first row to the third to make the other entries of the pivot column equal 0.

$$\left(\begin{array}{ccccc|c} 0.5 & 1 & 0.5 & 0 & 0 & 7 \\ 2.0 & 0 & -1.0 & 1 & 0 & 4 \\ \hline -5.0 & 0 & 15.0 & 0 & 1 & 210 \end{array} \right)$$

Observe that this is precisely the augmented matrix of the system (4.5) in which the basic variables are y and s. Thus the appropriate row and column labels for the new tableau are as shown below.

$$\begin{array}{c} \\ y \\ s \\ \\ \end{array} \begin{array}{c} x \quad y \quad r \quad s \quad P \\ \left(\begin{array}{ccccc|c} 0.5 & 1 & 0.5 & 0 & 0 & 7 \\ 2.0 & 0 & -1.0 & 1 & 0 & 4 \\ \hline -5.0 & 0 & 15.0 & 0 & 1 & 210 \end{array} \right) \end{array} \quad (4.9)$$

Comparing (4.9) with (4.8), we see that y (the variable corresponding to the pivot column) has replaced r (the variable corresponding to the pivot row) as a basic variable. Thus the basic feasible solution associated with (4.9) is $x = 0$, $y = 7$, $r = 0$, $s = 4$, and the value of the objective function (read from the last row and last column of the tableau) is 210 at this point.

Since a negative entry remains in the bottom row of the tableau, we know that the objective function can be increased even more. The previous steps can now be repeated to obtain another basic feasible solution at which the objective function will have a greater value. We begin by noting that the first column is the new pivot column, since it contains the most negative entry in the bottom row. To find the pivot row, we form the quotient of each entry in the last column above the dashed line divided by the corresponding entry of the pivot column:

$$\begin{array}{c} \\ y \\ s \end{array} \begin{array}{cccccc} x & y & r & s & P & \\ \left(\begin{array}{ccccc|c} 0.5 & 1 & 0.5 & 0 & 0 & 7 \\ \boxed{2.0} & 0 & -1.0 & 1 & 0 & 4 \\ \hline -5.0 & 0 & 15.0 & 0 & 1 & 210 \end{array} \right) & \begin{array}{l} \tfrac{7}{0.5} = 14 \\ \tfrac{4}{2} = 2 \end{array} \end{array}$$

↑
Pivot
column

From these calculations we see that the second row is the pivot row, and thus the circled entry above is the pivot element. We are now ready to perform a pivot. First multiply the second row by 0.5 to make the pivot element 1:

$$\left(\begin{array}{ccccc|c} 0.5 & 1 & 0.5 & 0.0 & 0 & 7 \\ \boxed{1.0} & 0 & -0.5 & 0.5 & 0 & 2 \\ \hline -5.0 & 0 & 15.0 & 0.0 & 1 & 210 \end{array} \right)$$

Now add appropriate multiples of the second row to the first and third rows to make the other entries of the pivot column equal 0:

$$\begin{array}{c} \\ y \\ x \end{array} \left(\begin{array}{ccccc|c} x & y & r & s & P & \\ 0 & 1 & 0.75 & -0.25 & 0 & 6 \\ 1 & 0 & -0.50 & 0.50 & 0 & 2 \\ \hline 0 & 0 & 12.50 & 2.50 & 1 & 220 \end{array} \right)$$

This tableau, which is the augmented matrix of system (4.6), is associated with the basic feasible solution $x = 2$, $y = 6$, $r = 0$, $s = 0$. Since there are no negative entries in the bottom row, the test for maximality guarantees that this basic feasible solution is the one at which the objective function assumes its maximum value. Moreover, the maximum value (220) can be read from the last row and last column of the tableau.

The simplex method can be summarized as follows:

The Simplex Method

Step 1 (Formulating the problem): Write the problem as a system of equations by introducing slack variables and determine a basic feasible solution for this system.[3]

Step 2 (Test for maximality): If all the entries in the bottom row of the tableau, except possibly the last entry, are nonnegative, then the maximum value of the objective function occurs at the basic feasible solution associated with the tableau. In this case stop; otherwise proceed to step 3.

Step 3 (Determining the pivot column): Ignoring the last entry of bottom row, locate the most negative entry elsewhere in this row of the tableau. The column containing this entry will be the pivot column. In case of ties for the most negative entry, choose any of the columns containing a most negative entry.

Step 4 (Determining the pivot row): Form quotients by dividing each entry of the last column of the tableau above the dashed line by the corresponding entry of the pivot column. The row corresponding to the smallest of the *nonnegative* quotients is the pivot row.[4]

Step 5 (The pivot): The entry lying in the pivot row and pivot column is the pivot element. Divide the pivot row by the pivot element in order to make the pivot element 1. Then add appropriate multiples of the pivot row to the other rows to make the other entries of the pivot column equal 0. Return to step 2.

EXAMPLE 14

We shall work Example 12 by the simplex method. From (4.3) we see that the first simplex tableau is

$$\begin{array}{c} \\ r \\ s \\ t \\ \\ \end{array} \left(\begin{array}{cccccc|c} x & y & r & s & t & P & \\ 1 & 1 & 1 & 0 & 0 & 0 & 100 \\ 2 & 1 & 0 & 1 & 0 & 0 & 180 \\ 1 & 3 & 0 & 0 & 1 & 0 & 240 \\ \hline -6 & -4 & 0 & 0 & 0 & 1 & 0 \end{array} \right)$$

Using steps 3 and 4, we find that the first column is the pivot column and the second row is the pivot row; thus the circled entry is the pivot element:

---

[3] When all the inequalities are of the form $a_1x_1 + a_2x_2 + \cdots + a_nx_n \leq b$ for $b \geq 0$, a basic feasible solution can be obtained by taking the slack variables as the basic variables and assigning the value 0 to the other variables.

[4] In the event of a tie for the smallest nonnegative quotient, special difficulties arise. This situation (called degeneracy) is not discussed in this book. Interested readers should consult an advanced linear programming book such as [5] or [12] for a discussion of this subject.

152 Chapter 4 Linear Programming

$$\begin{array}{c} r \\ s \\ t \end{array} \begin{pmatrix} x & y & r & s & t & P & \\ 1 & 1 & 1 & 0 & 0 & 0 & | & 100 \\ ② & 1 & 0 & 1 & 0 & 0 & | & 180 \\ 1 & 3 & 0 & 0 & 1 & 0 & | & 240 \\ \hline -6 & -4 & 0 & 0 & 0 & 1 & | & 0 \end{pmatrix} \begin{array}{l} \frac{100}{1} = 100 \\ \frac{180}{2} = 90 \\ \frac{240}{1} = 240 \end{array}$$

We are now ready to perform a pivot. Dividing the second row by 2 produces

$$\begin{pmatrix} 1 & 1 & 1 & 0 & 0 & 0 & | & 100 \\ ① & 0.5 & 0 & 0.5 & 0 & 0 & | & 90 \\ 1 & 3 & 0 & 0 & 1 & 0 & | & 240 \\ \hline -6 & -4 & 0 & 0 & 0 & 1 & | & 0 \end{pmatrix}$$

To complete the pivot, add -1 times the second row to the first and third rows and 6 times the second row to the fourth row.

$$\begin{array}{c} r \\ x \\ t \end{array} \begin{pmatrix} x & y & r & s & t & P & \\ 0 & 0.5 & 1 & -0.5 & 0 & 0 & | & 10 \\ 1 & 0.5 & 0 & 0.5 & 0 & 0 & | & 90 \\ 0 & 2.5 & 0 & -0.5 & 1 & 0 & | & 150 \\ \hline 0 & -1.0 & 0 & 3.0 & 0 & 1 & | & 540 \end{pmatrix}$$

We must now apply the test for maximality to this new tableau. Because there is a negative entry in the bottom row of this tableau other than in the last column, it will be necessary to repeat steps 3–5 again. The new pivot element is found to lie in the second column and first row:

$$\begin{array}{c} r \\ x \\ t \end{array} \begin{pmatrix} x & y & r & s & t & P & \\ 0 & ⓪.5 & 1 & -0.5 & 0 & 0 & | & 10 \\ 1 & 0.5 & 0 & 0.5 & 0 & 0 & | & 90 \\ 0 & 2.5 & 0 & -0.5 & & 0 & | & 150 \\ \hline 0 & -1.0 & 0 & 3.0 & 0 & 1 & | & 540 \end{pmatrix} \begin{array}{l} \frac{10}{0.5} = 20 \\ \frac{90}{0.5} = 180 \\ \frac{150}{2.5} = 60 \end{array}$$

Multiplying the first row of this tableau by 2 gives

$$\begin{pmatrix} 0 & ①.0 & 2 & -1.0 & 0 & 0 & | & 20 \\ 1 & 0.5 & 0 & 0.5 & 0 & 0 & | & 90 \\ 0 & 2.5 & 0 & -0.5 & 1 & 0 & | & 150 \\ \hline 0 & -1.0 & 0 & 3.0 & 0 & 1 & | & 540 \end{pmatrix}$$

Adding -0.5 times the first row to the second, -2.5 times the first row to the third, and 1 times the first row to the fourth completes the pivot as follows:

$$\begin{array}{c} \begin{array}{cccccc} x & y & r & s & t & P \end{array} \\ \begin{array}{c} y \\ x \\ t \\ \end{array}\left(\begin{array}{cccccc|c} 0 & 1 & 2 & -1 & 0 & 0 & 20 \\ 1 & 0 & -1 & 1 & 0 & 0 & 80 \\ 0 & 0 & -5 & 2 & 1 & 0 & 100 \\ \hline 0 & 0 & 2 & 2 & 0 & 1 & 560 \end{array}\right) \end{array}$$

Since there are no negative entries in the bottom row of this tableau, the associated basic feasible solution $x = 80$, $y = 20$, $r = 0$, $s = 0$, $t = 100$ gives the objective function its maximum value of 560. Thus in the original statement of the problem the optimum value of the objective function occurs when $x = 80$ and $y = 20$.

EXAMPLE 15

A small furniture finishing factory produces desks, buffets, and cocktail tables. Each desk requires 0.3 hour of sanding, 0.1 hour of staining, and 0.2 hour of varnishing. Each buffet requires 0.2 hour of sanding, 0.4 hour of staining, and 0.4 hour of varnishing. In addition, each cocktail table requires 0.1 hour of sanding, 0.1 hour of staining, and 0.2 hour of varnishing. During a particular week the factory will have at most 44 hours of time available for sanding, at most 40 hours of time available for staining, and at most 48 hours available for varnishing. If the factory earns profits of $10 on each desk, $14 on each buffet, and $7 on each cocktail table, how should production be scheduled in order to obtain a maximum profit?

Letting x, y, and z denote the number of desks, buffets, and cocktail tables to be made, respectively, we can formulate the following mathematical model of this problem.

Maximize $P = 10x + 14y + 7z$
Subject to
$$0.3x + 0.2y + 0.1z \le 44$$
$$0.1x + 0.4y + 0.1z \le 40$$
$$0.2x + 0.4y + 0.2z \le 48$$
$$x \ge 0,\ y \ge 0,\ z \ge 0$$

Introducing nonnegative slack variables r, s, and t, we can rewrite the problem in the form

Maximize $P = 10x + 14y + 7z$
Subject to
$$0.3x + 0.2y + 0.1z + r = 44$$
$$0.1x + 0.4y + 0.1z + s = 40 \quad (4.10)$$
$$0.2x + 0.4y + 0.2z + t = 48$$
$$x \ge 0,\ y \ge 0,\ z \ge 0,\ r \ge 0,\ s \ge 0,\ t \ge 0$$

Thus the first simplex tableau, associated with the basic feasible solution $x = 0, y = 0, z = 0, r = 44, s = 40, t = 48$ is

$$\begin{array}{c} \\ r \\ s \\ t \\ \\ \end{array} \left(\begin{array}{cccccc|c} x & y & z & r & s & t & P \\ 0.3 & 0.2 & 0.1 & 1 & 0 & 0 & 0 & 44 \\ 0.1 & \boxed{0.4} & 0.1 & 0 & 1 & 0 & 0 & 40 \\ 0.2 & 0.4 & 0.2 & 0 & 0 & 1 & 0 & 48 \\ \hline -10 & -14 & -7 & 0 & 0 & 0 & 1 & 0 \end{array} \right)$$

Then the second column is the pivot column, and the quotients for the first, second, and third rows are $\frac{44}{0.2} = 220$, $\frac{40}{0.4} = 100$, and $\frac{48}{0.4} = 120$, respectively. Therefore the second row is the pivot row.

To perform the pivot, we must first multiply the second row by 2.5. This operation produces

$$\left(\begin{array}{cccccc|c} 0.3 & 0.2 & 0.1 & 1 & 0 & 0 & 0 & 44 \\ 0.25 & \boxed{1.0} & 0.25 & 0 & 2.5 & 0 & 0 & 100 \\ 0.2 & 0.4 & 0.2 & 0 & 0 & 1 & 0 & 48 \\ \hline -10 & -14 & -7 & 0 & 0 & 0 & 1 & 0 \end{array} \right)$$

Now add -0.2 times the second row to the first, -0.4 times the second row to the third, and 14 times the second row to the fourth to obtain the following new tableau:

$$\begin{array}{c} \\ r \\ y \\ t \\ \\ \end{array} \left(\begin{array}{cccccc|c} x & y & z & r & s & t & P \\ 0.25 & 0 & 0.05 & 1 & -0.5 & 0 & 0 & 24 \\ 0.25 & 1 & 0.25 & 0 & 2.5 & 0 & 0 & 100 \\ \boxed{0.10} & 0 & 0.10 & 0 & -1.0 & 1 & 0 & 8 \\ \hline -6.50 & 0 & -3.50 & 0 & 35.0 & 0 & 1 & 1400 \end{array} \right)$$

Since negative entries occur in the bottom row of this tableau, we must perform another pivot. This time the first column is the pivot column and the third row is the pivot row. The first step in the pivot is to multiply the third row by 10:

$$\left(\begin{array}{cccccc|c} 0.25 & 0 & 0.05 & 1 & -0.5 & 0 & 0 & 24 \\ 0.25 & 1 & 0.25 & 0 & 2.5 & 0 & 0 & 100 \\ \boxed{1.00} & 0 & 1.00 & 0 & -10.0 & 10 & 0 & 80 \\ \hline -6.50 & 0 & -3.50 & 0 & 35.0 & 0 & 1 & 1400 \end{array} \right)$$

Then complete the pivot by adding -0.25 times the third row to the first and second rows and 6.5 times the third row to the fourth row. These operations yield

$$\begin{array}{c} \\ r \\ y \\ x \\ \\ \end{array} \left(\begin{array}{cccccc|c} x & y & z & r & s & t & P \\ 0 & 0 & -0.2 & 1 & \boxed{2} & -2.5 & 0 & 4 \\ 0 & 1 & 0.0 & 0 & 5 & -2.5 & 0 & 80 \\ 1 & 0 & 1.0 & 0 & -10 & 10.0 & 0 & 80 \\ \hline 0 & 0 & 3.0 & 0 & -30 & 65.0 & 1 & 1920 \end{array} \right)$$

Once again the presence of a negative entry in the bottom row indicates that another pivot is necessary. For this tableau the fifth column is the pivot column, and thus the quotients for the first, second, and third rows are $\frac{4}{2} = 2$, $\frac{80}{5} = 16$, and $\frac{80}{-10} = -8$, respectively. Recalling that the pivot row is the one corresponding to the smallest *nonnegative* quotient, we see that the first row is the pivot row. Hence we divide the first row by 2 to obtain

$$\begin{pmatrix} 0 & 0 & -0.1 & 0.5 & ① & -1.25 & 0 & | & 2 \\ 0 & 1 & 0.0 & 0.0 & 5 & -2.50 & 0 & | & 80 \\ 1 & 0 & 1.0 & 0.0 & -10 & 10.00 & 0 & | & 80 \\ 0 & 0 & 3.0 & 0.0 & -30 & 65.00 & 1 & | & 1920 \end{pmatrix}$$

Adding -5 times the first row to the second, 10 times the first row to the third, and 30 times the first row to the fourth yields the following new tableau:

$$\begin{array}{c} \\ s \\ y \\ x \\ \\ \end{array} \begin{array}{cccccccc} x & y & z & r & s & t & P & \\ \begin{pmatrix} 0 & 0 & -0.1 & 0.5 & 1 & -1.25 & 0 & | & 2 \\ 0 & 1 & 0.5 & -2.5 & 0 & 3.75 & 0 & | & 70 \\ 1 & 0 & 0.0 & 5.0 & 0 & -2.50 & 0 & | & 100 \\ 0 & 0 & 0.0 & 15.0 & 0 & 27.50 & 1 & | & 1980 \end{pmatrix} \end{array} \quad (4.11)$$

Since there are no negative entries in the bottom row of this tableau, the objective function assumes its maximum value (1980) at the basic feasible solution $x = 100$, $y = 70$, $z = 0$, $r = 0$, $s = 2$, $t = 0$ associated with this tableau. Thus in the context of the original problem the factory should manufacture 100 desks and 70 buffets for a profit of $1980. Recalling the meaning of the slack variables in (4.10), we see that the values of the slack variables in the final basic feasible solution ($r = 0$, $s = 2$, $t = 0$) mean that producing 100 desks and 70 buffets will require all the available time for sanding and varnishing but that 2 hours of the available time for staining is not needed.

We have already mentioned (see Theorem 4.1) that a linear programming problem may fail to have a solution if the set of feasible solutions is unbounded. If the simplex method is used on such a problem, a tableau will be obtained in which all the quotients used to determine the pivot row are negative or undefined. In this situation the rule for selecting the pivot rule (step 4) cannot be used. Thus we are alerted to the fact that the objective function is unbounded in the feasible set. For a problem of this type, see Exercise 23.

Exercises

For Exercises 1–10 solve Exercises 1–10 in Section 4.4 by the simplex method. Solve the following problems using the simplex method.

11. Maximize $P = 5x + 4y + 3z$
    Subject to $2x + y + z \leq 30$
    $y + 3z \leq 40$
    $x \geq 0, y \geq 0, z \geq 0$

12. Maximize $\quad P = 4x + 2y + 3z$
    Subject to
    $$0.1x + 0.25y \le 40$$
    $$0.2x + 0.30y + 0.4z \le 100$$
    $$x \ge 0, y \ge 0, z \ge 0$$

13. Maximize $\quad P = 4x + 3y + 5z$
    Subject to
    $$x - 2y + z \le 30$$
    $$-x + 4y + z \le 80$$
    $$-x + z \le 45$$
    $$x \ge 0, y \ge 0, z \ge 0$$

14. Maximize $\quad P = 5x + 8y + 6z$
    Subject to
    $$x + 2y + z \le 40$$
    $$-x + 4y + z \le 60$$
    $$3x + 2z \le 90$$
    $$x \ge 0, y \ge 0, z \ge 0$$

15. A manufacturer is considering the production of three new products. The first product requires 8 hours of cutting and 4 hours of finishing; the second product requires 2 hours of cutting and 5 hours of finishing; and the third product requires 4 hours of cutting and no finishing time. The company has 200 hours of cutting time available and 160 hours of finishing time available each week. The sales department of the company anticipates that the sales potential for the first and second products exceeds the production capacity, but that the sales of the third product will not exceed 20 per week. If the three products return profits of $30, $50, and $20, respectively, how many of each product should be made each week in order for the company to realize the largest weekly profit? What is the largest profit?

16. A merchant sells three assortments of mixed nuts—regular, deluxe, and special. Each regular assortment contains 1 pound of peanuts, 1 pound of cashews, and $\frac{1}{2}$ pound of walnuts; each deluxe assortment contains 2 pounds of peanuts, $1\frac{1}{2}$ pounds of cashews, and 1 pound of walnuts; and each special assortment contains 2 pounds of peanuts, 2 pounds of cashews, and $1\frac{1}{2}$ pounds of walnuts. On a certain day only 800 pounds of peanuts, 640 pounds of cashews, and 480 pounds of walnuts are available. If the profits on the regular, deluxe, and special assortments are $0.60, $0.90, and $0.75, respectively, how many of each type of assortment should be made for a maximum profit? What is the maximum profit?

17. In producing its three products, a chemical company emits carbon monoxide, sulfur dioxide, and particulates. For every 100 gallons of the first product that are produced, 0.1 pound of carbon monoxide, 0.2 pound of sulfur dioxide, and 0.1 pound of particulates are emitted. For every 100 gallons of the second product that are produced, 0.2 pound of carbon monoxide, 0.1 pound of sulfur dioxide, and 0.1 pound of particulates are emitted. In addition, for every 100 gallons of the third product that are produced, 0.2 pound of carbon monoxide, 0.3 pound of sulfur dioxide, and 0.1 pound of particulates are emitted. The Environmental Protection Agency has limited the company to weekly emissions of 120 pounds of carbon monoxide, 200 pounds of sulfur dioxide, and 160 pounds of particulates. If the company earns profits of $30, $20, and $50 on each 100 gallons of the first, second, and third products, respectively, how much of each of the three products should be made for a maximum weekly profit? What is the maximum weekly profit?

18. An electronics company manufactures three models of transistor radios. Production of each dozen model A radios requires 9 hours for manufacturing of parts, 5 hours for assembling, and 1 hour for packaging. Production of each dozen model B radios requires 4 hours for manufacturing, 4 hours for assembling, and 2 hours for packaging. Production of each dozen model C radios requires 12 hours for manufacturing, 6 hours for assembling, and 1 hour for packaging. Profits from the sale of a dozen radios of models A, B, and C are $40, $60, and $50, respectively. During a certain period there is at most 252 hours available for manufacturing, at most 136 hours available for assembling, and at most 36 hours available for packaging. Under these conditions, how should production be scheduled in order to earn a maximum profit? What is the maximum profit?

19. (a) In (4.11), perform another pivot using the third column as the pivot column and choosing the pivot row as usual.
    (b) What is the new basic feasible solution obtained by this pivot? What is the value of the objective function there?
    (c) What conclusion about this problem can be drawn from part (b)?
    (d) State a general rule that explains when this situation occurs.

Use Exercise 19(d) to find all the optimal basic feasible solutions of the linear programming problems in Exercises 20–22.

20. Maximize $P = 0.50x + 1.00y$
    Subject to
    $$5x + 2y \leq 3000$$
    $$0.2x + 0.4y \leq 160$$
    $$x \geq 0, y \geq 0$$

21. Maximize $P = 2x + y + 3z$
    Subject to
    $$0.1x + 0.2y + 0.2z \leq 120$$
    $$0.2x + 0.1y + 0.3z \leq 200$$
    $$0.1x + 0.1y + 0.1z \leq 160$$
    $$x \geq 0, y \geq 0, z \geq 0$$

22. Exercise 16 above.

Show that the linear programming problems in Exercises 23 and 24 have no maxima.

23. Maximize $P = 4x + 3y + 2z$
    Subject to
    $$x + 3y - 2z \leq 18$$
    $$x - 2y + z \leq 8$$
    $$x \geq 0, y \geq 0, z \geq 0$$

24. Maximize $P = 4x + 3y + 5z$
    Subject to
    $$x - 2y + z \leq 30$$
    $$x - 4y + z \leq 80$$
    $$-3x + 2z \leq 90$$
    $$x \geq 0, y \geq 0, z \geq 0$$

4.6 Artificial Variables and Minimization Problems

In Sections 4.4 and 4.5 we restricted our attention to constraints of the form

$$a_1x_1 + a_2x_2 + \cdots + a_nx_n \leq b \tag{4.12}$$

where $b \geq 0$. We now consider two additional types of constraints, those of the forms

$$a_1x_1 + a_2x_2 + \cdots + a_nx_n \geq b \tag{4.13}$$

and

$$a_1x_1 + a_2x_2 + \cdots + a_nx_n = b \tag{4.14}$$

where $b > 0$. Observe that multiplying an inequality or equation containing a negative right-side constant by -1 will transform it into one of these three forms. Of course, multiplication by -1 will change the sense of an inequality from "less than or equal to" to "greater than or equal to," and vice versa. So every linear inequality or equation containing a nonzero right-side constant can be written in the form of (4.12), (4.13), or (4.14).[5]

Because the simplex method as described in Section 4.5 assumes that the right-side constants are all nonnegative, we assume henceforth that all constraints are written in this way. Thus the inequality

$$3x - 2y + z \leq -5$$

must be multiplied by -1 in order to express it in the proper form

$$-3x + 2y - z \geq 5$$

To convert an inequality of the form (4.13) into an equation, we must *subtract* a nonnegative slack variable z from the left side. With this new variable (4.13) can be expressed as

$$a_1x_1 + a_2x_2 + \cdots + a_nx_n - z = b$$

Although we have converted the original inequality into an equation, this equation presents a difficulty in using the simplex method that did not occur in connection with inequalities of the form (4.12). The example below describes this difficulty.

EXAMPLE 16

We shall convert the constraints of the following linear programming problem into equations:

Maximize $\quad 4x + 5y$

Subject to $\quad 2x + y \leq 150$

$\qquad\qquad\quad x + 3y \leq 165 \tag{4.15}$

$\qquad\qquad\quad x + y \geq 50$

$\qquad\qquad\quad x \geq 0, y \geq 0$

The first two inequalities can be converted into equations by adding a nonnegative slack variable to the left side of each. The

---

[5] If $b = 0$, degeneracy occurs. See footnote 4.

4.6 Artificial Variables and Minimization Problems

resulting equations are

$$2x + y + r = 150 \quad \text{and} \quad x + 3y + s = 165$$

For the third inequality it is necessary to subtract a nonnegative slack variable from the left side to obtain

$$x + y - t = 50$$

So the constraints of the problem can be expressed as

$$\begin{aligned} 2x + y + r &= 150 \\ x + 3y + s &= 165 \\ x + y - t &= 50 \\ x \geq 0,\, y \geq 0,\, r \geq 0,\, s \geq 0,\, t \geq 0 \end{aligned} \quad (4.16)$$

In order to apply the simplex method to this problem, we must find a basic feasible solution with which to begin the process. If we attempt to obtain a basic feasible solution as in Section 4.5 by taking the slack variables as the basic variables, we obtain $x = 0$, $y = 0$, $r = 150$, $s = 165$, $t = -50$. This is *not* a feasible solution, since the value of t is negative. Notice that this negative value resulted because t was subtracted from the left side of the third inequality rather than added to it.

As the example above shows, there is no obvious choice of a basic feasible solution for problems involving constraints of the form (4.13). A similar difficulty exists for problems containing constraints of the form (4.14). To overcome these difficulties, we add to the left side of every constraint of forms (4.13) and (4.14) a nonnegative variable called an *artificial variable*. Thus in the case of inequalities of the form (4.13), we shall have both a nonnegative slack variable and a nonnegative artificial variable on the left side of the resulting equation. So the third inequality in (4.15) will be expressed as

artificial variable

$$x + y - t + w = 50$$

where t is a nonnegative slack variable and w is a nonnegative artificial variable.

EXAMPLE 17

Consider the problem

$$\begin{aligned} \text{Maximize} \quad & x + 2y + 3z \\ \text{Subject to} \quad & x + y + z \leq 4 \\ & x + z \geq 5 \\ & y - z = 1 \\ & x \geq 0,\, y \geq 0,\, z \geq 0 \end{aligned} \quad (4.17)$$

In order to use the simplex method to solve this problem, we must express the constraints as equations. The problem then takes the

Chapter 4 Linear Programming

following form:

$$\begin{aligned}
\text{Maximize} \quad & x + 2y + 3z \\
\text{Subject to} \quad & x + y + z + r = 4 \\
& x + z - s + v = 5 \\
& y - z + w = 1 \\
& x \geq 0, y \geq 0, z \geq 0, r \geq 0, s \geq 0, v \geq 0, w \geq 0
\end{aligned}$$

Here r and s are slack variables, and v and w are artificial variables. Observe that in this form we can easily obtain a basic feasible solution by taking r, v, and w as the basic variables: $x = 0$, $y = 0$, $z = 0$, $r = 4$, $s = 0$, $v = 5$, $w = 1$.

two-phase method

An artificial variable has no meaningful interpretation in the original problem; it simply serves as a device for obtaining a basic feasible solution with which to begin the simplex method. Consequently we must be certain that every artificial variable is made zero in the ultimate solution to the original problem. One method for accomplishing this objective is called the *two-phase method*. As its name suggests, this process involves two distinct parts. In phase I all the artificial variables are made zero (if possible). Thus if phase I is successful, it results in a basic feasible solution for the problem that contains no nonzero artificial variables. In phase II the usual simplex method is applied to this basic feasible solution in order to optimize the objective function.

Let us consider phase I in more detail, illustrating the ideas by referring to Example 16. After introducing slack and artificial variables, the problem can be written

$$\begin{aligned}
\text{Maximize} \quad & P = 4x + 5y \\
\text{Subject to} \quad & 2x + y + r = 150 \\
& x + 3y + s = 165 \\
& x + y - t + w = 50 \\
& x \geq 0, y \geq 0, r \geq 0, s \geq 0, t \geq 0, w \geq 0
\end{aligned} \quad (4.18)$$

The usual simplex tableau for (4.18) is

$$\left(\begin{array}{ccccccc|c}
2 & 1 & 1 & 0 & 0 & 0 & 0 & 150 \\
1 & 3 & 0 & 1 & 0 & 0 & 0 & 165 \\
1 & 1 & 0 & 0 & -1 & 1 & 0 & 50 \\
\hline
-4 & -5 & 0 & 0 & 0 & 0 & 1 & 0
\end{array} \right)$$

To this tableau we adjoin another row that will correspond to a new objective function. If artificial variables $w_1, w_2, \ldots, w_n$ have been included in the constraints, then we shall maximize the new objective function

$$P = -w_1 - w_2 - \cdots - w_n$$

Observe that, since the artificial variables are all required to be nonnegative, the maximum value of P will be zero when each artificial variable is zero. Thus by maximizing this new objective function we can remove all the artificial variables from the problem. Since there is only one artificial variable, w, in (4.18), the new objective function is $P = -w$, or equivalently, $w + P = 0$. When the new row corresponding to this equation is adjoined to the bottom of the tableau above, we obtain

$$\left(\begin{array}{ccccccc|c} 2 & 1 & 1 & 0 & 0 & 0 & 0 & 150 \\ 1 & 3 & 0 & 1 & 0 & 0 & 0 & 165 \\ 1 & 1 & 0 & 0 & -1 & 1 & 0 & 50 \\ \hline -4 & -5 & 0 & 0 & 0 & 0 & 1 & 0 \\ 0 & 0 & 0 & 0 & 0 & 1 & 1 & 0 \end{array}\right) \quad (4.19)$$

Before we can apply the simplex method to the basic feasible solution $x = 0$, $y = 0$, $r = 150$, $s = 165$, $t = 0$, $w = 50$ associated with (4.19), we must rewrite the bottom row of the tableau so that the coefficient of each basic variable is 0. This will express P in terms of the nonbasic variables only. Since the coefficient of the artificial variable w is 1, not 0, in the bottom row, we must subtract the third row from the bottom row. This operation amounts to performing a pivot in the column containing the artificial variable. In this way we obtain

$$\begin{array}{c} \\ r \\ s \\ w \\ \\ \end{array} \begin{array}{cccccccc} x & y & r & s & t & w & P & \\ \end{array}$$

$$\begin{array}{c} r \\ s \\ w \\ \\ \\ \end{array} \left(\begin{array}{ccccccc|c} 2 & 1 & 1 & 0 & 0 & 0 & 0 & 150 \\ 1 & 3 & 0 & 1 & 0 & 0 & 0 & 165 \\ 1 & 1 & 0 & 0 & -1 & 1 & 0 & 50 \\ \hline -4 & -5 & 0 & 0 & 0 & 0 & 1 & 0 \\ -1 & -1 & 0 & 0 & 1 & 0 & 1 & -50 \end{array}\right)$$

With this preliminary step completed, we proceed with the simplex method as described on page 151, continuing until no negative entries remain in the bottom row except possibly in the last column. Notice that no row below the dashed line may ever be used as a pivot row.

If the last entry of the bottom row is ignored in the tableau above, there is a tie for the most negative entry in the row. Consequently we may choose either the first or second column as the pivot column. Let us arbitrarily select the first column. Then the third row is the pivot row, and the result of this pivot is

$$\begin{array}{c} \\ r \\ s \\ x \\ \\ \end{array} \begin{array}{cccccccc} x & y & r & s & t & w & P & \\ \end{array}$$

$$\begin{array}{c} r \\ s \\ x \\ \\ \\ \end{array} \left(\begin{array}{ccccccc|c} 0 & -1 & 1 & 0 & 2 & -2 & 0 & 50 \\ 0 & 2 & 0 & 1 & 1 & -1 & 0 & 115 \\ 1 & 1 & 0 & 0 & -1 & 1 & 0 & 50 \\ \hline 0 & -1 & 0 & 0 & -4 & 4 & 1 & 200 \\ 0 & 0 & 0 & 0 & 0 & 1 & 1 & 0 \end{array}\right) \quad (4.20)$$

Since no negative entries remain in the bottom row of this tableau, phase I is complete. Notice that in the basic feasible solution $x = 50$, $y = 0$, $r = 50$, $s = 115$, $t = 0$, $w = 0$ associated with this tableau, the artificial variable w has the value 0; moreover, for this basic feasible solution $P = 0$. We can therefore delete from (4.20) the bottom row and the column corresponding to the artificial variable to obtain

$$\begin{array}{c} \\ r \\ s \\ x \\ {} \end{array} \begin{pmatrix} x & y & r & s & t & P & \\ 0 & -1 & 1 & 0 & 2 & 0 & | & 50 \\ 0 & 2 & 0 & 1 & 1 & 0 & | & 115 \\ 1 & 1 & 0 & 0 & -1 & 0 & | & 50 \\ \hline 0 & -1 & 0 & 0 & -4 & 1 & | & 200 \end{pmatrix}$$

In phase II we use the usual simplex method to maximize the original objective function $P = 4x + 5y$, beginning with the tableau above. Pivoting with the fifth column as the pivot column and the first row as the pivot row yields

$$\begin{array}{c} \\ t \\ s \\ x \\ {} \end{array} \begin{pmatrix} x & y & r & s & t & P & \\ 0 & -0.5 & 0.5 & 0 & 1 & 0 & | & 25 \\ 0 & 2.5 & -0.5 & 1 & 0 & 0 & | & 90 \\ 1 & 0.5 & 0.5 & 0 & 0 & 0 & | & 75 \\ \hline 0 & -3.0 & 2.0 & 0 & 0 & 1 & | & 300 \end{pmatrix}$$

Since a negative entry remains in the bottom row, another pivot is required. For this pivot the second column is the pivot column and the second row is the pivot row; this pivot produces

$$\begin{array}{c} \\ t \\ y \\ x \\ {} \end{array} \begin{pmatrix} x & y & r & s & t & P & \\ 0 & 0 & 0.4 & 0.2 & 1 & 0 & | & 43 \\ 0 & 1 & -0.2 & 0.4 & 0 & 0 & | & 36 \\ 1 & 0 & 0.6 & -0.2 & 0 & 0 & | & 57 \\ \hline 0 & 0 & 1.4 & 1.2 & 0 & 1 & | & 408 \end{pmatrix}$$

Because there are no negative entries in the bottom row, phase II is complete. Thus the basic feasible solution $x = 57$, $y = 36$, $r = 0$, $s = 0$, $t = 43$ associated with this tableau produces the maximum value of the objective function, which is 408. Observe that this solution does satisfy the constraints of the original problem as expressed in (4.16) without artificial variables.

EXAMPLE 18

Let us solve the problem

Maximize $P = 8x + 6y$
Subject to
$3x + 2y \leq 480$
$x + 3y \geq 300$
$2x + y \geq 250$
$x \geq 0, y \geq 0$

4.6 Artificial Variables and Minimization Problems 163

The constraints of this problem may be written as equations by introducing slack variables r, s, and t and artificial variables v and w. With these new variables the problem may be expressed as

Maximize $P = 8x + 6y$
Subject to
$$3x + 2y + r = 480$$
$$x + 3y - s + v = 300$$
$$2x + y - t + w = 250$$
$$x \geq 0, y \geq 0, r \geq 0, s \geq 0, t \geq 0, v \geq 0, w \geq 0$$

The simplex tableau for this problem is

$$\begin{pmatrix} 3 & 2 & 1 & 0 & 0 & 0 & 0 & 0 & | & 480 \\ 1 & 3 & 0 & -1 & 0 & 1 & 0 & 0 & | & 300 \\ 2 & 1 & 0 & 0 & -1 & 0 & 1 & 0 & | & 250 \\ \hline -8 & -6 & 0 & 0 & 0 & 0 & 0 & 1 & | & 0 \end{pmatrix}$$

To this tableau we adjoin a new row corresponding to the phase I objective function $P = -v - w$, or equivalently, $v + w + P = 0$. Thus the simplex tableau for phase I is

$$\begin{pmatrix} 3 & 2 & 1 & 0 & 0 & 0 & 0 & 0 & | & 480 \\ 1 & 3 & 0 & -1 & 0 & 1 & 0 & 0 & | & 300 \\ 2 & 1 & 0 & 0 & -1 & 0 & 1 & 0 & | & 250 \\ \hline -8 & -6 & 0 & 0 & 0 & 0 & 0 & 1 & | & 0 \\ 0 & 0 & 0 & 0 & 0 & 1 & 1 & 1 & | & 0 \end{pmatrix}$$

Before the simplex method can be started, we must rewrite the bottom row so that the entry in each column corresponding to an artificial variable is 0. This change can be made either by subtracting the second and third rows from the bottom row or by performing pivots in the sixth and seventh columns. In either case we obtain

$$\begin{array}{c} \\ r \\ v \\ w \\ \\ \end{array} \begin{pmatrix} x & y & r & s & t & v & w & P & | & \\ 3 & 2 & 1 & 0 & 0 & 0 & 0 & 0 & | & 480 \\ 1 & 3 & 0 & -1 & 0 & 1 & 0 & 0 & | & 300 \\ 2 & 1 & 0 & 0 & -1 & 0 & 1 & 0 & | & 250 \\ \hline -8 & -6 & 0 & 0 & 0 & 0 & 0 & 1 & | & 0 \\ -3 & -4 & 0 & 1 & 1 & 0 & 0 & 1 & | & -550 \end{pmatrix}$$

We are now ready to begin phase I by pivoting with the second column as the pivot column and the second row as the pivot row.

This pivot yields

$$
\begin{array}{c|ccccccc|c}
 & x & y & r & s & t & v & w & P & \\
\hline
r & \frac{7}{3} & 0 & 1 & \frac{2}{3} & 0 & -\frac{2}{3} & 0 & 0 & 280 \\
y & \frac{1}{3} & 1 & 0 & -\frac{1}{3} & 0 & \frac{1}{3} & 0 & 0 & 100 \\
w & \frac{5}{3} & 0 & 0 & \frac{1}{3} & -1 & -\frac{1}{3} & 1 & 0 & 150 \\
\hline
 & -6 & 0 & 0 & -2 & 0 & 2 & 0 & 1 & 600 \\
 & -\frac{5}{3} & 0 & 0 & -\frac{1}{3} & 1 & \frac{4}{3} & 0 & 1 & -150
\end{array}
$$

For the next pivot the first column will be the pivot column and the third row will be the pivot row. The result of this pivot is

$$
\begin{array}{c|ccccccc|c}
 & x & y & r & s & t & v & w & P & \\
\hline
r & 0 & 0 & 1 & \frac{1}{5} & \frac{7}{5} & -\frac{1}{5} & -\frac{7}{5} & 0 & 70 \\
y & 0 & 1 & 0 & -\frac{2}{5} & \frac{1}{5} & \frac{2}{5} & -\frac{1}{5} & 0 & 70 \\
x & 1 & 0 & 0 & \frac{1}{5} & -\frac{3}{5} & -\frac{1}{5} & \frac{3}{5} & 0 & 90 \\
\hline
 & 0 & 0 & 0 & -\frac{4}{5} & -\frac{18}{5} & \frac{4}{5} & \frac{18}{5} & 1 & 1140 \\
 & 0 & 0 & 0 & 0 & 0 & 1 & 1 & 1 & 0
\end{array}
$$

Since no negative entries remain in the bottom row of the tableau, phase I is complete. Observe that the phase I objective function has value 0, so that a basic feasible solution of the original problem has been obtained. We can now delete the bottom row and the sixth and seventh columns (the columns corresponding to the artificial variables v and w) from the preceding tableau to obtain

$$
\begin{array}{c|ccccc|c}
 & x & y & r & s & t & P & \\
\hline
r & 0 & 0 & 1 & \frac{1}{5} & \frac{7}{5} & 0 & 70 \\
y & 0 & 1 & 0 & -\frac{2}{5} & \frac{1}{5} & 0 & 70 \\
x & 1 & 0 & 0 & \frac{1}{5} & -\frac{3}{5} & 0 & 90 \\
\hline
 & 0 & 0 & 0 & -\frac{4}{5} & -\frac{18}{5} & 1 & 1140
\end{array}
$$

In phase II we apply the usual simplex method to this tableau in order to obtain a solution to the given problem. For the first pivot the fifth column is the pivot column and the first row is the pivot row. This pivot produces

$$
\begin{array}{c|ccccc|c}
 & x & y & r & s & t & P & \\
\hline
t & 0 & 0 & \frac{5}{7} & \frac{1}{7} & 1 & 0 & 50 \\
y & 0 & 1 & -\frac{1}{7} & -\frac{3}{7} & 0 & 0 & 60 \\
x & 1 & 0 & \frac{3}{7} & \frac{2}{7} & 0 & 0 & 120 \\
\hline
 & 0 & 0 & \frac{18}{7} & -\frac{2}{7} & 0 & 1 & 1320
\end{array}
$$

Using the fourth column as the pivot column and the first row as the pivot row, we obtain the following new tableau.

$$\begin{array}{c} \\ s \\ y \\ x \\ \\ \end{array} \begin{array}{c} x \\ \left(\begin{array}{cccccc|c} 0 & 0 & 5 & 1 & 7 & 0 & 350 \\ 0 & 1 & 2 & 0 & 3 & 0 & 210 \\ 1 & 0 & -1 & 0 & -2 & 0 & 20 \\ \hline 0 & 0 & 4 & 0 & 2 & 1 & 1420 \end{array}\right) \end{array}$$

Phase II is now complete. The maximum value of the objective function is therefore 1420, and this value is obtained at the basic feasible solution $x = 20$, $y = 210$, $r = 0$, $s = 350$, $t = 0$.

A linear programming problem may fail to have a solution because there are no feasible solutions for the problem. In this case it will not be possible to obtain the value 0 for the objective function in phase I. The example below illustrates this situation.

EXAMPLE 19

We shall use the two-phase method to show that the problem

Maximize $P = x + 2y + 3z$
Subject to $x + y + z \le 4$
$\quad\quad\quad\quad x \quad\quad + z \ge 5$
$\quad\quad\quad\quad\quad\quad y - z = 1$
$\quad\quad\quad\quad x \ge 0, y \ge 0, z \ge 0$

has no feasible solutions. First introduce slack variables r and s and artificial variables v and w as in Example 17 to express the problem in the form

Maximize $P = x + 2y + 3z$
Subject to $x + y + z + r \quad\quad\quad\quad\quad = 4$
$\quad\quad\quad\quad x \quad\quad + z \quad - s + v \quad\quad = 5$
$\quad\quad\quad\quad\quad\quad y - z \quad\quad\quad\quad + w = 1$

Since the objective function for phase I is $P = -v - w$, the simplex tableau for phase I is

$$\left(\begin{array}{cccccccc|c} 1 & 1 & 1 & 1 & 0 & 0 & 0 & 0 & 4 \\ 1 & 0 & 1 & 0 & -1 & 1 & 0 & 0 & 5 \\ 0 & 1 & -1 & 0 & 0 & 0 & 1 & 0 & 1 \\ \hline -1 & -2 & -3 & 0 & 0 & 0 & 0 & 1 & 0 \\ 0 & 0 & 0 & 0 & 0 & 1 & 1 & 1 & 0 \end{array}\right)$$

Subtracting the second and third rows from the bottom row (or pivoting in the sixth and seventh columns), we obtain

$$\begin{array}{c} \\ r \\ v \\ w \\ \\ \\ \end{array} \left(\begin{array}{ccccccc|c} x & y & z & r & s & v & w & P \\ 1 & 1 & 1 & 1 & 0 & 0 & 0 & 0 \;\vrule\; 4 \\ 1 & 0 & 1 & 0 & -1 & 1 & 0 & 0 \;\vrule\; 5 \\ 0 & 1 & -1 & 0 & 0 & 0 & 1 & 0 \;\vrule\; 1 \\ \hline -1 & -2 & -3 & 0 & 0 & 0 & 0 & 1 \;\vrule\; 0 \\ -1 & -1 & 0 & 0 & 1 & 0 & 0 & 1 \;\vrule\; -6 \end{array} \right)$$

We are now ready to begin phase I. Either the first or second column can serve as the pivot column. If we select the second column, then the third row will be the pivot row. Performing this pivot yields

$$\begin{array}{c} \\ r \\ v \\ y \\ \\ \\ \end{array} \left(\begin{array}{ccccccc|c} x & y & z & r & s & v & w & P \\ 1 & 0 & 2 & 1 & 0 & 0 & -1 & 0 \;\vrule\; 3 \\ 1 & 0 & 1 & 0 & -1 & 1 & 0 & 0 \;\vrule\; 5 \\ 0 & 1 & -1 & 0 & 0 & 0 & 1 & 0 \;\vrule\; 1 \\ \hline -1 & 0 & -5 & 0 & 0 & 0 & 2 & 1 \;\vrule\; 2 \\ -1 & 0 & -1 & 0 & 1 & 0 & 1 & 1 \;\vrule\; -5 \end{array} \right)$$

Again there is a choice of pivot columns. If the first column is chosen, then the first row is the pivot row. The tableau resulting from this pivot is

$$\begin{array}{c} \\ x \\ v \\ y \\ \\ \\ \end{array} \left(\begin{array}{ccccccc|c} x & y & z & r & s & v & w & P \\ 1 & 0 & 2 & 1 & 0 & 0 & -1 & 0 \;\vrule\; 3 \\ 0 & 0 & -1 & -1 & -1 & 1 & 1 & 0 \;\vrule\; 2 \\ 0 & 1 & -1 & 0 & 0 & 0 & 1 & 0 \;\vrule\; 1 \\ \hline 0 & 0 & -3 & 1 & 0 & 0 & 1 & 1 \;\vrule\; 5 \\ 0 & 0 & 1 & 1 & 1 & 0 & 0 & 1 \;\vrule\; -2 \end{array} \right)$$

In the bottom row of this tableau there are no negative entries other than the last entry. Consequently phase I is complete, but the phase I objective function has the value $P = -2$ in this tableau. This nonzero value indicates that some artificial variable (in this case v) remains a basic variable. Thus the original problem has no feasible solutions.

Until now we have discussed the simplex method only in connection with problems in which the objective function was to be maximized. Fortunately there is a simple method for converting any minimization problem into a maximization problem. Using this technique, we shall be able to solve minimization problems without any modifications in the simplex method. The key idea is illustrated in Figure 4.20: If v is the minimum value of a function f, then the maximum value of the function $-f$ is $-v$, and it occurs at the same point as the minimum value of f. This suggests that an objective

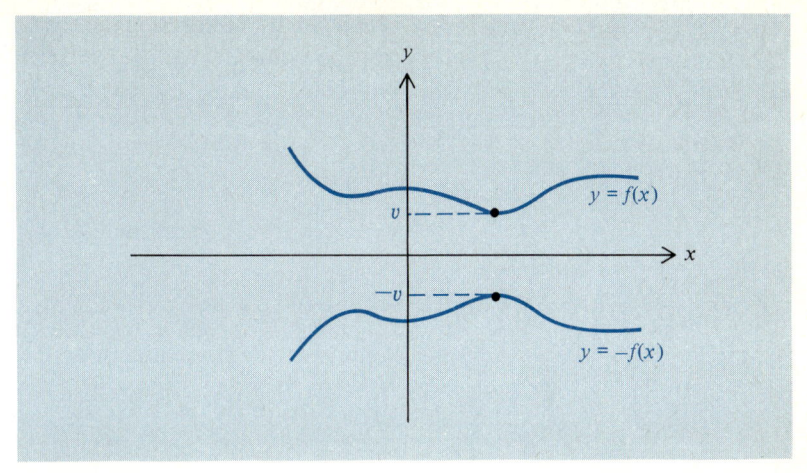

Figure 4.20

function can be minimized by maximizing its negative. Example 20 demonstrates this technique.

EXAMPLE 20

Let us use the simplex method to solve the problem

Minimize $\quad 8x + 5y + 2z$

Subject to $\quad 2x + y + z \geq 150$
$\quad\quad\quad\quad\quad x + 2y + z \geq 120$
$\quad\quad\quad\quad\quad x \geq 0, y \geq 0, z \geq 0$

Rather than minimize the given objective function, we maximize its negative. Thus the objective function we use is

$\quad P = -8x - 5y - 2z$

As usual, the constraints must be written as equations involving slack and artificial variables. With these changes the problem takes the following form.

Maximize $\quad P = -8x - 5y - 2z$

Subject to $\quad\quad\quad 2x + y + z - r \quad\quad + v \quad\quad = 150$
$\quad\quad\quad\quad\quad\quad\quad x + 2y + z \quad\quad - s \quad\quad + w = 120$
$\quad\quad\quad\quad\quad\quad\quad x \geq 0, y \geq 0, z \geq 0, r \geq 0, s \geq 0, v \geq 0, w \geq 0$

The simplex tableau for phase I is

$$\begin{pmatrix} 2 & 1 & 1 & -1 & 0 & 1 & 0 & 0 & | & 150 \\ 1 & 2 & 1 & 0 & -1 & 0 & 1 & 0 & | & 120 \\ \hline 8 & 5 & 2 & 0 & 0 & 0 & 0 & 1 & | & 0 \\ 0 & 0 & 0 & 0 & 0 & 1 & 1 & 1 & | & 0 \end{pmatrix}$$

We begin by subtracting the first and second rows from the bottom row (or equivalently, by pivoting in the sixth and seventh columns) to obtain

$$\begin{array}{c} \\ v \\ w \\ \\ \\ \end{array} \left(\begin{array}{ccccccc|c} x & y & z & r & s & v & w & P \\ 2 & 1 & 1 & -1 & 0 & 1 & 0 & 0 & 150 \\ 1 & 2 & 1 & 0 & -1 & 0 & 1 & 0 & 120 \\ \hline 8 & 5 & 2 & 0 & 0 & 0 & 0 & 1 & 0 \\ -3 & -3 & -2 & 1 & 1 & 0 & 0 & 1 & -270 \end{array} \right)$$

Choosing the first column as the pivot column, we find that the first row is the pivot row. The resulting pivot yields

$$\begin{array}{c} \\ x \\ w \\ \\ \\ \end{array} \left(\begin{array}{ccccccc|c} x & y & z & r & s & v & w & P \\ 1 & \frac{1}{2} & \frac{1}{2} & -\frac{1}{2} & 0 & \frac{1}{2} & 0 & 0 & 75 \\ 0 & \frac{3}{2} & \frac{1}{2} & \frac{1}{2} & -1 & -\frac{1}{2} & 1 & 0 & 45 \\ \hline 0 & 1 & -2 & 4 & 0 & -4 & 0 & 1 & -600 \\ 0 & -\frac{3}{2} & -\frac{1}{2} & -\frac{1}{2} & 1 & \frac{3}{2} & 0 & 1 & -45 \end{array} \right)$$

The next tableau is found by using the second column as the pivot column and the second row as the pivot row.

$$\begin{array}{c} \\ x \\ y \\ \\ \\ \end{array} \left(\begin{array}{ccccccc|c} x & y & z & r & s & v & w & P \\ 1 & 0 & \frac{1}{3} & -\frac{2}{3} & \frac{1}{3} & \frac{2}{3} & -\frac{1}{3} & 0 & 60 \\ 0 & 1 & \frac{1}{3} & \frac{1}{3} & -\frac{2}{3} & -\frac{1}{3} & \frac{2}{3} & 0 & 30 \\ \hline 0 & 0 & -\frac{7}{3} & \frac{11}{3} & \frac{2}{3} & -\frac{11}{3} & -\frac{2}{3} & 1 & -630 \\ 0 & 0 & 0 & 0 & 0 & 1 & 1 & 1 & 0 \end{array} \right)$$

Phase I is now complete. Since the phase I objective function has assumed the value 0, a basic feasible solution has been found in which all the artificial variables are 0. Thus we delete the bottom row and the sixth and seventh columns from the tableau above to obtain

$$\begin{array}{c} \\ x \\ y \\ \\ \end{array} \left(\begin{array}{ccccc|c} x & y & z & r & s & P \\ 1 & 0 & \frac{1}{3} & -\frac{2}{3} & \frac{1}{3} & 0 & 60 \\ 0 & 1 & \frac{1}{3} & \frac{1}{3} & -\frac{2}{3} & 0 & 30 \\ \hline 0 & 0 & -\frac{7}{3} & \frac{11}{3} & \frac{2}{3} & 1 & -630 \end{array} \right)$$

The first pivot in phase II will be made using the third column as the pivot column and the second row as the pivot row. This pivot yields

$$\begin{array}{c} \\ x \\ z \\ \\ \end{array} \left(\begin{array}{ccccc|c} x & y & z & r & s & P \\ 1 & -1 & 0 & -1 & 1 & 0 & 30 \\ 0 & 3 & 1 & 1 & -2 & 0 & 90 \\ \hline 0 & 7 & 0 & 6 & -4 & 1 & -420 \end{array} \right)$$

Next use the fifth column as the pivot column and the first row as the pivot row to obtain

$$\begin{array}{c} \\ s \\ z \\ \end{array} \begin{array}{ccccccc} x & y & z & r & s & P & \\ \left(\begin{array}{cccccc|c} 1 & -1 & 0 & -1 & 1 & 0 & 30 \\ 2 & 1 & 1 & -1 & 0 & 0 & 150 \\ \hline 4 & 3 & 0 & 2 & 0 & 1 & -300 \end{array}\right) \end{array}$$

Phase II is now complete. Thus the objective function $P = -8x - 5y - 2z$ assumes its maximum value of -300 at the basic feasible solution $x = 0$, $y = 0$, $z = 150$, $r = 0$, $s = 30$. It follows that 300 is the minimum value of the original function $8x + 5y + 2z$ and that this value occurs at the basic feasible solution $x = 0$, $y = 0$, $z = 150$, $r = 0$, $s = 30$.

Exercises

Solve the following linear programming problems using the simplex method.

1. Maximize $3x + 5y$
   Subject to $x + y \leq 20$
   $3x + y \geq 36$
   $x \geq 0, y \geq 0$

2. Maximize $3x + 4y$
   Subject to $x + y \leq 40$
   $2x + y \geq 50$
   $x \geq 0, y \geq 0$

3. Maximize $3x + y$
   Subject to $x + 2y \leq 200$
   $2x + y \geq 250$
   $x \geq 0, y \geq 0$

4. Maximize $3x + 2y$
   Subject to $2x + y \leq 75$
   $x + y \geq 60$
   $x \geq 0, y \geq 0$

5. Maximize $3x + 2y$
   Subject to $4x + y \leq 400$
   $2x + y \geq 300$
   $x \geq 0, y \geq 0$

6. Maximize $5x + 2y$
   Subject to $x + 2y \leq 150$
   $2x + 3y \geq 240$
   $x \geq 0, y \geq 0$

7. Maximize $8x + 4y$
   Subject to $5x + 3y \leq 600$
   $3x + 2y \geq 390$
   $x \geq 0, y \geq 0$

8. Maximize $4x + 6y$
   Subject to $x + 3y \leq 180$
   $3x + 5y \geq 480$
   $x \geq 0, y \geq 0$

9. Minimize $3x + 6y$
   Subject to $2x + y \leq 75$
   $x + y \geq 60$
   $x \geq 0, y \geq 0$

10. Minimize $4x + y$
    Subject to $x + 2y \leq 200$
    $2x + y \geq 250$
    $x \geq 0, y \geq 0$

11. Minimize $6x + 4y$
    Subject to $x + 2y \leq 150$
    $2x + 3y \geq 240$
    $x \geq 0, y \geq 0$

12. Minimize $5x + 3y$
    Subject to $4x + y \leq 400$
    $2x + y \geq 300$
    $x \geq 0, y \geq 0$

13. Minimize $2x + 5y$
    Subject to $x + 3y \leq 180$
    $3x + 5y \geq 480$
    $x \geq 0, y \geq 0$

14. Minimize $10x + 2y$
    Subject to $5x + 3y \leq 600$
    $3x + 2y \geq 390$
    $x \geq 0, y \geq 0$

15. Minimize $3x + 4y$
    Subject to $x + y \geq 100$
    $x + 4y \geq 160$
    $2x + 4y \geq 260$
    $x \geq 0, y \geq 0$

16. Minimize $9x + 5y$
    Subject to $x + y \geq 36$
    $2x + 5y \geq 120$
    $x + 5y \geq 80$
    $x \geq 0, y \geq 0$

170 Chapter 4 Linear Programming

17. Minimize $\quad 2x + 3y + 5z$
    Subject to $\quad x - y - z \le 30$
    $\qquad\qquad\ x - y + z \ge 40$
    $\qquad\qquad\ x \ge 0, y \ge 0, z \ge 0$

18. Minimize $\quad 2x + 6y + 3z$
    Subject to $\quad x + y + z \ge 120$
    $\qquad\qquad -2x + 2y + z \ge 108$
    $\qquad\qquad\ x \ge 0, y \ge 0, z \ge 0$

19. Minimize $\quad 2x + y + 3z$
    Subject to $\quad x - y + 2z \ge 24$
    $\qquad\qquad -x + 2y + z \ge 30$
    $\qquad\qquad\ x \ge 0, y \ge 0, z \ge 0$

20. A hospital dietician must prepare a special diet from two foods. The first food provides 1 unit of iron, 1 unit of magnesium, and 20 calories at a cost of 3¢ per gram. The second food provides 1 unit of iron, 4 units of magnesium, and 40 calories at a cost of 4¢ per gram. If the diet must provide at least 100 units of iron, 160 units of magnesium, and 2600 calories, what combination of the two foods will satisfy these conditions at the least cost? What is the least cost?

21. A jeweler makes rings, stickpins, and pendants from semiprecious stones. For each ring, 1 hour is required to cut the stones and 3 hours are needed to polish them; for each stickpin, 2 hours are required to cut the stones and 1 hour is needed to polish them; and for each pendant, 2 hours are required to cut the stones and 5 hours are required to polish them. During a particular week the jeweler wants to devote at least 9 hours to cutting and at least 30 hours to polishing. If it costs the jeweler $34 to cut and polish the stones for each ring, $28 to cut and polish the stones for each stickpin, and $60 to cut and polish the stones for each pendant, how many rings, stickpins, and pendants should be made in order to minimize the jeweler's costs? What is the minimum cost?

22. A manufacturer would like to produce a total of at least 30 ceramic tiles, which are available in three styles. The first style requires 5 minutes of shaping and no painting time; the second style requires 2 minutes of shaping and 3 minutes of painting; and the third style requires 2 minutes of shaping and 5 minutes of painting. Profits on the three styles are $3, $4, and $6 per tile, respectively. If at most 160 minutes are available for shaping and at most 125 minutes are available for painting, how many tiles of each style should be made for a maximum profit? What is the maximum profit?

23. A certain diet specifies a minimum daily requirement of 50 units of food supplement R and 60 units of supplement S. These supplements are obtained most economically by eating three foods. One gram of the first food provides 2 units of R and 5 units of S, one gram of the second food provides 1 unit of R and 3 units of S, and one gram of the third food provides 1 unit of R and 6 units of S. If a gram of each food costs $0.04, $0.05, and $0.03, respectively, what amounts of each food should be eaten in order to satisfy the minimum daily requirements at the least cost? What is the least daily cost?

24. (a) A factory produces ceramic tiles and saucers which it sells at profits of $8 and $9 per piece, respectively. Each tile requires 1 minute of

shaping and 2 minutes of painting, whereas each saucer requires 3 minutes of shaping and 1 minute of painting. On a certain day the factory has 150 minutes available for shaping and 120 minutes available for painting. Under these conditions, how many tiles and saucers should be made in order to earn a maximum profit? What is the maximum profit?

(b) Let y_1 denote the factory's cost per minute for shaping and y_2 denote the factory's cost per minute for painting. Then $C = 150y_1 + 120y_2$ represents the total cost of 150 minutes of shaping and 120 minutes of painting. Determine the values of y_1 and y_2 that minimize C under the following conditions:

$$y_1 + 2y_2 \geq 8$$
$$3y_1 + y_2 \geq 9$$
$$y_1 \geq 0, y_2 \geq 0$$

In the context of part (a) these restrictions ensure that the profit derived from each product never exceeds the value of the labor used for shaping and painting.

(c) What similarities are there in the mathematical formulations of parts (a) and (b)?

(d) What similarities are there in the solutions to parts (a) and (b)?

25. Show that the following linear programming problem has no solution.

  Maximize $3x + 6y + 2z$
  Subject to $x + 3y - 2z \leq 25$
              $x - 2y + 3z \leq 35$
              $4x + 2y + z \geq 150$
              $x \geq 0, y \geq 0, z \geq 0$

*4.7 Duality

One of the most important theoretical discoveries in the development of linear programming was that linear programming problems occur in pairs, one being a maximization problem and the other a minimization problem. This discovery led to a number of important practical results that provide valuable information about the solution of a linear programming problem. In this section we consider some of the properties of these pairs of related problems.

As was true for systems of linear equations, it will prove convenient to formulate linear programming problems in matrix notation. For example, the linear programming problem

  Maximize $4x_1 + 3x_2$
  Subject to $3x_1 + 2x_2 \leq 36$
              $2x_1 + x_2 \leq 48$ (4.21)
              $x_1 + 4x_2 \leq 42$
              $x_1 \geq 0, x_2 \geq 0$

can be written in the following form:

$$\text{Maximize} \quad (4 \ 3)\begin{pmatrix} x_1 \\ x_2 \end{pmatrix}$$

$$\text{Subject to} \quad \begin{pmatrix} 3 & 2 \\ 2 & 1 \\ 1 & 4 \end{pmatrix}\begin{pmatrix} x_1 \\ x_2 \end{pmatrix} \leq \begin{pmatrix} 36 \\ 48 \\ 42 \end{pmatrix}$$

$$\begin{pmatrix} x_1 \\ x_2 \end{pmatrix} \geq \begin{pmatrix} 0 \\ 0 \end{pmatrix}$$

Here the inequality signs between matrices of the same dimensions have the obvious meaning: $A \leq B$ or $B \geq A$ means that each entry of A is less than or equal to the corresponding entry of B.

More generally, any linear programming problem involving maximization can be expressed in the form

$$\text{Maximize} \quad CX$$
$$\text{Subject to} \quad AX \leq B \qquad\qquad (4.22)$$
$$X \geq 0$$

where 0 is a zero matrix of the appropriate dimensions, $C = (c_1 \ c_2 \ \cdots \ c_n)$,

$$X = \begin{pmatrix} x_1 \\ x_2 \\ \vdots \\ x_n \end{pmatrix} \quad B = \begin{pmatrix} b_1 \\ b_2 \\ \vdots \\ b_m \end{pmatrix} \quad \text{and} \quad A = \begin{pmatrix} a_{11} & a_{12} & \cdots & a_{1n} \\ a_{21} & a_{22} & \cdots & a_{2n} \\ \vdots & \vdots & & \vdots \\ a_{m1} & a_{m2} & \cdots & a_{mn} \end{pmatrix}$$

EXAMPLE 21

Consider the following problem.

$$\text{Maximize} \quad 8x_1 + 9x_2$$
$$\text{Subject to} \quad x_1 + 3x_2 \leq 150$$
$$\qquad\qquad\quad 2x_1 + x_2 \leq 120$$
$$\qquad\qquad\quad x_1 \geq 0, x_2 \geq 0$$

In the notation of (4.22) we have

$$C = (8 \ 9) \quad X = \begin{pmatrix} x_1 \\ x_2 \end{pmatrix} \quad B = \begin{pmatrix} 150 \\ 120 \end{pmatrix} \quad \text{and} \quad A = \begin{pmatrix} 1 & 3 \\ 2 & 1 \end{pmatrix}$$

Another linear programming problem that uses the same matrices A, B, and C is

$$\text{Minimize} \quad YB$$
$$\text{Subject to} \quad YA \geq C \qquad\qquad (4.23)$$
$$\qquad\qquad\quad Y \geq 0$$

where
$$Y = (y_1 \quad y_2 \quad \cdots \quad y_m)$$

dual Problem (4.23) is called the *dual* of problem (4.22), and vice versa. Observe that the objective function is maximized in one problem and minimized in the other and that the sense of the inequalities is reversed in the two problems. The following list contains further information about the corresponding parts of the two problems.

Original problem	Dual problem
n variables	n inequalities
m inequalities	m variables
Coefficients of the objective function	Right-side constants
Right-side constants	Coefficients of the objective function
Coefficients in the ith inequality	Coefficients of the ith variable
Coefficients of the jth variable	Coefficients in the jth inequality

For example, the matrix form of the dual of problem (4.21) is

$$\text{Minimize} \quad (y_1 \quad y_2 \quad y_3) \begin{pmatrix} 36 \\ 48 \\ 42 \end{pmatrix}$$

$$\text{Subject to} \quad (y_1 \quad y_2 \quad y_3) \begin{pmatrix} 3 & 2 \\ 2 & 1 \\ 1 & 4 \end{pmatrix} \geq (4 \quad 3)$$

$$(y_1 \quad y_2 \quad y_3) \geq (0 \quad 0 \quad 0)$$

Thus the dual of (4.21) can be written as

$$\text{Minimize} \quad 36y_1 + 48y_2 + 42y_3$$
$$\text{Subject to} \quad 3y_1 + 2y_2 + y_3 \geq 4$$
$$2y_1 + y_2 + 4y_3 \geq 3$$
$$y_1 \geq 0, y_2 \geq 0, y_3 \geq 0$$

EXAMPLE 22

The dual of the problem in Example 21 is

$$\text{Minimize} \quad 150y_1 + 120y_2$$
$$\text{Subject to} \quad y_1 + 2y_2 \geq 8$$
$$3y_1 + y_2 \geq 9$$
$$y_1 \geq 0, y_2 \geq 0$$

EXAMPLE 23

The dual of the problem

$$\text{Minimize} \quad 40y_1 + 50y_2$$
$$\text{Subject to} \quad 25y_1 + 20y_2 \geq 320$$
$$3y_1 + 4y_2 \geq 48$$
$$y_1 + 4y_2 \geq 24$$
$$y_1 \geq 0, y_2 \geq 0$$

is

$$\text{Maximize} \quad 320x_1 + 48x_2 + 24x_3$$
$$\text{Subject to} \quad 25x_1 + 3x_2 + x_3 \leq 40$$
$$20x_1 + 4x_2 + 4x_3 \leq 50$$
$$x_1 \geq 0, x_2 \geq 0, x_3 \geq 0$$

The pair of dual problems in Examples 21 and 22 was solved in Exercise 24 of Section 4.6. There the maximum value of $8x_1 + 9x_2$ in the set of feasible solutions was found to be 660 when $x_1 = 42$ and $x_2 = 36$, and the minimum value of $150y_1 + 120y_2$ in the set of feasible solutions was found to be 660 when $y_1 = 2$ and $y_2 = 3$. The fact that the optimal value of each objective function is 660 is no coincidence, as the following theorem shows.

THEOREM 4.4

If both members of a pair of dual linear programming problems have feasible solutions, then optimal solutions exist for both problems. Moreover, the optimal values of the objective functions in the two problems are the same.

Surprisingly, the simplex method makes implicit use of duality. In fact, solving either of a pair of dual problems by the simplex method automatically produces a solution to the dual problem as well: *In the final simplex tableau the optimal values for the variables in the dual problem are found in the bottom row of the columns containing the slack variables.* For example, the pair of dual problems in Examples 21 and 22 was solved by the simplex method in Exercise 24 of Section 4.6. The final tableau for the maximization problem is

$$\begin{array}{c c c c c c | c}
 & x_1 & x_2 & r & s & P & \\
x_2 & 0 & 1 & 0.4 & -0.2 & 0 & 36 \\
x_1 & 1 & 0 & -0.2 & 0.6 & 0 & 42 \\
\hline
 & 0 & 0 & 2.0 & 3.0 & 1 & 660
\end{array}$$

and so the solution to the minimization problem is $y_1 = 2$ and $y_2 = 3$. Likewise, the optimal solution, $x_1 = 42$ and $x_2 = 36$, to the maximum problem can be read from the final tableau for (phase II of) the minimization problem:

$$\begin{array}{c} \\ y_2 \\ y_1 \\ \\ \end{array} \left(\begin{array}{ccccc|c} y_1 & y_2 & r & s & P & \\ 0 & 1 & -0.6 & 0.2 & 0 & 3 \\ 1 & 0 & 0.2 & -0.4 & 0 & 2 \\ \hline 0 & 0 & 42.0 & 36.0 & 1 & -660 \end{array} \right)$$

The optimal values of the variables in the dual problem have a significant interpretation in the context of the original problem. The meaning of the optimal values of the dual variables in a maximization problem is this: Each dual variable measures the rate at which the objective function will change per unit increase in the right-side constant of the corresponding inequality. Consequently each dual variable represents the maximum price per unit that can profitably be paid in order to increase the available amount of the corresponding resource.[6]

For example, in the maximization problem in Exercise 24 in Section 4.6 and Example 21, an increase of 1 unit in the right-side constant of the first inequality will produce an increase in the objective function equal to the value of y_1. So increasing the right-side constant from 150 to 151 will increase the maximum profit from $660 to $662. (The new optimal solution will be $x_1 = 41.8$ and $x_2 = 36.4$.) Likewise, increasing the right-side constant in the second inequality from 120 to 121 will increase the objective function by $3, the value of y_2. (The new optimal solution will be $x_1 = 42.6$ and $x_2 = 35.8$.) Thus if the factory decides to devote more time to shaping or painting and *if the additional time does not change the solution to the dual problem*, the factory can afford to pay up to $2 per minute for additional shaping time and up to $3 per minute for additional painting time without loss of profit.

EXAMPLE 24

The dual of the problem in Example 15 is

Minimize $\quad 44y_1 + 40y_2 + 48y_3$
Subject to $\quad 0.3y_1 + 0.1y_2 + 0.2y_3 \geq 10$
$\qquad\qquad\quad 0.2y_1 + 0.4y_2 + 0.4y_3 \geq 14$
$\qquad\qquad\quad 0.1y_1 + 0.1y_2 + 0.2y_3 \geq 7$
$\qquad\qquad\quad y_1 \geq 0, y_2 \geq 0, y_3 \geq 0$

From (4.11) we see that the minimum value of $44y_1 + 40y_2 + 48y_3$ is 1980 and that it is attained when $y_1 = 15$, $y_2 = 0$, and $y_3 = 27.50$.

---

[6] In this context the dual variables are often called *shadow prices*.

In the context of Example 15 we see that adding an additional hour of time for sanding will increase the factory's profit by $15.00, and adding an additional hour of time for varnishing will increase its profit by $27.50. On the other hand, adding an additional hour of time for staining will not increase the factory's profit because there are already 2 hours of time for staining that are not being utilized.

Exercises

For Exercises 1–10, write the duals of the linear programming problems in Exercises 1–10 of Section 4.4.

11. Write the dual of the linear programming problem in Exercise 15 in Section 4.6.
12. Write the dual of the linear programming problem in Exercise 16 in Section 4.6.
13. Write the dual of the linear programming problem in Exercise 19 in Section 4.6.
14. Write the dual of the linear programming problem in Exercise 18 in Section 4.6.

For Exercises 15–24, use the results of Exercises 1–10 in Section 4.5 to solve the linear programming problems in Exercises 1–10 above.

25. Use the result of Exercise 19 in Section 4.6 to solve the linear programming problem in Exercise 13 above.
26. Use the result of Exercise 16 in Section 4.6 to solve the linear programming problem in Exercise 12 above.
27. In Exercise 15 in Section 4.5, how much additional profit could the manufacturer expect if there were an additional 10 hours of finishing time available?
28. Use the result of Exercise 18 in Section 4.6 to solve the linear programming problem in Exercise 14 above.
29. In Exercise 17 in Section 4.5, how much additional profit could the chemical company expect if it were allowed to emit an additional 10 pounds of carbon monoxide per week?
30. In Exercise 16 in Section 4.5, how much additional profit could the merchant receive if there were an additional 60 pounds of cashews available?
31. In Exercise 21 in Section 4.6, what would be the reduction in cost if the jeweler wanted to devote at least 27 hours to polishing instead of at least 30 hours?
32. In Exercise 18 in Section 4.5, how much additional profit could be earned by the electronics company if there were an additional 4 hours available for packaging?
33. In Exercise 23 in Section 4.6, what would be the reduction in cost if only 48 units of supplement R were required instead of 50 units?
34. In Exercise 20 in Section 4.6, what would be the additional cost if an additional 15 units of iron were required in the diet?

Chapter Review

New Terms

artificial variable (p. 159)
basic feasible solution (p. 142)
bounded feasible set (p. 130)
constraints (p. 127)
dual linear programming problem (p. 173)
feasible set (p.122)
half-plane (p. 118)
linear inequality (p. 118)
nonbinding constraint (p. 134)
objective function (p. 129)

pivot (p. 149)
pivot column (p. 148)
pivot element (p. 149)
pivot row (p. 149)
set of feasible solutions (p. 122)
simplex method (p. 151)
simplex tableau (p. 147)
slack variable (p. 141)
two-phase method (p. 160)
unbounded feasible set (p. 130)
vertex of a feasible set (p. 130)

Review Exercises

1. Label the following statements true or false.
   (a) If $a \neq 0$ and $b \neq 0$, the graph of the linear inequality $ax + by > c$ is the upper half-plane determined by the line $ax + by = c$.
   (b) The graph of the linear inequality $ax + by \leq c$, where $a \neq 0$ or $b \neq 0$, consists of all points on the line $ax + by = c$ and all points in one of the half-planes determined by the line.
   (c) In a linear programming problem the objective function always assumes a maximum and a minimum value in the feasible set.
   (d) The maximum or minimum value of the objective function in a linear programming problem can only occur at a vertex of the feasible set.
   (e) When a linear programming problem has a solution, the solution is unique.
   (f) In a linear programming problem containing no artificial variables, if every entry of the bottom row of a simplex tableau is nonnegative except possibly the last entry, then the optimum value of the objective function occurs at the basic feasible solution associated with the tableau.
   *(g) The optimal value of the objective function in a pair of dual linear programming problems is the same.
   *(h) The optimal value of each dual variable measures the rate at which the objective function will change per unit increase in the right-side constant of the corresponding inequality of the original problem.

2. Graph each of the following linear inequalities.
   (a) $3x + 7y > 42$
   (b) $5x - 3y < 30$
   (c) $5x + 2y \leq 20$
   (d) $3x - 8y \geq 48$

3. Graph each of the following systems of linear inequalities.
   (a) $x - 3y > -8$
   $2x + y \geq -9$
   $3x - y \leq 24$
   $y > -3$
   (b) $x + y \leq 15$
   $x + 4y > 36$
   $y \geq 2x$
   $x > -4$

Solve the linear programming problems in Exercises 4–6 geometrically.

4. (a) Maximize $6x + 7y$
Subject to $2x + 3y \leq 360$
$x + y \leq 150$
$x \geq 0, y \geq 0$

(b) Minimize $x + 2y$
Subject to $2x + 3y \geq 90$
$4x + y \geq 80$
$x + y \leq 35$
$x \geq 0, y \geq 0$

5. Each unit of product A requires 4 minutes on a milling machine and 4 minutes on a lathe, and each unit of product B requires 3 minutes on a milling machine and 5 minutes on a lathe. One unit of either product yields a profit of $1.50. If there are at most 1200 minutes available on a milling machine and at most 1600 minutes available on a lathe, how many of each product should be made for a maximum profit? What is the maximum profit?

6. An insurance company with offices in Baltimore and Cleveland wants to send teams of management personnel to regional sales meetings in Pittsburgh, Wheeling, and Philadelphia. It intends to send the same number of teams from Baltimore to each of the three meetings; however, each team sent to Pittsburgh and Wheeling will consist of a single person, whereas each team sent to Philadelphia will consist of three individuals. Likewise the company intends to send the same number of teams from Cleveland to each of the three meetings, but whereas a team sent to Wheeling or Philadelphia will consist of a single person, a team sent to Pittsburgh will consist of two people. The transportation cost of sending a team from Baltimore is $50, and the transportation cost of sending a team from Cleveland is $40. If the company wants to send at least 20 people to Pittsburgh, at least 16 people to Wheeling, and at least 30 people to Philadelphia, how many teams should be sent to each meeting from Baltimore and Cleveland in order to minimize the transportation costs?

Solve the linear programming problems in Exercises 7–9 by the simplex method.

7. (a) Maximize $6x + 8y + 3z$
Subject to $2x + 4y + 3z \leq 228$
$5x + 6y + 7z \leq 280$
$x + 2y - z \leq 84$
$x \geq 0, y \geq 0, z \geq 0$

(b) Minimize $5x + 4y + 6z$
Subject to $3y + 5z \leq 125$
$5x + 2y + 2z \leq 150$
$x + y + z \geq 15$
$x \geq 0, y \geq 0, z \geq 0$

8. A company manufactures mouthwash, which it sells in small, medium, and large bottles. Each small bottle requires 1 minute on the filling machine and 1 minute on the labeling machine; each medium-sized bottle requires 2 minutes on the filling machine and 1 minute on the labeling machine; and each large bottle requires 3 minutes on the filling machine and 2 minutes on the labeling machine. The profit on each small bottle is $0.30, the profit on each medium-sized bottle is $0.40, and the profit on each large bottle is $0.60. If the filling machine is available for at most 120 minutes and the labeling machine is available for at most 100 minutes, what combination of bottles should be filled and labeled for a maximum profit? What is the maximum profit?

9. A company is committed to developing a new product line in its Boston, Minneapolis, and Seattle plants. Manufacturing one unit requires 0.4 hour in Boston and Seattle and 0.3 hour in Minneapolis; packaging one unit requires 0.3 hour in Minneapolis and Seattle and 0.2 hour in Boston; and inspecting one unit requires 0.1 hour in Minneapolis and Seattle and 0.2 hour in Boston. The company is committed to a total of at least 660 hours of manufacturing time, at least 240 hours of packaging time, and at least 180 hours of inspection time at the three plants. If the cost per unit for this product is $20 in Boston, $18 in Minneapolis, and $16 in Seattle, how many units should be produced in each city in order to minimize the total cost? What is the minimum cost?

References

1. Adams, F. Gerard and James M. Griffin, "Economic Linear Programming Model of the U.S. Petroleum Refining Industry," *J. Am. Stat. Assoc.*, vol. 67 (September 1972), pp. 542–551.
2. Allman, William P., "An Optimization Approach to Freight Car Allocation Under Time-Mileage Per Diem Rental Rates," *Manage. Sci.*, vol. 18, no. 10 (June 1972), pp. B567–B574.
3. Broaddus, A., "Linear Programming: A New Approach to Bank Portfolio Management," *Fed. Reserve Bank Richmond: Mon. Rev.*, vol. 58, no. 11 (November 1972), pp. 3–11.
4. Cohen, K. J. and F. S. Hammer, "Linear Programming and Optimal Bank Asset Management Decisions," *J. Finan.*, vol. 22 (May 1967), pp. 147–165.
5. Cooper, Leon and David Steinberg, *Methods and Applications of Linear Programming*. Philadelphia: Saunders, 1974.
6. Crandall, Robert H., "A Constrained Choice Model for Student Housing," *Manage. Sci.*, vol. 16, no. 2 (October 1969), pp. B112–B120.
7. Hanssmann, Fred and Sidney W. Hess, "A Linear Programming Approach to Production and Employment Scheduling," *Manage. Technol.*, vol. 1 (January 1960), pp. 46–51.
8. Kohn, Robert E., "Application of Linear Programming to a Controversy on Air Pollution Control," *Manage. Sci.*, vol. 17, no. 10 (June 1971), pp. B609–B621.
9. Lee, Sang M. and Edward R. Clayton, "Goal Programming Model for Academic Resource Allocation," *Manage. Sci.*, vol. 18, no. 8 (April 1972), pp. B395–B408.
10. Loucks, Daniel P., Charles S. Revelle, and Walter R. Lynn, "Linear Programming Models for Water Pollution Control," *Manage. Sci.*, vol. 14, no. 4 (December 1967), pp. B166–B181.
11. Raun, Donald L., "Product-Mix Analysis by Linear Programming," *Manage. Account.*, vol. 47, pp. 3–13.
12. Spivey, W. Allen and Robert M. Thrall, *Linear Optimization*. New York: Holt, 1970.
13. Sweeney, Robert B., "Business Use of Linear Programming," *Manage. Account.* (September 1965), pp. 39–47.

14. Thomas, Harold A., Jr., and Roger Revelle, "On the Efficient Use of High Aswan Dam for Hydropower and Irrigation," *Manage. Sci.*, vol. 12, no. 8 (April 1966), pp. B296–B311.
15. Wardle, P. A., "Forest Management and Operations Research: A Linear Programming Study," *Manage. Sci.*, vol. 11, no. 10 (August 1965), pp. B260–B270.

5
An Introduction to Statistics

In the year 1977, an average American household consisted of 2.86 persons, had an annual income of $16,009, and owned 1.35 cars and 1.59 television sets. Statements such as these are statistical statements that describe an imaginary "typical" family.

statistics

Statistics is concerned with the collection, organization, analysis, and interpretation of numerical data. As the fields of business and social science have become more quantified, their use of statistics has greatly increased. Business executives, for example, rely on statistical data to analyze problems and to make decisions, psychologists use statistical methods to design and study behavioral experiments, and political scientists use sophisticated sampling procedures to measure public opinion.

descriptive statistics

inferential statistics

There are two main branches of statistics. *Descriptive statistics* is concerned with collecting, organizing, and summarizing data, whereas *inferential statistics* is concerned with drawing conclusions from data. In this chapter we shall primarily discuss topics from descriptive statistics, but one topic from inferential statistics will be presented in Section 5.3.

5.1 Frequency Distributions

In this section we shall be concerned with organizing given sets of data into forms that will permit easier interpretation. Without such organization, raw data are often incomprehensible. Consider, for example, Table

Table 5.1 Scores Obtained by College Algebra Students on a Basic Algebra Examination

16	20	16	17	21	22
10	14	13	8	11	17
17	16	22	17	19	18
17	17	23	21	19	13
22	21	13	20	11	13

Table 5.2 Distribution of Scores Obtained by College Algebra Students on a Basic Algebra Examination

Interval	Tally	Frequency	Relative frequency
6.5– 9.5	|	1	0.03
9.5–12.5	|||	3	0.10
12.5–15.5	⧗⧘	5	0.17
15.5–18.5	⧗⧘ ⧗⧘	10	0.33
18.5–21.5	⧗⧘ ||	7	0.23
21.5–24.5	||||	4	0.13

5.1, which lists the number of questions answered correctly by each student in a college algebra class on a basic algebra examination.

In order to better organize these data, let us group the 30 individual scores into intervals according to size. The choice of intervals will be made in accordance with the following general rules:

1. Every score should lie in exactly one interval.
2. If possible, the intervals should be of equal length.
3. The upper endpoint of one interval should equal the lower endpoint of the next interval.
4. The number of intervals should be large enough to show the distribution of the scores yet small enough to simplify analysis of the data. As a rule of thumb, the number of intervals should be between 5 and 15.

Since the largest of the scores in Table 5.1 is 23 and the smallest is 8, all the scores can be included in 6 intervals of width 3. Although it may seem natural to use intervals such as 6–9, 9–12, 12–15, 15–18, 18–21, and 21–24 to group the scores, such a choice violates the first of the rules above because certain scores (namely, 9, 12, 15, 18, and 21) will lie in more than one interval. Instead, we choose the intervals 6.5–9.5, 9.5–12.5, 12.5–15.5, 15.5–18.5, 18.5–21.5, and 21.5–24.5. With these intervals the data in Table 5.1 can be grouped as in Table 5.2.

5.1 Frequency Distributions

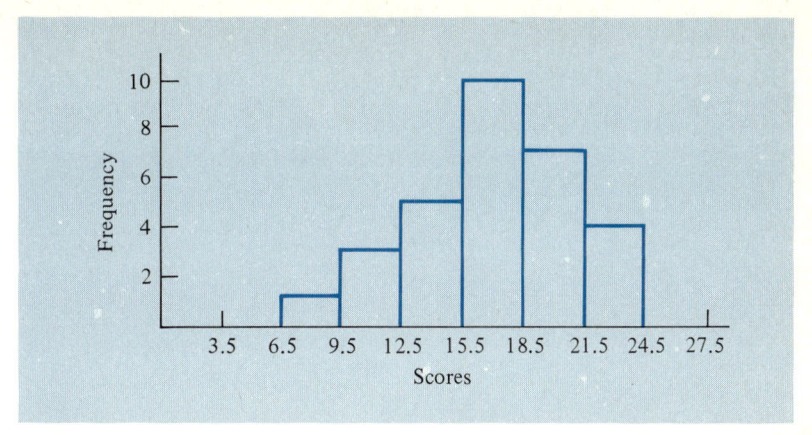

Figure 5.1

frequency

frequency distribution
relative frequency

The number of measurements that lie in an interval is called the *frequency* of the interval. Consequently the collection of all the intervals and their frequencies (such as is presented in Table 5.2) is called a *frequency distribution*. The *relative frequency* of an interval is found by dividing the frequency of the interval by the total number of pieces of data (30 in the case of Table 5.2). Thus the relative frequency of any interval is the proportion of the data that lie within the interval.

Although tables express information precisely, trends or relationships in data are often difficult to detect from a table. Graphs, on the other hand, may not present the data as accurately as tables (because it is sometimes possible to read only approximate values from a graph), yet they display trends and relationships more easily.

histogram

The most common way of depicting a frequency distribution is with a form of bar graph called a *histogram*. In a histogram the endpoints of the intervals used to group the data are plotted on the horizontal axis and the interval frequencies (or relative frequencies) are plotted on the vertical axis. Figure 5.1 shows a histogram for the frequency distribution in Table 5.2. Observe that it is customary to include one interval with zero frequency at both the left and right ends of the histogram. For the data in Table 5.2 it is easy to include the entire horizontal and vertical scales. Sometimes, however, it is convenient to omit a portion of either the horizontal or vertical scale; in such a case the omission is indicated by the symbol ⌇.

EXAMPLE 1

Table 5.3 contains the number of tornadoes reported in the United States for each year during the period 1953–1977.

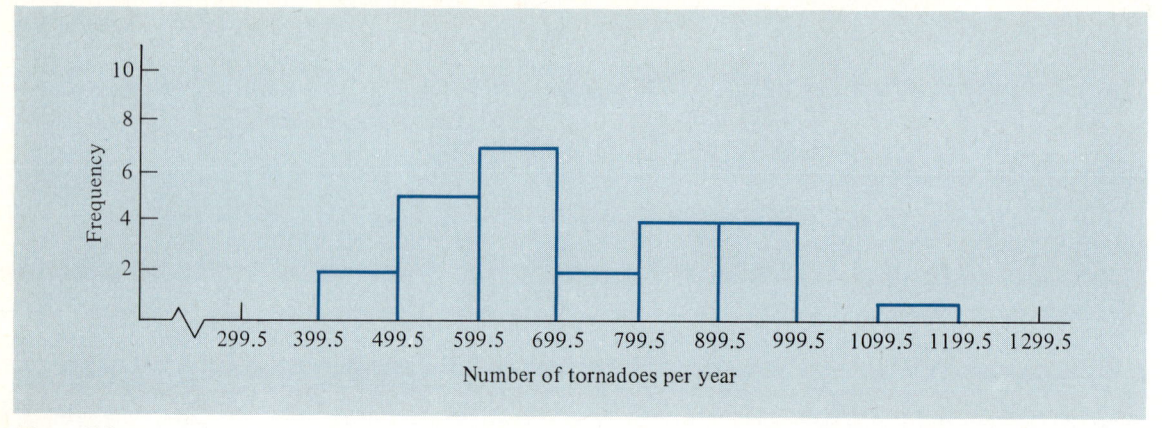

Figure 5.2

Table 5.3 *Number of Tornadoes Reported in the United States, 1953–1977*

1953-422	1958-563	1963-461	1968-660	1973-1109
1954-550	1959-604	1964-703	1969-608	1974- 945
1955-595	1960-616	1965-901	1970-652	1975- 920
1956-503	1961-698	1966-585	1971-889	1976- 835
1957-856	1962-658	1967-929	1972-741	1977- 852

Source: The World Almanac and Book of Facts. New York: Newspaper Enterprise Association, 1979.

Since the largest entry in Table 5.3 is 1109 and the smallest is 422, we can organize these data in eight intervals of width 100. One such arrangement is contained in Table 5.4.

Table 5.4 *Frequency Distribution for the Number of Tornadoes Reported in the United States, 1953–1977*

Interval	Tally	Frequency	Relative frequency
399.5– 499.5	||	2	0.08
499.5– 599.5	⋈	5	0.20
599.5– 699.5	⋈ ||	7	0.28
699.5– 799.5	||	2	0.08
799.5– 899.5	||||	4	0.16
899.5– 999.5	||||	4	0.16
999.5–1099.5		0	0.00
1099.5–1199.5	|	1	0.04

A histogram for the distribution in Table 5.4 is shown in Figure 5.2.

5.1 Frequency Distributions

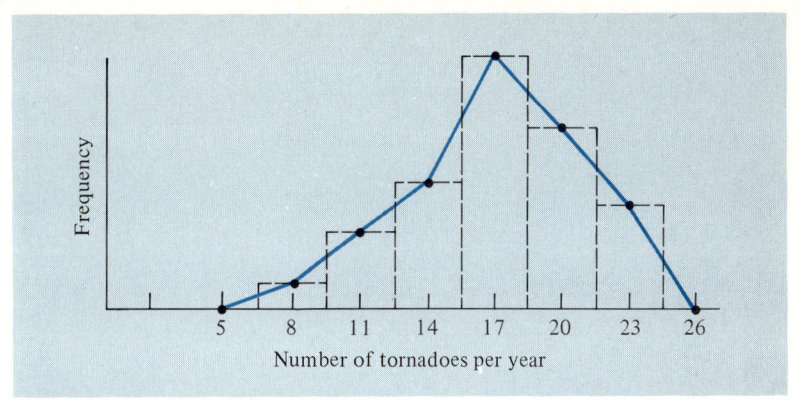

Figure 5.3

frequency polygon

A *frequency polygon* is a broken-line graph which can be constructed by connecting the midpoints of the tops of adjacent bars in a histogram with straight-line segments. Of course, it is possible to draw a frequency polygon without first constructing a histogram; to do so merely requires plotting the frequency of each interval at the midpoint of the interval and joining successive points by line segments. Since the first and last intervals have zero frequencies, the first and last points on the frequency polygon will always lie on the horizontal axis.

EXAMPLE 2

Figure 5.3 shows a frequency polygon for the data in Table 5.2 superimposed on a histogram for these data (as shown in Figure 5.1).

EXAMPLE 3

The frequency of marriage among 1000 American women of various age groups is listed in Table 5.5. (These data are based on information from the 1970 census.)

Table 5.5 *Frequency of Marriage Among 1000 American Women of Various Age Groups*

Age	15–20	20–25	25–30	30–35	35–40	40–45	45–50
Number of marriages per thousand	88.2	237.1	129.2	60.6	38.5	22.2	14.5

Figure 5.4 shows a frequency polygon for these data.

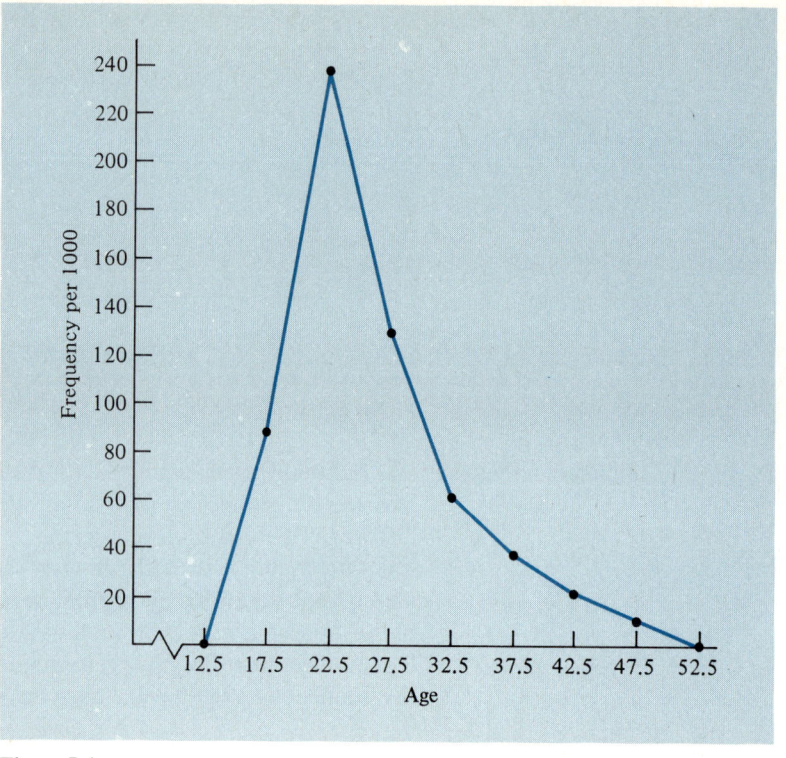

Figure 5.4

Exercises

In Exercises 1–6 construct a histogram and a frequency polygon for the given frequency distributions.

1. In 1969, the 150 largest corporations in the United States had net incomes (expressed as a percentage of their sales) distributed as follows.[1]

Net income (percentage of sales)	Number of corporations	Net income (percentage of sales)	Number of corporations
0–1	8	6–7	12
1–2	8	7–8	10
2–3	18	8–9	9
3–4	25	9–10	4
4–5	30	10–11	5
5–6	19	11–12	2

2. An experiment described in [3] required school superintendents to respond to 37 items on a questionnaire with one of five responses: (1) abso-

---

[1] These data were tabulated from *Fortune* (May 15, 1968), vol. 79, no. 6, pp. 166–185.

lutely must, (2) preferably should, (3) may or may not, (4) preferably should not, or (5) absolutely must not. Responses (1) and (5) were regarded as being moralistic. The total number of moralistic responses given by the subjects was as follows:

Number of moralistic responses	Number of subjects	Number of moralistic responses	Number of subjects
0.5–3.5	5	15.5–18.5	15
3.5–6.5	11	18.5–21.5	10
6.5–9.5	10	21.5–24.5	8
9.5–12.5	18	24.5–27.5	4
12.5–15.5	23	27.5–30.5	1

3. The length of service by Supreme Court justices (excluding those presently serving) is distributed as follows:

Years of service	Number of justices	Years of service	Number of justices
0–3	10	18–21	10
3–6	15	21–24	5
6–9	11	24–27	5
9–12	4	27–30	5
12–15	12	30–33	5
15–18	8	33–36	4

4. The record low temperatures for all states and the District of Columbia are distributed as follows:

Low temperature (degrees Fahrenheit)	Number of states	Low temperature (degrees Fahrenheit)	Number of states
−80.5 to −70.5	1	−30.5 to −20.5	7
−70.5 to −60.5	2	−20.5 to −10.5	6
−60.5 to −50.5	9	−10.5 to −0.5	1
−50.5 to −40.5	11	−0.5 to 9.5	0
−40.5 to −30.5	13	9.5 to 19.5	1

5. The record high temperatures for each state and the District of Columbia are distributed as follows:

High temperature (degrees Fahrenheit)	Number of states	High temperature (degrees Fahrenheit)	Number of states
99.5–102.5	2	117.5–120.5	11
102.5–105.5	4	120.5–123.5	3
105.5–108.5	4	123.5–126.5	0
108.5–111.5	8	126.5–129.5	1
111.5–114.5	11	129.5–132.5	0
114.5–117.5	6	132.5–135.5	1

6. The distribution of IQ scores in the standardization group for the 1937 Stanford-Binet intelligence test was as follows:

IQ	Percentage	IQ	Percentage
29.5–39.5	0.03	99.5–109.5	23.5
39.5–49.5	0.2	109.5–119.5	18.1
49.5–59.5	0.4	119.5–129.5	8.2
59.5–69.5	2.0	129.5–139.5	3.1
69.5–79.5	5.6	139.5–149.5	1.1
79.5–89.5	14.5	149.5–159.5	0.2
89.5–99.5	23.0	159.5–169.5	0.03

In Exercises 7–12 construct a frequency distribution, compute the relative frequency of each interval, and form a histogram and frequency polygon for the given data.

7. The ages of the 38 United States presidents at the time of their first inauguration were as follows:

57	57	49	52	50	51	51	55
61	61	64	56	47	56	50	61
57	54	50	46	55	55	62	52
57	68	48	54	54	51	43	
58	51	65	49	42	54	55	

8. During the period July 1 through December 31, 1977, the circulation of the leading U.S. magazines was as follows:

Magazine	Circulation	Magazine	Circulation
American Legion	2,616,027	Penthouse	4,606,134
Better Homes and Gardens	8,056,355	People	2,394,979
Cosmopolitan	2,581,157	Playboy	4,970,753
Family Circle	8,498,517	Reader's Digest	18,371,000
Good Housekeeping	5,170,007	Redbook	4,613,908
Ladies' Home Journal	6,004,334	Senior Scholastic	2,927,108
McCall's	6,512,186	Star	2,708,495
National Enquirer	5,208,375	Time	4,273,962
National Geographic	9,756,312	TV Guide	20,443,254
Newsweek	2,947,406	Woman's Day	8,404,618

9. In [1] Anderson reports the IQ scores of 26 children prior to a nursery school experience to be as follows:

108	107	93	128	133	126	125
117	113	115	111	122	100	100
139	108	117	127	119	150	
117	108	95	111	127	86	

10. The number of deaths in the United States caused by tornadoes for each year during the period 1953–1977 is as follows:

515	66	31	131	87
36	58	73	66	361
126	47	296	72	60
83	51	99	156	44
191	28	114	27	43

11. The number of home runs hit by the leading home run hitter in the American League during each season from 1936 to 1977 was as follows:

49	36	39	32	40	49	37
46	34	43	37	61	44	32
58	22	37	52	48	44	32
35	24	33	42	45	49	36
41	44	32	42	49	44	32
37	32	43	42	32	33	39

12. The number of points scored by the leading scorer in the National Football League for each season during the period 1935–1976 was as follows:

55	95	102	114	94	132	117
73	138	110	114	176	119	128
69	117	102	96	147	117	130
58	85	128	99	137	145	94
68	110	102	77	113	129	138
57	100	94	108	155	125	109

5.2 Measures of Central Tendency and Measures of Dispersion

In Section 5.1 we saw that the use of graphs made it possible to depict data in a more readily understood form. Often, however, it is necessary to compare two or more sets of data, and for this purpose graphs are of only limited value. What is needed to compare different sets of data are numerical measures that describe the data. The most common of such measures are *measures of central tendency*, which locate an approximate center of the data, and *measures of dispersion*, which indicate the amount of spread around a central point.

We begin this section by discussing three measures of central tendency that describe the size of a "typical" piece of data in different ways.

The most useful and most common measure of central tendency is the *mean* (or *average*). To compute the mean of n numbers $x_1, x_2, \ldots, x_n$, we divide their sum by n. If we denote the mean of the numbers $x_1, x_2, \ldots, x_n$ by the Greek letter mu (μ), then the mean is defined by

$$\mu = \frac{x_1 + x_2 + \cdots + x_n}{n} \tag{5.1}$$

EXAMPLE 4

A student received grades of 84, 94, 87, and 79 on four hourly examinations. Her mean (average) score is therefore

$$\frac{84 + 94 + 87 + 79}{4} = \frac{344}{4} = 86$$

As we saw in Section 5.1, it is helpful to group raw data into intervals when considering a large number of pieces of data. For grouped data the mean can be approximated by assuming that each value lies at the midpoint of the interval containing it. Thus if there are n pieces of data grouped into k intervals, and if m_i and f_i denote the midpoint and frequency of the ith interval, then the mean μ of the data is approximated by

$$\mu \approx \frac{f_1 m_1 + f_2 m_2 + \cdots + f_k m_k}{n} \tag{5.2}$$

EXAMPLE 5

For the grouped data in Table 5.2, the midpoints of the six intervals are 8, 11, 14, 17, 20, and 23. So we can arrange the data as follows:

Interval	Midpoint m_i	Frequency f_i	Product $f_i m_i$
6.5–9.5	8	1	8
9.5–12.5	11	3	33
12.5–15.5	14	5	70
15.5–18.5	17	10	170
18.5–21.5	20	7	140
21.5–24.5	23	4	92
Total	—	30	513

Hence by (5.2)

$$\mu \approx \tfrac{513}{30} = 17.1$$

For comparison, if the exact value of μ is computed directly from the raw data in Table 5.1 by using Equation (5.1), we obtain (by a much more tedious calculation)

$$\mu = \tfrac{504}{30} = 16.8$$

median   The *median* of a set of data is found by arranging the data in either increasing or decreasing order and selecting the "middle" term. When the number of pieces of data is odd, there is a unique middle term and consequently it is the median. When the number of pieces of data is even, however, there are two "middle" terms, and in this case the median is defined to be the average of these two values. For example, the median score for the student described in Example 4 is

$$\frac{84 + 87}{2} = 85.5$$

EXAMPLE 6

To find the medians of the two sets of data

(a) 10, 2, 8, 7, 4, 5, 3
(b) 9, 9, 1, 3, 10, 5, 3, 6

we first arrange each list in increasing order. These orderings are

(a) 2, 3, 4, 5, 7, 8, 10
(b) 1, 3, 3, 5, 6, 9, 9, 10

In list (a) there are seven pieces of data (an odd number), and so the fourth number in the ordered list (5) is the unique middle term. Thus 5 is the median of (a).

In list (b) there are eight pieces of data (an even number). In this case there is no single middle term, but rather both the fourth and fifth numbers in the ordered list (5 and 6) are middle terms. Consequently, the median of (b) is $(5 + 6)/2 = 5.5$.

Note that the mean of a set of numbers is affected by every number in the set, whereas the median is unaffected by extremely large or extremely small values. Consequently the median will often be more typical of the data than the mean if the data set contains a few abnormally large or small values. Consider, for example, the data in Table 5.6. The median population of these 10 cities is 68,950.5, and the mean population is 145,765. In this case (because of the abnormally large population of Baltimore in comparison to the other nine cities), the median population represents the data better than the mean population.

Table 5.6 *Population of the 10 Largest Cities in Maryland (Based on the 1970 Census)*

Baltimore	905,759	Wheaton	66,280
Dundalk	85,377	Catonsville	54,812
Towson	77,768	Rockville	41,821
Silver Spring	77,411	Glen Burnie	38,608
Bethesda	71,621	Essex	38,193

The median occurs much less often than the mean in connection with grouped data. Thus, since the procedure for estimating the median of grouped data is somewhat complicated, we shall not discuss it here.

mode   The least common measure of central tendency, the *mode*, is simply the entry that occurs most frequently. For example, the mode of the scores in Table 5.1 is 17, since there are more scores of 17 (six)

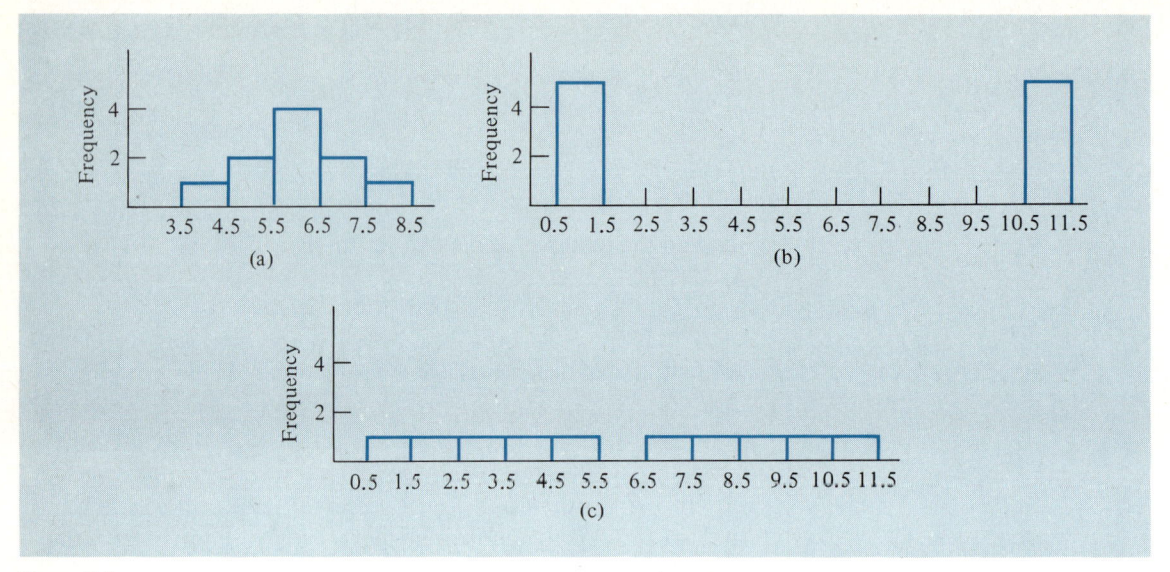

Figure 5.5

than any other. The mode is usually easy to determine and, like the median, is unaffected by abnormally large or small values. On the other hand, the mode has two significant disadvantages: It does not exist if all the data occur with the same frequency [as in list (a) in Example 6], and there may be more than one mode [as in list (b) in Example 6, in which both 3 and 9 are modes].

Similarly, in a frequency distribution, the interval having the largest frequency is called the *modal class*. In Table 5.4, for instance, the interval 599.5–699.5 is the modal class.

modal class

Although the mean is undoubtedly the single most important number that can be used to describe a set of data, the mean alone is inadequate to give a complete representation of the data—it is also necessary to indicate the dispersion of the data around the mean. For example, the three sets of data

(a) 4, 5, 5, 6, 6, 6, 6, 7, 7, 8
(b) 1, 1, 1, 1, 1, 11, 11, 11, 11, 11
(c) 1, 2, 3, 4, 5, 7, 8, 9, 10, 11

all have means of 6. Yet the histograms of the three distributions, shown in Figure 5.5, are quite different.

Consider a set of data $x_1, x_2, \ldots, x_n$ with mean μ. Since we are interested in knowing how the data are distributed about the mean, we form the differences $x_1 - \mu, x_2 - \mu, \ldots, x_n - \mu$. It seems natural at first to measure the dispersion of the data as the average of these differences. However this average is always zero, since the positive and negative differences always offset each other. Instead, we consider the squares of the differences from the mean $(x_1 - \mu)^2, (x_2 - \mu)^2, \ldots, (x_n - \mu)^2$. The average of the differences is called the *variance* of

variance

the data.[2] Symbolically, the variance of $x_1, x_2, \ldots, x_n$ is defined by

$$\text{Variance} = \frac{(x_1 - \mu)^2 + (x_2 - \mu)^2 + \cdots + (x_n - \mu)^2}{n} \tag{5.3}$$

where μ denotes the mean of the data.

EXAMPLE 7

We shall compute the variance of the four test scores 84, 94, 87, and 79 in Example 4. Recall that the mean of these scores is 86. It is convenient to perform the calculations required to use Equation (5.3) as shown below.

Data x_i	Difference from the mean $x_i - \mu$	Square of the difference from the mean $(x_i - \mu)^2$
84	-2	4
94	8	64
87	1	1
79	-7	49
Total		118

Thus the variance of the four scores is $\frac{118}{4} = 29.5$.

EXAMPLE 8

Let us compute the variance of the three data sets shown in Figure 5.5. Recall that each data set has a mean of 6.

(a) x_i	$x_i - \mu$	$(x_i - \mu)^2$	(b) x_i	$x_i - \mu$	$(x_i - \mu)^2$	(c) x_i	$x_i - \mu$	$(x_i - \mu)^2$
4	-2	4	1	-5	25	1	-5	25
5	-1	1	1	-5	25	2	-4	16
5	-1	1	1	-5	25	3	-3	9
6	0	0	1	-5	25	4	-2	4
6	0	0	1	-5	25	5	-1	1
6	0	0	11	5	25	7	1	1
6	0	0	11	5	25	8	2	4
7	1	1	11	5	25	9	3	9
7	1	1	11	5	25	10	4	16
8	2	4	11	5	25	11	5	25
Total		12	Total		250	Total		110

Thus the variances are $\frac{12}{10} = 1.2$ for (a), $\frac{250}{10} = 25$ for (b), and $\frac{110}{10} = 11$ for (c).

These variances indicate that the data in (a) are clustered closely around the mean, the data in (c) are more dispersed, and the data in (b) are scattered even farther from the mean. These conclusions are consistent with the histograms shown in Figure 5.5.

---

[2] For technical reasons the variance is often computed by dividing the sum of the squares of the differences from the mean by $n - 1$ instead of n. Unless n is quite small, there will be little difference between the values computed by the two methods; so we divide by n for simplicity.

It is not difficult to see that, if each entry of a data set is multipled by the same number c, then the mean of the data is also multiplied by c. Unfortunately the corresponding statement about the variance is not true—if each entry of the data set is multiplied by c, then the variance is multiplied by c^2. In order to obtain a measure of dispersion that changes by a factor of c when the data are multiplied by c, we define the **standard deviation** to be the square root of the variance. The standard deviation of a data set is usually denoted by the Greek letter sigma (σ). Thus the standard deviation of a data set $x_1, x_2, \ldots, x_n$ with mean μ is defined by

$$\sigma = \sqrt{\frac{(x_1 - \mu)^2 + (x_2 - \mu)^2 + \cdots + (x_n - \mu)^2}{n}} \tag{5.4}$$

Observe that with this notation the variance is σ^2.

EXAMPLE 9

Since the variance of 84, 94, 87, and 79 is 29.5 from Example 7, the standard deviation of these numbers is $\sigma = \sqrt{29.5} \approx 5.43$.

EXAMPLE 10

We shall compute the mean and standard deviation of the numbers 24, 11, 8, 25, and 10. The mean is

$$\mu = \frac{24 + 11 + 8 + 25 + 10}{5} = \frac{78}{5} = 15.6$$

Next we compute the variance.

x_i	$x_i - \mu$	$(x_i - \mu)^2$
24	8.4	70.56
11	−4.6	21.16
8	−7.6	57.76
25	9.4	88.36
10	−5.6	31.36
Total		269.20

It follows from the calculations above that the variance is

$$\sigma^2 = \frac{269.20}{5} = 53.84$$

Hence the standard deviation is

$$\sigma = \sqrt{53.84} \approx 7.34$$

Just as we were able to approximate the mean for grouped data by assuming that each piece of data lay at the midpoint of the interval containing it, the same assumption will produce an approximation to the variance and standard deviation for grouped data. Specifically, if there are n pieces of data grouped into k intervals, and if m_i and f_i denote the midpoint and frequency of the ith interval, then the variance σ^2 of the data can be approximated by

$$\sigma^2 \approx \frac{(m_1 - \mu)^2 f_1 + (m_2 - \mu)^2 f_2 + \cdots + (m_k - \mu)^2 f_k}{n} \tag{5.5}$$

where μ is the mean of the data.[3]

EXAMPLE 11

Let us compute the standard deviation of the grouped data in Table 5.2. Recall from Example 5 that the mean of these data is $\mu \approx 17.1$. As usual it is helpful to arrange the calculations as shown below.

Interval	m_i	f_i	$m_i - \mu$	$(m_i - \mu)^2$	$(m_i - \mu)^2 f_i$
6.5– 9.5	8	1	−9.1	82.81	82.81
9.5–12.5	11	3	−6.1	37.21	111.63
12.5–15.5	14	5	−3.1	9.61	48.05
15.5–18.5	17	10	−0.1	0.01	0.10
18.5–21.5	20	7	2.9	8.41	58.87
21.5–24.5	23	4	5.9	34.81	139.24
Total	—	30	—	—	440.70

So from (5.5) the variance of the data is

$$\sigma^2 \approx \frac{440.70}{30} = 14.69$$

Hence the standard deviation is approximately $\sqrt{14.69} \approx 3.83$. By comparison, a much longer calculation of the exact value of σ using the data in Table 5.1 and (5.4) yields $\sigma = \sqrt{462.8/30} \approx 3.93$.

Exercises

In Exercises 1–8 determine the mean, median, mode (if it exists), and standard deviation for the given data sets.

1. 3, 7, 9, 4, 7
2. 3, 5, 7, 3, 7
3. 26, 38, 16, 32
4. 12, 9, 18, 21
5. 4, 10, 9, 4, 6, 9
6. 8, 7, 2, 6, 2, 11
7. 2, 6, 2, 7, 8, 6, 2, 7
8. 4, 12, 7, 9, 6, 5, 8, 13

For Exercises 9–20 estimate the mean and standard deviation for the frequency distributions found in Exercises 1–12 in Section 5.1.

---

[3] Equation (5.5) frequently underestimates the actual variance. For this reason, it is usually modified by adding $w^2/12$ to the right side, where w is the width of the interval used in grouping the data. In Example 11, for instance, the actual variance is $462.8/30 \approx 15.43$, whereas the approximate value from (5.5) is 14.69. By adding the correction term $3^2/12 = 0.75$, however, (5.5) yields a value of 15.44.

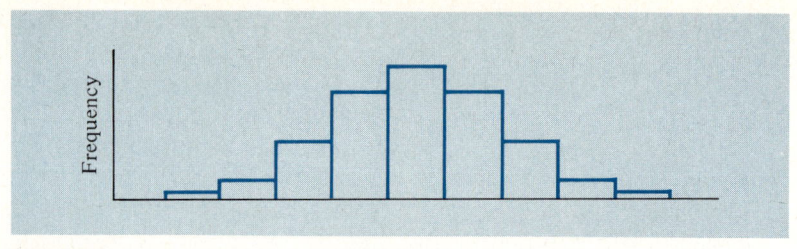

Figure 5.6

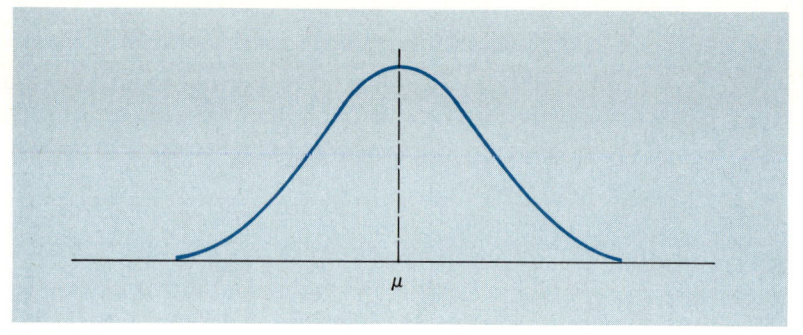

Figure 5.7

5.3 The Normal Distribution

It is surprising that the frequency distributions of many natural phenomena have the same basic shape. For example, if a histogram of the weights of all the women in a particular city were plotted, it would look very much like the one shown in Figure 5.6. Moreover the distribution of IQ scores in a particular elementary school would have a similar appearance. Consequently the distribution of many different phenomena can be described by the same mathematical model.

In this section we shall examine this model, which is called the *normal distribution*. A normal distribution is a bell-shaped curve as in Figure 5.7. Notice that this curve is symmetric with respect to a vertical line drawn through its highest point; this line passes through the point on the horizontal axis that corresponds to the mean of the distribution.

normal distribution

EXAMPLE 12

Scores on the 1960 revision of the Stanford-Binet intelligence test are normally distributed (i.e., distributed as in a normal distribution) with a mean of 100 and a standard deviation of 16. The distribution of these scores therefore appears as in Figure 5.8.

Even though a normal distribution is symmetrically distributed about its mean, there can be many different normal distributions having

5.3 The Normal Distribution

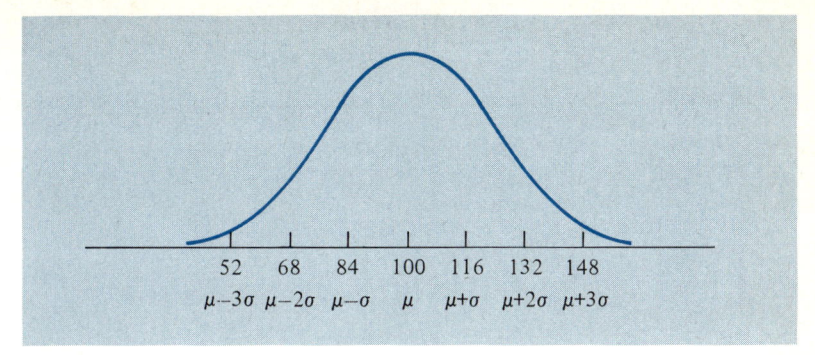

Figure 5.8

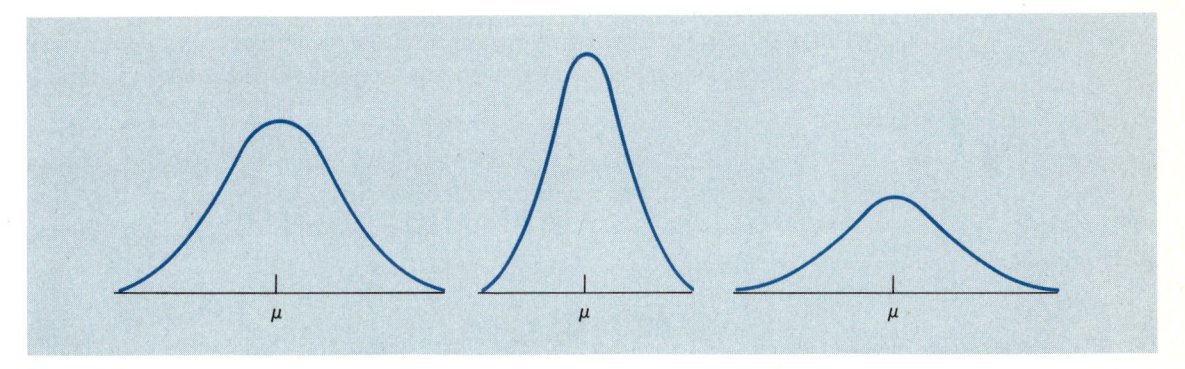

52 68 84 100 116 132 148
μ−3σ μ−2σ μ−σ μ μ+σ μ+2σ μ+3σ

Figure 5.9

μ   μ   μ

standard normal distribution

the same mean. Figure 5.9 shows three different normal distributions with the same mean μ. The difference between any two of these distributions is in the dispersion of the outcomes around the mean; that is, the difference in shape is caused by a difference in the standard deviation. In fact, it can be shown that for any given values of μ and σ there is only one normal distribution having those values as its mean and standard deviation.[4] The particular normal distribution with mean 0 and standard deviation 1 is called the *standard normal distribution*.

In any experiment with normally distributed outcomes, the proportion of the outcomes falling between values a and b is approximated by the area under the corresponding normal curve between the vertical lines $x = a$ and $x = b$. (See Figure 5.10.) We can determine such areas with the use of a table. Since the shape of a normal distribution depends on its standard deviation, it may at first seem necessary to have different tables for different standard deviations. But fortunately, the area under a normal distribution between the mean and a given number of standard deviations to the right (or left) of the mean is always the same. Thus

---

[4] The equation of the normal distribution with mean μ and standard deviation σ is $y = (1/\sigma\sqrt{2\pi}) e^{-(x-\mu)^2/2\sigma^2}$, where e and π are irrational numbers with values that equal approximately 2.71828 and 3.14159, respectively.

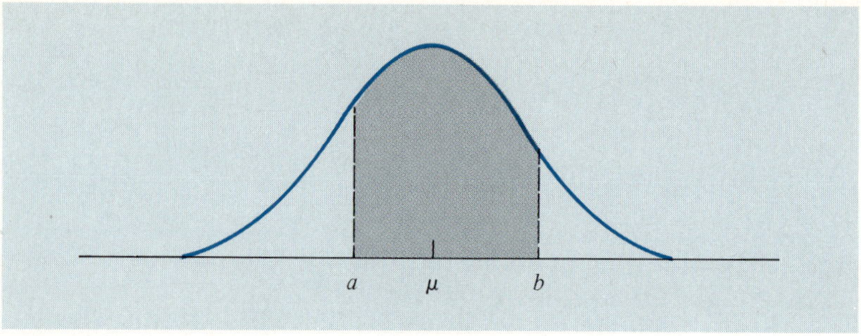

Figure 5.10

the table of areas under the standard normal distribution can be used to determine the areas under portions of any normal distribution. Such a table is Table 1 in the appendix. The following example demonstrates the use of this table in computing areas under the standard normal distribution.

EXAMPLE 13

We shall determine the area under the standard normal distribution between

(a) $x = 0$ and $x = 1.52$
(b) $x = -2.13$ and $x = 0$
(c) $x = -0.86$ and $x = 1.35$
(d) $x = 0.46$ and $x = 1.28$

(a) The desired area is pictured in Figure 5.11(a). Since this is the area between the mean and a positive number of standard deviations to the right of the mean, the value can be read directly from Table 1: It is the entry in the table corresponding to $z = 1.52$. To find this entry, locate the row labeled 1.5 and the column labeled 0.02; the intersection of this row and column contains the number 0.4357. This is the area under the curve between $x = 0$ and $x = 1.52$.

(b) In this case we are seeking the area in Figure 5.11(b) between the mean and a number of standard deviations to the left of the mean. Since any normal distribution is symmetric about its mean, this area is the same as the area between $x = 0$ and $x = 2.13$, the corresponding number of standard deviations to the right of the mean. This area can be found as in part (a) to be 0.4834. Thus the area between $x = -2.13$ and $x = 0$ is also 0.4834.

(c) To compute the area between a point to the left of the mean and a point to the right of the mean, we separately compute the areas between the mean and each of the given values. The desired area is easily seen to be the sum of these two areas. [Refer to Figure 5.11(c).] Since the area between $x = -0.86$ and $x = 0$ is 0.3051 and the area between $x = 0$ and $x = 1.35$ is 0.4115, it follows that the total area between $x = -0.86$ and $x = 1.35$ is

$$0.3051 + 0.4115 = 0.7166$$

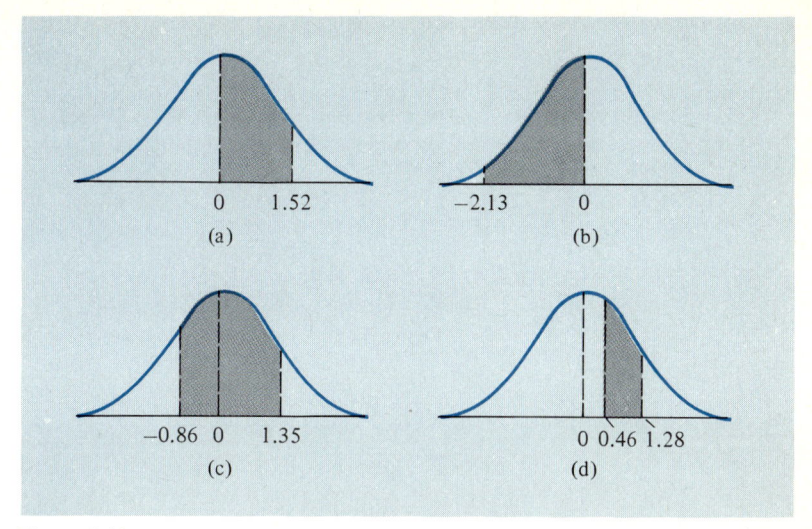

Figure 5.11

(d) To determine the area between $x = 0.46$ and $x = 1.28$, note that it equals the difference of the areas between $x = 0$ and $x = 1.28$ and $x = 0$ and $x = 0.46$. [See Figure 5.11(d).] Since these areas are 0.3997 and 0.1772, the area between $x = 0.46$ and $x = 1.28$ is

$$0.3997 - 0.1772 = 0.2225$$

In order to use Table 1 to compute areas under normal distributions other than the standard normal distribution, it is necessary to measure distances from the mean in terms of standard deviations. These distances are usually called *z scores*. Conversion of a value of x into a z score is done by means of the formula

z scores

$$z = \frac{x - \mu}{\sigma} \tag{5.6}$$

where μ and σ denote the mean and standard deviation of the given distribution.

EXAMPLE 14

For a normal distribution with mean 50 and standard deviation 5, x values of 44 and 62 correspond to z scores of

$$\frac{44 - 50}{5} = \frac{-6}{5} = -1.2 \quad \text{and} \quad \frac{62 - 50}{5} = \frac{12}{5} = 2.4$$

The area under a normal distribution between two z scores can be computed by determining the area under the standard normal distribution between these values. The next example demonstrates this technique.

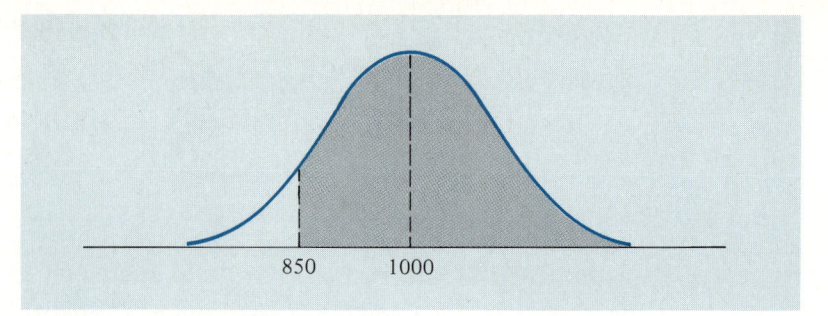

Figure 5.12

EXAMPLE 15

What is the area under the normal distribution with mean 60 and standard deviation 8 that lies between $x = 50$ and $x = 64$?

To answer this question, we must first convert the given values into z scores. By using (5.6), we find that $x = 50$ and $x = 64$ correspond to z scores of

$$\frac{50 - 60}{8} = \frac{-10}{8} = -1.25 \quad \text{and} \quad \frac{64 - 60}{8} = \frac{4}{8} = 0.50$$

So the area under the given normal distribution between $x = 50$ and $x = 64$ is the same as the area under the standard normal distribution between -1.25 and 0.50. This area [computed as in Example 13(c)] is

$$0.3944 + 0.1915 = 0.5859$$

Recall that for normally distributed outcomes the area under the appropriate normal distribution between $x = a$ and $x = b$ approximates the proportion of outcomes falling between the values a and b. Thus for normally distributed outcomes, the likelihood that an outcome will fall within a specified interval can be computed as in Example 15. The following examples illustrate this process.

EXAMPLE 16

The length of time a certain brand of 60-watt light bulbs will burn is normally distributed with a mean of 1000 hours and a standard deviation of 100 hours. What proportion of these bulbs will burn at least 850 hours?

This proportion equals the area under the normal distribution with mean 1000 and standard deviation 100 that lies to the right of the line $x = 850$. (See Figure 5.12.) Notice that this area equals the area between $x = 850$ and $x = 1000$ plus the area to the right of $x = 1000$. Since this latter area is 0.5 (because a normal distribution is symmetrically distributed about its mean), we need to determine only the area between $x = 850$ and $x = 1000$, that is, the area between z scores of -1.50 and 0. This area is 0.4332; so the proportion of these light bulbs that will burn at least 850 hours is

$$0.4332 + 0.5000 = 0.9332$$

EXAMPLE 17

Scores on the 1960 revision of the Stanford-Binet intelligence test are normally distributed with a mean of 100 and a standard deviation of 16. What percentage of the population has IQ scores in the superior range (120–140)?

To answer this question, we must determine the area under the normal distribution with mean 100 and standard deviation 16 that lies between $x = 120$ and $x = 140$. The z scores corresponding to these values are 1.25 and 2.50, respectively. So the area under consideration equals

$$0.4938 - 0.3944 = 0.0994$$

(See Figure 5.13.) Thus approximately 9.94% of the population has IQ scores between 120 and 140.

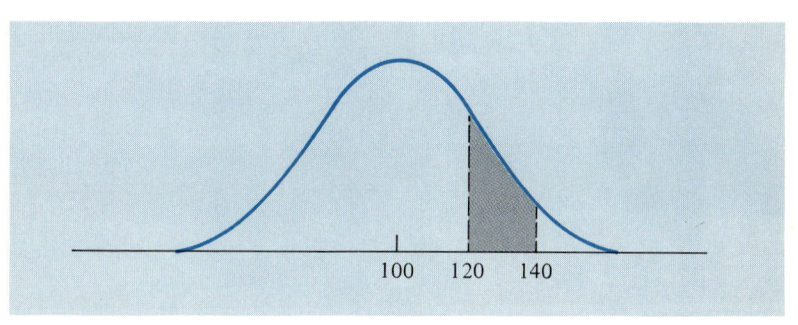

Figure 5.13

Exercises

In Exercises 1–12 find the area under the standard normal distribution between the given values.

1. 0 and 0.79
2. -1.32 and 0
3. -0.48 and 1.65
4. -1.23 and 0.57
5. -0.64 and 0.36
6. -0.50 and 0.75
7. -0.25 or more
8. 1.63 or less
9. 1.13 or more
10. -2.13 or less
11. 1.39 and 2.05
12. -1.47 and -0.32

In Exercises 13–20 convert the given values of x into z scores for a normal distribution with mean μ and standard deviation σ.

13. $x = 450$, $\mu = 600$, $\sigma = 100$
14. $x = 62$, $\mu = 50$, $\sigma = 20$
15. $x = 89$, $u = 80$, $\sigma = 5$
16. $x = 63$, $\mu = 90$, $\sigma = 12$

17. $x = 4.36, \mu = 3.5, \sigma = 1$ 18. $x = 3.24, \mu = 6, \sigma = 2.4$
19. $x = 13.82, \mu = 17.85, \sigma = 1.55$ 20. $x = 8.5, \mu = 6.1, \sigma = 1.5$

In Exercises 21–32 find the area under the normal distribution with mean μ and standard deviation σ that lies in the given interval.

21. Between 38 and 50 if $\mu = 50$ and $\sigma = 12$
22. Between 25 and 32 if $\mu = 25$ and $\sigma = 10$
23. Between 71 and 92 if $\mu = 80$ and $\sigma = 15$
24. Between 44 and 54 if $\mu = 48$ and $\sigma = 5$
25. Between 28 and 36 if $\mu = 40$ and $\sigma = 10$
26. Between 104 and 124 if $\mu = 100$ and $\sigma = 16$
27. Between 158 and 168 if $\mu = 150$ and $\sigma = 20$
28. Between 50 and 60 if $\mu = 64$ and $\sigma = 8$
29. 46 or less if $\mu = 36$ and $\sigma = 8$
30. 54 or more if $\mu = 75$ and $\sigma = 15$
31. 90 or more if $\mu = 72$ and $\sigma = 24$
32. 45 or less if $\mu = 60$ and $\sigma = 12$

33. The number of girls in families with 8 children can be approximated by a normal distribution with mean 4 and standard deviation $\sqrt{2}$. Calculate the proportion of such families that contain 3 or more girls.

34. The weights of men in a certain physical education class were found to be normally distributed with a mean of 160 pounds and a standard deviation of 8 pounds. What proportion of these men weigh less than 150 pounds?

35. A certain brand of 100-watt light bulbs has a mean life of 750 hours and a standard deviation of 50 hours. What proportion of these bulbs will burn at least 820 hours?

36. During the period from October 1974 to September 1977, the Graduate Record Examination's advanced mathematics test was given to 12,375 students. During this time the scores were normally distributed with a mean of 687 and a standard deviation of 160. Approximately how many of the students who took the test during this period scored above 900?

37. Suppose that 54% of the people intending to vote in a particular election favor a certain candidate. If a survey of 400 is taken among these voters, the number favoring the candidate will be normally distributed with a mean of 216 and a standard deviation of 10. In what proportion of such surveys will the candidate fail to receive a majority?

38. Under normal conditions, the number of bottles from a lot of 1200 that are filled improperly by a certain machine is normally distributed with a mean of 36 and a standard deviation of 5.9. When this machine is operating under normal conditions, what proportion of the time will it produce between 30 and 40 improperly filled bottles?

39. Scores on the 1960 revision of the Stanford-Binet intelligence test are normally distributed with a mean of 100 and a standard deviation of 16. What proportion of the population has IQ scores between 80 and 120?

40. During the fall semester of 1979, the first-year class at Illinois State University had a mean score of 20.9 and a standard deviation of 6.1 on the ACT natural science test. Assuming that the scores were normally distributed, calculate the proportion of students who scored above 30.

41. Suppose that the scores on a particular examination are normally distributed with a mean of 74 and a standard deviation of 8. Determine the grading curve that should be used in order to obtain 9% A's, 18% B's, 46% C's, 18% D's, and 9% F's.

42. The mean life of a particular automobile battery is 39 months with a standard deviation of 6 months. If these batteries are sold with a 36-month warranty, what proportion of them will fail before the warranty expires? (Assume that the life of these batteries is normally distributed.)

5.4 Linear Regression

It is not surprising that the normal weight of a boy is related to his height. If we knew the nature of this relationship, we could predict the normal weight for a boy from his height.

The area of statistics concerned with making predictions about an unknown variable based upon its relationship with a known variable is called *regression analysis*. In this section we shall discuss a special case of regression analysis in which the known and unknown variables are connected by an essentially linear relationship.

Table 5.7 contains data relating the normal weight of a boy to his height.

Table 5.7 *Normal Weight for Boys of Various Heights*

Height (inches)	49	56	61	65	68	71
Weight (pounds)	60	80	100	120	140	160

In order to investigate the relationship between these heights and weights, let us denote each of the corresponding measurements as an ordered pair (x_i, y_i), where x_i denotes the height in inches and y_i denotes the weight in pounds. The six resulting ordered pairs will then be plotted to obtain a picture of the data. Such a picture is called a *scatter diagram*. The scatter diagram for the data in Table 5.7 is shown in Figure 5.14.

In this figure the data are clustered closely around the dashed line. This fact suggests that the relationship between the normal weights and heights is almost linear. Note that this relationship is not truly linear; for if this were the case, all the data points would lie on the same line. Nevertheless these data can be approximated quite well by assuming that there is a linear relationship between the x_i and the y_i. On the other hand if, as in Figure 5.15, the data points are not clustered around a single line, the relationship between the x_i and y_i would not be linear.

When a scatter diagram reveals an essentially linear relationship between two variables, there will be many lines that approximate the data reasonably well. A line that has proved to be a good fit to the

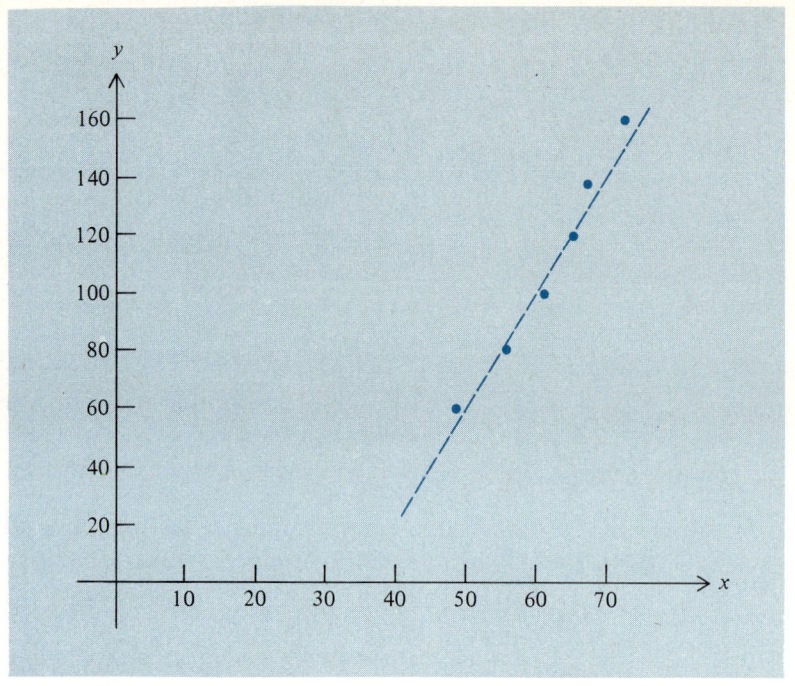

Figure 5.14

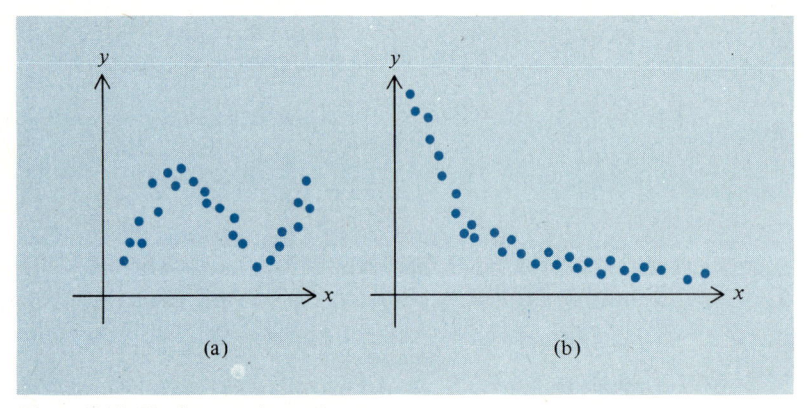

Figure 5.15 *Nonlinear relationships*

data is one for which the sum of the squares of the vertical distances from the data points to the line is as small as possible. This line is called the *least squares line*, and its equation is called the *linear regression equation*. For the data points $(x_1, y_1), (x_2, y_2), \ldots, (x_n, y_n)$ the least squares line has slope

$$m = \frac{nZ - XY}{nV - X^2} \quad (5.7)$$

and *y* intercept

$$b = \frac{Y - mX}{n} \tag{5.8}$$

where

$X = x_1 + x_2 + \cdots + x_n$ (the sum of the x_i)
$Y = y_1 + y_2 + \cdots + y_n$ (the sum of the y_i)
$Z = x_1 y_1 + x_2 y_2 + \cdots + x_n y_n$ (the sum of the products $x_i y_i$)
$V = x_1^2 + x_2^2 + \cdots + x_n^2$ (the sum of the squares of the x_i)

The computations that must be made in order to use (5.7) and (5.8) to compute the linear regression equation for the data in Table 5.7 can be conveniently arranged as follows. (For future reference we have included a column listing the squares of the y_i values.)

	x_i	y_i	$x_i y_i$	x_i^2	y_i^2
	49	60	2,940	2,401	3,600
	56	80	4,480	3,136	6,400
	61	100	6,100	3,721	10,000
	65	120	7,800	4,225	14,400
	68	140	9,520	4,624	19,600
	71	160	11,360	5,041	25,600
Total	$X = 370$	$Y = 660$	$Z = 42,200$	$V = 23,148$	$W = 79,600$

Thus from (5.7) and (5.8) the least squares line has slope

$$m = \frac{nZ - XY}{nV - X^2} = \frac{6(42,200) - (370)(660)}{6(23,148) - (370)^2} = \frac{9,000}{1,988} \approx 4.527$$

and y intercept

$$b = \frac{Y - mX}{n} \approx \frac{660 - (4.527)(370)}{6} \approx \frac{-1014.99}{6} \approx -169.165$$

So the linear regression equation is $y = 4.527x - 169.165$. By using this equation we can predict the normal weight of a boy with a given height. For instance, the normal weight for a boy of height 60 inches is

$$4.527(60) - 169.165 = 271.620 - 169.165 = 102.455 \text{ pounds}$$

EXAMPLE 18

Consider the data points (2, 10), (3, 7), (5, 3), and (6, 2).
The scatter diagram for these four points, shown in Figure 5.16, suggests that there is an essentially linear relationship between the x_i and y_i.
To compute the linear regression equation for these data,

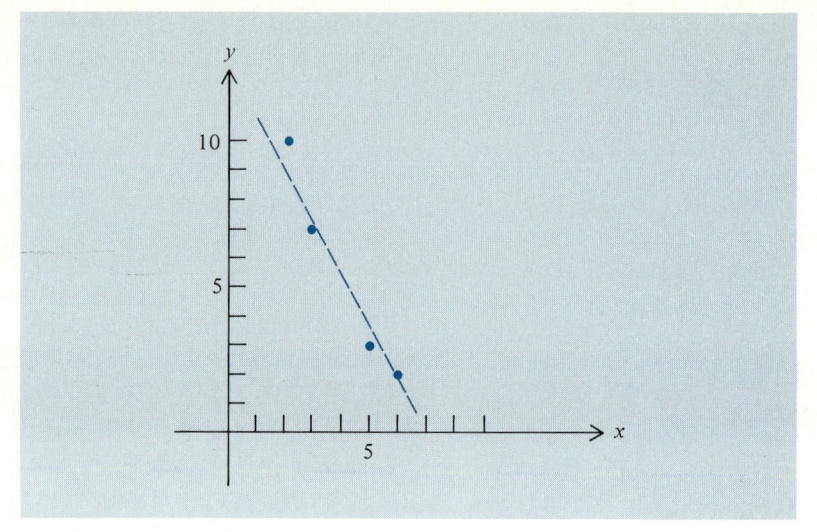

Figure 5.16

we begin by computing the sum of the x_i, y_i, x_iy_i, x_i^2, and y_i^2 values as shown below.

	x_i	y_i	x_iy_i	x_i^2	y_i^2
	2	10	20	4	100
	3	7	21	9	49
	5	3	15	25	9
	6	2	12	36	4
Total	$X = 16$	$Y = 22$	$Z = 68$	$V = 74$	$W = 162$

Now using (5.7) and (5.8), we obtain

$$m = \frac{nZ - XY}{nV - X^2} = \frac{4(68) - (16)(22)}{4(74) - (16)^2} = \frac{-80}{40} = -2$$

and

$$b = \frac{Y - mX}{n} = \frac{22 - (-2)(16)}{4} = \frac{54}{4} = 13.5$$

So the linear regression equation is $y = -2x + 13.5$.

The dashed lines in Figures 5.14 and 5.16 are the least squares lines for the corresponding data sets. Although both these lines approximate the data reasonably well, the line in Figure 5.16 fits the data somewhat better than the one in Figure 5.14. It is often useful to have a way of measuring how well the least squares line approximates the data. The *coefficient of correlation*, denoted r, provides a way of measuring the "goodness of fit" between the data and its least squares line. The value of r is computed using the formula

$$r = \frac{nZ - XY}{\sqrt{nV - X^2}\sqrt{nW - Y^2}} \tag{5.9}$$

where

$\quad X = x_1 + x_2 + \cdots + x_n \quad$ (the sum of the x_i)
$\quad Y = y_1 + y_2 + \cdots + y_n \quad$ (the sum of the y_i)
$\quad Z = x_1 y_1 + x_2 y_2 + \cdots + x_n y_n \quad$ (the sum of the products $x_i y_i$)
$\quad V = x_1^2 + x_2^2 + \cdots + x_n^2 \quad$ (the sum of the squares of the x_i)
$\quad W = y_1^2 + y_2^2 + \cdots + y_n^2 \quad$ (the sum of the squares of the y_i)

Observe that X, Y, Z, and V have the same meaning in (5.9) as in (5.7) and (5.8).

Using the values obtained on page 205, we see that the coefficient of correlation for the data in Table 5.7 is

$$r = \frac{nZ - XY}{\sqrt{nV - X^2}\sqrt{nW - Y^2}}$$

$$= \frac{6(42{,}200) - (370)(660)}{\sqrt{6(23{,}148) - (370)^2}\sqrt{6(79{,}600) - (660)^2}}$$

$$= \frac{9000}{\sqrt{1988}\sqrt{42{,}000}} \approx \frac{9000}{(44.59)(204.94)} \approx .985$$

EXAMPLE 19

For the data in Example 18 we have

$$r = \frac{nZ - XY}{\sqrt{nV - X^2}\sqrt{nW - Y^2}} = \frac{4(68) - (16)(22)}{\sqrt{4(74) - (16)^2}\sqrt{4(162) - (22)^2}}$$

$$= \frac{-80}{\sqrt{40}\sqrt{164}} \approx \frac{-80}{(6.32)(12.81)} \approx -.99$$

It can be shown that r is always a number between -1 and 1 (inclusive). Values of r close to ± 1 indicate that the least squares line provides an excellent approximation to the data, whereas values of r close to 0 indicate that the relationship between x_i and y_i is not linear. Note that the numerators in (5.7) and (5.9) are the same. Thus, because the denominators in (5.7) and (5.9) are always positive, the sign of r determines the sign of m. In other words, the slope of the least squares line will be positive or negative according to whether the coefficient of correlation is positive or negative.

EXAMPLE 20

We shall examine the data in Table 5.8 to see if there is a linear relationship between the number of automobiles in use in the United States and domestic motor fuel consumption.

Table 5.8 *Number of Automobiles in Use and Domestic Motor Fuel Consumption in the United States, 1950–1975*

Year	Millions of automobiles in use	Billions of gallons of motor fuel consumed
1950	35.8	35.6
1955	47.1	47.6
1960	56.9	57.9
1965	68.9	71.1
1970	80.4	92.3
1975	95.2	109.0

Source: Statistical Abstract of the United States, 1978. Washington, D.C.: U.S. Department of Commerce, Bureau of the Census.

Performing the calculations required to use (5.9), we obtain the following values.

x_i	y_i	$x_i y_i$	x_i^2	y_i^2
35.8	35.6	1,274.48	1,281.64	1,267.36
47.1	47.6	2,241.96	2,218.41	2,265.76
56.9	57.9	3,294.51	3,237.61	3,352.41
68.9	71.1	4,898.79	4,747.21	5,055.21
80.4	92.3	7,420.92	6,464.16	8,519.23
95.2	109.0	10,376.80	9,063.04	11,881.00

Total $X = 384.3$ $Y = 413.5$ $Z = 29,507.46$ $V = 27,012.07$ $W = 32,341.03$

Thus

$$r = \frac{nZ - XY}{\sqrt{nV - X^2}\sqrt{nW - Y^2}}$$

$$= \frac{6(29,507.46) - (384.3)(413.5)}{\sqrt{6(27,012.07) - (384.3)^2}\sqrt{6(32,341.03) - (413.5)^2}}$$

$$= \frac{18,136.71}{\sqrt{14,385.93}\sqrt{23,063.93}} \approx \frac{18,136.71}{(119.94)(151.87)} \approx .996$$

Hence there is a strong linear relationship between the number of automobiles in use and domestic motor fuel consumption.

From (5.7) and (5.8) we see that the least squares line has slope

$$m = \frac{nZ - XY}{nV - X^2} = \frac{18,136.71}{14,385.93} \approx 1.26$$

and y intercept

$$b = \frac{Y - mX}{n} = \frac{413.5 - (1.26)(384.3)}{6} \approx -11.83$$

(Notice that some of the calculations performed in computing r can be used in computing m.) So the linear regression equation is $y = 1.26x - 11.83$.

This equation can be used to predict the amounts of domestic motor fuel consumption at various times. For example, when there were 110 million automobiles in use, the predicted amount of motor fuel consumption was

$$1.26(110) - 11.83 = 126.77 \quad \text{billion gallons}$$

Exercises

In Exercises 1–10, plot a scatter diagram and compute the coefficient of correlation and the linear regression equation for the given data sets.

1. (1, 10), (3, 18), (4, 20), (6, 20)
2. (1, 4), (3, 7), (5, 9), (7, 10)
3. (1, 20), (2, 17), (4, 11), (7, 4)
4. (1, 3), (3, 4), (4, 5), (7, 10)
5. (3, 8), (8, 16), (12, 24), (15, 25)
6. (−3, 10), (−2, 7), (0, 3), (1, 2)
7. (1, 30), (3, 26), (7, 13), (8, 11), (10, 3)
8. (1, 9), (2, 7), (3, 6), (4, 4), (5, 2)
9. (1, 5), (2, 6), (3, 8), (4, 10), (5, 11)
10. (1, 2), (2, 4), (3, 7), (4, 8), (5, 10)

11. Hanford, Washington, located on the Columbia River, is the site of a storage facility for radioactive wastes. In [2], Fadeley investigated the relationship between deaths from cancer in the city of Portland and the Oregon counties bordering the Columbia River and the degree to which the population in these counties is exposed to wastes that may be carried by the river from the Hanford facility. The data that he obtained are shown below.

County	Index of exposure	Cancer mortality (per 100,000)
Umatilla	2.49	147.1
Morrow	2.57	130.1
Gilliam	3.41	129.9
Sherman	1.25	113.5
Wasco	1.62	137.5
Hood River	3.83	162.3
Portland	11.64	207.5
Columbia	6.41	177.9
Clatsop	8.34	210.3

Show that there is a strong linear relationship between the index of exposure and the cancer mortality rate and compute the linear regression equation.

12. Prevailing currents in the Pacific Ocean normally divert the waters of the Columbia River southward along the coast of Oregon. Thus the population of the Oregon counties bordering the Pacific Ocean is also exposed to radioactive wastes from the Hanford storage facility described in Exercise

11. Using the data below, show that for Oregon's five predominantly coastal counties there is a strong linear relationship between the index of exposure and the cancer mortality rate and compute the linear regression equation.

County	Index of exposure	Cancer mortality (per 100,000)
Clatsop	8.34	210.3
Tillamook	5.51	163.8
Lincoln	6.21	170.4
Coos	1.85	117.6
Curry	2.81	73.6

13. During the years 1970–1976, disposable personal income in the United States was as shown below.[5]

Year	1970	1972	1973	1974	1975	1976
Disposable personal income (billions of dollars)	685.9	801.3	901.7	982.9	1080.9	1181.7

(a) Letting $x = 0$ denote the year 1970, $x = 2$ denote 1972, and so forth, determine the linear regression equation that expresses disposable personal income as a function of the year.
(b) Compute the coefficient of correlation.
(c) Predict the disposable personal income in 1971.

14. In [5], Lux, Peterson, and Hutton investigate the relationship between the mean number of dorsal and anal fin rays in 18 samples of flounder caught in various locations off the coast of Massachusetts. Their data are as follows:

Sample number	Mean number of dorsal fin rays	Mean number of anal fin rays
1	64.35	48.54
2	64.34	48.36
3	64.00	47.80
4	63.74	48.34
5	64.23	48.29
6	64.94	48.89
7	65.50	49.09
8	67.22	50.68
9	66.59	50.02
10	66.65	50.21
11	66.87	50.42
12	65.94	49.90
13	64.89	48.67
14	67.26	50.57
15	67.66	50.73
16	69.53	51.94
17	69.58	52.14
18	70.28	52.61

[5] Source: *Statistical Abstract of the United States, 1977.* Washington, D.C.: U.S. Department of Commerce, Bureau of the Census.

Compute the coefficient of correlation and the linear regression equation that describes the relationship between the number of dorsal and anal fin rays.

15. Before beginning construction of a dam on the Kootenai River at Newgate, British Columbia, it was necessary to collect data on the rate of stream flow there. Unfortunately, stream records for Newgate were not kept until 1931, but records have existed since 1925 for Libby, Montana, further downstream. These data appear in Table 5.9.

   (a) Compute the linear regression equation for the stream flow rates at Libby and Newgate during the period 1931–1943.
   (b) Predict the stream flow rates at Newgate for the years 1925–1930.

   (These predicted values were actually used in planning construction of the dam at Newgate.)

Table 5.9 *Water Flow at Two Points on the Kootenai River in January*

Year	Flow at Libby (hundreds of cubic feet per second)	Flow at Newgate (hundreds of cubic feet per second)
1925	42.0	
1926	24.0	
1927	38.0	
1928	49.4	
1929	24.6	
1930	24.2	
1931	27.1	19.7
1932	20.9	18.0
1933	33.4	26.1
1934	77.6	44.9
1935	37.0	26.1
1936	21.6	19.9
1937	17.6	15.7
1938	35.1	27.6
1939	32.6	24.9
1940	26.0	23.4
1941	27.6	23.1
1942	38.7	31.3
1943	27.8	23.8

Source: Extending Stream-Flow Records, U.S. Department of the Interior, Geological Survey, Water Resources Branch, September 1947, pp. 7–8.

Chapter Review

New Terms

coefficient of correlation (p. 206)
frequency (p. 183)
frequency distribution (p. 183)
frequency polygon (p. 185)
histogram (p. 183)
least squares line (p. 204)

linear regression equation (p. 204)
mean (p. 189)
measure of central tendency (p. 189)
measure of dispersion (p. 189)
median (p. 190)
modal class (p. 192)

mode (p. 191)
normal distribution (p. 196)
relative frequency (p. 183)
scatter diagram (p. 203)

standard deviation (p. 194)
standard normal distribution (p. 197)
variance (p. 193)
z score (p. 199)

Review Exercises

1. Label the following statements true or false.
   (a) When constructing a frequency distribution, the intervals should be of the same length if possible.
   (b) The number of intervals in a frequency distribution should be between 5 and 15 whenever possible.
   (c) A histogram is a type of bar graph that can be used to depict a frequency distribution.
   (d) Measures of dispersion indicate a central point for a data set.
   (e) The mean is the most important measure of dispersion.
   (f) Unlike the mean, the median of a data set is always a number in the data set.
   (g) Every data set has a unique mode.
   (h) The standard deviation of a data set is the square root of the variance.
   (i) There is exactly one normal distribution having mean μ.
   (j) A normal distribution is symmetric about its mean.
   (k) The standard normal distribution has mean 0 and standard deviation 1.
   (l) For normally distributed outcomes, the proportion of outcomes falling between a and b can be approximated by the area under the appropriate normal distribution between the values a and b.
   (m) A z score measures the distance from the mean using one standard deviation as a unit of measurement.
   (n) The coefficient of correlation is a number between 0 and 1.
   (o) If the coefficient of correlation between two data sets is close to -1, then there is no linear relationship between these data sets.

2. The mean annual incidence of Hodgkin's disease in the population of Connecticut during the years 1950–1959 is as shown below.[6]

Age at Diagnosis	0–10	10–20	20–30	30–40	40–50	50–60	60–70	70–80
Number of Patients	8	48	118	97	94	89	76	62

Prepare a histogram and a frequency polygon for these data.

3. The age at death of deceased presidents of the United States is shown below. Construct a frequency distribution, a histogram, and a frequency polygon for these data.

67	80	53	56	56	72	63
90	78	65	66	71	67	88
83	79	74	63	67	57	78
85	68	64	70	58	60	46
73	71	77	49	60	90	64

[6] Source: *Cancer in Connecticut, Incidence and Rates.* Hartford: Connecticut State Department of Health, 1967.

4. The number of home runs hit by the leading home run hitter in the National League during each season from 1936 to 1977 is shown below. Construct a frequency distribution, a histogram, and a frequency polygon for these data.

33	30	40	49	41	44	40
31	29	54	51	46	39	44
36	33	47	43	49	36	36
28	28	42	44	44	45	38
43	23	37	47	47	45	38
34	51	47	46	52	48	52

5. Compute the mean, median, mode (if it exists), and standard deviation for each of the following data sets.
   (a) 2, 7, 8, 2, 5, 7, 4   (b) 2, 7, 5, 11, 4, 8, 5, 6

6. Estimate the mean and standard deviation of the frequency distribution in Exercise 2.

7. Estimate the mean and standard deviation of the frequency distribution constructed in Exercise 3.

8. In a normal distribution with mean 45 and standard deviation 5, what z scores correspond to the following values?
   (a) 45   (b) 55   (c) 38   (d) 49

9. Find the area under the normal distribution with mean 200 and standard deviation 40 that lies in the given interval.
   (a) Between 200 and 250   (b) Between 180 and 226
   (c) Between 140 and 188   (d) Between 216 and 274
   (e) 230 or less   (f) 210 or more

10. A mill must cut wood into strips 72 inches long. The length of the strips is normally distributed with a mean of 72 inches and a standard deviation of $\frac{1}{8}$ inch. If strips less than $71\frac{13}{16}$ inches in length must be rejected, what proportion of strips will be rejected because of shortness?

11. During the fall semester of 1979, the Illinois State University first-year class had a mean ACT composite score of 19.0 with a standard deviation of 5.4. Assuming that these scores were normally distributed, what proportion of the freshman class had ACT composite scores between 20 and 30?

12. Plot a scatter diagram, compute the coefficient of correlation, and determine the linear regression equation for the data (2, 3), (6, 7), (8, 10), and (10, 12).

13. In [7], Sharpe and Johnsgard investigate the relationship between the physical and behavioral characteristics of 11 offspring resulting from the mating of pintail and mallard ducks. The physical and behavioral characteristics were measured by a plumage index and a behavioral index, respectively. Their data are shown below.

Total plumage index	7	7	6	4	9	8	13	14	14	14	15
Total behavioral index	3	4	5	7	9	10	10	11	11	15	15

Plot a scatter diagram, compute the coefficient of correlation, and determine the linear regression equation for these data.

References

1. Anderson, L. Dewey, "A Longitudinal Study of the Effects of Nursery-School Training on Successive Intelligence-Test Ratings," in *Intelligence: Its Nature and Nurture*, Guy M. Whipple, ed. Bloomington, Ill.: National Society for the Study of Education, 1940.

2. Fadeley, Robert Cunningham, "Oregon Malignancy Pattern Physiographically Related to Hanford Washington Radioisotope Storage," *J. Environ. Health*, vol. 27 (May–June 1965), pp. 883–897.

3. Gross, Neal, Ward S. Mason, and Alexander W. McEachern, *Explorations in Role Analysis*, p. 297. New York: Wiley, 1958.

4. Larsen, Richard J. and Donna Fox Stroup, *Statistics in the Real World: A Book of Examples*. New York: Macmillan, 1976.

5. Lux, F. E., A. E. Peterson, Jr., and R. F. Hutton, "Geographical Variation in Fin Ray Number in Winter Flounder *Pseudopleuronectes americanus* (Walbaum) off Massachusetts, *Trans. Am. Fish. Soc.*, vol. 99, no. 3 (July 1970), pp. 483–488.

6. Mosteller, Frederick, William H. Kruskal, Richard F. Link, Richard S. Pieters, and Gerald R. Rising, eds., *Statistics by Example*. Reading Mass.: Addison-Wesley, 1973.

7. Sharpe, Roger S. and Paul A. Johnsgard, "Inheritance of Behavioral Characters in F_2 Mallard × Pintail (*Anas platyrhynchos* L. × *Anas acuta* L.) Hybrids," *Behaviour*, vol. 27 (1966), pp. 259–272.

8. Tanur, Judith M., Frederick Mosteller, William H. Kruskal, Richard F. Link, Richard S. Pieters, and Gerald R. Rising, eds. *Statistics: A Guide to the Unknown*. San Francisco: Holden-Day, 1972.

9. Tanur, Judith M., Frederick Mosteller, William H. Kruskal, Richard F. Link, Richard S. Pieters, Gerald R. Rising, and E. L. Lehmann, eds., *Statistics: A Guide to Business and Economics*. San Francisco: Holden-Day, 1976.

6

Sets and Techniques for Counting

The terminology and notation of set theory are often useful in describing collections of objects and the relationships among such collections. In Chapter 7, for example, this terminology and notation will be used in the study of probability. We shall see there that in situations involving only a finite number of possible outcomes, the computation of probabilities reduces to the problem of counting the number of elements in various sets.

In this chapter the fundamental concepts of set theory needed for the study of probability are introduced. In addition, several techniques are presented for counting the number of different ways in which certain tasks can be performed, a type of counting which occurs frequently in Chapter 7.

6.1 Introduction to Set Theory

The widespread use of the terminology and notation of set theory is a relatively recent occurrence. The concepts of set theory enable us to discuss certain mathematical ideas concisely, yet with great precision. This section introduces the basic terms and notation from set theory that will be used in our study of probability.

set

elements of a set

By a *set* we mean any collection of objects for which it is possible to decide whether or not a particular object belongs to the collection. The objects that compose the set are called *elements* or *members* of the set. In this book we usually denote sets by capital letters (such as A, B, and X) and elements of sets by lowercase letters (such as a, b, and x).

To denote that a particular object x is an element of set X, we write

$$x \in X$$

read "x is an element of X" or "x belongs to X." If, on the other hand, x is not an element of set X, then we write

$$x \notin X$$

read "x is not an element of X" or "x does not belong to X."

equality of sets Sets A and B are said to be *equal*, denoted $A = B$, if they contain precisely the same elements. If A and B are not equal, then we write $A \neq B$.

There are two possible ways of describing a set: All the elements of the set may be listed, or the elements of the set may be described by a rule. Both methods utilize *set braces* { }. For example, the set consisting of the positive integers 1, 2, 3, and 4 may be written as

$$\{1, 2, 3, 4\} \quad \text{or} \quad \{x | x \text{ is a positive integer less than 5}\}$$

set braces

The latter form is read "the set of all x such that x is a positive integer less than 5." In this notation the letter x denotes only a typical element of the set and can be replaced by any other letter without changing the set being described.

Notice that the definition of set equality requires only that the sets in question contain the same elements. No consideration is given to the order in which the elements are listed. Thus

$$\{1, 2, 3, 4\} = \{4, 3, 2, 1\} = \{3, 1, 2, 1, 4\}$$

In particular, there is no reason to list an element of a set more than once.

EXAMPLE 1

If
$$A = \{x | x \text{ is an even positive integer less than 9}\}$$
then $6 \in A$, $5 \notin A$, and $12 \notin A$. Since the elements of A are precisely 2, 4, 6, and 8, we may also write A as
$$\{2, 4, 6, 8\}$$

EXAMPLE 2

The set
$$\{\text{Illinois, Indiana, Michigan, Wisconsin}\}$$
may be written as
$$\{y | y \text{ is a state that borders Lake Michigan}\}$$

EXAMPLE 3

The set
$$\{x | x \text{ is a positive integer less than 100}\}$$

can be written as

$$\{1, 2, \ldots, 99\}$$

where the dots indicate that the pattern established by the elements 1, 2, and 3 continues through the element 99.

EXAMPLE 4

The set

$$\{x \mid x \text{ is an integer and } |x| < 4\}$$

can be written as

$$\{-3, -2, -1, 0, 1, 2, 3\}$$

EXAMPLE 5

Let

$$B = \{x \mid x^3 - x = 0\}$$

By factoring

$$x^3 - x = x(x^2 - 1) = x(x - 1)(x + 1)$$

we see that

$$B = \{-1, 0, 1\}$$

subset

proper subset

If the elements of set A are all elements of set B, then A is called a *subset* of B. In this case we write $A \subset B$ or $B \supset A$. Observe that every set is automatically a subset of itself. If A is a subset of B and B contains at least one element not in A, then A is called a *proper* subset of B. Finally, we denote that A is not a subset of B by writing $A \not\subset B$ or $B \not\supset A$. Notice that, if A is not a subset of B, then there must be at least one element of A that does not belong to B.

EXAMPLE 6

Let

$$A = \{1, 3, 5\} \qquad B = \{1, 4, 5, 6\} \quad \text{and} \quad C = \{1, 2, 3, 4, 5, 6, 7\}$$

Then $A \subset C$ and $B \subset C$, but $A \not\subset B$ and $B \not\subset A$. In this case both A and B are proper subsets of C.

empty set

We discuss below three operations that can be used to produce new sets from existing ones. When operations such as these are performed, the resulting set may contain no elements. Such a set is called the *empty set* or *null set* and is denoted symbolically by $\emptyset$. It should be noted that the empty set is a subset of every set. In fact, the empty set is a proper subset of every nonempty set.

EXAMPLE 7

The set $X = \{2, 4, 6, 8\}$ has 16 subsets, of which 15 are proper. The subsets of X are

$\emptyset, \{2\}, \{4\}, \{6\}, \{8\}, \{2,4\}, \{2,6\}, \{2,8\}, \{4,6\}, \{4,8\},$
$\{6,8\}, \{2,4,6\}, \{2,4,8\}, \{2,6,8\}, \{4,6,8\},$ and X

For logical reasons it is necessary to assume that in any discussion of sets the elements under consideration all belong to some set called a *universal set*. Throughout this chapter universal sets are denoted by the letter U. Frequently there are many possible universal sets for a particular situation, and the universal set often is not explicitly defined. For instance, in problems dealing with the sets $\{1, 3, 4, 5\}, \{2, 5, 8, 12\},$ and $\{1, 6, 9, 13\}$, the set of positive integers, the set of integers, and the set of real numbers are three possible universal sets.

universal set

intersection of sets

The *intersection* of two sets A and B, denoted $A \cap B$, is the set consisting of all elements in both A and B. Symbolically,

$$A \cap B = \{x | x \in A \text{ and } x \in B\}$$

Of course, A and B may have no elements in common, in which case $A \cap B = \emptyset$; such sets are called *disjoint*. Since the elements in $A \cap B$ belong to both A and B, it is clear that $A \cap B$ is always a subset of A and also a subset of B.

disjoint sets

EXAMPLE 8

If
$$A = \{1, 2, 5, 8\} \quad B = \{2, 3, 4, 5, 6\} \quad \text{and} \quad C = \{3, 4, 6, 7\}$$
then
$$A \cap B = \{2, 5\} \quad B \cap C = \{3, 4, 6\} \quad \text{and} \quad A \cap C = \emptyset$$
Hence A and C are disjoint.

union of sets

The *union* of two sets A and B, denoted $A \cup B$, is the set consisting of all elements that belong to A or B. Here, as always in mathematics, the word "or" is used in the inclusive sense; that is, the union of A and B consists of all the elements that belong to A or B or both. Symbolically, we write

$$A \cup B = \{x | x \in A \text{ or } x \in B\}$$

In this case, since all the elements in A belong to $A \cup B$ and all the elements in B belong to $A \cup B$, it is clear that A and B are always subsets of $A \cup B$.

EXAMPLE 9

If
$$A = \{1, 2, 5, 8\} \quad B = \{2, 3, 4, 5, 6\} \quad \text{and} \quad C = \{3, 4, 6, 7\}$$
then
$$A \cup B = \{1, 2, 3, 4, 5, 6, 8\} \quad B \cup C = \{2, 3, 4, 5, 6, 7\}$$
and
$$A \cup C = \{1, 2, 3, 4, 5, 6, 7, 8\}$$

complement of a set

The *complement* of a set A is the set consisting of all elements of the universal set U that do not belong to A. In this book we denote the complement[1] of set A by A'. Thus
$$A' = \{x | x \in U \text{ and } x \notin A\}$$

It follows easily from the definition of A' that
$$A \cap A' = \emptyset \quad \text{and} \quad A \cup A' = U$$

EXAMPLE 10

If
$$A = \{1, 2, 5, 8\} \quad B = \{2, 3, 4, 5, 6\} \quad C = \{3, 4, 6, 7\}$$
and
$$U = \{1, 2, 3, 4, 5, 6, 7, 8, 9, 10\}$$
then
$$A' = \{3, 4, 6, 7, 9, 10\} \quad B' = \{1, 7, 8, 9, 10\}$$
and
$$C' = \{1, 2, 5, 8, 9, 10\}$$

Exercises

Label the statements in Exercises 1–8 true or false.

1. $3 \in \{-3, 2, 5\}$
2. $2 \subset \{-3, 2, 5\}$
3. $\{2, -4\} \supset \{-4, 0, 2\}$
4. $\{|-3|, \sqrt{4}\} = \{2, 3\}$
5. $\{1, 3, 5\} \subset \{0, 1, 2, 3, 4, 5\}$
6. $\{-2, 1, 7\} \neq \{7, -2, 1\}$
7. $1 \notin \{-1, 0, 7, 8\}$
8. $\{0, 5\} \not\subset \{1, 2, 3, 4, 5\}$

In Exercises 9–14, write each of the given sets by listing its elements.

9. $\{y | y \text{ is an integer and } y < 7\}$
10. $\{x | x(x - 2)(x + 5) = 0\}$
11. $\{z | z \text{ is an integer and } |z| < 3\}$
12. $\{w | w \text{ is a state bordering Lake Erie}\}$
13. $\{x | x \text{ is one of the original 13 states}\}$
14. $\{y | y \text{ is a state beginning with the letter "M"}\}$

In Exercises 15–20, write each of the given sets by giving a rule describing its elements.

[1] Another common notation for the complement of set A is $\bar{A}$.

15. $\{2, 4, 6, 8, 10\}$ 16. $\{4, 5, 6, 7, 8\}$ 17. $\{-3, 3\}$
18. $\{\text{Alaska, California, Hawaii, Oregon, Washington}\}$
19. $\{\text{Arizona, California, New Mexico, Texas}\}$
20. $\{\text{Truman, Eisenhower, Kennedy, Johnson, Nixon, Ford, Carter}\}$

Let U denote the set of all students at this university, M denote the set of all students taking a mathematics course at this university, B denote the set of all students taking a business course at this university, and E denote the set of all students taking an economics course at this university. Describe in words the elements of each of the sets given in Exercises 21–30.

21. $B \cup E$ 22. $B \cap M$ 23. M'
24. $M \cup B'$ 25. $B \cap E'$ 26. $B \cap M \cap E$
27. $B \cup E \cup M$ 28. $M \cap (B \cup E)$ 29. $B \cup (E \cap M)$
30. $M \cap (B \cup E)'$

Determine all the subsets of each of the sets in Exercises 31–34. How many proper subsets are there?

31. $\{5\}$ 32. $\{5, 6\}$ 33. $\{5, 6, 8\}$ 34. $\{5, 6, 8, 9\}$

Compute $A \cup B$, $A \cap B$, A', and B' for each of the sets A, B, and U in Exercises 35–44.

35. $A = \{1, 3\}$, $B = \{1, 2, 4\}$, $U = \{0, 1, 2, 3, 4\}$
36. $A = \{-5, -4, -2\}$, $B = \{-3, -1, 2\}$, $U = \{-5, -4, -3, -2, -1, 0, 1, 2, 3\}$
37. $A = \{-3, 1, 5\}$, $B = \{-4, -3, 0, 1, 2, 5\}$,
    $U = \{-5, -4, -3, -2, -1, 0, 1, 2, 3, 4, 5\}$
38. $A = \{-2, -1, 0, 1, 2, 3\}$, $B = \{-2, 0, 2\}$, $U = \{-4, -3, -2, -1, 0, 1, 2, 3, 4\}$
39. $A = \{1, 4, 7, 10, 13\}$, $B = \{2, 4, 6, 8, 10, 12, 14\}$, $U = \{1, 2, \ldots, 15\}$
40. $A = \{2, 3, 4\}$, $B = \{2, 3, 4\}$, $U = \{1, 2, \ldots, 10\}$
41. $A = \{x | x \text{ is an integer and } x \geq 10\}$, $B = \{x | x \text{ is a positive integer and } x \leq 100\}$, $U = \{x | x \text{ is a positive integer}\}$
42. $A = \{x | x \text{ is an even positive integer}\}$, $B = \{x | x \text{ is a positive integer that is a multiple of } 3\}$, $U = \{x | x \text{ is a positive integer}\}$
43. $A = \{x | x \text{ is an integer and } x > 20\}$, $B = \{x | x \text{ is an integer and } x \geq 30\}$, $U = \{x | x \text{ is a positive integer}\}$
44. $A = \{x | x \text{ is a real number and } -2 \leq x \leq 3\}$, $B = \{x | x \text{ is a real number and } 0 \leq x \leq 5\}$, $U = \{x | x \text{ is a real number}\}$

6.2 Venn Diagrams and Counting

Many of the concepts introduced in Section 6.1 can be represented pictorially by means of Venn diagrams. In this section we shall use Venn diagrams not only to visualize the relationships between sets but also to compute the number of elements in the union of two sets in terms of the number of elements in the original sets.

A *Venn diagram* consists of circles representing sets that are contained in a rectangle representing the universal set. The points within each circle represent the elements of the respective sets, and the points within the rectangle represent the elements of the universal set. The basic Venn diagram involving two sets A and B and a universal set U is shown in Figure 6.1.

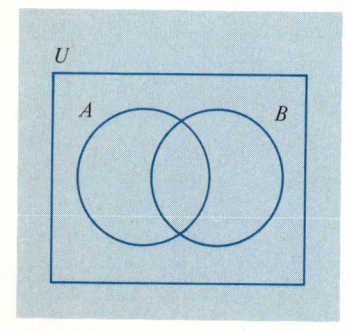

Figure 6.1

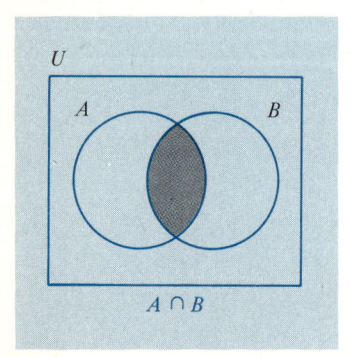

Figure 6.2

$A \cap B$

Venn diagram

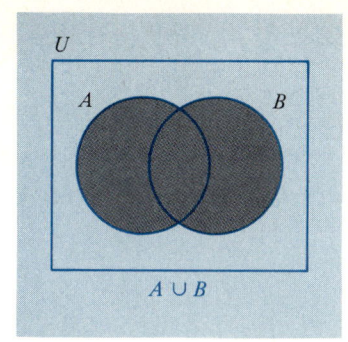

6.2 Venn Diagrams and Counting

Figure 6.3 (A ∪ B shaded)

Figure 6.4 (A' shaded)

Figure 6.5 (Three interlocking circles A, B, C)

Sets formed by intersections and unions of other sets can be easily depicted by means of Venn diagrams. For example, the intersection of sets A and B, which consists of the elements common to both A and B, corresponds to the overlap of circles A and B. This region is shaded in Figure 6.2.

Likewise, the union of sets A and B, which consists of all the elements in A or B or both, corresponds to the region enclosed by the circles representing A and B. This region is shaded in Figure 6.3. Similarly, since the complement of A consists of all the elements of the universal set that do not belong to A, the shaded region in Figure 6.4 represents A'.

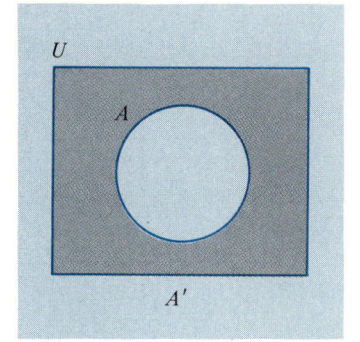

EXAMPLE 11

To depict the set $(A \cap B) \cup C$, we must draw a rectangle containing three interlocking circles representing the sets A, B, and C. This configuration will be like that shown in Figure 6.5. Notice that each pair of circles overlaps.

In order to construct a Venn diagram for the set $(A \cap B) \cup C$ we must first shade the region corresponding to $A \cap B$ (as in Figure 6.2). If we now shade the circle corresponding to set C, then the shaded region will correspond to the set $(A \cap B) \cup C$. (See Figure 6.6.)

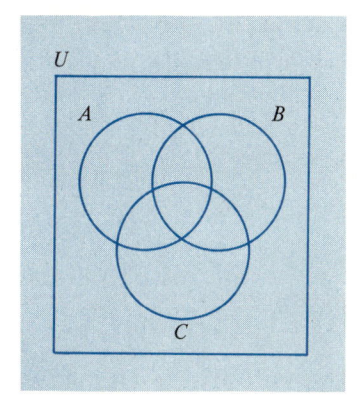

In the Venn diagrams contained in Figures 6.1–6.6, we have not assumed any special relationship among the sets depicted. Sometimes, however, we have additional information about the sets under consideration that allows us to refine our Venn diagrams accordingly. For example, if we know that A is a subset of B, then we can draw the circle representing A entirely within the circle representing B (as in Figure 6.7). Likewise, if we know that A and B are disjoint, then we can draw the circles representing A and B so that they do not overlap (as in Figure 6.8).

It will be important in our study of probability to be able to determine the number of elements in the union of two finite sets in terms of the number of elements in each of the two sets. For convenience of notation we denote the number of elements in a finite set A by $n(A)$. Thus we are interested in computing $n(A \cup B)$ in terms of $n(A)$ and $n(B)$. At first thought it may seem that $n(A \cup B) = n(A) + n(B)$. However, it is easy to find an example that will show this equation to be incorrect. For instance, if

$$A = \{1, 3, 5\} \quad \text{and} \quad B = \{2, 3, 4, 5\}$$

then

$$A \cup B = \{1, 2, 3, 4, 5\}$$

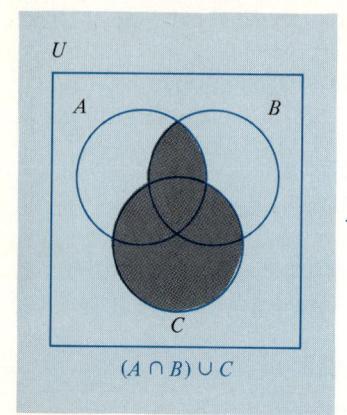

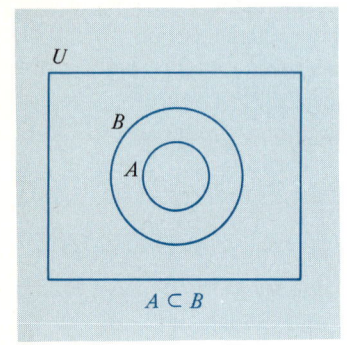

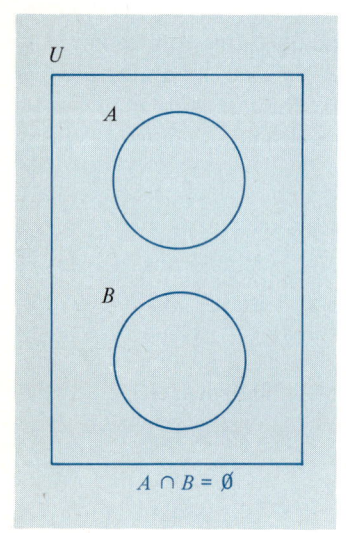

it is easy to see why $n(A \cup B) \neq n(A) + n(B)$: There are two elements (namely, 3 and 5) contained in both A and B, which are being counted twice in the sum $n(A) + n(B)$ but only once in $n(A \cup B)$. Thus in the sum $n(A) + n(B)$ we are counting each element of $A \cap B$ twice. It is now easy to see that the correct formula for $n(A \cup B)$ is as stated below.

THEOREM 6.1

If A and B are sets containing a finite number of elements, then

$$n(A \cup B) = n(A) + n(B) - n(A \cap B)$$

Figure 6.6 $(A \cap B) \cup C$

Figure 6.7 $A \subset B$

Figure 6.8 $A \cap B = \emptyset$

EXAMPLE 12

Suppose that among 50 people, 16 have blond hair and 20 have blue eyes. If 9 of these persons are known to have both blond hair and blue eyes, then Theorem 6.1 can be used to determine the number of persons having blond hair or blue eyes. For if we let H denote the set of persons with blond hair and E denote the set of persons with blue eyes, then the people having blond hair or blue eyes are members of the set $H \cup E$. So by Theorem 6.1 the number of persons with blond hair or blue eyes is

$$n(H \cup E) = n(H) + n(E) - n(H \cap E) = 16 + 20 - 9 = 27$$

Example 12 is a simple case of a problem requiring analysis of data involving several different attributes. Similar situations often arise when analyzing data from a survey. In order to further clarify the conclusion in Example 12, note that, since there are 9 persons with blond hair and blue eyes, there must be

$$n(H) - n(H \cap E) = 16 - 9 = 7$$

persons with blond hair but without blue eyes and

$$n(E) - n(H \cap E) = 20 - 9 = 11$$

persons with blue eyes but without blond hair. This information can be stored conveniently in the Venn diagram shown in Figure 6.9: There are 7 elements in $H \cap E'$ (the set of blond persons without blue eyes), 9 elements in $H \cap E$ (the set of blond, blue-eyed persons), and 11 elements in $E \cap H'$ (the set of blue-eyed persons without blond hair). The total number of persons in these three sets is the number of persons in $H \cup E$ (the set of people having blond hair or blue eyes).

The same type of analysis as that used in Example 12 can be used when more than two sets are involved. Consider, for example, the following problem.

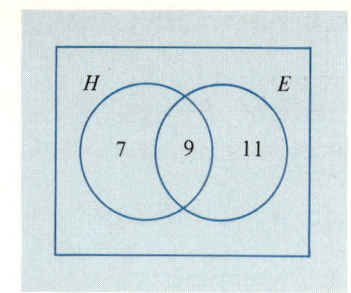

6.2 Venn Diagrams and Counting

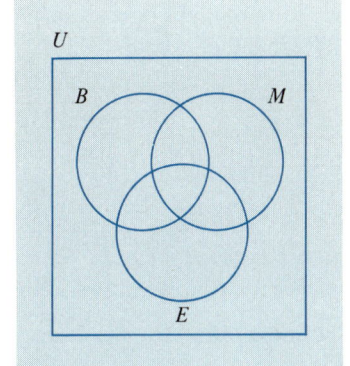

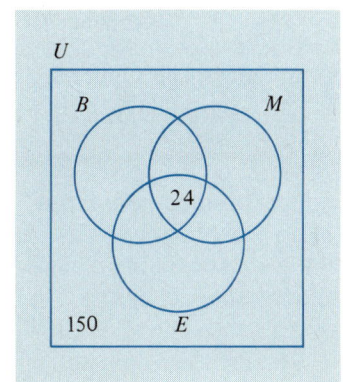

In a survey of students at a certain college the following data were obtained:

244 were taking a business course.
208 were taking a mathematics course.
152 were taking an economics course.
72 were taking courses in business and mathematics.
46 were taking courses in business and economics.
60 were taking courses in mathematics and economics.
24 were taking courses in business, mathematics, and economics.
150 were not taking a course in business, mathematics, or economics.

1. How many students were taking a business course but not taking a course in mathematics or economics?
2. How many students were taking a mathematics course but not taking a course in business or economics?
3. How many students were taking an economics course but not taking a course in business or mathematics?
4. How many students were surveyed?

To solve this problem, we use the Venn diagram in Figure 6.10, where B, M, and E denote the sets of students taking business, mathematics, and economics courses, respectively, and where U denotes the set of all students who were surveyed. The given data can then be expressed as follows:

$n(B) = 244$ $n(B \cap E) = 46$
$n(M) = 208$ $n(M \cap E) = 60$
$n(E) = 152$ $n(B \cap M \cap E) = 24$
$n(B \cap M) = 72$ $n[(B \cup M \cup E)'] = 150$

Since $n(B \cap M \cap E) = 24$ and $n[(B \cup M \cup E)'] = 150$, we can immediately insert the number of students in two of the eight regions in the Venn diagram in Figure 6.10. (See Figure 6.11.) Next we can determine the number of students taking courses in exactly two of the three subjects. Since 72 students are taking both business and mathematics courses and 24 students are taking courses in business, mathematics, and economics, the number of students taking both business and mathematics courses but not taking an economics course is $72 - 24 = 48$. Symbolically,

$$n(B \cap M \cap E') = n(B \cap M) - n(B \cap M \cap E) = 72 - 24 = 48$$

Likewise the number of students taking both business and economics courses but not taking a mathematics course is

$$n(B \cap E \cap M') = n(B \cap E) - n(B \cap M \cap E) = 46 - 24 = 22$$

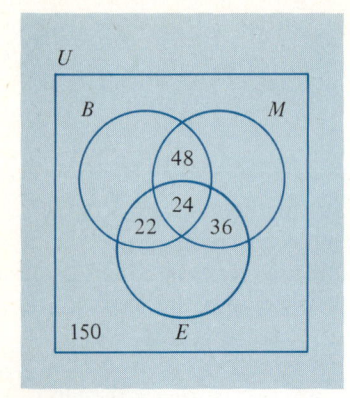

Figure 6.12

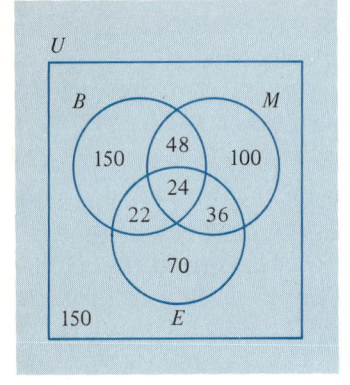

Figure 6.13

and the number of students taking both mathematics and economics courses but not taking a business course is

$$n(M \cap E \cap B') = n(M \cap E) - n(B \cap M \cap E) = 60 - 24 = 36$$

These three numbers can be placed in the appropriate regions of the Venn diagram as in Figure 6.12.

Only the computation of the number of students taking courses in exactly one of the three subjects remains. To find the number of students taking a business course but not taking a mathematics course or an economics course, we note that there are $48 + 24 + 22 = 94$ students already included in set B. (See Figure 6.12.) Since $n(B) = 244$, there must be $244 - 94 = 150$ students in the remaining part of set B (the region corresponding to $B \cap M' \cap E'$). In other words

$$n(B \cap M' \cap E') = n(B) - n(B \cap M \cap E') - n(B \cap M \cap E)$$
$$- n(B \cap E \cap M') = 244 - 48 - 24 - 22 = 150$$

Likewise the number of students taking a mathematics course but not taking a business course or an economics course is

$$n(M \cap B' \cap E') = n(M) - n(B \cap M \cap E') - n(B \cap M \cap E)$$
$$- n(M \cap E \cap B') = 208 - 48 - 24 - 36 = 100$$

and the number of students taking an economics course but not taking a business course or a mathematics course is

$$n(E \cap B' \cap M') = n(E) - n(B \cap E \cap M') - n(B \cap M \cap E)$$
$$- n(M \cap E \cap B') = 152 - 22 - 24 - 36 = 70$$

Writing these three numbers in the appropriate regions in Figure 6.12 produces the Venn diagram in Figure 6.13.

From this Venn diagram we see that:

1. There are 150 students who are taking a business course but not taking a mathematics course or an economics course.
2. There are 100 students who are taking a mathematics course but not taking a business course or an economics course.
3. There are 70 students who are taking an economics course but not taking a business course or a mathematics course.
4. The number of students who were surveyed was 600, the sum of all the numbers in the Venn diagram.

EXAMPLE 13

On May 7, 1970, Miami University (Oxford, Ohio) was closed for 10 days by the university administration in response to student protests following the invasion of Cambodia by the United States. An attitude questionnaire was prepared to sample student views regarding the closing of the university, and the results were reported in [6].

6.2 Venn Diagrams and Counting   225

Among the statements to which the students responded were these three:

1. Miami University will drastically have to change its educational policies in the future.
2. Trouble will never end at Miami until the whole university administrative structure is overturned.
3. Violence seems to be the only way to get the administration to listen to us.

Let N_1, N_2, and N_3 denote the set of students who indicated that statements 1, 2, and 3, respectively, were probably true or definitely true. The following data were reported from 434 responses.

$n(N_1) = 193$ $n(N_1 \cap N_3) = 69$
$n(N_2) =82$ $n(N_2 \cap N_3) = 36$
$n(N_3) = 112$ $n(N_1 \cap N_2 \cap N_3) = 30$
$n(N_1 \cap N_2) = 62$

By an analysis similar to that used in the problem above, we obtain the Venn diagram in Figure 6.14. From this diagram we see that 184 of the responders regarded none of the three statements as being probably true or definitely true.

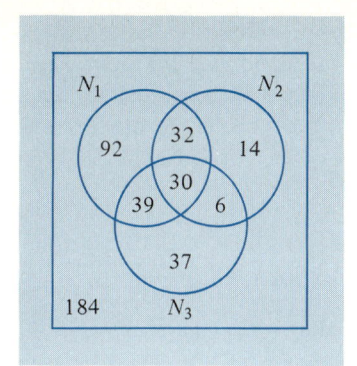

Figure 6.14

EXAMPLE 14

Human blood types are classified according to the presence or absence of three antigens called A, B, and Rh. The eight possible blood types are AB+, AB−, A+, A−, B+, B−, O+, and O−. In this classification the letters A and B denote the presence of the corresponding antigens, O denotes the absence of both A and B antigens, + denotes the presence of Rh antigen, and − denotes the absence of Rh antigen. Thus blood of type A− contains only A antigen, blood of type O+ contains only Rh antigen, and blood of type AB+ contains all three antigens. The possible blood types are displayed in the Venn diagram in Figure 6.15(a).

Among a random sample of 400 blacks, the following distribution of antigens can be expected:

140 will have A antigen.
100 will have B antigen.
340 will have Rh antigen.
 20 will have both A and B antigens.
119 will have both A and Rh antigens.
 85 will have both B and Rh antigens.
 17 will have all three antigens.

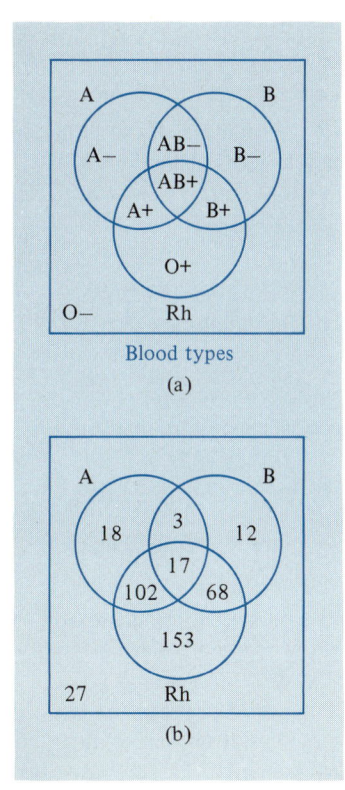

Figure 6.15

If these data are analyzed by the technique described above, then the Venn diagram in Figure 6.15(b) will be obtained. Thus we see, for example, that 102 persons (25.5%) can be expected to have blood type A+, 12 persons (3%) can be expected to have blood type B−, and 153 (38.25%) can be expected to have blood type O+.

Exercises

Depict each of the sets in Exercises 1–12 by shading a Venn diagram.

1. A'
2. $A \cap B$
3. $A \cup B$
4. $A' \cup B$
5. $A' \cap B$
6. $A \cap B \cap C$
7. $(A \cap C) \cup B$
8. $(B \cup C) \cap A$
9. $(A \cup B)' \cap C$
10. $(A \cap C)' \cup B$
11. $(A \cup B) \cap (C \cup B)$
12. $(B \cap A') \cup (C \cap A)$

13. Use Theorem 6.1 to compute $n(A \cup B)$ if $A = \{1, 2, 3, 4\}$ and $B = \{3, 4, 5, 6\}$.

14. Use Theorem 6.1 to compute $n(A \cup B)$ if $A = \{1, 3, 5, 7, 9\}$ and $B = \{4, 5, 6, 7\}$.

15. Prehistoric animals can be classified in various ways. (See [1].) Let S denote the set of prehistoric animals that had short limbs and T be the set of prehistoric animals that lived in the temperate zone. It is known that:

    1. Caseids, finbacks, and freshwater thecodonts had short limbs but did not live in the temperate zone.
    2. Most land thecodonts and therapsids had short limbs and lived in the temperate zone.
    3. Cenozoic mammals and dinosaurs lived in the temperate zone but did not have short limbs.

    Place caseids, finbacks, freshwater and most land thecodonts, therapsids, Cenozoic mammals, and dinosaurs in the proper parts of a Venn diagram containing sets S and T.

16. In a survey of 100 moviegoers it was found that 44 liked Bergman films, 37 liked Fellini films, and 23 liked both men's films. How many of the persons surveyed did not like the films of either man?

17. In [4] Dooley states: "The institution of the interlocking directorate is extensive and enduring." He found 3165 different persons serving on the boards of directors of the 200 largest nonfinancial corporations and the 50 largest financial corporations in the United States. Of these people, 544 held positions on two, three, or four different boards, and 67 held positions on four or more boards. If 49 people held positions on exactly four different boards, how many people held positions on exactly one board?

18. Among a random sample of 2000 whites, the following distribution of antigens can be expected:

    860 will have A antigen.
    340 will have B antigen.

1700 will have Rh antigen.
 100 will have both A and B antigens.
 731 will have both A and Rh antigens.
 289 will have both B and Rh antigens.
  85 will have all three antigens.

Use Figure 6.15(a) to determine the expected number of persons with each blood type.

19. The following data were obtained from 25 fast-food restaurants in a certain city:

12 served hamburgers.
10 served roast beef sandwiches.
 9 served pizza.
 4 served hamburgers and roast beef sandwiches.
 2 served hamburgers and pizza.
 3 served roast beef sandwiches and pizza.
 1 served all three of these foods.

(a) How many of these restaurants served hamburgers but neither roast beef sandwiches nor pizza?
(b) How many of these restaurants served pizza but neither hamburgers nor roast beef sandwiches?
(c) How many of these restaurants served none of the three foods?

20. The following information was obtained from persons at a shopping mall:

563 were adults.
414 were female.
310 had come alone.
296 were adult females.
213 adults had come alone.
124 females had come alone.
 92 adult females had come alone.
 54 were neither adult nor female and had not come alone.

(a) How many adult males had come alone?
(b) How many children had come alone?
(c) How many people were questioned?

21. In a survey of 350 registered voters, the following data were found:

175 were college-educated.
158 came from high-income families.
 90 were registered as Republicans.
104 were college-educated and came from high-income families.
 55 were college-educated and registered as Republicans.
 65 were from high-income families and registered as Republicans.
 42 were college-educated, from high-income families, and registered as Republicans.

How many persons were not college-educated, not from high-income families, and not registered as Republicans?

22. In tabulating the responses to a questionnaire sent to his constituents, a congressman found that

   2471 wanted tax reform.
   2952 wanted a balanced budget.
   1936 wanted increased aid to education.
   1997 wanted tax reform and a balanced budget.
   1713 wanted tax reform and increased aid to education.
   1504 wanted a balanced budget and increased aid to education.
   1376 wanted tax reform, a balanced budget, and increased aid to education.
    167 did not want tax reform, a balanced budget, or increased aid to education.

   How many questionnaires were returned to the congressman?

23. An insurance company claimed to have 900 new policyholders, of which

   796 bought automobile insurance.
   402 bought life insurance.
   667 bought fire insurance.
   347 bought automobile and life insurance.
   580 bought automobile and fire insurance.
   291 bought life insurance and fire insurance.
   263 bought automobile, life, and fire insurance.

   Explain why the state office of insurance ordered an audit of the company's records.

6.3 The Multiplication Principle

In Chapter 7 we shall see that under certain circumstances the relative frequency of occurrence of an event can be computed by counting the number of elements in certain related sets. Although the problem of counting the number of elements in a set may appear at first to be easy, often it is not, especially when the number of elements is very large. For example, determining the number of possible bridge hands by a direct count is difficult and tedious. In this section we shall develop formulas that will allow us to perform certain types of counting tasks with relative ease.

Let us begin, however, with a simple example. Suppose that we are interested in determining the number of possible outcomes when a die is rolled and then a coin is flipped. In this case, since the number of outcomes of each action is small, it is not difficult to list all the possibilities. The *tree diagram* in Figure 6.16 displays the results of both actions. Thus we see that there are 12 possible outcomes when a die is rolled and a coin is flipped.

Notice that in this situation there are 6 outcomes for the die, 2 outcomes for the coin, and $6 \cdot 2 = 12$ outcomes for the die and coin together. This example illustrates the following general result.

6.3 The Multiplication Principle 229

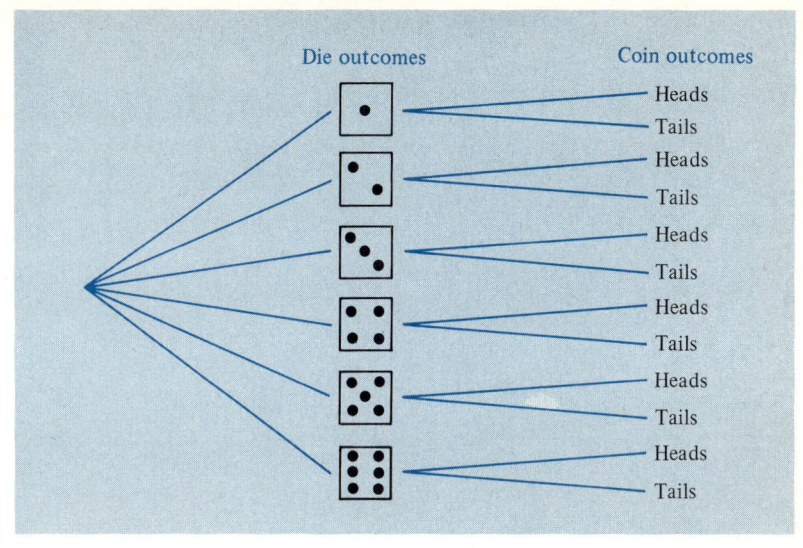

Figure 6.16

THEOREM 6.2 *The multiplication principle*

Suppose that k operations are to be performed in sequence and that the first can be performed in n_1 different ways, the second in n_2 different ways, ..., and the last in n_k different ways. Then the total number of ways of performing all k operations in sequence is $n_1 \cdot n_2 \cdot \cdots \cdot n_k$.

EXAMPLE 15

Broadhurst, in [3], describes an experiment with male albino rats designed to test the Yerkes-Dodson law which asserts that the optimum motivation for a learning task decreases as the difficulty of the task increases. The experiment involved a task having 3 levels of difficulty and rats having 4 levels of motivation and 2 levels of emotionality. The total number of classifications involved is therefore $3 \times 4 \times 2 = 24$. The tree diagram for this situation is shown in Figure 6.17.

EXAMPLE 16

Many universities administer examinations via computer terminals. In the typical situation the examiner stores several comparable questions about a particular subject in the computer, and on each examination the computer randomly selects one of them. If such a test is to consist of six questions, and if there are 8 possibilities for the first question, 7 for the second, 10 for the third, 5 for the fourth, 6 for the fifth, and 8 for the sixth, then there are $8 \cdot 7 \cdot 10 \cdot 5 \cdot 6 \cdot 8 = 134{,}000$ different tests the computer can administer.

Chapter 6 Sets and Techniques for Counting

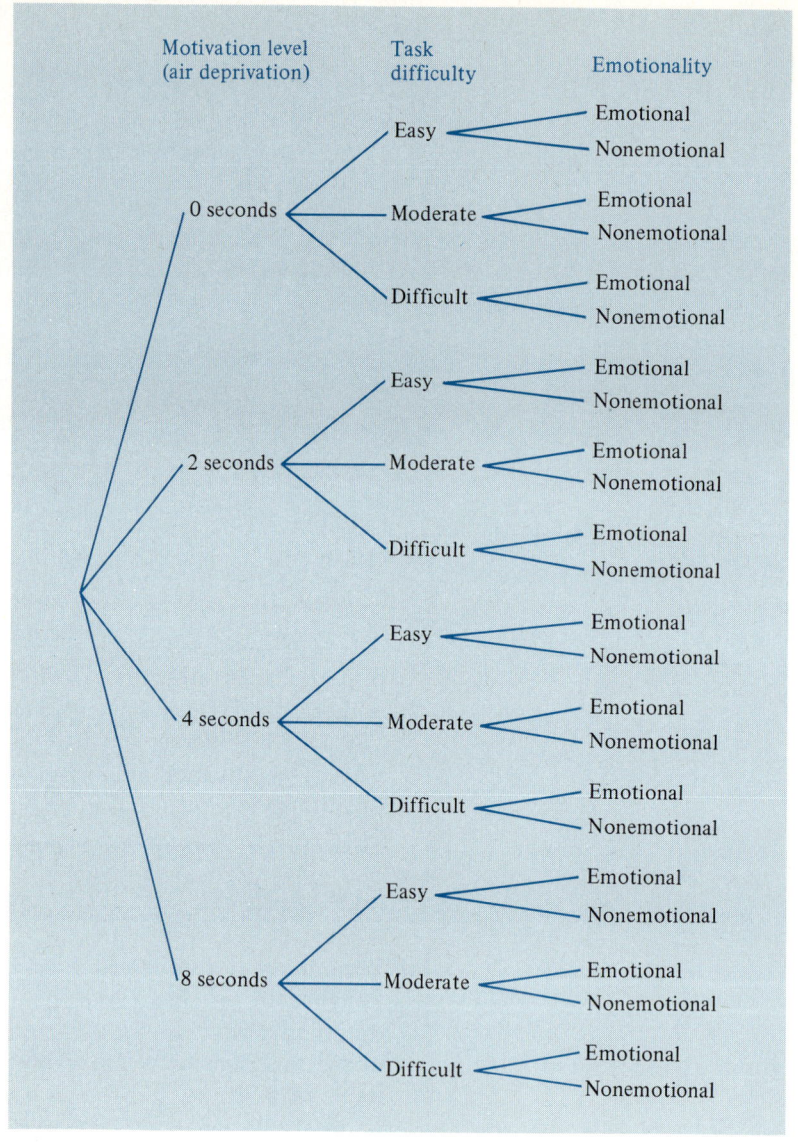

Motivation level (air deprivation)	Task difficulty	Emotionality
0 seconds	Easy	Emotional / Nonemotional
	Moderate	Emotional / Nonemotional
	Difficult	Emotional / Nonemotional
2 seconds	Easy	Emotional / Nonemotional
	Moderate	Emotional / Nonemotional
	Difficult	Emotional / Nonemotional
4 seconds	Easy	Emotional / Nonemotional
	Moderate	Emotional / Nonemotional
	Difficult	Emotional / Nonemotional
8 seconds	Easy	Emotional / Nonemotional
	Moderate	Emotional / Nonemotional
	Difficult	Emotional / Nonemotional

Figure 6.17

EXAMPLE 17

In Example 5 we saw that the set $A = \{2, 4, 6, 8\}$ has 16 possible subsets. Any particular subset can be thought of as being obtained by choosing whether or not to include each element of A in that subset. Thus there are 2 choices for each element of A (whether to include the element in the subset or not), hence a total of $2 \cdot 2 \cdot 2 \cdot 2 = 2^4 = 16$ possible sequences of choices, each of which corresponds to one of the subsets of A. More generally, a set containing n elements will have 2^n possible subsets.

EXAMPLE 18

> At Wendy's a hamburger can be ordered with any combination of 8 toppings—cheese, ketchup, lettuce, mayonnaise, mustard, onion, pickles, and tomatoes. Each combination of toppings can be regarded as a selection of a subset from a set containing 8 elements. So as in Example 17 the number of different combinations of toppings available at Wendy's is
>
> $2^8 = 256$

Exercises

1. Hal's Hot Dog Haven sells 7 types of hot dogs and 5 types of beverages. How many different orders of one hot dog and one beverage are possible?

2. A particular model of automobile is available in 3 body styles, 8 exterior colors, and 10 interior colors. How many different cars of this model can be ordered?

3. A questionnaire consists of 6 questions to be answered "always," "often," "sometimes," "seldom," or "never" followed by 4 questions to be answered "true" or "false." How many different questionnaires can be completed?

4. How many 3-digit numbers are there? (Assume that zero is not permitted as the first digit.)

5. (a) How many different license plate numbers can be formed using 3 letters followed by 3 digits?
   (b) Of the license plate numbers in part (a), how many contain no repeated letters and no repeated digits?
   (c) How many different license plate numbers can be formed using 2 letters followed by 4 digits?

6. In the United States, radio station call letters consist of 3 or 4 letters beginning with the letter "K" or "W."
   (a) How many 4-letter call letters are possible?
   (b) How many 3-letter call letters are possible?
   (c) How many of the call letters in part (a) contain no repeated letters?
   (d) How many of the call letters in part (a) end in "Z" and contain no repeated letters?

7. Kotler, in [5], discusses the measurement of market demand in terms of 6 different product levels (product item, product class, product line, company sales, industry sales, and national sales), 5 different space levels (customer, territory, region, country, and world), and 3 different time levels (short-range, medium-range, and long-range). In how many different ways can market demand be measured with one product level, one space level, and one time level?

8. A hospital classifies its patients according to sex and blood type. (Recall from Example 12 that there are 8 blood types.)
   (a) How many such classifications are there?
   (b) Display all these classifications with a tree diagram.

9. In [2], Baron hypothesizes that a subject cannot attend to more than one task at a time. Thus, when confronted with two tasks that must be performed simultaneously, the subject must either abandon one task or divide his or her attention between both.

(a) If there are 3 possible states of attention (focused on the first task, the second task, or neither task), 2 possible responses to the first task (correct or incorrect), and 2 possible responses to the second task (correct or incorrect), in how many ways may a state of attention followed by a response to each question occur?

(b) Construct a tree diagram showing all the possibilities described in part (a).

10. (a) How many arrangements of the digits 1, 2, 3, and 4 are there?
    (b) Construct a tree diagram showing all the possibilities described in part (a).

Determine the number of subsets of the sets given in Exercises 11–14.

11. $\{2\}$ 12. $\{4, -3\}$
13. $\{0, 1, 2, 3\}$ 14. $\{5, -3, 0, 9, 7\}$

15. At Avanti's a pizza can be ordered with any combination of 7 toppings: green pepper, ham, hamburger, mushrooms, onions, pepperoni, and sausage. How many different pizzas can be ordered at Avanti's?

16. The following items may be purchased as optional equipment on a certain model of new car: air conditioning, automatic transmission, bucket seats, power steering, AM/FM radio, and rear window defroster. How many different choices of optional equipment are there for this model of car?

17. How many different answer sheets are possible on a true-false test containing 10 questions if
    (a) Each question must be answered?
    (b) Each question need not be answered?

18. On a multiple-choice test in which each question can be answered with 5 possible responses, how many different answer sheets are possible if there are ten questions and no more than one answer can be chosen for each question?

19. In how many different orders can 3 men and 3 women be seated in a row of 6 seats if
    (a) Anyone may sit in any of the seats?
    (b) The first and last seats must be filled by men?
    (c) Men occupy the first 3 seats and women occupy the last 3 seats?
    (d) All members of the same sex are seated in adjacent seats?
    (e) Men and women are seated alternately?

20. Three women and two men are to be presented awards. In how many different orders can the awards be given if
    (a) The awards can be presented in any order?
    (b) The awards are presented to the women before the men?
    (c) The first award is presented to a woman and subsequent awards are given alternately to a man and then to a woman?
    (d) The first and last awards are made to women?
    (e) The first and last awards are made to men?

6.4 Permutations and Combinations

Two particular types of counting problems occur very frequently. The first involves counting the number of different ways of arranging or ordering objects, and the second involves counting the number of different ways of selecting objects. In this section we shall use the multiplication principle to obtain formulas that will enable us to determine how many ways there are of arranging or selecting objects chosen from among some designated set of objects.

In the discussion that follows we frequently encounter a product of consecutive integers. For convenience of notation we therefore define *n factorial*, denoted $n!$, to be the product of the integers 1 through n. It is helpful also to define *zero factorial*, denoted $0!$, to be 1. Thus the values of $n!$ for $n = 0, 1, 2, 3, 4, 5,$ and 6 are

n factorial
zero factorial

$0! = 1$
$1! = 1$
$2! = 2 \cdot 1 = 2$
$3! = 3 \cdot 2 \cdot 1 = 6$
$4! = 4 \cdot 3 \cdot 2 \cdot 1 = 24$
$5! = 5 \cdot 4 \cdot 3 \cdot 2 \cdot 1 = 120$
$6! = 6 \cdot 5 \cdot 4 \cdot 3 \cdot 2 \cdot 1 = 720$

Notice that for any positive integer n

$$n! = n(n-1)! \tag{6.1}$$

An arrangement or ordering of r objects taken from a set of n different objects is called a *permutation of the n objects taken r at a time*. The number of possible permutations of n objects taken r at a time will be denoted $P(n, r)$.

permutation

Suppose, for example, that a department head has been asked to select 3 persons from among 8 applicants for a particular job and to rank them in order of preference. The number of possible rankings is $P(8, 3)$, the number of permutations of 8 objects taken 3 at a time. In order to evaluate this number, notice that for the highest-ranking position the department head has 8 possible choices. After the first choice is made, there are 7 remaining persons from which to select the second-ranked person. Finally, when the second choice is made, there will be 6 remaining persons available from which to make the third choice. Thus the number of possible rankings is $8 \cdot 7 \cdot 6 = 336$; so $P(8, 3) = 336$.

Generalizing from the example above, we see that the number of permutations of n objects taken r at a time is

$$P(n, r) = n \cdot (n - 1) \cdot (n - 2) \cdot \cdots \cdot (n - r + 1)$$

This formula may be rewritten using factorial notation in the following useful form:

$$P(n, r) = n \cdot (n - 1) \cdot (n - 2) \cdot \cdots \cdot (n - r + 1) \frac{(n-r)!}{(n-r)!}$$

$$= \frac{n!}{(n-r)!} \tag{6.2}$$

EXAMPLE 19

A book exhibitor intends to display 5 of her company's 9 new books side by side. The number of possible arrangements of books in this way is

$$P(9, 5) = \frac{9!}{(9-5)!} = \frac{9!}{4!} = \frac{9 \cdot 8 \cdot 7 \cdot 6 \cdot 5 \cdot 4!}{4!}$$
$$= 9 \cdot 8 \cdot 7 \cdot 6 \cdot 5 = 15{,}120$$

EXAMPLE 20

A psychologist has trained 8 mice to run a maze. If all 8 mice are to run the maze consecutively, the number of possible orderings in which the mice are placed in the maze is

$$P(8, 8) = \frac{8!}{0!} = \frac{8!}{1} = 8! = 8 \cdot 7 \cdot 6 \cdot 5 \cdot 4 \cdot 3 \cdot 2 \cdot 1 = 40{,}320$$

It is important to remember that (6.2) is valid only when the n objects are all different. If some of the objects are indistinguishable, then the number of possible arrangements will be less than if the objects are all different. For example, the number of possible arrangements of the letters in the word "TEA" is $P(3, 3) = 6$:

TEA, TAE, ETA, ATE, EAT, and AET

There are only 3 possible arrangements of the letters in the word "TEE," however:

TEE, ETE, and EET

Notice that in the arrangements of the letters in "TEE," each placement of the letter "T" determined one arrangement, whereas in the first case each placement of the letter "T" determined two arrangements (one with "E" preceding "A" and one with "A" preceding "E"). This illustrates the following result.

If there are k different types of objects among a set of n objects, and if there are n_1 objects of one type, n_2 objects of a second type, $\cdots$, and n_k objects of the last type, then the number of different arrangements of the n objects is

$$\frac{n!}{n_1! n_2! \cdots n_k!}$$

EXAMPLE 21

The word "MISSISSIPPI" contains 11 occurrences of four different letters: "M" occurs once, "I" and "S" occur 4 times each, and "P" occurs 2 times. Thus the number of different arrangements of the letters in the word "MISSISSIPPI" is

$$\frac{11!}{1!4!4!2!} = 34{,}650$$

EXAMPLE 22

A concert pianist is preparing a recital that will consist of 2 classical pieces, 3 romantic pieces, and 1 contemporary piece. If pieces of the same period are regarded as indistinguishable for the sake of programming, then the number of different arrangements of the 6 pieces is

$$\frac{6!}{2!3!1!} = 60$$

combination

The second type of counting problem that we shall consider involves counting the number of possible ways of selecting r objects from among n different objects. Such a selection is called a *combination of n objects taken r at a time*. The number of combinations of n objects taken r at a time will be denoted $C(n, r)$.[2]

Each combination of n objects taken r at a time can be considered as a subset of r objects selected from a set of n objects. For example, the number of combinations of 5 objects taken 2 at a time is 10, since there are 10 subsets of $\{1, 2, 3, 4, 5\}$ containing exactly 2 elements, namely,

$$\{1,2\}\ \{1,3\},\ \{1,4\},\ \{1,5\},\ \{2,3\},\ \{2,4\},\ \{2,5\},\ \{3,4\},\ \{3,5\},\ \text{and } \{4,5\}$$

Observe that each permutation of 5 objects taken 2 at a time can be obtained by first selecting the two objects and then arranging them in the proper order. For example, the permutation 4, 3 of the 5 numbers 2, 3, 4, 5, and 6 taken 2 at a time can be obtained by first selecting the two-element subset $\{3, 4\}$ and then ordering the numbers as 4, 3. More generally, every permutation of n objects taken r at a time can be obtained by first selecting the r elements and then arranging them in order. Since the number of ways of selecting the r elements is $C(n, r)$ and the number of ways of arranging the r elements is $P(r, r)$, we see that

$$P(n, r) = C(n, r) \cdot P(r, r)$$

by the multiplication principle. This equation yields the following formula for $C(n, r)$:

$$C(n, r) = \frac{P(n, r)}{P(r, r)} = \frac{n!}{r!(n-r)!} \tag{6.3}$$

---

[2] Another common notation for the number of combinations of n objects taken r at a time is $\binom{n}{r}$.

EXAMPLE 23

If 3 police officers are to be selected for promotion from a list of 8 eligible persons, the number of different selections is

$$C(8,3) = \frac{8!}{3!5!} = \frac{8 \cdot 7 \cdot 6 \cdot 5!}{3!5!} = \frac{8 \cdot 7 \cdot 6}{3!} = \frac{8 \cdot 7 \cdot 6}{3 \cdot 2 \cdot 1} = 8 \cdot 7 = 56$$

EXAMPLE 24

Suppose that a laboratory technician wishes to perform experiments to determine the effects of certain drug interactions on mice. If the technician wants to consider the interactions of all possible pairs of 6 drugs, then the number of experiments that must be performed is

$$C(6,2) = \frac{6!}{2!4!} = \frac{6 \cdot 5 \cdot 4!}{2!4!} = \frac{6 \cdot 5}{2 \cdot 1} = 15$$

EXAMPLE 25

The number of possible bridge hands equals the number of ways of selecting 13 cards from among 52; so the number of possible bridge hands is

$$C(52,13) = \frac{52!}{13!39!} = 635{,}013{,}559{,}600$$

EXAMPLE 26

A student organization that consists of 4 freshmen, 5 sophomores, 8 juniors, and 7 seniors wants to select a 4-member executive board.

(a) How many different executive boards can be formed?
(b) How many different boards consisting entirely of seniors can be formed?
(c) How many different boards consisting entirely of juniors or seniors can be formed?

First, note that each of these questions concerns the number of ways that the members of the executive board may be selected. Thus each question will require computing a certain combination.

(a) Since there are 24 members in the organization, the number of different 4-member boards is

$$C(24,4) = \frac{24!}{4!20!} = 10{,}626$$

(b) Since there are 7 seniors in the organization, the number of different 4-member boards consisting entirely of seniors is

$$C(7,4) = \frac{7!}{4!3!} = 35$$

(c) Since there are 15 juniors and seniors in the organization, the number of different 4-member boards consisting entirely of juniors or seniors is

$$C(15,4) = \frac{15!}{4!11!} = 1365$$

Problems involving permutations and combinations often require use of the multiplication principle as well. The following example is of this type.

EXAMPLE 27

In Example 26, how many different boards can be formed if

(a) The board is to contain 2 juniors and 2 seniors?
(b) The board is to contain 1 junior and 3 seniors?
(c) The board is to contain 1 sophomore, 1 junior, and 2 seniors?

The number of different choices of 2 junior members is $C(8,2)$, and the number of different choices for 2 senior members is $C(7,2)$. Thus the number of different boards consisting of 2 junior members and 2 senior members is

$$C(8,2) \cdot C(7,2) = 28 \cdot 21 = 588$$

Likewise, the number of different ways of selecting 1 junior member is $C(8,1)$, and the number of different ways of selecting 3 senior members is $C(7,3)$. So the number of different boards containing 1 junior and 3 seniors is

$$C(8,1) \cdot C(7,3) = 8 \cdot 35 = 280$$

As above, the number of different boards containing 1 sophomore, 1 junior, and 2 seniors is

$$C(5,1) \cdot C(8,1) \cdot C(7,2) = 5 \cdot 8 \cdot 21 = 840$$

As the examples and exercises in this section demonstrate, it is sometimes difficult to determine whether a particular problem involves permutations or combinations. In order to distinguish permutations from combinations remember that *if the order of selection is important, permutations are involved, but if the order of selection is unimportant, combinations are involved.* Also be aware that the use of permutations and combinations is limited to situations involving distinct objects (i.e., no repetition of elements).

Exercises

Evaluate each of the numbers in Exercises 1–16.

1. 4!
2. 7!
3. 8!
4. 10!
5. $C(5, 3)$
6. $P(7, 5)$
7. $P(6, 3)$
8. $C(10, 7)$
9. $P(8, 3)$
10. $C(8, 4)$
11. $C(9, 4)$
12. $P(6, 2)$
13. $C(n, 1)$
14. $P(n, 1)$
15. $P(n, n)$
16. $C(n, n)$

17. Six candidates are running for the same seat in the state legislature. In how many different orders can their names be listed on the ballot?
18. Four speakers have been scheduled to address a convention. In how many different orders can the speakers appear?
19. In a test of consumer preferences, a person is asked to taste 7 brands of butter or margarine and rate (in order of preference) the 4 that taste best. How many possible ratings are there?
20. From among the 10 members of a committee, a chairperson and a secretary are to be selected. On a nominating ballot each member is asked to submit 2 different names, 1 for each office. How many different responses are possible?
21. Five chairs are placed in a row.
    (a) How many different ways are there of seating 5 people in the chairs?
    (b) If there are 8 people available, in how many different ways can the 5 chairs be occupied?

Determine the number of arrangements of the letters in the words given in Exercises 22–26.

22. TATTOO
23. REDBIRD
24. SASSAFRAS
25. STATISTICS
26. TENNESSEE

27. Four subcommittees are to be formed from a committee of 15 members. Each member will serve on exactly one subcommittee, and the subcommittees will consist of 6, 4, 3, and 2 members, respectively. How many different subcommittees can be formed?
28. In how many different orders can 7 $1 bills, 3 $2 bills, and 2 $5 bills be arranged?
29. If 20 children are to be grouped into 4 teams of 5 members each, how many different groupings are possible?
30. How many different 5-card poker hands are there?
31. A sample of 50 professors is to be taken at a university having 832 faculty members. How many different samples can be selected?
32. If there are 9 candidates running for 3 seats on a city council, how many different election results are possible
    (a) If the order of finish is disregarded?
    (b) If the order of finish of all 9 candidates is considered?
33. A grievance committee consisting of 5 members is to be selected from among 9 women and 7 men.
    (a) How many different subcommittees can be selected?
    (b) How many different committees consisting entirely of women can be selected?

(c) How many different committees consisting entirely of men can be selected?

34. For marketing purposes a company has divided the United States into 8 regions. It wishes to test a new product in 3 of these regions. How many different choices of regions are possible?

35. A 5-member committee is to be selected from among 4 representatives of management and 5 representatives of labor. In how many different ways can the members of the committee be selected if

   (a) Anyone is eligible to be chosen?
   (b) 3 representatives of management and 2 representatives of labor are to be chosen?
   (c) 1 representative of management and 4 representatives of labor are to be chosen?
   (d) The committee cannot contain 4 representatives of management?

36. Twelve of the houses on a particular street receive cable television and 8 do not. A researcher studying the amount of time that various categories of people watch television intends to visit 3 of the houses that receive cable television and 2 of the houses that do not. How many different choices of houses to visit can the researcher make?

37. A basketball team has 3 persons who play center, 5 who play guard, and 6 who play forward. How many different lineups consisting of 1 center, 2 guards, and 2 forwards can be selected?

38. Suppose that 5 seniors, 4 juniors, 3 sophomores, and 2 freshmen are candidates for 4 identical service awards. In how many different ways can the awards be given if

   (a) Any of the candidates may receive an award?
   (b) Only seniors receive an award?
   (c) No freshman receives an award?
   (d) 2 seniors and 2 juniors receive an award?
   (e) 1 member of each class receives an award?
   (f) 1 senior, 2 juniors, and 1 sophomore receive awards?

39. An electric mixer is available in three colors—avocado, gold, and white. An appliance store has 24 of these mixers in stock; 6 are avocado, 8 are gold, and 10 are white. Suppose that 5 of the mixers are selected from stock.

   (a) How many different selections are possible? (Regard two selections as different unless they contain exactly the same 5 mixers.)
   (b) How many of the selections in part (a) contain only white mixers?
   (c) How many of the selections in part (a) contain 2 gold and 3 white mixers?
   (d) How many of the selections in part (a) contain 1 avocado, 2 gold, and 2 white mixers?

40. How many different 5-card poker hands contain
   (a) Only hearts?
   (b) Only black cards?
   (c) 2 diamonds and 3 spades?
   (d) Exactly 2 aces?
   (e) Exactly 3 cards of the same denomination?
   (f) A full house (3 cards of one denomination and 2 of another)?

41. How many different 5-card poker hands contain
    (a) No cards above a 10?
    (b) 3 red cards and 2 black cards?
    (c) A flush (5 cards of the same suit)?
    (d) No pair of cards having the same denomination?
    (e) One 5, one 6, one 7, one 8, and one 9?
42. Figure 6.18 shows a portion of the map of a city. How many different routes can be traveled from location A to location B without moving south or west?

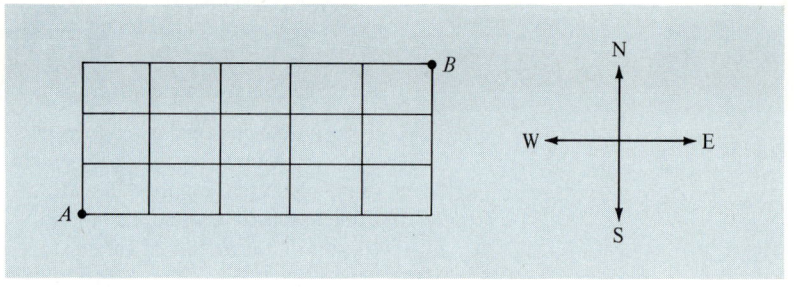

Figure 6.18

43. In how many different arrangements can n persons be seated around a *circular* table, taking into account only the position of each person relative to the others?
44. Show that $C(n, r) = C(n, n - r)$. Interpret this result.

Chapter Review

New Terms

combination (p. 235)
complement of a set (p. 219)
disjoint sets (p. 218)
element of a set (p. 215)
empty set (p. 217)
equality of sets (p. 216)
factorial (p. 233)
intersection of sets (p. 218)

permutation (p. 233)
set (p. 215)
set braces (p. 216)
subset (p. 217)
tree diagram (p. 228)
union of sets (p. 218)
universal set (p. 218)
Venn diagram (p. 220)

Review Exercises

1. Label the following statements true or false.
   (a) $\{3\} \notin \{1, 2, 3, 4, 5\}$
   (b) $\{2, 3, 4\} \subset \{1, 2, 3, 4, 5\}$
   (c) The sets $\{x | x$ is an odd positive integer$\}$ and $\{y | y$ is an even positive integer$\}$ are disjoint.
   (d) $n(A \cup B) = n(A) + n(B)$
   (e) $n! = 1 \cdot 2 \cdot \cdots \cdot n$

(f) $P(n,r) = \dfrac{n!}{r!}$

(g) $C(n,r) = \dfrac{n!}{r!(n-r)!}$

(h) The number of ways of selecting r objects from among n objects is $P(n,r)$.

2. Let $A = \{2, 5, 6, 8\}$, $B = \{1, 2, 3, 4, 5, 6\}$, and $U = \{1, 2, 3, 4, 5, 6, 7, 8, 9, 10\}$. Compute each of the following:
   (a) $A \cup B$ (b) $A \cap B$ (c) A' (d) B'

3. Depict the set $(A' \cap B) \cup C$ by shading a Venn diagram.

4. In a survey of 100 families it was found that 61 had a large car and 59 had a small car. If 24 of the families had both a large and a small car, how many had neither a large car nor a small car?

5. Among the houses in a particular subdivision it was found that

   195 had central air conditioning.
   92 had a finished basement.
   201 had a two-car garage.
   72 had central air conditioning and a finished basement.
   151 had central air conditioning and a two-car garage.
   66 had a finished basement and a two-car garage.
   54 had central air conditioning, a finished basement, and a two-car garage.
   7 did not have central air conditioning, a finished basement, or a two-car garage.

   (a) How many houses in this subdivision had a two-car garage but neither central air conditioning nor a finished basement?
   (b) How many houses in this subdivision had a finished basement and a two-car garage but did not have central air conditioning?
   (c) How many houses were in this subdivision?

6. Evaluate each of the following:
   (a) $5!$ (b) $9!$ (c) $C(8,6)$ (d) $P(7,3)$
   (e) $P(8,4)$ (f) $C(10,5)$ (g) $C(7,4)$ (h) $P(9,3)$

7. Godfather's Pizza has 13 different toppings that can be added to a pizza. How many different pizzas with 3 toppings can be purchased?

8. In [5] Kotler discusses the division of markets into segments based on geographic, demographic, and psychographic variables. He lists 5 geographic variables, 11 demographic variables, and 8 psychographic variables. How many different segmentations are possible using 1 geographic variable, 1 demographic variable, and 1 psychographic variable?

9. How many permutations of the letters in "SPRING" are possible?

10. How many permutations of the letters in "DECIDED" are possible?

11. An investor intends to buy stock in 4 of 10 companies. How many different selections of companies can be made?

12. First, second, and third prizes are to be awarded in a pie-baking contest. If there are 12 entries, how many different winning results are possible?

13. Six liberal candidates and 5 conservative candidates are running for 4 positions on a city council.

(a) How many different orders of finish are possible?
(b) How many different winning results are possible?
(c) In how many of the results in part (b) are 4 liberals elected?
(d) In how many of the results in part (b) are 2 liberals and 2 conservatives elected?

References

1. Bakker, Robert T., "Dinosaur Renaissance," *Sci. Am.*, vol. 232, no. 4 (April 1975), pp. 58–78.
2. Baron, Jonathan, "Division of Attention in Successiveness Discrimination," in *Attention and Performance IV*, Sylvan Kornblum, ed. New York: Academic, 1973, pp. 703–711.
3. Broadhurst, P. L., "Emotionality and the Yerkes-Dodson Law," *J. Exp. Psychol.*, vol. 54 (1957), pp. 345–352.
4. Dooley, Peter C., "The Interlocking Directorate," *Am. Econ. Rev.*, vol. 59, no. 3 (June 1969), pp. 314–323.
5. Kotler, Philip, *Marketing Management*, 3rd ed. Englewood Cliffs, N.J.: Prentice-Hall, 1976.
6. Rudestam, Kjell Erik and Bruce John Morrison, "Student Attitudes Regarding the Temporary Closing of a Major University," *Am. Psychol.*, vol. 26, no. 5 (May 1971), pp. 519–525.

7

Probability

Experiments in the physical sciences often produce exactly the same results when performed under identical conditions because there is some underlying principle (such as the principal of gravitational attraction) that governs the precise behavior of objects in certain situations. Such experiments are called *deterministic* because the results are completely determined by the underlying principle and the conditions under which the experiment is performed.

deterministic experiment

Other experiments will not yield the same results when repeated under identical conditions because there is an element of chance inherent in the experiment. For example, a coin flipped under identical conditions may fall heads in one case and tails in another, or children conceived under identical conditions may be of different sexes. Experiments that involve an element of chance are called *stochastic*.

stochastic experiment

This chapter is concerned with the study of probability, the branch of mathematics concerned with stochastic experiments. Intuitively, the probability of an event is a measure of its likelihood of occurrence. In this chapter we restrict our attention primarily to situations in which there is a finite number of equally likely outcomes.

7.1 Sample Spaces and Elementary Properties of Probability

In this section we shall introduce certain fundamental concepts that will form the basis for our work throughout this chapter. The terminology and notation introduced in Chapter 6 will be particularly

experiment

sample space

useful in discussing many of these concepts, and consequently we freely use the language of sets in what follows.

By an *experiment* we mean any observable occurrence. For example, we may speak of the experiment of flipping a coin (and observing whether it falls heads or tails), selecting a card from a deck (and noting its suit and denomination), observing the time of arrival of a bus at a particular stop, or observing the frequency of an automobile accident among a certain set of drivers.

Often there may be many possible types of outcomes that can be observed about a particular experiment. In the experiment of reading the obituary notices in a newspaper, for instance, we may be interested in observing the name, age, sex, or date of death for each person in the list. Once we have determined what observations are to be made, we can form the set consisting of all possible outcomes of the experiment; this set is called the *sample space* of the experiment. The reader should note that there may be many possible sample spaces for the same experiment, each depending upon the type of observations to be made.

EXAMPLE 1

Suppose that a box contains one red marble (R), one yellow marble (Y), one blue marble (B), and one green marble (G). Let us consider an experiment consisting of selecting one of the marbles from the box and then flipping a coin. The possible outcomes of this experiment can easily be enumerated using the tree diagram in Figure 7.1. (Heads and tails are denoted by H and T, respectively.) Thus one possible sample space for this experiment is

{RH, RT, YH, YT, BH, BT, GH, GT}

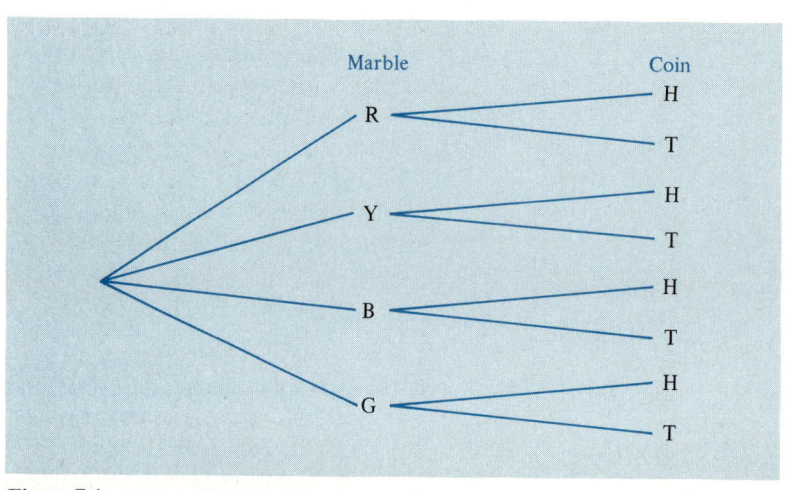

Figure 7.1

EXAMPLE 2

In the experiment of rolling a die, if we observe the number that appears, a sample space for the experiment is

$\{1, 2, 3, 4, 5, 6\}$

But perhaps we are only interested in whether the number that appears is even or odd; in this case a sample space is

$\{\text{even, odd}\}$

In a different context we may be interested only in whether or not a number greater than 2 appears; in this setting a sample space is

$\{2 \text{ or less, greater than } 2\}$

event
simple event
impossible event

Any subset of a sample space is called an *event*. Any event containing only one element, that is, a set consisting of a single outcome of an experiment, is called a *simple event*. An event E is said to *occur* if any of the outcomes in E occur and is said to be *impossible* if $E = \emptyset$.

EXAMPLE 3

In the experiment of rolling a die and observing the number that appears, the sample space is

$S = \{1, 2, 3, 4, 5, 6\}$

The event "a number greater than 4 appears" is the subset

$E = \{5, 6\}$

If a 5 or 6 is rolled, then E has occurred; otherwise E has not occurred. The event "a 7 appears" is the subset $\emptyset$, hence is impossible.

EXAMPLE 4

Consider the experiment of listing the sex of the children in a three-child family, where the children are listed in order of decreasing age. The sample space for this experiment is

$\{\text{GGG, GGB, GBG, GBB, BGG, BGB, BBG, BBB}\}$

where G and B represent a girl and boy, respectively. The event "the family has three girls" is the simple event $\{\text{GGG}\}$, while the event "the family has at least two boys" is the event

$\{\text{GBB, BGB, BBG, BBB}\}$

Because events are sets, we may speak of the intersection, union, or complement of events. It is important to note that for any events

E and F the event $E \cap F$ is the event consisting of the outcomes for which both E *and* F occur, and $E \cup F$ is the event consisting of the outcomes for which E *or* F occurs. Moreover, E' occurs exactly when E does not occur.

EXAMPLE 5

In Example 4 let E be the event "the family has exactly two girls," and let F be the event "the third child is a boy." Then

$$E = \{\text{GGB, GBG, BGG}\} \quad \text{and} \quad F = \{\text{GGB, GBB, BGB, BBB}\}$$

Thus

$$E \cap F = \{\text{GGB}\}$$

is the event "the family has exactly two girls and the third child is a boy," and

$$E \cup F = \{\text{GGB, GBG, BGG, GBB, BGB, BBB}\}$$

is the event "the family has exactly two girls or the third child is a boy." The event

$$E' = \{\text{GGG, GBB, BGB, BBG, BBB}\}$$

is the event "the family does not have exactly two girls."

For the remainder of this chapter we shall consider only experiments having a finite number of possible outcomes, hence a finite sample space.

Let us consider an experiment for which the sample space is

$$S = \{s_1, s_2, \ldots, s_m\}$$

For each simple event $\{s_i\}$ we assume that there is a real number denoted $Pr(s_i)$ associated with the event subject to the following conditions:

1. $0 \leq Pr(s_i) \leq 1$.
2. The sum of the numbers assigned to all the simple events equals 1; that is,

$$Pr(s_1) + Pr(s_2) + \cdots + Pr(s_m) = 1$$

probability of a simple event

The number $Pr(s_i)$ is called the *probability of the event* $\{s_i\}$.[1]

It is important to recognize that no statement has been made regarding how the probabilities $Pr(s_i)$ are to be determined. Sometimes they are determined theoretically, while in other situations they are estimated empirically as long-term relative frequencies.

---

[1] Actually we should write $Pr(\{s_i\})$ rather than $Pr(s_i)$ for the probability of the simple event $\{s_i\}$. Since no confusion will result from writing $Pr(s_i)$ rather than $Pr(\{s_i\})$, we omit the set braces for convenience of notation.

Suppose, for example, that we wish to assign probabilities to the two simple events in a coin-flipping experiment where the outcomes are H (the coin lands heads) and T (the coin lands tails). Since a perfectly balanced coin is just as likely to land heads as tails, we can theoretically assign the probabilities

$$Pr(H) = \tfrac{1}{2} \quad \text{and} \quad Pr(T) = \tfrac{1}{2}$$

On the other hand, we may actually flip the coin a large number of times and note the relative frequency with which each outcome occurs. If the coin is flipped 1000 times with the results shown in Table 7.1, then we may empirically assign the probabilities

$$Pr(H) = .476 \quad \text{and} \quad Pr(T) = .524$$

since these are the relative frequencies with which heads and tails appeared.

Table 7.1 *Results of 1000 Coin Flips*

Number of flips	Number of heads	Number of tails	Proportion of heads[a]	Proportion of tails[a]
100	54	46	0.540	0.460
200	96	104	0.480	0.520
300	138	162	0.460	0.540
400	189	211	0.473	0.528
500	232	268	0.464	0.536
600	278	322	0.463	0.537
700	327	373	0.467	0.533
800	380	420	0.475	0.525
900	428	472	0.476	0.524
1000	476	524	0.476	0.524

[a] Entries are rounded to three decimal places.

Of course, when problems arise that require the determination of various probabilities, it is important that the probability assigned to each simple event reflects the likelihood that the event will occur. But choosing which probabilities to assign to simple events is a decision that must be made by the problem solver according to experience, intuition, or personal taste.

Once probabilities have been assigned to the simple events, it is possible to assign a probability $Pr(E)$ to an arbitrary event E. There are three possibilities:

Case 1: If $E = \emptyset$, then we let $Pr(E) = 0$.
Case 2: If E is a simple event, then $Pr(E)$ has already been assigned.
Case 3: In any other case E is the union of two or more simple events, and we let $Pr(E)$ equal the sum of the probabilities of all the simple events whose union is E.

EXAMPLE 6

The distribution of scores on a particular English test was as follows:

Score	0–59	60–64	65–69	70–74	75–79	80–84	85–89	90–94	95–100
Proportion of students	0.07	0.09	0.12	0.21	0.23	0.13	0.08	0.05	0.02

We shall regard the proportion of students who earn a score in each interval as the empirical probability of obtaining a score in that interval. Suppose that the instructor announces the grading scale

A: 90–100
B: 80–89
C: 70–79
D: 60–69
F: 0–59

Then the event E_1 of receiving an A on the test is the union of the simple events F_1 and F_2, where F_1 is the event "the score is in the interval 95–100" and F_2 is the event "the score is in the interval 90–94." So

$$Pr(E_1) = Pr(F_1 \cup F_2) = Pr(F_1) + Pr(F_2) = .02 + .05 = .07$$

Likewise the event E_2 of receiving at least a B on the test is the union of the simple events $F_1, F_2, F_3,$ and F_4, where F_3 and F_4 are the events "the score is in the interval 85–89" and "the score is in the interval 80–84," respectively. Hence

$$\begin{aligned} Pr(E_2) &= Pr(F_1 \cup F_2 \cup F_3 \cup F_4) \\ &= Pr(F_1) + Pr(F_2) + Pr(F_3) + Pr(F_4) \\ &= .02 + .05 + .08 + .13 = .28 \end{aligned}$$

EXAMPLE 7

Suppose that after 600 times at bat during a particular season a baseball player's batting statistics show that

$Pr(S) = .175$ $\quad$ $Pr(W) = .150$
$Pr(D) = .025$ $\quad$ $Pr(HP) = .010$
$Pr(T) = .010$ $\quad$ $Pr(R) = .590$
$Pr(HR) = .040$

where S, D, T, HR, and W represent the events of getting a single, double, triple, home run, or walk, respectively, HP represents the event of being hit by a pitch, and R represents any other result.

Then this player's probability of reaching first base by getting a single, getting a walk, or being hit by a pitch is

$$Pr(S \cup W \cup HP) = Pr(S) + Pr(W) + Pr(HP)$$
$$= .175 + .150 + .010 = .335$$

Likewise this player's probability of getting a hit is

$$Pr(S \cup D \cup T \cup HR) = Pr(S) + Pr(D) + Pr(T) + Pr(HR)$$
$$= .175 + .025 + .010 + .040 = .250$$

and the probability of getting an extra base hit is

$$Pr(D \cup T \cup HR) = Pr(D) + Pr(T) + Pr(HR)$$
$$= .025 + .010 + .040 = .075$$

In many experiments it is reasonable to assign the same probability to each simple event. For example, we have already discussed assignment of the value $\frac{1}{2}$ as the probability of both simple events in a coin-flipping experiment. Likewise, in rolling a die, we can expect that each face is equally likely to appear if the die is perfectly symmetric and properly balanced; so under these conditions it is reasonable to assign the value $\frac{1}{6}$ as the probability that any face will appear. More generally, if an experiment has n possible outcomes that intuitively can be expected to occur with the same relative frequency, then we can assign the value $1/n$ as the probability of each simple event. This type of situation frequently occurs when items are chosen randomly.

EXAMPLE 8

If a card is randomly chosen from a standard deck of playing cards, then the theoretical probability of randomly selecting each card is $\frac{1}{52}$.

EXAMPLE 9

If the integers 1 through 845 are each written on a separate slip of paper and dropped in a barrel, the theoretical probability of randomly selecting each number is $\frac{1}{845}$.

Henceforth, whenever a sample space is constructed, it will be constructed so that the outcomes are equally likely, and consequently the same probability will be assigned to each simple event.[2] In this

---

[2] It must be recognized that assigning the same probability to each simple event involves an assumption that may prove to be unrealistic. For example, although it may seem reasonable to assign the probability $\frac{1}{2}$ to the event "a newborn child is a girl," census figures since 1950 show that in the United States the proportion of girls born has been only .488. Nevertheless, we assume in what follows that newborn infants are equally likely to be girls or boys.

context the assignment of the value $Pr(E)$ to an arbitrary event E (as described on page 247) takes the following simple form.

THEOREM 7.1

In an experiment having a sample space S consisting of m equally likely outcomes, let E be an event consisting of k outcomes. Then the probability of the event E is

$$Pr(E) = \frac{n(E)}{n(S)} = \frac{k}{m}$$

EXAMPLE 10

If a die is rolled, the event "a number greater than 4 appears" is the set $E = \{5, 6\}$. Since there are 6 possible outcomes in the sample space $S = \{1, 2, 3, 4, 5, 6\}$, it follows that

$$Pr(E) = \frac{n(E)}{n(S)} = \frac{2}{6} = \frac{1}{3}$$

Likewise the event "an odd number appears" is the set $F = \{1, 3, 5\}$; hence

$$Pr(F) = \frac{n(F)}{n(S)} = \frac{3}{6} = \frac{1}{2}$$

EXAMPLE 11

If the integers 1 through 845 are each written on a separate slip of paper and dropped in a barrel from which a slip is to be randomly selected, then the probability that any one of the numbers 1–10 will be selected is $\frac{10}{845} = \frac{2}{169}$.

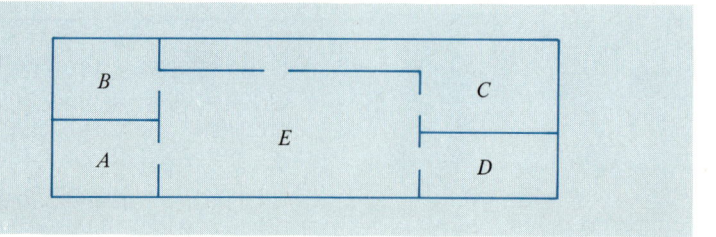

Figure 7.2

EXAMPLE 12

Suppose that a rat is placed in room E of the maze shown in Figure 7.2. If it selects a door at random, then the probability that it will next enter room C is $\frac{2}{5}$.

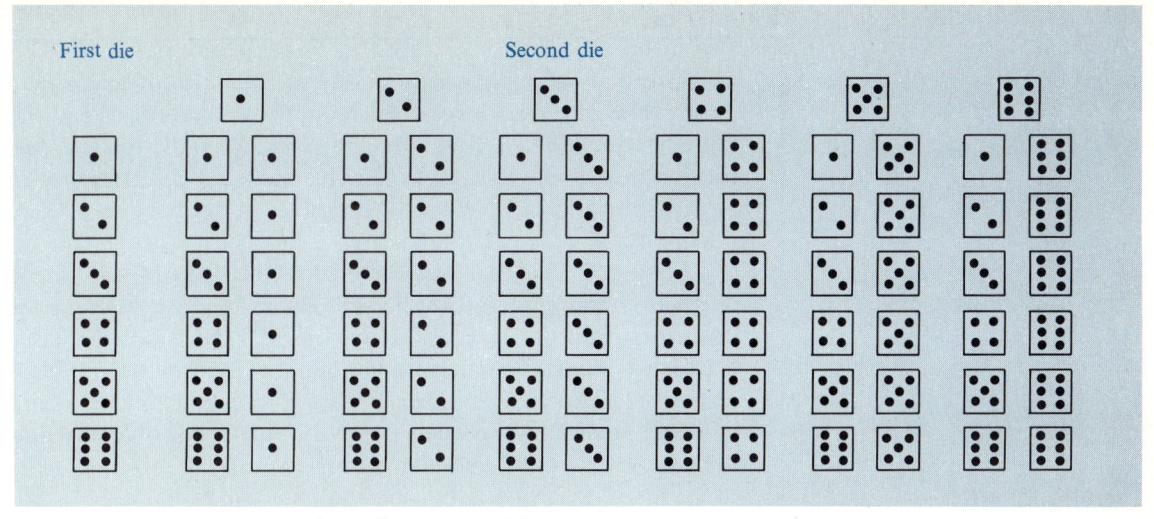

Figure 7.3 *Possible outcomes when rolling a pair of dice.*

EXAMPLE 13

If a pair of dice is rolled or one die is rolled twice, the multiplication principle shows that there are $6 \cdot 6 = 36$ possible outcomes. These outcomes are shown in Figure 7.3. Since there are 5 outcomes in which the sum of the numbers showing equals 8, the probability of rolling an 8 equals $\frac{5}{36}$. Likewise the probability of any number from 2 through 12 can be shown to be as follows:

Number	2	3	4	5	6	7	8	9	10	11	12
Probability of occurrence	$\frac{1}{36}$	$\frac{2}{36}$	$\frac{3}{36}$	$\frac{4}{36}$	$\frac{5}{36}$	$\frac{6}{36}$	$\frac{5}{36}$	$\frac{4}{36}$	$\frac{3}{36}$	$\frac{2}{36}$	$\frac{1}{36}$

When there are a large number of possible outcomes for an experiment, the counting techniques discussed in Chapter 6 are useful in computing probabilities. The following examples illustrate how permutations and combinations can be used with Theorem 7.1.

EXAMPLE 14

Suppose that 6 students enter a classroom and randomly select seats in the first row. Since there are $P(6,6) = 6! = 720$ possible arrangements of the students in 6 seats, the probability that the students are seated in alphabetical order from left to right is $\frac{1}{720}$.

EXAMPLE 15

Suppose that an appliance store stocks 8 models of microwave ovens, of which 3 leak excessive amounts of radiation. If 2 of the 8 models are selected randomly and tested for radiation leakage, the sample of 2 may contain 0 defective models, 1 defective model, or 2 defective models. We shall compute the probability of each possibility.

First, note that the number of possible ways of selecting 2 ovens from among 8 is $C(8,2) = 28$. Hence the sample space for this experiment has 28 possible outcomes. If the sample contains 0 defective models, then it must contain 2 of the 5 models without excessive leakage. The number of ways of selecting 2 models from among 5 nondefective models is $C(5,2)$. Thus the probability that the sample contains 0 defective models is

$$Pr(0 \text{ defectives}) = \frac{C(5,2)}{C(8,2)} = \frac{10}{28} = \frac{5}{14}$$

Likewise, since there are 3 defective models, the probability that the sample contains only defective models is

$$Pr(2 \text{ defectives}) = \frac{C(3,2)}{C(8,2)} = \frac{3}{28}$$

We shall see in Section 7.2 that the probability of the sample containing exactly 1 defective model can be computed easily in terms of $Pr(0 \text{ defectives})$ and $Pr(2 \text{ defectives})$. It is possible, however, to compute $Pr(1 \text{ defective})$ directly. If a sample contains exactly 1 defective model, then it must also contain exactly 1 nondefective model. The number of ways of selecting 1 defective model is $C(3,1)$, and the number of ways of selecting 1 nondefective model is $C(5,1)$. Thus, by the multiplication principle, the number of ways of selecting 1 defective model and 1 nondefective model is $C(3,1) \cdot C(5,1)$. Hence

$$Pr(1 \text{ defective}) = \frac{C(3,1) \cdot C(5,1)}{C(8,2)} = \frac{3 \cdot 5}{28} = \frac{15}{28}$$

EXAMPLE 16

If 7 objects of one kind are mixed with 13 objects of another kind, then the probability of randomly selecting an object of the first kind is easily seen to be $\frac{7}{20}$ (since there are a total of 20 objects of both kinds). Suppose, however, that 8 of the 20 objects are randomly selected and removed without being seen. If one of the remaining 12 objects is now selected at random, what is the probability that it will be an object of the first kind?

The answer to this question can be obtained by using facts about permutations from Section 6.3. Let us think of randomly selecting 9 of the 20 objects in succession and discarding the first 8. We would like to determine the probability that an object of the first kind will be chosen on the ninth selection. Since each possible sequence of choices can be thought of as an ordering of 9 objects from among the original 20, Theorem 7.1 shows that the desired probability equals $n(E)/n(S)$, where S is the set of all orderings of 9 objects from among 20 and E is the subset of S consisting of the orderings in which an object of the first kind occurs last. Clearly S is the set of permutations of 20 objects taken 9 at a time; so

$$n(S) = P(20, 9) = \frac{20!}{11!}$$

To count the number of sequences in E, we note that the last selection (the choice of an object of the first kind) can occur in one of 7 possible ways because there are 7 objects of the first kind. In addition, since an object of the first kind is to be selected ninth, there are only 19 objects from which to make the first 8 selections. So the number of ways of selecting the first 8 objects is $P(19, 8) = 19!/11!$. Thus by the multiplication principle

$$n(E) = \begin{pmatrix} \text{number of ways of} \\ \text{selecting the first 8 objects} \end{pmatrix} \begin{pmatrix} \text{number of ways of} \\ \text{selecting the ninth} \end{pmatrix}$$

$$= \frac{19!}{11!} \cdot 7$$

Hence the probability that an object of the first kind will be selected after 8 objects have been removed is

$$\frac{n(E)}{n(S)} = \frac{(19!/11!) \cdot 7}{20!/11!} = \frac{7 \cdot 19!}{11!} \cdot \frac{11!}{20!} = \frac{7 \cdot 19!}{20!} = \frac{7}{20}$$

Therefore the probability of choosing an object of the first kind on the ninth selection is the same as on the first selection. Similar reasoning shows that, when successive random selections are made, the probability of choosing an object of the first kind on any subsequent selection is the same as on the first selection. Moreover, this conclusion remains true no matter how many objects of each type there are initially.

Exercises

For each experiment described in Exercises 1–10, write the sample space using set notation. Note that in these exercises some of the sample spaces may be infinite.

1. One coin is flipped.
2. One two-headed coin is flipped.
3. A person's month of birth is recorded.
4. One marble is selected from a box containing a red, a yellow, and a blue marble, and then one marble is selected from a box containing a green, a black, an orange, and a white marble.
5. A die is rolled once, and a coin is flipped twice.
6. A Democrat and a Republican are the only candidates for the offices of governor, attorney general, and comptroller. A voter is asked how he or she intends to vote for these three offices.
7. The number of persons riding the subway in New York is counted on a particular day.
8. At a particular location the number of hours of sunlight is recorded on a certain day. (Assume that this time can be measured exactly.)
9. A light bulb is lit, and the length of time it burns is recorded. (Assume that this time can be measured exactly.)
10. A coin is flipped until it lands tails.
11. Suppose that a rat is released from the room labeled "START" in the maze pictured in Figure 7.4 and that a psychologist records each left turn (L) and right turn (R) made by the rat. If the rat is allowed to move through the maze without retracing its steps until it reaches a room containing food, what will be the sample space for this experiment?

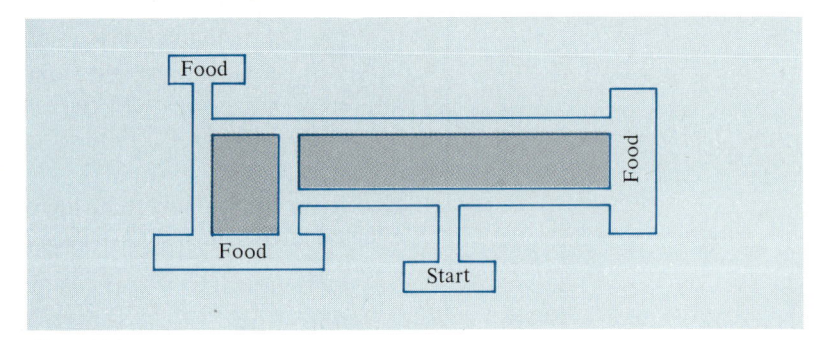

Figure 7.4

12. A firm that conducts public polls classifies persons according to sex (male or female), age (18–24, 25–34, 35–64, or 65 and over), and education (college graduate, high school graduate, or other). When a person is stopped and classified in this way, what is the sample space?

For each pair of events E and F in Exercises 13–20 describe the events $E \cup F$, $E \cap F$, E', and F'.

13. In the experiment of flipping a coin twice, let E be the event "the same side of the coin shows on both flips" and F be the event "the second flip is tails."
14. In the experiment of selecting a card from a standard deck of playing cards, let E be the event "a club is drawn" and F be the event "a face card is drawn."

15. In the experiment of rolling a red die and a white die, let E be the event "an even number appears on the red die" and F be the event "5 or 6 appears on the white die."
16. In the experiment of selecting a member from a committee consisting of students, faculty, and administrators, let E be the event "a student is selected" and F be the event "a female is selected."
17. In the experiment described in Exercise 5, let E be the event "at least one heads appears" and F be the event "a number less than 3 is rolled."
18. In the experiment described in Exercise 6, let E be the event "the voter votes for 3 candidates from the same party" and F be the event "the voter votes for the Democratic candidate for governor."
19. In the experiment of recording the last digit in someone's social security number, let $E = \{0, 1, 2, 3, 4\}$ and $F = \{1, 3, 5, 7, 9\}$.
20. In the experiment of recording the last two digits in someone's social security number, let $E = \{x | 60 \leq x \leq 99\}$ and $F = \{x | x \leq 80\}$.

Let E, F, and G be three events in the same experiment. Using set notation, describe the events in Exercises 21–28 in terms of E, F, and G.

21. F does not occur.
22. E and G occur.
23. F or G occurs.
24. E occurs or G does not occur.
25. G occurs and E does not occur.
26. E, F, and G all occur.
27. At least one of the events E, F, or G occurs.
28. F occurs but E and G do not occur.

Let $S = \{s_1, s_2, s_3, s_4\}$ be the sample space of an experiment. Which of the functions in Exercises 29–34 are permissible probability assignments (not necessarily having equally likely outcomes)?

29. $Pr(s_1) = \frac{1}{3}$, $Pr(s_2) = \frac{1}{3}$, $Pr(s_3) = \frac{1}{3}$, $Pr(s_4) = 0$
30. $Pr(s_1) = .6$, $Pr(s_2) = -.1$, $Pr(s_3) = .3$, $Pr(s_4) = .2$
31. $Pr(s_1) = .3$, $Pr(s_2) = .3$, $Pr(s_3) = .3$, $Pr(s_4) = .3$
32. $Pr(s_1) = .2$, $Pr(s_2) = .3$, $Pr(s_3) = .1$, $Pr(s_4) = .4$
33. $Pr(s_1) = .3$, $Pr(s_2) = .1$, $Pr(s_3) = .2$, $Pr(s_4) = .2$
34. $Pr(s_1) = \frac{1}{4}$, $Pr(s_2) = \frac{1}{4}$, $Pr(s_3) = \frac{1}{4}$, $Pr(s_4) = \frac{1}{4}$

For the experiment with sample space $S = \{s_1, s_2, s_3, s_4, s_5\}$, let $Pr(s_1) = .15$, $Pr(s_2) = .20$, $Pr(s_3) = .30$, $Pr(s_4) = .10$, $Pr(s_5) = .25$. Compute the probability of each of the events in Exercises 35–38.

35. $\{s_1, s_3, s_5\}$
36. $\{s_2, s_3\}$
37. $\{s_1, s_2, s_3, s_4\}$
38. $\{s_3, s_5\}$

Using Example 6, compute the probability of the events in Exercises 39–42.

39. Receiving less than an A
40. Receiving a B
41. Receiving a D or an F
42. Receiving an A, a B, or a C

Using Example 13, compute the probability of the events in Exercises 43–48.

43. Both dice showing the same number.
44. A number less than 7 being rolled.
45. A number greater than 9 being rolled.
46. A 3 appearing on at least one die.
47. A 7 or an 11 being rolled.
48. The number on the second die being less than the number on the first die.

49. If a coin is flipped 5 times, find the probability that
    (a) Exactly 3 heads will appear.
    (b) Exactly 2 heads will appear.
    (c) At least 2 heads will appear.
    (d) The same side of the coin will show each time.
50. A student guesses the answer to 3 true-false questions. Compute the probability that
    (a) All the answers are wrong.
    (b) All the answers are correct.
    (c) At least 1 answer is correct.
    (d) Exactly 2 answers are correct.

The integers 2 through 9 are written (once each) on separate slips of paper, placed in a box, and thoroughly mixed. If two slips are selected simultaneously, find the probability of the events in Exercises 51–58.

51. 4 will be chosen.
52. 3 will not be chosen.
53. An even number will be chosen.
54. A multiple of 3 will be chosen.
55. 7 and 8 will be chosen.
56. Two odd numbers will be chosen.
57. Two multiples of 3 will be chosen.
58. The sum of the numbers chosen will exceed 13.
59. One brand of margarine in a supermarket dairy case has two different latest sale dates. Suppose that the manager counts 24 packages with the earlier date and 37 with the later date and then mixes the packages together.
    (a) If the next customer to buy this brand of margarine selects a package at random, what is the probability that it will have the later date?
    (b) Suppose that after several hours the manager notices that there are only 12 packages of this margarine remaining in the dairy case. If the next customer to buy this brand selects a package at random, what is the probability that it will have the earlier date?
60. A supervisor randomly selects the personnel files of 4 employees. What is the probability that the files will be in order of decreasing age?
61. In a taste test 4 crackers are spread with butter and 4 with margarine. A consumer is asked to taste each cracker and identify the 4 spread with butter. What is the probability of identifying the 4 crackers spread with butter by guessing randomly?
62. In an 8-horse race, a bettor bet the trisecta, which requires that the first 3 horses be identified in order of finish. What is the probability of winning the trisecta by randomly selecting 3 numbers?
63. In a lot of 20 transistors, 4 are known to be defective. If the transistors are packaged in 2 boxes of 10 transistors each, what is the probability that
    (a) All the defective transistors are packed in the same box?
    (b) 3 of the defective transistors are packed in the same box?
    (c) 2 of the defective transistors are packed in each box?
64. The 12 finalists in a state lottery consist of 7 men and 5 women. From among these 12 finalists 3 persons are to be randomly selected to win $50,000.

(a) What is the probability that any 1 of the 12 will win?
(b) What is the probability that all the winners will be women?
(c) What is the probability that 2 of the winners will be men and 1 will be a woman?

In Exercises 65–72, suppose a box contains 4 red marbles, 6 blue marbles, and 5 green marbles. If 5 of the marbles are randomly selected, what is the probability that

65. All will be blue?
66. All will be green?
67. All will be red?
68. None will be red?
69. None will be green?
70. 3 will be blue and 2 will be green?
71. 1 will be red, 2 will be blue, and 2 will be green?
72. 1 will be red, 1 will be blue, and 3 will be green?

odds in favor of an event The *odds in favor of an event E* are defined to be the ratio

$$\frac{Pr(E)}{Pr(E')} \quad \text{if } Pr(E') \neq 0$$

odds against an event Likewise the *odds against an event E* are defined to be the ratio

$$\frac{Pr(E')}{Pr(E)} \quad \text{if } Pr(E) \neq 0$$

For example, if $Pr(E) = \frac{3}{7}$ and $Pr(E') = \frac{4}{7}$, then the odds in favor of E are $\frac{3/7}{4/7} = \frac{3}{4}$, or 3 to 4, and the odds against E are $\frac{4/7}{3/7} = \frac{4}{3}$, or 4 to 3.

In Exercises 73–78, calculate the indicated odds when a single die is rolled.

73. The odds in favor of rolling a 5 or 6
74. The odds against rolling a 5 or 6
75. The odds against rolling a number greater than 1
76. The odds in favor of rolling a number greater than 1
77. The odds in favor of rolling a 2
78. The odds against rolling an even number

7.2 Probability of the Complement and Union of Events

In Section 7.1 we mentioned that the complement E' of an event E occurs precisely when the event E does not occur and that the union $E \cup F$ of events E and F occurs precisely when E occurs or F occurs. These facts lead to a relationship between $Pr(E')$ and $Pr(E)$ and to a relationship among $Pr(E \cup F)$, $Pr(E)$, and $Pr(F)$, which we now discuss.

Suppose that E is an event in an experiment with sample space S. If E contains k outcomes and S contains m equally likely outcomes, it is easily seen that E' contains $m - k$ outcomes. Thus

$$Pr(E') = \frac{n(E')}{n(S)} = \frac{m-k}{m} = 1 - \frac{k}{m} = 1 - Pr(E)$$

Moreover, the same conclusion is true when the sample space does not consist of equally likely outcomes. We state this more general result as Theorem 7.2.

THEOREM 7.2

For any event E, the probability of the complementary event E' is

$$Pr(E') = 1 - Pr(E)$$

The following examples illustrate a common situation in which this theorem can be used advantageously.

EXAMPLE 17

Suppose that a medical school can admit only 5 of 20 qualified applicants, 8 of whom are women. If the school decides to fill the 5 openings by randomly selecting from among the qualified applicants, we can use Theorem 7.2 to find the probability of the event "at least 1 woman is admitted."

Letting E denote this event, we see that the complementary event E' is "no women are admitted." As in Example 15, it can be seen that

$$Pr(E') = \frac{C(12,5)}{C(20,5)} = \frac{792}{15{,}504} \approx .051$$

Therefore the probability that at least 1 woman will be admitted is

$$Pr(E) = 1 - Pr(E') \approx 1 - .051 = .949$$

EXAMPLE 18

A committee of 6 is to be formed from among 13 executives, 10 of whom hold master's degrees and 3 of whom do not. If the committee members are randomly selected, we can use Theorem 7.2 to determine the probability that at most 5 of the members hold master's degrees. For if E is the event "at most 5 members hold master's degrees," then E' is the event "all 6 committee members hold master's degrees." Since

$$Pr(E') = \frac{C(10,6)}{C(13,6)} = \frac{210}{1716} \approx .122$$

it follows that

$$Pr(E) = 1 - Pr(E') \approx 1 - .122 = .878$$

7.2 Probability of the Complement and Union of Events

Now let us compute $Pr(E \cup F)$ when E and F are events in an experiment with a sample space S consisting of equally likely outcomes. Recall from Theorem 6.1 that

$$n(E \cup F) = n(E) + n(F) - n(E \cap F)$$

Thus

$$Pr(E \cup F) = \frac{n(E \cup F)}{n(S)} = \frac{n(E) + n(F) - n(E \cap F)}{n(S)}$$

$$= \frac{n(E)}{n(S)} + \frac{n(F)}{n(S)} - \frac{n(E \cap F)}{n(S)}$$

$$= Pr(E) + Pr(F) - Pr(E \cap F)$$

Again the same result is true even if the sample space does not contain equally likely outcomes.

THEOREM 7.3

For any events E and F in the same experiment,

$$Pr(E \cup F) = Pr(E) + Pr(F) - Pr(E \cap F)$$

EXAMPLE 19

In the experiment of rolling a pair of dice, let E be the event "the sum is 6" and let F be the event "the same number appears on each die." Referring to Example 13, we see that $Pr(E) = \frac{5}{36}$ and $Pr(F) = \frac{6}{36}$. Now $E \cap F$ is the event "the sum is 6 and the same number appears on each die." Since $E \cap F$ occurs only when a 3 appears on each die, $Pr(E \cap F) = \frac{1}{36}$. Thus

$$Pr(E \cup F) = Pr(E) + Pr(F) - Pr(E \cap F)$$

$$= \frac{5}{36} + \frac{6}{36} - \frac{1}{36} = \frac{10}{36} = \frac{5}{18}$$

Of course, $Pr(E \cup F)$ could have been computed directly by counting the number of outcomes in Figure 7.3 in which the sum is 6 or the same number appears on each die.

EXAMPLE 20

In the experiment of randomly selecting a card from a standard deck[3] of playing cards, let E be the event "a heart is drawn" and F

---

[3] A standard deck of playing cards consists of 4 suits (clubs, diamonds, hearts, and spades), each containing 13 cards (2 through 10, jack, queen, king, and ace). The clubs and spades are black suits, whereas the diamonds and hearts are red suits. Any jack, queen, or king is called a *face card*.

be the event "a 9 is drawn." Then $E \cap F$ is the event "a heart is drawn and a 9 is drawn" and $E \cup F$ is the event "a heart is drawn or a 9 is drawn." Now

$$Pr(E) = \tfrac{13}{52} \quad \text{and} \quad Pr(F) = \tfrac{4}{52}$$

and, because there is only one card that is both a heart and a 9 (namely, the 9 of hearts),

$$Pr(E \cap F) = \tfrac{1}{52}$$

Thus from Theorem 7.3

$$Pr(E \cup F) = Pr(E) + Pr(F) - Pr(E \cap F)$$
$$= \tfrac{13}{52} + \tfrac{4}{52} - \tfrac{1}{52} = \tfrac{16}{52} = \tfrac{4}{13}$$

Here again $Pr(E \cup F)$ could have been computed directly by counting, since there are 16 cards in the deck that are hearts or 9s (13 hearts and the 9s of clubs, diamonds, and spades).

EXAMPLE 21

Suppose that among the students at a certain college 36% frequently read a local newspaper and 62% frequently watch local news on television. Suppose further that 27% of these students frequently read a local newspaper and also frequently watch local news on television. Then the probability that one of these students frequently reads a local newspaper or frequently watches local news on television can be determined by Theorem 7.3.

Let E and F be the events "a student frequently reads a local newspaper" and "a student frequently watches local news on television," respectively. Then $E \cap F$ is the event "a student frequently reads a local newspaper and frequently watches local news on television," and $E \cup F$ is the event "a student frequently reads a local newspaper or frequently watches local news on television." Hence

$$Pr(E \cup F) = Pr(E) + Pr(F) - Pr(E \cap F)$$
$$= .36 + .62 - .27 = .71$$

Notice that, if $Pr(E \cap F) = 0$, then Theorem 7.3 simplifies to the form

$$Pr(E \cup F) = Pr(E) + Pr(F) \tag{7.1}$$

mutually exclusive events Two events E and F in the same experiment are called *mutually exclusive*. if $E \cap F = \emptyset$. Thus if E and F are mutually exclusive events, then $Pr(E \cap F) = 0$ and (7.1) holds. More generally, we have the following result.

THEOREM 7.4

If $E_1, E_2, \ldots, E_k$ are events in the same experiment, each pair of which is mutually exclusive, then

$$Pr(E_1 \cup E_2 \cup \cdots \cup E_k) = Pr(E_1) + Pr(E_2) + \cdots + Pr(E_k)$$

Notice that, in the special case where $E_1, E_2, \ldots, E_k$ are simple events, Theorem 7.4 reduces to case 3 on page 247.

EXAMPLE 22

In the experiment of randomly selecting a card from a standard deck, let E be the event "a spade is chosen" and F be the event "a red card is chosen." These events are mutually exclusive, since no card can be both a spade and a red card. Hence by Theorem 7.4

$$Pr(E \cup F) = Pr(E) + Pr(F) = \tfrac{1}{4} + \tfrac{1}{2} = \tfrac{3}{4}$$

EXAMPLE 23

Recall from Example 4 the experiment of listing the sex of the children in a three-child family in order of decreasing age. Let E denote the event "the youngest child is a girl" and F denote the event "the youngest two children are boys." From the sample space in Example 4 we see that

$$Pr(E) = \tfrac{4}{8} \quad \text{and} \quad Pr(F) = \tfrac{2}{8}$$

Since E and F are mutually exclusive, the probability of $E \cup F$ (the event "the youngest child is a girl or the youngest two children are boys") is

$$Pr(E \cup F) = Pr(E) + Pr(F) = \tfrac{4}{8} + \tfrac{2}{8} = \tfrac{6}{8} = \tfrac{3}{4}$$

EXAMPLE 24

In the experiment of rolling a pair of dice, let $E_1, E_2,$ and E_3 denote the events "a 10 is rolled," "an 11 is rolled," and "a 12 is rolled," respectively. From Example 13 we see that

$$Pr(E_1) = \tfrac{3}{36} \quad Pr(E_2) = \tfrac{2}{36} \quad \text{and} \quad Pr(E_3) = \tfrac{1}{36}$$

Since the events $E_1, E_2,$ and E_3 are mutually exclusive, the probability of the event "a number 10 or greater is rolled" is

$$Pr(E_1 \cup E_2 \cup E_3) = Pr(E_1) + Pr(E_2) + Pr(E_3)$$
$$= \tfrac{3}{36} + \tfrac{2}{36} + \tfrac{1}{36} = \tfrac{6}{36} = \tfrac{1}{6}$$

EXAMPLE 25

Let E be the set of all 6-member subcommittees containing 2 or more men that can be formed from a committee containing 8 women and 7 men, and let F_i ($i = 0, 1, 2, 3, 4, 5,$ and 6) be the set of all subcommittees containing exactly i men that can be formed from this committee. Since $E = F_2 \cup F_3 \cup F_4 \cup F_5 \cup F_6$ and each pair of the sets $F_2, F_3, F_4, F_5,$ and F_6 is mutually exclusive,

$$Pr(E) = Pr(F_2) + Pr(F_3) + Pr(F_4) + Pr(F_5) + Pr(F_6)$$

by Theorem 7.4. Unfortunately, this method of computing $Pr(E)$ requires calculating the five values $Pr(F_2), Pr(F_3), Pr(F_4), Pr(F_5),$ and $Pr(F_6)$.

An easier method using Theorem 7.2 can be found if we note that the complement of E is $F_0 \cup F_1$. Now the probability of selecting a subcommittee containing no men is

$$Pr(F_0) = \frac{C(8,6)}{C(15,6)} = \frac{28}{5005} \approx .0056$$

and the probability of selecting a subcommittee containing exactly 1 man is

$$Pr(F_1) = \frac{C(7,1) \cdot C(8,5)}{C(15,6)} = \frac{7(56)}{5005} = \frac{392}{5005} \approx .0783$$

Hence

$$Pr(E') = Pr(F_0 \cup F_1) = Pr(F_0) + Pr(F_1)$$
$$\approx .0056 + .0783 = .0839$$

since F_0 and F_1 are mutually exclusive, and so

$$Pr(E) = 1 - Pr(E') \approx 1 - .0839 = .9161$$

The reader is cautioned that (7.1) and Theorem 7.4 are true only for mutually exclusive events. For events that are not mutually exclusive Theorem 7.3 must be used.

Exercises

Compute $Pr(E'), Pr(F'),$ and $Pr(E \cup F)$ under the conditions given in Exercises 1–4.

1. $Pr(E) = .6, Pr(F) = .2,$ and $Pr(E \cap F) = .1$
2. $Pr(E) = .3, Pr(F) = .4,$ and $Pr(E \cap F) = .2$
3. $Pr(E) = .50, Pr(F) = .30,$ and $Pr(E \cap F) = .15$
4. $Pr(E) = .25, Pr(F) = .45,$ and $Pr(E \cap F) = .05$
5. In a certain town the probability of reading *The Times* is .51 and the probability of reading *The Herald* is .43. If the probability of reading both papers is .16, what is the probability of reading *The Times* or *The Herald*?

6. During a certain year, automobile sales in a large city showed that 53% of the cars sold were American cars and 63% were economy cars. If 21% of the cars sold in the city during the year were American economy cars, what percentage of cars sold were not American cars or economy cars?

7. In a certain subdivision, 67% of the houses have central air conditioning, 32% have a fireplace, and 13% have both central air conditioning and a fireplace. What percentage of these houses have central air conditioning or a fireplace?

In the experiment of rolling a pair of dice, which of the pairs of events in Exercises 8–15 are mutually exclusive?

8. $\{2, 5, 8, 11\}$ and $\{9, 10, 11, 12\}$
9. $\{7, 8, 9, 10\}$ and $\{2, 3, 11, 12\}$
10. "One die shows 4" and "one die shows 2"
11. "One die shows 2" and "the sum of the dice is at least 10"
12. "Both dice show the same number" and "the sum of the dice is 7"
13. "One die shows 3 or less" and "one die shows an even number"
14. "The sum of the dice is 2 or 3" and "no die shows 1"
15. "The sum of the dice is a multiple of 3" and "both dice show odd numbers"

In the experiment of selecting 2 cards sequentially from a standard deck of playing cards, which of the pairs of events in Exercises 16–21 are mutually exclusive?

16. "The first card is red" and "the first card is a spade"
17. "The first card is red" and "the second card is a spade"
18. "The first card is a 3" and "the first card is a 4"
19. "The first card is a king" and "the first card is a diamond"
20. "The first card is a 10" and "the first card is black"
21. "Both cards are diamonds" and "the second card is a 10"

If E and F are mutually exclusive events, compute $Pr(E')$, $Pr(F')$, $Pr(E \cup F)$, and $Pr(E \cap F)$ under the conditions given in Exercises 22–25.

22. $Pr(E) = .4$ and $Pr(F) = .3$
23. $Pr(E) = .15$ and $Pr(F) = .80$
24. $Pr(E) = .2$ and $Pr(F) = .2$
25. $Pr(E) = .6$ and $Pr(F) = .3$

26. A researcher studying voting patterns among the upper, middle, and lower classes intends to interview persons from a group of 12 consisting of 3 upper-class, 5 middle-class, and 4 lower-class.
    (a) When 1 person is randomly chosen, what is the probability that the person is from the upper class? From the middle class?
    (b) When 3 of the 12 persons are randomly selected, find the probability that at least 1 is from the upper class, at most 2 are from the middle class, and at least 2 are from the lower class.

27. In a particular barbershop the probability of a given number of persons waiting for a haircut is as shown below.

Number waiting	0	1	2	3	4 or more
Probability	.2	.5	.2	.1	0

    (a) What is the probability that at least 2 are waiting?
    (b) What is the probability that at least 1 is waiting?
    (c) What is the probability that no more than 2 are waiting?

28. From the set $\{1, 2, 3, 4, 5, 6, 7\}$ four distinct elements are chosen randomly.
    (a) What is the probability that 2 will be chosen?
    (b) What is the probability that 3 and 4 will be chosen?
    (c) What is the probability that 3 or 4 will be chosen?

In Exercises 29–36, one card is to be drawn from a standard deck of playing cards. What is the probability of drawing

29. A heart or a face card?
30. A heart or a red card?
31. A 7 or an 8?
32. A card that is not a face card?
33. A black card or an ace?
34. A card that is not a club?
35. A diamond or a black card?
36. A card that is not red?

Determine the probability of the events in Exercises 37–44 when a pair of dice is rolled.

37. The sum of the dice does not exceed 5.
38. The sum of the dice is 2 or 12.
39. A 6 appears on at least one die.
40. A 6 appears on at least one die or the sum of the dice is 4.
41. A 6 appears on at least one die or the sum of the dice is 8.
42. The sum of the dice is even or at least one die shows 6.
43. At least one die shows 5 or at least one die shows 6.
44. At least one die is 3 or less or at least one die shows 6.
45. Four marbles are chosen at random from a box containing 3 green and 6 blue marbles.
    (a) What is the probability that at least 2 will be green?
    (b) What is the probability that at most 2 will be green?
46. A committee of 3 is to be chosen from among 4 students and 3 faculty members. If selection of the committee members is made randomly, what is the probability that
    (a) At most 2 students will be selected?
    (b) At least 2 students will be selected?
47. A committee meets randomly every four weeks. Of the next 5 meetings, what is the probability that
    (a) All will be held on Tuesday?
    (b) At least one will be held on Wednesday?
    (c) One meeting will be held on each weekday?
    (d) No meetings will be held on Tuesday or Thursday?

7.3 Conditional Probability and the Probability of the Intersection of Events

In Section 7.2 we saw that it was possible to compute the probability of the union of two events in terms of the probability of each event. It is natural to expect a similar formula that will allow us to compute the probability of the intersection of events in terms of the probability of each event. In this section we shall obtain such a formula. The most

conditional probability of an event

general statement of this result, however, requires a new concept which we must introduce first.

Ordinarily a flood is an unlikely occurrence. After three days of heavy rain, however, flooding is much more likely. This example illustrates that the probability of an event (such as flooding) may change if some prior event (heavy rain) is known to have occurred. The probability that an event F will occur given that an event E has occurred is called the *conditional probability of F given E* and is denoted $Pr(F|E)$.

Consider the experiment of rolling a pair of dice, which was described in Example 13. If F denotes the event "a number greater than 8 is rolled," then we see from Theorem 7.4 and Example 13 that

$$Pr(F) = Pr(9 \text{ appears}) + Pr(10 \text{ appears})$$
$$+ Pr(11 \text{ appears}) + Pr(12 \text{ appears})$$
$$= \tfrac{4}{36} + \tfrac{3}{36} + \tfrac{2}{36} + \tfrac{1}{36} = \tfrac{10}{36} = \tfrac{5}{18}$$

Now suppose that E is the event "the first die shows 6." If we know that E has occurred, then the sum of the numbers showing on the dice will be greater than 8 whenever a 3, 4, 5, or 6 appears on the other die. Hence

$$Pr(F|E) = \tfrac{4}{6} = \tfrac{2}{3}$$

Notice that this computation of $Pr(F|E)$ amounts to reducing the sample space of the experiment from the 36 events in Figure 7.3 to the 6 events that are possible when the first die shows 6. In other words, we have calculated $Pr(F|E)$ by restricting the original sample space to the outcomes for which E has occurred.

The computation in the preceding paragraph suggests the following formula for a sample space of equally likely outcomes:

$$Pr(F|E) = \frac{n(E \cap F)}{n(E)} \quad \text{if } n(E) \neq 0$$

EXAMPLE 26

A sample space of equally likely outcomes for the experiment of flipping a coin twice is

$$S = \{HH, HT, TH, TT\}$$

where H and T represent heads and tails, respectively. If E is the event "the first flip lands heads" and F is the event "the second flip lands tails," then

$$E = \{HH, HT\} \quad F = \{HT, TT\} \quad \text{and} \quad E \cap F = \{HT\}$$

Hence

$$Pr(F) = \frac{n(F)}{n(S)} = \frac{2}{4} = \frac{1}{2} \quad \text{and} \quad Pr(F|E) = \frac{n(E \cap F)}{n(E)} = \frac{1}{2}$$

EXAMPLE 27

In the experiment of randomly selecting one card from a standard deck of playing cards, let E be the event "a face card is drawn" and F be the event "a jack is drawn." Since there are 4 jacks and 12 face cards in the deck,

$$Pr(F) = \tfrac{4}{52} = \tfrac{1}{13} \quad \text{and} \quad Pr(F|E) = \tfrac{4}{12} = \tfrac{1}{3}$$

EXAMPLE 28

Berelson, Lazarsfeld, and McPhee thoroughly studied the voting patterns of the residents of Elmira, New York, in the 1948 presidential election. Some of the data they present in [1] is contained in Table 7.2, which shows the number of persons who voted for the Republican candidate (Thomas E. Dewey) categorized by sex and socioeconomic status.

Table 7.2 *Number of Persons Voting for Dewey by Sex and Socioeconomic Status*

	High	Middle	Low	Total
Men	66	48	74	188
Women	60	80	90	230
Total	126	128	164	418

Suppose that a person is selected randomly from among the 418 who are described in Table 7.2, and let M, W, H, and L be the events described below.

M: A man is selected.
W: A woman is selected.
H: A person of high socioeconomic status is selected.
L: A person of low socioeconomic status is selected.

Then

$$Pr(W) = \tfrac{230}{418} = \tfrac{115}{209} \approx .550 \qquad Pr(H) = \tfrac{126}{418} = \tfrac{63}{209} \approx .301$$
$$Pr(W|H) = \tfrac{60}{126} = \tfrac{10}{21} \approx .476 \qquad Pr(H|W) = \tfrac{60}{230} = \tfrac{6}{23} \approx .261$$
$$Pr(W'|H) = \tfrac{66}{126} = \tfrac{11}{21} \approx .524 \qquad Pr(H'|W) = \tfrac{170}{230} = \tfrac{17}{23} \approx .739$$

Notice that $Pr(W|H) \neq Pr(H|W)$, but that $Pr(W'|H) = 1 - Pr(W|H)$ and $Pr(H'|W) = 1 - Pr(H|W)$.

In the formula $Pr(F|E) = n(E \cap F)/n(E)$, if we divide the numerator and denominator of the right side by $n(S)$, where S is the sample space of the experiment, we obtain

$$Pr(F|E) = \frac{P(E \cap F)}{P(E)}$$

7.3 Conditional Probability and the Probability of the Intersection of Events

Once again it can be shown that this equation is true even if the sample space does not consist of equally likely outcomes. This equation can be written in the following useful form.

THEOREM 7.5

For any events E and F in the same experiment[4]

$$Pr(E \cap F) = Pr(E) \cdot Pr(F|E)$$

Theorem 7.5 contains the general formula for computing the probability of the intersection of two events in terms of the probability of the original events. It is especially useful when a sample space for the experiment is large.

EXAMPLE 29

Suppose that an insurance agent telephones randomly selected persons in hopes of arranging appointments to discuss insurance. If 8% of those who are called agree to an appointment and if 30% of those who agree to an appointment actually buy insurance, we can use Theorem 7.5 to determine the percentage of those who are called that agree to an appointment and buy insurance. For if E denotes the event of agreeing to an appointment and if F denotes the event of buying insurance, then

$$Pr(E \cap F) = Pr(E) \cdot Pr(F|E) = .08(.30) = .024$$

So 2.4% of those who are called agree to an appointment and buy insurance.

EXAMPLE 30

Suppose that, in a shipment of 100 items, 5 are defective. If 2 of these 100 items are chosen at random, we have seen in Section 7.1 that the probability of both being defective equals

$$\frac{C(5,2)}{C(100,2)} = \frac{10}{4950} = \frac{1}{495}$$

It is easier, however, to compute this value using Theorem 7.5. Letting E be the event "the first item is defective" and F be the event "the second item is defective," we have

$$Pr(E \cap F) = Pr(E) \cdot Pr(F|E) = \frac{5}{100} \cdot \frac{4}{99} = \frac{1}{495}$$

[4] Notice that, since $E \cap F = F \cap E$, we also have $Pr(E \cap F) = Pr(F \cap E) = Pr(F) \cdot Pr(E|F)$.

EXAMPLE 31

By repeated use of Theorem 7.5 we can evaluate the probability of the intersection of more than two events. For example,

$$Pr(E \cap F \cap G) = Pr(E \cap F) \cdot Pr(G|E \cap F)$$
$$= Pr(E) \cdot Pr(F|E) \cdot Pr(G|E \cap F)$$

To illustrate this equation, suppose that three cards are selected sequentially from a standard deck of playing cards, and let E, F, and G be the following events.

E: The first card is a jack.
F: The second card is a 5.
G: The third card is a face card.

Then

$$Pr(E) = \tfrac{4}{52} \qquad Pr(F|E) = \tfrac{4}{51} \quad \text{and} \quad Pr(G|E \cap F) = \tfrac{11}{50}$$

So the probability that the first card is a jack, the second card is a 5, and the third card is a face card is

$$Pr(E \cap F \cap G) = Pr(E) \cdot Pr(F|E) \cdot Pr(G|E \cap F)$$
$$= \tfrac{4}{52} \cdot \tfrac{4}{51} \cdot \tfrac{11}{50} = \tfrac{22}{3825} \approx .006$$

Observe that in Example 26 $Pr(F) = Pr(F|E)$, whereas in Example 27 $Pr(F) \neq Pr(F|E)$. Two events E and F such that $Pr(F) = Pr(F|E)$ or, equivalently,[5] such that $Pr(E) = Pr(E|F)$ are called *independent*. Events that are not independent are called *dependent*. Intuitively, two events are independent if the occurrence of one does not affect the occurrence of the other.

independent events
dependent events

EXAMPLE 32

In the experiment of randomly selecting a card from a standard deck of playing cards, let H, K, and B denote the events "a heart is drawn," "a king is drawn," and "a black card is drawn," respectively. Then

$$Pr(\text{H}) = \tfrac{13}{52} = \tfrac{1}{4} \quad \text{and} \quad Pr(\text{H}|\text{K}) = \frac{n(\text{H} \cap \text{K})}{n(\text{K})} = \tfrac{1}{4}$$

So $Pr(\text{H}) = Pr(\text{H}|\text{K})$, and thus events H and K are independent. More generally, since it is intuitively clear that the suit of a card does not affect its denomination, drawing a card having a partic-

---

[5]It can be shown that the equalities $Pr(F) = Pr(F|E)$ and $Pr(E) = Pr(E|F)$ either both hold or both fail. So if either holds, then E and F are independent, but if either fails, then E and F are not independent.

ular suit is independent of drawing a card having a particular denomination.

On the other hand, $Pr(H|B) = 0$. So $Pr(H) \neq Pr(H|B)$, and therefore H and B are dependent. More generally, it is clear that the suit of a card is related to its color, hence drawing a card of a particular suit and drawing a card of a particular color are dependent events.

EXAMPLE 33

In a random sample of 200 persons having either type AB or type O blood, the numbers shown in Table 7.3 can be expected.

Table 7.3 *Classification of Persons by Blood Type and Rh Factor*

	Blood type		
Rh factor	AB	O	Total
+	17	153	170
−	3	27	30
Total	20	180	200

Consider the following events.

Rh+ : A person having Rh antigen is selected.
AB: A person having blood type AB is selected.
O: A person having blood type O is selected.

Since

$$Pr(Rh+) = \tfrac{170}{200} = .85 \qquad Pr(Rh+|AB) = \tfrac{17}{20} = .85$$

and

$$Pr(Rh+|O) = \tfrac{153}{180} = .85$$

Rh+ and AB are independent events, as are Rh+ and O. In fact, the presence or absence of Rh antigen can be shown to be independent of the presence or absence of A or B antigen; that is, the Rh factor is independent of the blood types A, B, AB, and O.

If E and F are independent events, then $Pr(F|E) = Pr(F)$. So in this case Theorem 7.5 takes the simpler form

$$Pr(E \cap F) = Pr(E) \cdot Pr(F) \tag{7.2}$$

EXAMPLE 34

In Example 32 we remarked that, in the experiment of selecting a card from a standard deck of playing cards, drawing a card with a particular suit and drawing a card with a particular denomination are independent events. Letting A denote the event "an ace is drawn" and C denote the event "a club is drawn," we see as a result that

$$Pr(A \cap C) = Pr(A) \cdot Pr(C) = \tfrac{1}{13} \cdot \tfrac{1}{4} = \tfrac{1}{52}$$

This conclusion is obvious, of course, since there is only one card in the deck that is both an ace and a club.

EXAMPLE 35

In Example 33 we mentioned that the Rh factor is independent of blood types A, B, AB, and O. Consider the following events.

Rh+: A person having Rh antigen is selected.
Rh−: A person not having Rh antigen is selected.
A: A person having blood type A is selected.
B: A person having blood type B is selected.

Now $Pr(Rh+) = .85$ and $Pr(Rh-) = .15$, and for whites $Pr(A) = .38$ and $Pr(B) = .12$. Thus the probability that a white person has blood type A+ is

$$Pr(A \cap Rh+) = Pr(A) \cdot Pr(Rh+) = .38(.85) = .323$$

and the probability that a white person has blood type B− is

$$Pr(B \cap Rh-) = Pr(B) \cdot Pr(Rh-) = .12(.15) = .018$$

When more than two sets are involved, the definition of independence is more complicated than when only two sets are involved. Consequently, we shall not give a formal definition of independence in this case. Intuitively, however, the meaning of independence remains the same: Several events are called independent if the occurrence of any collection of the events does not affect the occurrence of the others. Moreover, the generalization of (7.2) is true in this context; that is, if $E_1, E_2, \ldots, E_k$ are independent events, then

$$Pr(E_1 \cap E_2 \cap \cdots \cap E_k) = Pr(E_1) \cdot Pr(E_2) \cdot \cdots \cdot Pr(E_k) \qquad (7.3)$$

EXAMPLE 36

Suppose that a coin is flipped, a die is rolled, and a card is randomly selected from a standard deck of playing cards. Let E_1, E_2, and E_3 be the following events.

E_1: The coin lands tails.
E_2: A 3 appears on the die.
E_3: A diamond is drawn from the deck.

Clearly the outcome of any of these three actions is not affected by the outcome of the others. Thus E_1, E_2, and E_3 are independent. Hence from (7.3) the probability that the coin lands tails, a 3 appears on the die, and a diamond is drawn from the deck is

$$Pr(E_1 \cap E_2 \cap E_3) = Pr(E_1) \cdot Pr(E_2) \cdot Pr(E_3) = \tfrac{1}{2} \cdot \tfrac{1}{6} \cdot \tfrac{1}{4} = \tfrac{1}{48}$$

EXAMPLE 37

It is clear that the outcome of one roll of a die does not affect the outcome of a subsequent roll. Hence if a die is rolled 8 times, the rolls are independent events. So the probability that a 4 will appear on each roll is

$$\left(\frac{1}{6}\right)^8 = \frac{1}{1,679,616}$$

EXAMPLE 38

Suppose that a company sells a stereo system consisting of a receiver, a turntable, and speakers. Let $Pr(E_1) = .06$, $Pr(E_2) = .02$, and $Pr(E_3) = .05$, where $E_1, E_2,$ and E_3 are the events defined below.

E_1: The receiver is defective.
E_2: The turntable is defective.
E_3: The speakers are defective.

If each of the three components of the system is manufactured separately, then it is reasonable to assume that the events $E_1, E_2,$ and E_3 are independent. Hence the probability of obtaining one of these stereo systems with a defective receiver, a defective turntable, and defective speakers is

$$Pr(E_1 \cap E_2 \cap E_3) = Pr(E_1) \cdot Pr(E_2) \cdot Pr(E_3)$$
$$= .06(.02)(.05) = .00006$$

One final remark is appropriate here. The concepts of mutually exclusive events and independent events are often confused with each other. Notice this difference between these concepts: Whereas the occurrence of one of a pair of independent events has no bearing on the outcome of the other event, the occurrence of one of a pair of mutually exclusive events precludes the occurrence of the other.

Exercises

In a study on nightmares in 352 subjects (see [5]), the following data concerning the frequency of nightmares were obtained.

	\multicolumn{4}{c}{Frequency of nightmares}	
	Frequent	Sometimes	Seldom	Never	Total
Males	14	41	38	67	160
Females	12	48	48	84	192
Total	26	89	86	151	352

Let events M, F, Sm, Sl, and N be defined as follows.

    M: A subject is male.
    F: A subject has frequent nightmares.
    Sm: A subject sometimes has nightmares.
    Sl: A subject seldom has nightmares.
    N: A subject never has nightmares.

Compute each of the probabilities in Exercises 1–8.

1. $Pr(Sl)$
2. $Pr(M')$
3. $Pr(M|N)$
4. $Pr(F|M)$
5. $Pr(Sm|M)$
6. $Pr(M|Sl)$
7. $Pr(F|M')$
8. $Pr(M'|N)$

The data below from [1] show the 1948 presidential vote of 626 residents of Elmira, New York.

	Presidential candidate voted for		
Religion	Democratic	Republican	Total
Catholic	124	67	191
Protestant	90	345	435
Total	214	412	626

Let C, D, T, and R be the events of being Catholic, voting Democratic, being Protestant, and voting Republican, respectively.

9. Compute $Pr(C)$.
10. Compute $Pr(R)$.
11. Compute $Pr(C|D)$.
12. Compute $Pr(R|T)$.
13. Compute $Pr(R|C)$.
14. Compute $Pr(D|T)$.
15. Are C and D independent?
16. Are T and R independent?
17. Are C and R independent?
18. Are T and D independent?
19. If $Pr(E) = .6$ and $Pr(F) = .2$, compute $Pr(E \cap F)$ under the following conditions:

    (a) E and F are independent.   (b) E and F are mutually exclusive.

20. A mathematics student would like to know the probability of not giving a wrong answer in class. She can avoid giving a wrong answer if the teacher does not ask her a question or by answering correctly if questioned. She estimates that the probability of being questioned by the teacher is .2 and that the probability of answering correctly if questioned is .6. Assuming that she will not be questioned more than once, what is the probability that she will not give an incorrect answer in class?

21. On a multiple-choice question with 5 possible responses but only 1 correct answer, what is the probability that

    (a) The correct answer will be obtained by guessing randomly?
    (b) If 1 response is known to be incorrect, the correct answer will be obtained by randomly guessing from among the other 4 responses?
    (c) If 2 responses are known to be incorrect, the correct answer will be obtained by randomly guessing from among the other 3 responses?

Use Example 4 to determine which of the pairs of events in Exercises 22–25 are independent.

22. "All 3 children have the same sex" and "at least 1 child is a boy"
23. "The family has exactly 2 girls" and "the first child is a boy"

24. "The family has children of both sexes" and "the last child is a girl"
25. "The first 2 children are of opposite sexes" and "the family has exactly 2 boys"

Suppose that a box contains 12 blue marbles and 15 green marbles and that 2 marbles are selected sequentially from the box. If the first marble is returned to the box before the second is selected, then the selection is said to be made *with replacement*, whereas if the first marble is not returned to the box before the second is selected, then the selection is said to be made *without replacement*. In Exercises 26–31, compute each probability for selection with replacement and for selection without replacement.

selection with replacement
selection without replacement

26. Both marbles will be blue.
27. Both marbles will be green.
28. The first marble will be green and the second blue.
29. The first marble will be blue and the second green.
30. The first and second marbles will be different colors.
31. The first and second marbles will be of the same color.

A desk drawer contains 9 pens, 3 of which are out of ink. Suppose that 3 pens are selected randomly from the drawer. Compute each of the probabilities described in Exercises 32–35.

32. At least 1 of the pens will be out of ink.
33. The third pen selected will not be out of ink.
34. Exactly 1 of the pens will be out of ink.
35. At least 2 of the pens will not be out of ink.

If 2 cards are drawn sequentially from a standard deck of playing cards, determine each of the probabilities in Exercises 36–45.

36. The first will be red and the second will be black.
37. Both will be black.
38. Both will be of the same color.
39. Both will be clubs.
40. The first will be a diamond and the second will not.
41. The first will be a 10 and the second will be a 4.
42. Both cards will be face cards.
43. Both cards will be queens.
44. The first card will be a club and the second will be black.
45. The first card will be black and the second will be a club.
46. Using the information in Example 35, compute the probability that a white person will have blood type A− and the probability that a white person will have blood type B+.
47. For black persons $Pr(Rh+) = .85$, $Pr(Rh-) = .15$, $Pr(A) = .30$, and $Pr(B) = .20$. Use the fact that the presence or absence of Rh antigen is independent of the presence or absence of A and B antigens to compute the probability that a black person will have each of the following blood types.
    (a) A+   (b) A−   (c) B−   (d) B+

A box contains 4 red marbles, 6 yellow marbles, and 5 white marbles. Use the results of this section to compute the probability of the events in Exercises 48–55 if 3 of the marbles are randomly selected in succession.

48. All 3 marbles will be yellow. 49. All 3 marbles will be white.
50. None of the marbles will be red.
51. None of the marbles will be yellow.
52. The first marble will be red, the second white, and the third yellow.
53. The first marble will be yellow, the second red, and the third white.
54. The first two marbles will be yellow and the third not yellow.
55. The second and third marbles will be white.
56. Show that, if E and F are independent events, then E' and F are independent events.
57. (a) In Example 28 verify that $Pr(L'|M) = 1 - Pr(L|M)$ but that $Pr(L|M) \neq Pr(M|L)$.
    (b) If E and F are events in an experiment with equally likely outcomes, verify that $Pr(E'|F) = 1 - Pr(E|F)$. Hint: $n(E' \cap F) = n(F) - n(E \cap F)$.

7.4 Binomial Experiments

Many experiments are concerned with counting the number of times a particular outcome occurs. For example, we may be interested in knowing the number of times a girl is born in 1000 live births or the number of times a defective item is found in a sample of 100 items.

Experiments in which there are only two possible outcomes are called *Bernoulli experiments* after the Swiss mathematician Jacob Bernoulli who was among the first to study such problems. It is customary to call the outcome being counted a *success* and the other outcome a *failure*, even though the outcome being counted is not necessarily favorable. For instance, in testing whether a drug produces severe side effects, we call the occurrence of severe side effects a success and the absence of severe side effects a failure.

In many experiments, of course, there are more than two possible outcomes. If only one of the outcomes is of interest, however, we can regard the experiment as a Bernoulli experiment by calling the outcome in which we are interested a success and any other outcome a failure. Thus if we are interested in determining the number of times a 5 appears in 100 rolls of a die, we consider the appearance of a 5 a success and any other result (that is, the appearance of a 1, 2, 3, 4, or 6) a failure.

The probability of a success in a Bernoulli experiment will be denoted by p and the probability of a failure by q. Since success and failure are complementary events, it follows from Theorem 7.2 that

$$q = 1 - p$$

EXAMPLE 39

In the experiment of rolling a die, if the appearance of a 5 is regarded as a success, then

$$p = \tfrac{1}{6} \quad \text{and} \quad q = \tfrac{5}{6}$$

EXAMPLE 40

In the experiment of flipping a coin, if landing heads is considered a success, then

$$p = \tfrac{1}{2} \quad \text{and} \quad q = \tfrac{1}{2}$$

EXAMPLE 41

In a certain type of learning experiment a subject is regarded as being conditioned to give a correct response or as being unconditioned. In one such experiment,[6] described in [2], Bower determined that the probability of becoming conditioned to a correct response was approximately .344. Regarding the occurrence of conditioning as a success, we have

$$p = .344 \quad \text{and} \quad q = .656$$

binomial experiment

A *binomial experiment* is an experiment consisting of a finite number of independent trials (repetitions) of a Bernoulli experiment. Thus, for example, counting the number of heads that appear when a coin is flipped 20 times or counting the number of times a number less than 3 appears in 50 rolls of a die is a binomial experiment. On the other hand, if a card is selected and removed from an ordinary deck of playing cards and if this process is continued until 5 cards are removed, counting the number of clubs that occur is not a binomial experiment, because the repeated selections are not independent events. If each of the cards selected were replaced and the deck were shuffled before the next was drawn, however, then this experiment would be a binomial experiment.

In a binomial experiment we are interested in knowing the probability that k successes will occur in n trials. As a simple example, let us determine the probability that a 1 will appear exactly 3 times in 4 rolls of a die. Thus we let s denote a success (that is, the appearance of a 1) and f denote a failure and compute the probability of exactly 3 successes in 4 repetitions when the probability of success is $p = \tfrac{1}{6}$ and the probability of failure is $q = \tfrac{5}{6}$. Note that there are 4 outcomes in which exactly 3 successes occur:

sssf, ssfs, sfss, and fsss

These correspond to the $C(4, 3) = 4$ ways of selecting 3 successes from among 4 trials. Since the rolls are independent, (7.3) shows that

$$Pr(\text{sssf}) = Pr(s) \cdot Pr(s) \cdot Pr(s) \cdot Pr(f) = p \cdot p \cdot p \cdot q = p^3 q = (\tfrac{1}{6})^3(\tfrac{5}{6})$$
$$Pr(\text{ssfs}) = Pr(s) \cdot Pr(s) \cdot Pr(f) \cdot Pr(s) = p \cdot p \cdot q \cdot p = p^3 q = (\tfrac{1}{6})^3(\tfrac{5}{6})$$
$$Pr(\text{sfss}) = Pr(s) \cdot Pr(f) \cdot Pr(s) \cdot Pr(s) = p \cdot q \cdot p \cdot p = p^3 q = (\tfrac{1}{6})^3(\tfrac{5}{6})$$

---

[6] This experiment will be discussed in Section 8.4.

and

$$Pr(\text{fsss}) = Pr(\text{f}) \cdot Pr(\text{s}) \cdot Pr(\text{s}) \cdot Pr(\text{s}) = q \cdot p \cdot p \cdot p = p^3 q = (\tfrac{1}{6})^3(\tfrac{5}{6})$$

Notice that the four simple events {sssf}, {ssfs}, {sfss}, and {fsss} all occur with the same probability. Hence, since these four simple events are mutually exclusive, we have

$$Pr(\text{exactly 3 successes}) = Pr(\text{sssf}) + Pr(\text{ssfs}) + Pr(\text{sfss}) + Pr(\text{fsss})$$
$$= 4(\tfrac{1}{6})^3(\tfrac{5}{6}) = \tfrac{5}{324} \approx .015$$

This example illustrates the following result.

THEOREM 7.6

In a binomial experiment in which the probability of a success is p and the probability of a failure is q, the probability that exactly k successes occur in n trials is

$$Pr(\text{exactly } k \text{ successes}) = C(n, k) p^k q^{n-k}$$

EXAMPLE 42

In a certain community the probability that a marriage will end in divorce is .4. What is the probability that there will be exactly 3 divorces among 7 unacquainted married couples?

Since the 7 couples are unacquainted, it is reasonable to regard this situation as 7 independent trials of a binomial experiment in which the probability of success (a divorce) is .4. Thus the probability of exactly 3 divorces is given by Theorem 7.6 as

$$Pr(\text{exactly 3 successes}) = C(7, 3) p^3 q^{7-3}$$
$$= 35(.4)^3(.6)^4 = .290304$$

EXAMPLE 43

Deutsch and Madow [3] discuss the problem of recognizing the competence of decision makers in large bureaucratic organizations. They point out that chance alone may account for the existence of a bureaucrat who has made only correct decisions.

In one of their examples, they consider the likelihood of finding someone who has made correct decisions on each of 8 occasions when the probability of making a successful decision is $\tfrac{2}{3}$. If the 8 decisions are independent (as Deutsch and Madow assume), then the probability of correctly making all 8 decisions is

$$Pr(\text{exactly 8 successes}) = C(8, 8) p^8 q^{8-8} = 1(\tfrac{2}{3})^8(\tfrac{1}{3})^0 = \tfrac{256}{6561}$$

We shall see in Section 7.6 that the organization can expect to have at least 1 person who has made only correct decisions under these circumstances if it has at least $\frac{6561}{256} \approx 26$ employees making decisions independently.

EXAMPLE 44

In [10] Pascal and Suttell report a test devised to determine whether a graphologist (handwriting expert) could distinguish normal persons from psychotic individuals on the basis of their handwriting. Ten psychotic persons were chosen and matched with normal persons of the same sex, comparable age, and comparable education. Each person was given five minutes to study a short story and then asked to write it from memory. From the 10 pairs of answer sheets, the graphologist correctly identified the psychotic member of each pair six times.

To determine whether or not the graphologist's performance was unusual, Pascal and Suttell computed the probability of correctly identifying 6 or more of the 10 psychotic persons by chance. Since the probability of correctly identifying the psychotic individual in each pair by guessing is $\frac{1}{2}$, this experiment is a binomial experiment with 10 trials in which $p = \frac{1}{2}$ and $q = \frac{1}{2}$. Hence

$$Pr(\text{exactly 6 successes}) = C(10,6)p^6 q^{10-6} = 210(\tfrac{1}{2})^6(\tfrac{1}{2})^4$$
$$= \tfrac{210}{1024}$$
$$Pr(\text{exactly 7 successes}) = C(10,7)p^7 q^{10-7} = 120(\tfrac{1}{2})^7(\tfrac{1}{2})^3$$
$$= \tfrac{120}{1024}$$
$$Pr(\text{exactly 8 successes}) = C(10,8)p^8 q^{10-8} = 45(\tfrac{1}{2})^8(\tfrac{1}{2})^2$$
$$= \tfrac{45}{1024}$$
$$Pr(\text{exactly 9 successes}) = C(10,9)p^9 q^{10-9} = 10(\tfrac{1}{2})^9(\tfrac{1}{2})^1$$
$$= \tfrac{10}{1024}$$

and

$$Pr(\text{exactly 10 successes}) = C(10,10)p^{10} q^{10-10} = 1(\tfrac{1}{2})^{10}(\tfrac{1}{2})^0$$
$$= \tfrac{1}{1024}$$

Since each pair of these events is mutually exclusive, we have from Theorem 7.4 that

$$Pr(\text{6 or more successes}) = Pr(\text{exactly 6 successes})$$
$$+ \cdots + Pr(\text{exactly 10 successes})$$
$$= \tfrac{210}{1024} + \tfrac{120}{1024} + \tfrac{45}{1024} + \tfrac{10}{1024} + \tfrac{1}{1024}$$
$$= \tfrac{386}{1024} \approx .377$$

Thus there is a .377 probability of obtaining 6 or more correct identifications by chance alone. On this basis Pascal and Suttell dismissed the graphologist's claim to be able to distinguish normal persons from psychotic ones on the basis of handwriting.

Exercises

For each of the binomial experiments in Exercises 1–6, determine the probability of success p and the probability of failure q.

1. A die is rolled 20 times, and the number of appearances of 5 or 6 is counted.
2. A die is rolled 15 times, and the number of even numbers that appear is counted.
3. The number of boys born is recorded in 40 live births.
4. A digit is randomly selected, and the number of 7s, 8s, and 9s is counted.
5. Ten human blood samples are checked for the presence of Rh antigen. (See Example 33.)
6. One card is selected from each of 12 standard decks of playing cards, and the number of diamonds that appear is counted.

In 8 trials of a binomial experiment where the probability of success is $p = .8$, compute each of the probabilities in Exercises 7–14.

7. Pr(exactly 1 success)
8. Pr(exactly 2 successes)
9. Pr(no successes)
10. Pr(8 successes)
11. Pr(at least 2 successes)
12. Pr(at least 7 successes)
13. Pr(at most 3 successes)
14. Pr(at most 5 successes)

A die is rolled 6 times. Determine each of the probabilities in Exercises 15–18.

15. Exactly one 5 occurs.
16. Exactly two 5s occur.
17. At least one 5 occurs.
18. At most three 5s occur.
19. When flipping a coin, which event in each pair is more likely?
    (a) 3 consecutive tails or 7 tails out of 10 flips
    (b) 4 consecutive tails or 8 tails out of 11 flips
20. In a 4-child family, what is the probability that at least 3 children are girls?
21. Twelve mice have been conditioned so that the probability of their turning right in a T maze is .4. What is the probability that exactly 8 of the 12 mice will turn right? More than 10 will turn right?
22. If the probability that a baseball team will win any game is .6, what is the probability that it will win exactly 4 games in a 7-game series? Assume that the games are independent events.
23. In a certain city the weather bureau takes temperature readings in the center of the city and at the airport several miles away. From past experience it is known that the downtown readings are higher 70% of the time. What is the probability that, in 10 independent readings, the downtown temperature will be higher exactly 7 times? At least 7 times?
24. When subjected to a certain dose of radiation the probability that a genetic mutation will occur is .001. What is the probability that at least one mutation will occur in 1000 doses of radiation?
25. On Main Street there are 4 traffic lights which operate independently. Each light remains green for 2 minutes and red for 1 minute. What is the probability that a car traveling on Main Street
    (a) Will not find any of the lights red?
    (b) Will find all the lights red?
    (c) Will find at least 1 of the lights red?

(d) Will find exactly 1 of the lights red?
(e) Will find at least 2 of the lights red?
(f) Will find at least 3 of the lights green?

26. If a softball player has a .300 batting average (that is, if the probability of the player's getting a hit is .3), what is the probability that the player will get no hits in 4 independent times at bat?

27. A manufacturer has found that, when his automated machinery is functioning properly, 10% of the items produced are defective. To check whether the machinery is working properly, he periodically selects 10 finished items at random and tests them for defects. What is the probability that the machinery is working properly and yet the sample tested contains

    (a) 2 or more defective items?
    (b) 3 or more defective items?

7.5 Bayes' Formula

A doctor making a diagnosis observes a patient's symptoms and then determines the possible cause of these symptoms. This example illustrates a common situation in which an experimenter observes a particular outcome of an experiment and determines the likelihood that the observed result was due to each of several possible causes. In this section we shall be concerned with situations where we are interested in finding the probability of a prior event given the occurrence of some later event. This situation is the reverse of that encountered in Section 7.3, where we asked for the probability of a later event given the occurrence of an earlier event.

In the simplest situation of this type, we must calculate $Pr(E|F)$ when $Pr(F|E)$ is known. The relationship between these two conditional probabilities can be easily found as a consequence of Theorem 7.5, for

$$Pr(F) \cdot Pr(E|F) = Pr(E) \cdot Pr(F|E)$$

since both sides equal $Pr(E \cap F)$. If $Pr(F) \neq 0$, we can divide the equation above by $Pr(F)$ to obtain

$$Pr(E|F) = \frac{Pr(E) \cdot Pr(F|E)}{Pr(F)} \tag{7.4}$$

EXAMPLE 45

An insurance company estimates that $\frac{1}{2}$ of those who apply for positions in its data processing department are able to begin work without further training, but only $\frac{1}{5}$ of the applicants are hired. If the probability is .34 that an applicant will be hired given that he or she can begin work without further training, what is the probability that someone who is hired will be able to begin work without further training?

To answer this question, let E and F be the events "an applicant can begin work without further training" and "an applicant is hired," respectively. Then

$$Pr(E) = \frac{1}{2} = .5 \qquad Pr(F) = \frac{1}{5} = .2 \quad \text{and} \quad Pr(F|E) = .34$$

So from (7.4) the probability that someone who is hired can begin work without further training is

$$Pr(E|F) = \frac{Pr(E) \cdot Pr(F|E)}{Pr(F)} = \frac{.5(.34)}{.2} = .85$$

EXAMPLE 46

If two cards are drawn from a standard deck of playing cards and the second card is a face card, what is the probability that the first card will be a jack?

The answer to this question is $Pr(E|F)$, where E denotes the event "a jack is obtained on the first draw" and F denotes the event "a face card is obtained on the second draw." Since it is easy to calculate that $Pr(F|E) = \frac{11}{51}$, (7.4) can be used to determine $Pr(E|F)$. Noting that $Pr(E) = \frac{4}{52} = \frac{1}{13}$ and $Pr(F) = \frac{12}{52} = \frac{3}{13}$ (the latter from Example 16), we have

$$Pr(E|F) = \frac{Pr(E) \cdot Pr(F|E)}{Pr(F)} = \frac{\frac{1}{13} \cdot \frac{11}{51}}{\frac{3}{13}} = \frac{11}{153}$$

Equation (7.4) is the basis for a result called Bayes' formula[7] which permits the computation of certain conditional probabilities when the sample space is subdivided in a certain way. To illustrate the basic ideas involved in Bayes' formula, we begin with a simple example.

Suppose that there are two boxes containing pennies and nickels; the first box contains 5 pennies and 3 nickels, and the second box contains 2 pennies and 4 nickels. (See Figure 7.5.) If one of the boxes is randomly selected and a coin is randomly chosen from that box and found to be a nickel, what is the probability that the coin came from the first box?

Let the events E_1, E_2, and F be defined as follows.

E_1: The first box is chosen.
E_2: The second box is chosen.
F: A nickel is chosen.

In this notation, we wish to compute $Pr(E_1|F)$. Since it follows from Theorem 7.5 that

First box

Second box

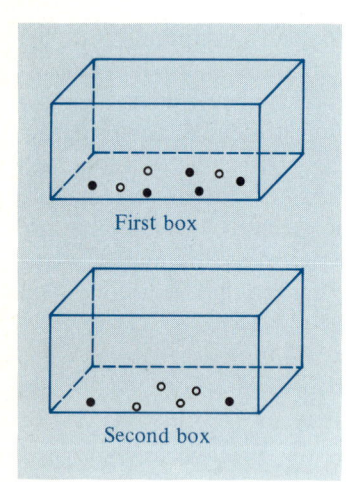

Figure 7.5

---

[7] In 1763 a paper by Thomas Bayes, a Presbyterian minister, was published in *The Philosophical Transactions* of the Royal Society. This paper, entitled "An Essay Toward Solving a Problem in the Doctrine of Chances," contained the first statement and proof of (7.4). This result later was generalized, and the statement of Theorem 7.8 is now called Bayes' formula.

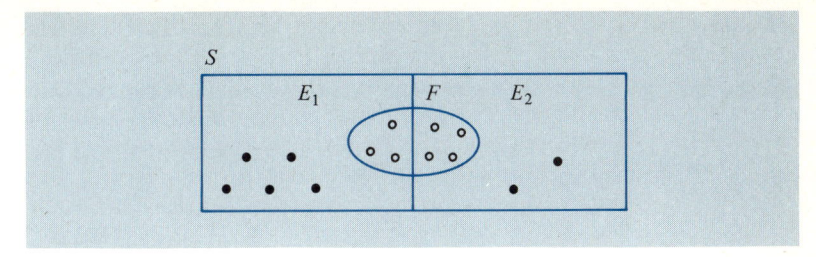

Figure 7.6

$$Pr(E_1|F) = \frac{Pr(E_1 \cap F)}{Pr(F)} \tag{7.5}$$

we shall be able to compute the desired value if we can determine $Pr(F)$.

We may regard the sample space S consisting of all 14 coins as being subdivided into two disjoint parts, coins that come from the first box and those that come from the second. (See Figure 7.6.) Because $S = E_1 \cup E_2$ and $E_1 \cap E_2 = \emptyset$, it follows that

$$F = (E_1 \cap F) \cup (E_2 \cap F)$$

is the union of the mutually exclusive events $E_1 \cap F$ and $E_2 \cap F$. Hence

$$Pr(F) = Pr(E_1 \cap F) + Pr(E_2 \cap F) \tag{7.6}$$

Combining (7.5) and (7.6) gives

$$Pr(E_1|F) = \frac{Pr(E_1 \cap F)}{Pr(E_1 \cap F) + Pr(E_2 \cap F)} \tag{7.7}$$

This equation can be rewritten using Theorem 7.5 in the following equivalent form:

$$Pr(E_1|F) = \frac{Pr(E_1) \cdot Pr(F|E_1)}{Pr(E_1) \cdot Pr(F|E_1) + Pr(E_2) \cdot Pr(F|E_2)} \tag{7.8}$$

The tree diagram in Figure 7.7 is helpful in understanding these formulas. Equation (7.6), which enables us to compute $Pr(F)$, can be

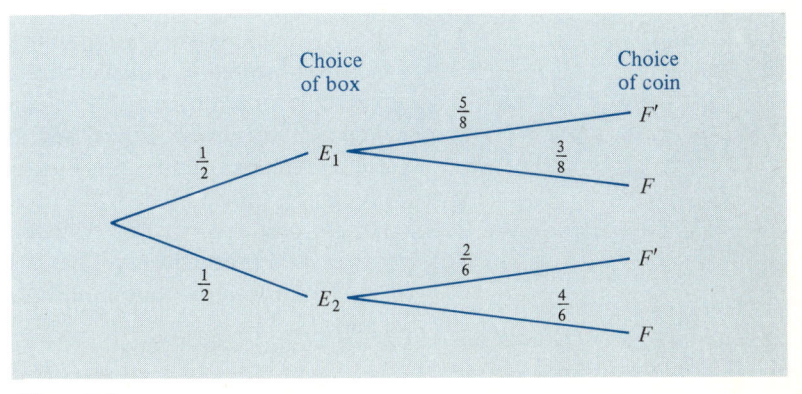

Figure 7.7

interpreted in the tree diagram as stating that $Pr(F)$ equals the sum of the probabilities of all the branches of the tree diagram that include event F. Moreover, (7.7) can be interpreted as stating that $Pr(E_1|F)$ equals the probability of the branch through E_1 and F divided by the sum of the probabilities of all the branches that include F. So

$$Pr(E_1|F) = \frac{Pr(E_1 \cap F)}{Pr(E_1 \cap F) + Pr(E_2 \cap F)}$$

$$= \frac{Pr(E_1) \cdot Pr(F|E_1)}{Pr(E_1) \cdot Pr(F|E_1) + Pr(E_2) \cdot Pr(F|E_2)}$$

$$= \frac{\frac{1}{2} \cdot \frac{3}{8}}{\frac{1}{2} \cdot \frac{3}{8} + \frac{1}{2} \cdot \frac{4}{6}} = \frac{\frac{3}{16}}{\frac{25}{48}} = \frac{9}{25}$$

In Figure 7.5 the sample space was subdivided into two mutually exclusive events E_1 and E_2. More generally, the procedure illustrated above can be used whenever the sample space can be subdivided into any finite number of events $E_1, E_2, \ldots, E_k$ such that:

1. Each pair of events is mutually exclusive.
2. The union of $E_1, E_2, \ldots, E_k$ is the entire sample space.

partitioned sample space When these two conditions hold, we say that the sample space is *partitioned* by the events $E_1, E_2, \ldots, E_k$. In this case (7.6) can be generalized as follows.

THEOREM 7.7

If a sample space is partitioned by events $E_1, E_2, \ldots, E_k$, then for any event F

$$Pr(F) = Pr(E_1 \cap F) + Pr(E_2 \cap F) + \cdots + Pr(E_k \cap F)$$
$$= Pr(E_1) \cdot Pr(F|E_1) + Pr(E_2) \cdot Pr(F|E_2) + \cdots + Pr(E_k) \cdot Pr(F|E_k)$$

EXAMPLE 47

A nationwide company manufactures plastic containers in three factories located in Philadelphia, St. Louis, and Los Angeles. For one style of container 50% of the production is done in Philadelphia, 30% in St. Louis, and 20% in Los Angeles. If 2.2% of the containers produced in Philadelphia are defective, 2.8% of the containers produced in St. Louis are defective, and 3.3% of the containers produced in Los Angeles are defective, what percentage of the total production of this container is defective?

To answer this question, let E_1, E_2, E_3, and F be the events defined below.

E_1: A container is manufactured in Philadelphia.
E_2: A container is manufactured in St. Louis.

E_3: A container is manufactured in Los Angeles.
F: A container is defective.

Thus we wish to determine $Pr(F)$. Since $E_1, E_2,$ and E_3 partition the sample space of containers under consideration, we have from Theorem 7.7

$$Pr(F) = Pr(E_1) \cdot Pr(F|E_1) + Pr(E_2) \cdot Pr(F|E_2) + Pr(E_3) \cdot Pr(F|E_3)$$
$$= .50(.022) + .30(.028) + .20(.033)$$
$$= .0110 + .0084 + .0066 = .026$$

Hence for this style of container the overall percentage of defective items is 2.6%.

Note once again that $Pr(F)$ equals the sum of the probabilities of all the branches of the tree diagram in Figure 7.8 that contain event F.

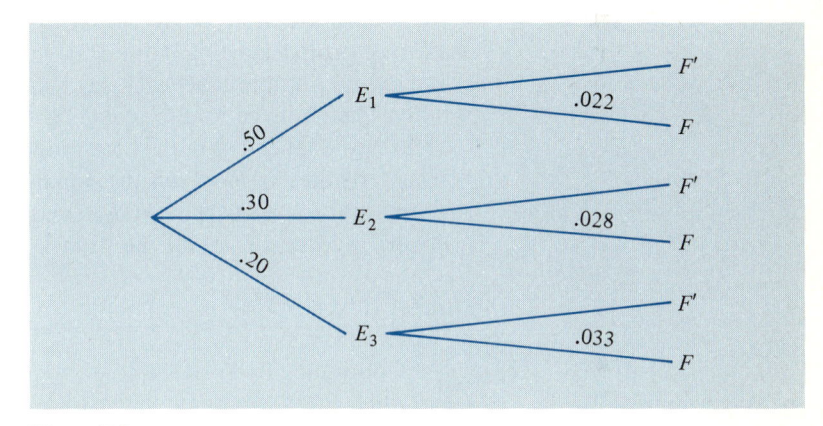

Figure 7.8

Combining Theorems 7.5 and 7.7 yields the following formula for computing the probability of a prior event given the occurrence of a later event.

THEOREM 7.8 *Bayes' formula*

Let $E_1, E_2, \ldots, E_k$ be events that partition a sample space. Then for any event F and any $i = 1, 2, \ldots, k$

$$Pr(E_i|F)$$
$$= \frac{Pr(E_i \cap F)}{Pr(E_1 \cap F) + Pr(E_2 \cap F) + \cdots + Pr(E_k \cap F)}$$
$$= \frac{Pr(E_i) \cdot Pr(F|E_i)}{Pr(E_1) \cdot Pr(F|E_1) + Pr(E_2) \cdot Pr(F|E_2) + \cdots + Pr(E_k) \cdot Pr(F|E_k)}$$

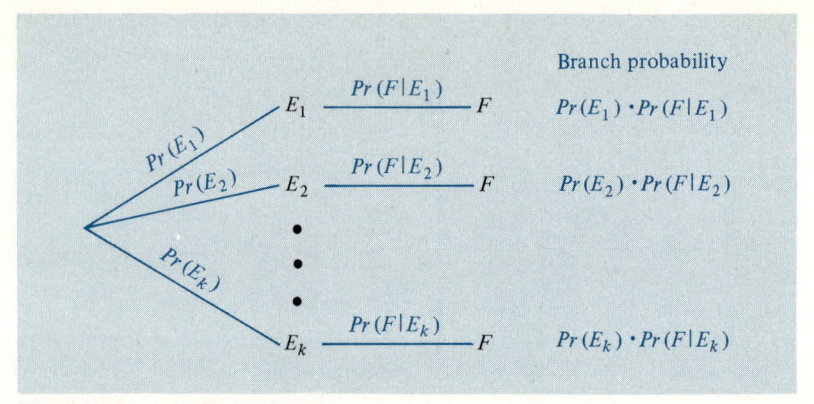

Figure 7.9

Observe that both Theorems 7.7 and 7.8 can be easily remembered with the aid of the diagram in Figure 7.9, which is constructed as follows. From a starting point draw line segments to each of the events $E_1, E_2, \ldots, E_k$ and label each segment with the corresponding probability. Then from each of the events E_i draw another line segment to the event F and label it with the conditional probability $Pr(F|E_i)$. Theorem 7.7 asserts that $Pr(F)$ equals the sum of all the branch probabilities, and Theorem 7.8 asserts that $Pr(E_i|F)$ equals the ith branch probability divided by the sum of all the branch probabilities.

EXAMPLE 48

Continuing from Example 47, we can use Bayes' formula to determine the percentage of the total number of defective containers produced by each of the three factories. From Figure 7.8 we see that

$$Pr(E_1|F) = \frac{.50(.022)}{.50(.022) + .30(.028) + .20(.033)} = \frac{.011}{.026} \approx .423$$

$$Pr(E_2|F) = \frac{.30(.028)}{.50(.022) + .30(.028) + .20(.033)} = \frac{.0084}{.026} \approx .323$$

and

$$Pr(E_3|F) = \frac{.20(.033)}{.50(.022) + .30(.028) + .20(.033)} = \frac{.0066}{.026} \approx .254$$

Thus approximately 42.3% of the defective containers are produced in Philadelphia, approximately 32.3% are produced in St. Louis, and approximately 25.4% are produced in Los Angeles.

EXAMPLE 49

Suppose that a public health agency in a particular state predicts that, of those who catch the flu during the coming winter, 80% will

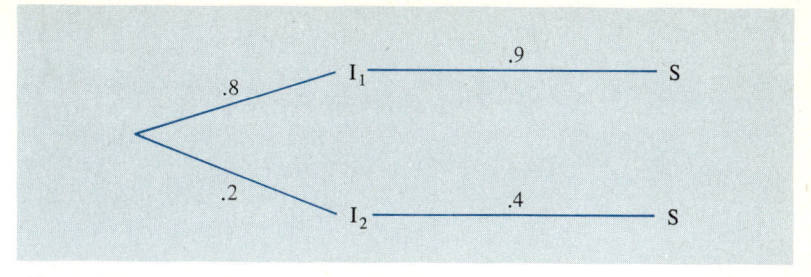

Figure 7.10

catch one strain of influenza and 20% will catch another. Although persons with either strain may show symptoms of nausea, 90% of those with the first strain of influenza experience nausea, and only 40% of those with the second strain experience nausea. Given that a person with the flu shows symptoms of nausea, what is the probability that he or she has each strain of influenza?

This question can be answered by the use of Bayes' formula. Let I_1 and I_2 be the events of contracting the first and second strains of influenza, respectively, and let S be the event of showing symptoms of nausea. Then

$$Pr(I_1) = .8 \qquad Pr(I_2) = .2 \qquad Pr(S|I_1) = .9$$

and

$$Pr(S|I_2) = .4$$

Hence from Figure 7.10 and Bayes' formula

$$Pr(I_1|S) = \frac{.8(.9)}{.8(.9) + .2(.4)} = \frac{.72}{.80} = .90$$

and

$$Pr(I_2|S) = \frac{.2(.4)}{.8(.9) + .2(.4)} = \frac{.08}{.80} = .10$$

Therefore if someone with the flu shows symptoms of nausea, the probability is .90 that the person has the first strain of influenza and .10 that the person has the second strain.

EXAMPLE 50

A factory employs its workers on three shifts; the first shift employs 60% of the workers, the second shift employs 30% of the workers, and the third shift employs 10% of the workers. Management has found that the absentee rate for the first shift is 1.5% but increases to 5% for the second shift and 6% for the third shift.

The percentage of all the absentees who are employed on each shift can be computed from this information using Bayes' formula.

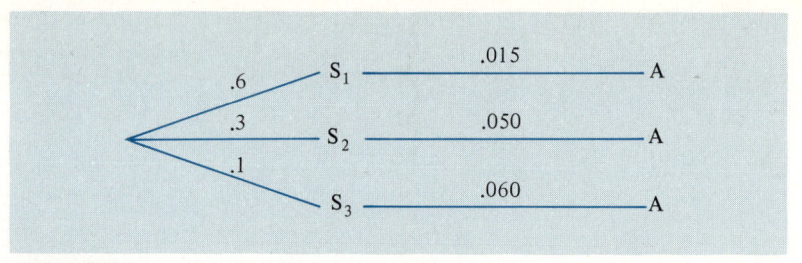

Figure 7.11

Define

S_1: A worker is employed on the first shift.
S_2: A worker is employed on the second shift.
S_3: A worker is employed on the third shift.
A: A worker is absent.

Then

$$Pr(S_1) = .6 \qquad Pr(S_2) = .3 \quad \text{and} \quad Pr(S_3) = .1$$
$$Pr(A|S_1) = .015 \qquad Pr(A|S_2) = .050 \quad \text{and} \quad Pr(A|S_3) = .060$$

From Figure 7.11 we see that

$$Pr(S_1|A) = \frac{.6(.015)}{.6(.015) + .3(.050) + .1(.060)} = \frac{.009}{.030} = .30$$

$$Pr(S_2|A) = \frac{.3(.050)}{.6(.015) + .3(.050) + .1(.060)} = \frac{.015}{.030} = .50$$

and

$$Pr(S_3|A) = \frac{.1(.060)}{.6(.015) + .3(.050) + .1(.060)} = \frac{.006}{.030} = .20$$

Thus 30% of the absentees work on the first shift, 50% on the second shift, and 20% on the third shift.

Exercises

In Exercises 1–4, evaluate $Pr(E|F)$ under the given conditions.

1. $Pr(E) = .30$, $Pr(F) = .12$, and $Pr(F|E) = .22$
2. $Pr(E) = .15$, $Pr(F) = .42$, and $Pr(F|E) = .56$
3. $Pr(E) = .24$, $Pr(F) = .66$, and $Pr(F|E) = .11$
4. $Pr(E) = .25$, $Pr(F) = .15$, and $Pr(F|E) = .21$
5. From a standard deck of playing cards someone randomly selects one card. You then randomly select a second card and find that it is a 10. What is the probability that the other person has a card with a higher denomination (that is, a jack, queen, king, or ace)?

6. In a particular factory 14% of all applicants are hired and, of those who are hired, 85% are high school graduates. If 70% of all applicants are high school graduates, what is the probability that an applicant who is a high school graduate will be hired?

7. In a small town 10% of the labor force is employed in a factory that produces a strong pesticide. After several years it was noticed that, among the residents of the town who had a certain form of cancer, 80% had worked in the factory for at least one year. If it is known that this form of cancer normally occurs in only 2% of the population, determine the probability that someone who was employed in the factory for at least one year will contract this form of cancer.

8. In analyzing the vote in a certain precinct, an election poll found that 42% of the voters were registered as Democrats and 28% of those who were registered as Democrats voted for the Republican gubernatorial candidate. If 56% of the voters in this precinct voted for the Republican gubernatorial candidate, what proportion of those who voted for the Republican gubernatorial candidate were registered as Democrats?

Suppose that E_1 and E_2 partition the sample space of an experiment. Compute $Pr(F)$ under the conditions given in Exercises 9–12.

9. $Pr(E_1) = .7$, $Pr(F|E_1) = .4$, and $Pr(F|E_2) = .1$
10. $Pr(E_2) = .4$, $Pr(F|E_1) = .2$, and $Pr(F|E_2) = .7$
11. $Pr(E_2) = .8$, $Pr(F|E_1) = .3$, and $Pr(F|E_2) = .4$
12. $Pr(E_1) = .25$, $Pr(F|E_1) = .32$, and $Pr(F|E_2) = .12$

Suppose that E_1, E_2, and E_3 partition the sample space of an experiment. Compute $Pr(F)$ under the condition given in Exercises 13–16.

13. $Pr(E_1) = .3$, $Pr(E_2) = .6$, $Pr(F|E_1) = .7$, $Pr(F|E_2) = .2$, and $Pr(F|E_3) = .4$
14. $Pr(E_1) = .5$, $Pr(E_3) = .1$, $Pr(F|E_1) = .4$, $Pr(F|E_2) = .6$, and $Pr(F|E_3) = .2$
15. $Pr(E_2) = .2$, $Pr(E_3) = .6$, $Pr(F|E_1) = .35$, $Pr(F|E_2) = .45$, and $Pr(F|E_3) = .15$
16. $Pr(E_1) = .4$, $Pr(E_2) = .3$, $Pr(F|E_1) = .5$, $Pr(F|E_2) = .2$, and $Pr(F|E_3) = .3$

17. A teacher found that only 60% of the class completed a particular examination. Of those who completed the examination, 80% passed, but only 55% of the others passed. What percentage of students passed this examination?

18. An automobile dealer sells Buicks, Oldsmobiles, and Pontiacs. His sales records show that 45% of his new car sales are Buicks, 25% are Oldsmobiles, and 30% are Pontiacs. Of those who buy Buicks, 60% say that they will buy another car from him; for purchasers of Oldsmobiles and Pontiacs this percentage is 40 and 20%, respectively. What is the probability that someone who has bought a new car from this dealer will buy another car from him?

19. Three boxes contain blue marbles and green marbles. In the first box $\frac{2}{3}$ of the marbles are green, in the second box $\frac{3}{8}$ of the marbles are green, and in the third box $\frac{1}{2}$ of the marbles are green. A die will be rolled, and if a 1, 2, or 3 appears, then a marble will be randomly selected from the first box; if a 4 or 5 appears, then a marble will be randomly selected from the second box; if a 6 appears, then a marble will be randomly selected from the third box. What is the probability that the marble selected will be green?

20. A placement test has been devised to predict success in a certain mathematics course. For those who score above 30 on the test, the probability of success is .8; for those who score 21–30, the probability of success is 6; for those who score 11–20 the probability of success is .5; and for those who score 0–10, the probability of success is .1. When the placement test was given, 15% of the students scored above 30, 25% scored 21–30, 40% scored 11–20, and 20% scored 0–10. What is the probability that one of these students selected at random will succeed in the mathematics course?

For Exercises 21–24, compute $Pr(E_1|F)$ and $Pr(E_2|F)$ using the data in Exercises 9–12.

For Exercises 25–28, compute $Pr(E_1|F)$, $Pr(E_2|F)$, and $Pr(E_3|F)$ using the data in Exercises 13–16.

29. Suppose that a cancer test indicates the presence of a certain form of cancer in 96% of those who have the cancer and in 2% of those who do not. If 3% of the population has this form of cancer, what is the probability that
    (a) Someone actually has the cancer if the test indicates that the cancer is present?
    (b) Someone has the cancer if the test indicates that the cancer is not present?

30. In a particular county, 50% of the registered voters are Democrats, 30% are Republicans, and 20% are independents. During a recent election, 40% of the Democrats voted, 60% of the Republicans voted, and 70% of the independents voted. What is the probability that someone who voted is a Democrat? A Republican? An independent?

31. In a small town there are three builders who do all the home construction. East Side Construction builds 20% of the new houses, Beach Builders constructs 50% of the new houses, and Tragbaum Construction builds 30% of the new houses. A survey of the purchasers of new houses in this town showed that, one year after moving in, 72% of those who bought from East Side were completely satisfied with their houses, 46% of those who bought from Beach were completely satisfied, and 62% of those who bought from Tragbaum were completely satisfied. What percentage of the completely satisfied buyers bought a house built by East Side? By Beach? By Tragbaum?

32. An insurance company finds that 25% of its automobile insurance policies cover drivers under 25, 15% cover drivers 25–34, 40% cover drivers 35–60, and 20% cover drivers over 60. The probability of an accident for each age group is as follows: .020 for those under 25, .008 for those aged 25–34, .005 for those aged 35–60, and .012 for those over 60. What proportion of the accidents involving this company's policyholders involve drivers of each age group?

7.6 Expected Value

In Section 5.2 we saw the need to obtain a measure of the size of a "typical" element in a data set. Similarly, it is useful to have some indication of an "average" value for a stochastic experiment. Such a measure should reflect the probability that each outcome of the

7.6 Expected Value   289

experiment will occur. In this section one such measure, the expected value, will be discussed.

Suppose that a random experiment has n possible outcomes and that associated with each outcome is one of the numerical values $x_1, x_2, \ldots, x_n$. If the probability of each outcome is $p_1, p_2, \ldots, p_n$, respectively, then the *expected value* of the experiment is the quantity $p_1 x_1 + p_2 x_2 + \cdots + p_n x_n$.

expected value

EXAMPLE 51

A contractor anticipates a $10,000 loss if there is a strike by construction workers and a $50,000 profit if there is no strike. If the probability of a strike is .2, then the probability of there being no strike is $1 - .2 = .8$. So we have the following data:

Outcome	Probability	Value
Strike	.2	$-\$10,000$
No strike	.8	$\$50,000$

Hence the contractor's expected value (expected profit) is

$$.2(-\$10,000) + .8(\$50,000) = -\$2000 + \$40,000 = \$38,000$$

EXAMPLE 52

An air traveler can purchase a life insurance policy for $1 which will pay $25,000 in the event of death due to an airplane accident. If the probability of death due to an airplane accident is .00002, what is the expected value to the traveler of such a policy?

To determine this expected value, note that there are two possible outcomes: death due to an airplane accident or not. If death occurs, the policy will pay $24,999 ($25,000 less the $1 premium) to the traveler; otherwise, the traveler loses the $1 premium. Hence we have the following data:

Outcome	Probability	Value
Death	.00002	$\$24,999$
No death	.99998	$-\$1$

So the expected value for the traveler of such a policy is

$$.00002(\$24,999) + .99998(-\$1) = \$0.49998 - \$0.99998 = -\$0.50$$

We see therefore that the expected value of such a policy for the insurance company will be $0.50.

EXAMPLE 53

Let us compute the expected number of spots showing on one roll of a fair die. In this case we have the following data:

Outcome	Probability	Value
1 is rolled	$\frac{1}{6}$	1
2 is rolled	$\frac{1}{6}$	2
3 is rolled	$\frac{1}{6}$	3
4 is rolled	$\frac{1}{6}$	4
5 is rolled	$\frac{1}{6}$	5
6 is rolled	$\frac{1}{6}$	6

So the expected value of this experiment is

$$\tfrac{1}{6}(1) + \tfrac{1}{6}(2) + \tfrac{1}{6}(3) + \tfrac{1}{6}(4) + \tfrac{1}{6}(5) + \tfrac{1}{6}(6) = \tfrac{21}{6} = \tfrac{7}{2}$$

Observe that in Examples 51–53 the expected value is not one of the values associated with an outcome in the experiment, but rather that the expected value represents a long-term average value when the experiment is performed many times. More precisely, the expected value of an experiment is a weighted average of the numerical values associated with the outcomes of the experiment that reflects the likelihood that each outcome occurs.

As we have seen, the calculation of the expected value of an experiment is quite easy when the values of the outcomes and the corresponding probabilities are known. Determining these values and probabilities is sometimes difficult, however, as the following examples demonstrate.

EXAMPLE 54

A lottery offers 1 first prize of $3000, 2 second prizes of $1000, and 10 third prizes of $100. If 10,000 tickets are sold at a cost of $1 each, what is the expected value of each ticket?

In this experiment there are four possible outcomes: the first prize is won, a second prize is won, a third prize is won, and no prize is won. The respective values of these outcomes are $2999, $999, $99, and $-$1. (These values are obtained by subtracting the ticket price from the amount won.) By Example 16 in Section 7.1, it follows that the corresponding probabilities are 1/10,000, 2/10,000, 10/10,000, and 9987/10,000. Hence the expected value of each ticket is

$$\frac{1}{10{,}000}(\$2999) + \frac{2}{10{,}000}(\$999) + \frac{10}{10{,}000}(\$99) + \frac{9987}{10{,}000}(-\$1)$$

$$= \$0.2999 + \$0.1998 + \$0.0990 - \$0.9987 = -\$0.40$$

EXAMPLE 55

A sample of 3 transistors is chosen at random from a box containing 2 defective transistors and 10 nondefective transistors. What is the expected number of defective transistors selected?

Since the sample may contain 0, 1, or 2 defective transistors, these are the three possible outcomes for this experiment. As in Section 7.1, we see that

$$Pr(0 \text{ defective}) = \frac{C(10,3)}{C(12,3)} = \frac{120}{220} = \frac{6}{11}$$

$$Pr(1 \text{ defective}) = \frac{C(10,2) \cdot C(2,1)}{C(12,3)} = \frac{45 \cdot 2}{220} = \frac{9}{22}$$

and

$$Pr(2 \text{ defective}) = \frac{C(10,1) \cdot C(2,2)}{C(12,3)} = \frac{10 \cdot 1}{220} = \frac{1}{22}$$

So the expected number of defective transistors selected is

$$\tfrac{6}{11}(0) + \tfrac{9}{22}(1) + \tfrac{1}{22}(2) = 0 + \tfrac{9}{22} + \tfrac{2}{22} = \tfrac{1}{2}$$

The next example demonstrates how the calculation of expected values can be used to decide on a course of action involving several alternatives.

EXAMPLE 56

A farmer delivers eggs each Friday to her wholesale and retail customers in the city. From experience she knows that she will sell no less than 2 truckloads and no more than 5 truckloads each week; the probabilities of selling exactly 2, 3, 4, and 5 truckloads on any given week are .2, .4, .3, and .1, respectively. For each truckload that is sold, the farmer will receive a profit of $150, but each truckload that is not sold will spoil with a resulting loss of $50. How many truckloads of eggs should the farmer send to the city each week in order to obtain the maximum expected profit?

To answer this question, we must compute the expected value of each of the farmer's four alternatives (sending 2, 3, 4, or 5 truckloads).

If the farmer sends 2 truckloads of eggs, only one outcome is possible—both truckloads will be sold with a resulting profit of $300. So the expected value of this alternative is $300.

If the farmer sends 3 truckloads of eggs, there will be two possible outcomes—only 2 truckloads may be sold or all 3 truckloads may be sold. If only 2 truckloads are sold, the profit will be

$250 ($300 profit on the 2 truckloads that are sold less $50 loss on the truckload that is not sold), whereas the profit will be $450 if all 3 truckloads are sold. Since the probability of selling exactly 2 truckloads is .2 and the probability of selling at least 3 truckloads is $.4 + .3 + .1 = .8$, the expected value of this alternative is

$$.2(\$250) + .8(\$450) = \$50 + \$360 = \$410$$

If the farmer sends 4 truckloads of eggs, there are three possible outcomes as shown below

Outcome	Probability	Value
Sell exactly 2 truckloads	.2	$2(\$150) - 2(\$50) = \$200$
Sell exactly 3 truckloads	.4	$3(\$150) - 1(\$50) = \$400$
Sell at least 4 truckloads	$.3 + .1 = .4$	$4(\$150) \quad\quad = \$600$

Hence the expected value of this alternative is

$$.2(\$200) + .4(\$400) + .4(\$600) = \$40 + \$160 + \$240 = \$440$$

Finally, if the farmer sends 5 truckloads of eggs, there are four possible outcomes:

Outcome	Probability	Value
Sell exactly 2 truckloads	.2	$2(\$150) - 3(\$50) = \$150$
Sell exactly 3 truckloads	.4	$3(\$150) - 2(\$50) = \$350$
Sell exactly 4 truckloads	.3	$4(\$150) - 1(\$50) = \$550$
Sell exactly 5 truckloads	.1	$5(\$150) \quad\quad = \$750$

Thus the expected value of this alternative is

$$.2(\$150) + .4(\$350) + .3(\$550) + .1(\$750)$$
$$= \$30 + \$140 + \$165 + \$75 = \$410$$

We see therefore that the farmer's greatest expected profit ($440) is obtained by sending 4 truckloads of eggs to the city.

Exercises

In Exercises 1–8 compute the expected value of the experiment with sample space S under the given conditions.

1. $S = \{3, 5\}$, $Pr(3) = .6$, $Pr(5) = .4$
2. $S = \{1, 2, 6\}$, $Pr(1) = .2$, $Pr(2) = .7$, $Pr(6) = .1$
3. $S = \{-4, 0, 2, 8\}$, $Pr(-4) = .3$, $Pr(0) = .2$, $Pr(2) = .4$, $Pr(8) = .1$
4. $S = \{-30, -20, 50, 100\}$, $Pr(-30) = .4$, $Pr(-20) = .1$, $Pr(50) = .2$, $Pr(100) = .3$
5. $S = \{-60, -30, 0, 90\}$, $Pr(-60) = \frac{1}{6}$, $Pr(-30) = \frac{1}{4}$, $Pr(0) = \frac{1}{12}$, $Pr(90) = \frac{1}{2}$

6. $S = \{-24, -6, 12, 36\}$, $Pr(-24) = \frac{1}{8}$, $Pr(-6) = \frac{1}{3}$, $Pr(12) = \frac{1}{6}$, $Pr(36) = \frac{3}{8}$
7. $S = \{3, 4, 5, 6, 7\}$, $Pr(3) = \frac{5}{24}$, $Pr(4) = \frac{1}{4}$, $Pr(5) = \frac{1}{3}$, $Pr(6) = \frac{1}{6}$, $Pr(7) = \frac{1}{24}$
8. $S = \{-6, -2, 3, 5, 10\}$, $Pr(-6) = \frac{1}{4}$, $Pr(-2) = \frac{1}{10}$, $Pr(3) = \frac{1}{5}$, $Pr(5) = \frac{1}{4}$, $Pr(10) = \frac{1}{5}$
9. A die is loaded so that the probability of a given number being rolled is as follows: $Pr(1) = .22$, $Pr(2) = .26$, $Pr(3) = .18$, $Pr(4) = .13$, $Pr(5) = .10$, $Pr(6) = .11$. What is the expected value of a single roll of the die?
10. What is the expected value of one roll of a pair of ordinary dice?
11. A business venture is expected to earn a $250,000 profit if successful and to lose $100,000 if unsuccessful. If the probability of this venture succeeding is .4, what is its expected profit?
12. A farmer expects 220 bushels of corn per acre under normal weather conditions, 250 bushels per acre under excellent weather conditions, and 150 bushels per acre under poor weather conditions. If the probability of normal weather, excellent weather, and poor weather is .6, .1, and .3, respectively, what is the expected yield per acre?
13. An insurance company charges $25 for a policy that will pay $10,000 to a person aged 30 who dies before age 31. If the probability of someone aged 30 dying before age 31 is approximately .00213, estimate the expected value of such a policy to the policyholder.
14. An insurance company charges $300 for a policy that will pay $20,000 to a person aged 35 who dies before age 40. What is the expected value of such a policy to the company if the probability that someone aged 35 will die before age 40 is .01413?
15. A raffle offers a first prize of $2000, 2 second prizes of $500, and 10 third prizes of $100. If 10,000 tickets are sold at a price of $1 each, what is the expected value of each ticket?
16. A raffle offers 5 prizes of $200, 10 prizes of $100, and 20 prizes of $50. If 20,000 tickets are sold at a price of $0.50 each, what is the expected value of each ticket?
17. What is the expected number of boys in a 3-child family?
18. American roulette wheels usually have 38 slots numbered 00, 0, 1, 2, ..., 36, all of which are equally likely to occur. A person who bets $1 on a given number wins $35 (and receives the bet back) if that number occurs, and loses the bet otherwise. What is the expected value of such a bet?
19. Three prize winners are to be selected at random from among 6 women and 2 men. What is the expected number of men that will be selected?
20. A bargaining committee is to be appointed from among 6 union members and 3 nonunion workers. If the committee is to consist of 4 randomly chosen persons, what is the expected number of nonunion workers that will be selected?
21. A university committee consisting of 4 faculty members and 3 students intends to form a 3-member subcommittee. If the members of the subcommittee are chosen at random, what is the expected number of students that will be selected?
22. Three members are to be selected at random from among the members of the city council to serve on a planning committee. If there are 9 Republicans and 6 Democrats on the city council, what is the expected number of Republicans that will be appointed to the planning committee?

23. An investor must decide whether to put her money into a mutual fund or to buy a speculative stock. Her broker advises that the mutual fund will earn $400 profit during a time of great economic growth, will lose $100 during a recession, and will earn $300 profit otherwise. The stock is expected to yield $800 profit during a time of great economic growth, to lose $600 during a recession, and to earn $200 profit otherwise. If the investor believes that the probabilities of great economic growth and recession are .3 and .1, respectively, what is the expected profit for each investment?

24. A fruit grower delivers peaches to his wholesale and retail customers each week. From experience he knows that the probability of selling exactly 1, 2, 3, and 4 truckloads of peaches each week is .4, .3, .2, and .1, respectively. For each truckload of peaches sold, the grower will realize a profit of $200, but he will lose $80 because of spoilage for each truckload of peaches not sold. Under these conditions, what is the grower's maximum expected profit, and which alternative yields this profit?

Chapter Review

New Terms

Bernoulli experiment (p. 274)
binomial experiment (p. 275)
conditional probability (p. 265)
dependent events (p. 268)
event (p. 245)
expected value (p. 289)
experiment (p. 244)
failure (p. 274)
impossible event (p. 245)
independent events (p. 268)

mutually exclusive events (p. 260)
odds against an event (p. 257)
odds in favor of an event (p. 257)
partitioned sample space (p. 282)
probability of an event (p. 247)
sample space (p. 244)
selection with replacement (p. 273)
selection without replacement (p. 273)
simple event (p.245)
success (p. 274)

Review Exercises

1. Label the following statements true or false.
   (a) In an experiment with m equally likely outcomes the probability of each simple event is $1/m$.
   (b) In an experiment with m equally likely outcomes, if an event E consists of k outcomes, then $Pr(E) = k/m$.
   (c) For any event E, $Pr(E') = 1 - Pr(E)$.
   (d) For any events E and F, $Pr(E \cup F) = Pr(E) + Pr(F)$.
   (e) If $n(E) \neq 0$, then $Pr(F|E) = n(E \cap F)/n(E)$.
   (f) For any events E and F, $Pr(E \cap F) = Pr(E) \cdot Pr(F)$.
   (g) If $E_1, E_2, \ldots, E_k$ are independent events, then
   $Pr(E_1 \cap E_2 \cap \cdots \cap E_k) = Pr(E_1) \cdot Pr(E_2) \cdots Pr(E_k)$.
   (h) In a Bernoulli experiment $Pr(\text{success}) = Pr(\text{failure})$.
   (i) In a binomial experiment with a probability of success p and a probability of failure q, the probability of obtaining exactly k successes in n trials is $C(n, k)q^k p^{n-k}$.
   (j) For any events E and F, $Pr(E|F) = Pr(E) \cdot Pr(F|E)/Pr(F)$ if $Pr(F) \neq 0$.

(k) If a sample space is partitioned by events $E_1, E_2, \ldots, E_k$, then for any event $F \neq \emptyset$, $Pr(E_i|F)$

$$= \frac{Pr(E_i) \cdot Pr(F|E_i)}{Pr(E_1) \cdot Pr(F|E_1) + Pr(E_2) \cdot Pr(F|E_2) + \cdots + Pr(E_k) \cdot Pr(F|E_k)}$$

(l) The expected value of an experiment must be one of the possible outcomes of the experiment.

2. (a) Write a sample space for a family with 4 children that consists of equally likely outcomes. (Assume that the probability of a boy is $\frac{1}{2}$.)
   (b) What is the probability that 3 of the 4 children are of the same sex?
   (c) What is the probability that the 2 youngest children are of the same sex?
   (d) What is the probability that the oldest child is a boy or the last 3 children are girls?
   (e) What is the probability that the oldest child is a girl and the youngest is a boy?
   (f) What is the probability that there are 2 children of each sex?

3. In [6] Horvath and Reid conducted a study to determine whether experienced and inexperienced polygraph operators could successfully judge guilt and innocence by analyzing only the polygraph records for 20 innocent and 20 guilty suspects. This study yielded the following data:

	Correct decision	Incorrect decision	Total
Experienced examiners	256	24	280
Inexperienced examiners	95	25	120
Total	351	49	400

Determine the probability of the following events.
(a) A correct decision was made.
(b) An experienced examiner was tested.
(c) An inexperienced examiner made an incorrect decision.
(d) Someone who made a correct decision was an experienced examiner.

4. At a certain college, 6% of the students take Mathematics 105 and 4% take Economics 101. If 22% of the students taking Economics 101 have taken Mathematics 105, what percentage of students taking Mathematics 105 have taken Economics 101?

5. A city council consists of 4 liberals and 6 conservatives. If a delegation of 3 is selected at random, what is the probability that
   (a) The delegation will contain no liberals?
   (b) The delegation will contain no conservatives?
   (c) The delegation will contain exactly 2 liberals?
   (d) The delegation will contain exactly 1 liberal?

6. The probability that a certain brand of light bulb will burn for at least 1500 hours is .6. If 8 of these bulbs are randomly selected, what is the probability that exactly 5 will burn for at least 1500 hours? That 5 or more will burn for at least 1500 hours?

7. A box contains marbles of 2 sizes and 4 colors: $\frac{1}{12}$ are large red marbles, $\frac{1}{6}$ are small red marbles, $\frac{1}{8}$ are large yellow marbles, $\frac{1}{12}$ are small yellow marbles, $\frac{1}{3}$ are large blue marbles, $\frac{1}{12}$ are large green marbles, and $\frac{1}{8}$ are

small green marbles. If 1 marble is selected at random, what is the probability that it will be large? Red? Yellow or green? Yellow, blue, or green? Small or green?

8. Among the patients of a certain dentist, 15% are children under 18, 25% are aged 18–30, and 60% are over 30. Past experience shows that the probability of having a cavity is .6 for a child under 18, .2 for a person aged 18–30, and .1 for someone over 30. What is the probability that a randomly selected patient will have a cavity?

9. In a consumer test of a particular brand of cereal, 73% thought that the cereal had a good taste, and 64% thought that it stayed crisp in milk. If 51% of those tested thought that the cereal had a good taste and stayed crisp in milk, what percentage thought that the cereal had a good taste or stayed crisp in milk? What percentage thought that the cereal did not have a good taste?

10. A key chain contains 8 keys which look alike. If only 1 of the keys will open a particular door and the keys are tried successively until the door is opened, what is the probability that
    (a) The first key will open the door?
    (b) The second key will open the door?
    (c) The first or second key will open the door?
    (d) One of the first 7 keys will open the door?

11. A survey was taken to determine the frequency with which the computer language COBOL was used by various computer operations. Of the computer centers surveyed, 20% were universities or colleges, 30% were state or local governments, and 50% were industries. It was learned that 25% of the universities or colleges used COBOL, 50% of the state or local governments used COBOL, and 80% of the industries used COBOL. What is the probability that one of the computer centers that uses COBOL is an industry?

12. Three cards are randomly selected without replacement from a standard deck of playing cards. What is the probability that
    (a) The first 2 cards are hearts?
    (b) All 3 cards are red?
    (c) The first 2 cards are of the same denomination?
    (d) The first card is a club or a face card?
    (e) The first card is a jack, the second is a queen, and the third is a king?
    (f) Each card is a 5, 6, 7, 8, or 9?
    (g) At least 1 card is a face card?
    (h) The first card is a heart and the second card is a 10?
    (i) The first card is a club and the second card is red?
    (j) The first card is red and the second card is a diamond?

13. An economist has predicted that during the next year the probability of an 8% inflation rate will be .3, the probability of a 7% inflation rate will be .5, and the probability of a 6% inflation rate will be .2. What is the expected inflation rate according to this economist?

14. The administration of a large university expects that next year's enrollment will increase by 2000 with probability .1, will increase by 1000 with probability .3, will remain unchanged with probability .2, and will decrease by 1000 with probability .4. What is the expected increase in enrollment for next year?

15. A raffle offers a first prize of $3000, 2 second prizes of $1000, and 10 third prizes of $100. If 20,000 tickets are sold at a price of $0.50 each, what is the expected value of each ticket?

16. A subcommittee of 3 is to be selected from among 2 students and 4 faculty members. If the subcommittee members are selected at random, what is the expected number of students that will be on the subcommittee?

17. A baker can sell as many as 3 cakes besides those specially ordered. From experience he knows that he can sell 0, 1, 2, and 3 cakes with probability .1, .4, .3, and .2, respectively. If each cake that is sold results in a $3 profit and each cake that is not sold results in an $0.80 loss, how many cakes should the baker make in order to obtain the greatest expected profit? What is the baker's greatest expected profit?

References

1. Berelson, Bernard R., Paul F. Lazarsfeld, and William N. McPhee. *Voting*. Chicago: University of Chicago Press, 1954.
2. Bower, Gordon H., "Application of a Model to Paired-Associate Learning," *Psychometrika*, vol. 26, no. 3 (September 1961), pp. 255–280.
3. Deutsch, Karl W. and William G. Madow, "A Note on the Appearance of Wisdom in Large Bureaucratic Organizations," *Behav. Sci.*, vol. 6 (1961), pp. 72–78.
4. Gelfand, Alan E. and Herbert Solomon, "Modeling Jury Verdicts in the American Legal System," *J. Am. Stat. Assoc.*, vol. 69 (March 1974), pp. 32–37.
5. Hersen, Michel, "Personality Characteristics of Nightmare Sufferers," *J. Nerv. Ment. Dis.*, vol. 153, no. 1 (July 1971), pp. 27–31.
6. Horvath, Frank S. and John E. Reid, "The Reliability of Polygraph Examiner Diagnosis of Truth and Deception," *J. Crim. Law, Criminol. Police Sci.*, vol. 62, no. 2 (1971), pp. 276–281.
7. Mosteller, F. and D. L. Wallace, *Inference and Disputed Authorship: The Federalist*. Reading, Mass.: Addison-Wesley, 1964.
8. Mosteller, F. and D. L. Wallace, "Deciding Authorship," in *Statistics: A Guide to the Unknown*, Judith M. Tanur, ed. San Francisco: Holden-Day, 1972, pp. 164–175.
9. Overall, John E. and Clyde M. Williams, "Conditional Probability Program for Diagnosis of Thyroid Function," *J. Am Med. Assoc.*, vol. 183, no. 5 (February 2, 1963), pp. 307–313.
10. Pascal, Gerald R. and Barbara Suttell, "Testing the Claims of a Graphologist," *J. Pers.*, vol. 16 (1947), pp. 192–197.
11. Smith, Paul F., "Measuring Risk on Consumer Installment Credit," *Manage. Sci.*, vol. 11, no. 2 (November 1964), pp. 327–340.
12. Warner, Homer R., Alan F. Toronto, L. George Veasey, and Robert Stephenson, "A Mathematical Approach to Medical Diagnosis," *J. Am. Med. Assoc.*, vol. 177, no. 3 (July 22, 1961), pp. 177–183.

8

Markov Chains

In this chapter the study of probability will be combined with the use of matrices in considering a special type of repeated-trials experiment called a Markov chain. Whereas in Section 7.4 we studied repeated-trials experiments in which the trials were independent, a Markov chain is a repeated-trials experiment in which the outcome at some stage of the experiment is dependent upon the outcome of the immediately preceding trial of the experiment but not upon the outcome of any earlier stage.

Markov chains have been used in a number of disciplines to provide mathematical models of various phenomena. Unlike our previous models, which were concerned with predicting a single outcome or action, Markov chain models predict the probability of various possible outcomes. Thus Markov chain models are stochastic rather than deterministic.

We shall consider two special types of Markov chains in this chapter, the so-called regular and absorbing chains. But first we begin by examining ideas common to both.

8.1 Transition Matrices

state

Consider an experiment in which the possible outcomes of any trial are known in advance. It is convenient to regard the outcome of any trial as a *state* of the experiment. For example, the experiment may be an election, and the state of the experiment may be a particular voter's preferred candidate in the election. Or the experiment may be the purchase of a particular item, and the state of the experiment may be the brand of the item selected by a particular consumer. Normally, the probability of being in a particular state of the experiment will depend upon such factors as

1. The state in question
2. The time in question
3. The previous states of the experiment

If, however, there is only a finite number of possible states and the probability of being in a certain state depends only upon the immediately preceding state of the experiment, then the experiment is called a *Markov chain*.

Markov chain

Associated with a Markov chain having n possible states S_1, $S_2, \ldots, S_n$ is an $n \times n$ matrix $P = (p_{ij})$ in which p_{ij} represents the probability of moving from state i to state j in one trial. The matrix P is called the *transition matrix of the Markov chain*. More generally, any square matrix is called a *transition matrix* if it has the following two properties:

transition matrix

1. Each entry is a nonnegative number not exceeding 1.
2. The sum of the entries in each row of the matrix is 1.

Clearly the matrix P defined above will have these two properties because the entries of P are probabilities and the probability of being in one of the states $S_1, S_2, \ldots, S_n$ is 1.

EXAMPLE 1

Because of a high accident rate at a certain location, the chief of police has decided to assign a radar unit to operate once a week at that location. The radar unit is to be placed near one of four intersections as shown in Figure 8.1. The unit is instructed to begin at intersection 1 and to proceed randomly to other intersections during the following weeks subject to two conditions:

1. The unit will return to the same intersection as that of the preceding week with probability .4.
2. The unit will move to any of the adjacent intersections with equal probability.

Thus, for instance, if the unit is at intersection 2 during a given week, then it will be stationed at intersection 1, 2, 3, or 4 with the respective probability of .2, .4, .2, or .2 during the following week.

In this situation the movement of the radar unit can be described by the 4 × 4 transition matrix below in which state i represents being positioned at intersection i.

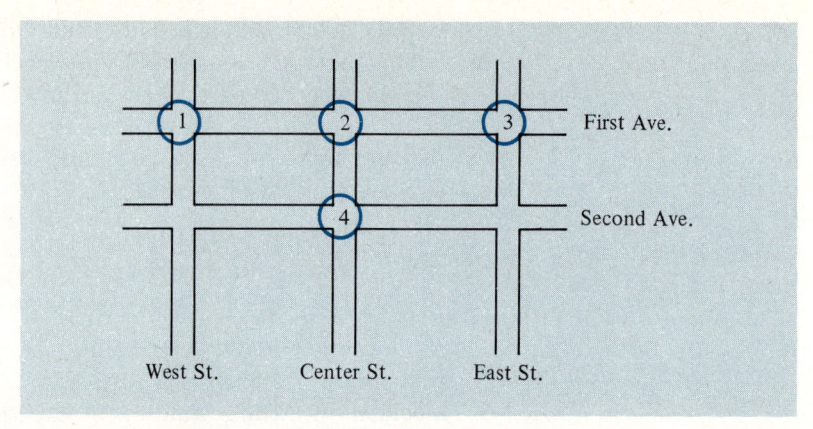

Figure 8.1 *Possible locations of the radar unit*

$$\begin{array}{c} \\ S_1 \\ S_2 \\ S_3 \\ S_4 \end{array} \begin{pmatrix} S_1 & S_2 & S_3 & S_4 \\ .4 & .6 & 0 & 0 \\ .2 & .4 & .2 & .2 \\ 0 & .6 & .4 & 0 \\ 0 & .6 & 0 & .4 \end{pmatrix}$$

Suppose that the population of a certain metropolitan area remains constant from one year to the next but that there is a continual movement of people between the city and the suburbs. Specifically, let the probability be .8 that someone who is living in the city as of January 1 will be living in the city on next January 1, and let the probability be .2 that this person will be living in the suburbs as of next January 1. Likewise, let the probability be .1 that someone who is living in the suburbs as of January 1 will be living in the city on next January 1, and let the probability be .9 that he or she will be living in the suburbs as of next January 1. The movement of people between the city and the suburbs is therefore a Markov chain with transition matrix

$$P = \begin{array}{c} \\ \text{City} \\ \text{Suburbs} \end{array} \begin{pmatrix} \text{City} & \text{Suburbs} \\ .8 & .2 \\ .1 & .9 \end{pmatrix}$$

Let us determine the probability that a city resident will be living in the suburbs after two years (trials). Observe that there are two different ways in which such a move can be made—either by remaining in the city for one year and then moving to the suburbs or by moving to the suburbs during the first year and remaining there the second.

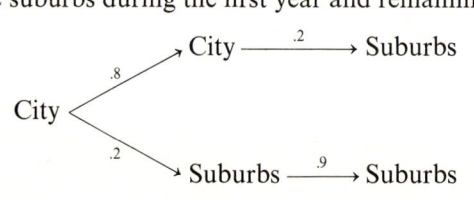

$$\text{City} \begin{array}{c} \overset{.8}{\nearrow} \text{City} \overset{.2}{\longrightarrow} \text{Suburbs} \\ \underset{.2}{\searrow} \text{Suburbs} \overset{.9}{\longrightarrow} \text{Suburbs} \end{array}$$

Since the probability that a city dweller will stay in the city during the next year is .8 and the probability of moving to the suburbs during the following year is .2, the probability that a city resident will remain in the city for one year and move to the suburbs during the following year is $.8(.2) = .16$. Likewise the probability of a city dweller moving to the suburbs during a given year and remaining there the following year is $.2(.9) = .18$. Thus the probability that a city resident will be living in the suburbs after two years is $.8(.2) + .2(.9) = .34$. Notice that this number is obtained by the same calculation as that which forms the 1, 2 entry of

$$P^2 = \begin{pmatrix} .8 & .2 \\ .1 & .9 \end{pmatrix}\begin{pmatrix} .8 & .2 \\ .1 & .9 \end{pmatrix} = \begin{pmatrix} .8(.8) + .2(.1) & .8(.2) + .2(.9) \\ .1(.8) + .9(.1) & .1(.2) + .9(.9) \end{pmatrix}$$

$$= \begin{matrix} \text{City} \\ \text{Suburbs} \end{matrix} \begin{matrix} \text{City} & \text{Suburbs} \\ \begin{pmatrix} .66 & .34 \\ .17 & .83 \end{pmatrix} \end{matrix}$$

It can be seen by similar reasoning that the other entries of P^2 can be interpreted in the same manner. This example illustrates the following result.[1]

THEOREM 8.1

If P is the transition matrix of a Markov chain, then the i, j entry of P^k (the kth power of P) represents the probability of moving from state i to state j in k trials.

Notice that, as a consequence of this interpretation of the entries of P^k, P^k must be a transition matrix.

Now suppose that in the city-suburbs problem we are told that, in 1970, 70% of the population of the metropolitan area lived in the city and 30% lived in the suburbs. This information can be described by a row vector $D = (.70 \quad .30)$ which is called the *initial distribution vector* of the Markov chain. Observe that the vector D contains nonnegative entries which sum to 1; such vectors are called *probability vectors*. It is not difficult to see that the entries of the matrix product

initial distribution vector

probability vectors

$$DP = (.70 \quad .30)\begin{pmatrix} .8 & .2 \\ .1 & .9 \end{pmatrix} = (.59 \quad .41)$$

will be the percentage of the metropolitan population living in each location in 1971 (that is, after one trial). Thus in 1971, 59% of the metropolitan population was living in the city and 41% in the suburbs. More generally, we have the following theorem.

---

[1] Readers who have read Section 3.4 should compare this theorem with the interpretation of powers of an incidence matrix on page 69.

THEOREM 8.2

Let P be the transition matrix of a Markov chain with initial distribution vector D. Then the probability of being in state i after k trials of the experiment is the ith entry of the row vector DP^k.

From this result we see that the distribution of people between the city and the suburbs in 1972 was

$$DP^2 = (DP)P = (.59 \quad .41)\begin{pmatrix} .8 & .2 \\ .1 & .9 \end{pmatrix} = (.513 \quad .487)$$

Notice that it is easier to compute DP^k by successively multiplying $D, DP, DP^2, \ldots, DP^{k-1}$ by P than to compute P^k directly. Also observe that each distribution vector DP^k is a probability vector.

EXAMPLE 2

Suppose that, during the year 1978, 50% of the drivers in a certain community had State Farm automobile insurance, 30% had Allstate insurance, and 20% were insured by some other company. Suppose also that one year later:

1. Of those who had been insured by State Farm in 1978, 98% continued to be insured by State Farm, but 2% had switched their insurance to Allstate.
2. Of those who had been insured by Allstate in 1978, 94% continued to be insured by Allstate, but 4% had switched to State Farm and 2% had switched to some other company.
3. Of those who had been insured by some other company in 1978, 77% continued with the other company, but 14% had switched to State Farm and 9% had switched to Allstate.

Using this information, determine

(a) What percentage of the drivers in this community were insured by State Farm and Allstate in 1979?
(b) If these trends continued for one more year, what percentage of the drivers in 1980 were insured by State Farm and Allstate?

The given information describes a three-state Markov chain with transition matrix

$$P = \begin{array}{c} \text{State Farm} \\ \text{Allstate} \\ \text{Other} \end{array} \begin{pmatrix} \overset{\text{State Farm}}{.98} & \overset{\text{Allstate}}{.02} & \overset{\text{Other}}{.00} \\ .04 & .94 & .02 \\ .14 & .09 & .77 \end{pmatrix}$$

and initial distribution vector

$$D = (.50 \quad .30 \quad .20)$$

So by Theorem 8.2 the answer to part (a) is provided by the entries of

$$DP = (.50 \quad .30 \quad .20) \begin{pmatrix} .98 & .02 & .00 \\ .04 & .94 & .02 \\ .14 & .09 & .77 \end{pmatrix} = (.53 \quad .31 \quad .16)$$

Thus 53% of the drivers in the community were insured by State Farm in 1979, 31% were insured by Allstate, and 16% were insured by some other company.

Likewise the answer to part (b) is given by the entries of

$$DP^2 = (DP)P = (.53 \quad .31 \quad .16) \begin{pmatrix} .98 & .02 & .00 \\ .04 & .94 & .02 \\ .14 & .09 & .77 \end{pmatrix}$$

$$= (.5542 \quad .3164 \quad .1294)$$

So 55.42% of the drivers in the community were insured by State Farm in 1980, 31.64% were insured by Allstate, and 12.94% were insured by some other company.

APPLICATION 1

In [12] Hans Hoffman describes a Markov chain model for analyzing the ages of men in the various age grades found in the Galla tribes of Ethiopia. Galla males are classified in five age grades, each of 8 years' duration. Regardless of a son's age, he enters the first (lowest) grade when his father retires from the fifth grade. Thus there is a 40-year interval between the time a father and a son enter the first grade. Because the important positions in the tribal government must be filled by men in the fifth age grade, it is important that there be an ample supply of men in this grade.

Hoffman discusses a Markov chain for analyzing the progression of Galla men through the age grade system. This Markov chain has three states: youth (ages 13–19), adult (ages 20–29), and senior citizen (age 30 or older), and the entries of the transition matrix represent the probability that the son will enter the lowest age grade while in state j, assuming that his father entered the lowest age grade in state i. Hoffman presents an example in which the initial distribution vector D and the transition matrix P are

$$D = (.250 \quad .550 \quad .200) \quad \text{and} \quad P = \begin{pmatrix} .154 & .384 & .462 \\ .367 & .400 & .233 \\ .200 & .600 & .200 \end{pmatrix}$$

Thus after one trial (one 40-year period) the distribution of Galla men among the three states is given by

$$DP \approx (.280 \quad .436 \quad .284)$$

and after two trials (80 years) the distribution of men among the three states is given by

$$DP^2 \approx (.260 \quad .452 \quad .288)$$

Notice the apparent stability of the proportion of men in each state.

APPLICATION 2

In species that reproduce sexually, the characteristics of an offspring with respect to inherited traits such as height and eye color are determined by a pair of genes, one inherited from each parent. Genes may be considered to occur in pairs at certain points (called *loci*) on chromosomes. Different genes that can occur at the same locus are called *alleles*. Let us consider a locus for which there are only two possible alleles, G (representing the dominant characteristic) and g (representing the recessive characteristic). At such a locus there are only three different genotypes (genetic pairings): GG, Gg (which is the same as gG), and gg.

Suppose that there is a large population in which the proportion of genotypes GG, Gg, and gg is p, q, and r, respectively. We assume that mating is random with respect to genotype, that the distribution of each genotype is independent of age and sex, and that half of the offspring are male and half are female. Then the possible genotypes can be shown to be the states of a Markov chain for which the transition matrix P is

Genotype of parent   **Genotype of offspring**

$$\begin{array}{c} \\ GG \\ Gg \\ gg \end{array} \begin{pmatrix} GG & Gg & gg \\ a & b & 0 \\ \tfrac{1}{2}a & \tfrac{1}{2} & \tfrac{1}{2}b \\ 0 & a & b \end{pmatrix}$$

where $a = p + \tfrac{1}{2}q$ and $b = \tfrac{1}{2}q + r$ are the proportion of G and g alleles, respectively, in the population. Note that $a + b = p + q + r = 1$.

Thus the probabilities of the various genotypes of second-generation offspring (grandchildren) of members of the original population having a specified genotype are entries of

Genotype of parent   **Genotype of grandchildren**

$$\begin{array}{c} \\ GG \\ Gg \\ gg \end{array} \begin{pmatrix} GG & Gg & gg \\ a^2 + \tfrac{1}{2}ab & ab + \tfrac{1}{2}b & \tfrac{1}{2}b^2 \\ \tfrac{1}{2}a^2 + \tfrac{1}{4}a & ab + \tfrac{1}{4} & \tfrac{1}{4}b + \tfrac{1}{2}b^2 \\ \tfrac{1}{2}a^2 & \tfrac{1}{2}a + ab & \tfrac{1}{2}ab + b^2 \end{pmatrix} = P^2$$

So, for example, the probability that a parent of genotype GG will have a grandchild of genotype gg is $\frac{1}{2}b^2$.

To determine the distribution of genotypes among the first-generation offspring, we must compute DP, where $D = (p \ q \ r)$ is the initial distribution vector. This computation yields

$$DP = (p \ q \ r)\begin{pmatrix} a & b & 0 \\ \frac{1}{2}a & \frac{1}{2} & \frac{1}{2}b \\ 0 & a & b \end{pmatrix}$$

$$= (ap + \tfrac{1}{2}aq \quad bp + \tfrac{1}{2}q + ar \quad \tfrac{1}{2}bq + br)$$
$$= (a(p + \tfrac{1}{2}q) \quad bp + \tfrac{1}{2}q(a+b) + ar \quad (\tfrac{1}{2}q + r)b)$$
$$= (a^2 \quad 2ab \quad b^2)$$

Likewise the distribution of genotypes among the second-generation offspring is given by the entries of

$$DP^2 = (DP)P = (a^2 \ 2ab \ b^2)\begin{pmatrix} a & b & 0 \\ \frac{1}{2}a & \frac{1}{2} & \frac{1}{2}b \\ 0 & a & b \end{pmatrix}$$

$$= (a^3 + a^2b \quad a^2b + ab + ab^2 \quad ab^2 + b^3)$$
$$= (a^2(a+b) \quad ab + ab(a+b) \quad (a+b)b^2)$$
$$= (a^2 \quad 2ab \quad b^2)$$

Hence $DP^2 = DP$; that is, the distribution of genotypes among the second-generation offspring (and thus the distribution of genotypes among all succeeding generations) is the same as that among the first-generation offspring. This result is called the Hardy-Weinberg law (see [10]).

Exercises

In Exercises 1–8, determine which of the given vectors are probability vectors.

1. $(\frac{1}{3} \ \frac{2}{3})$
2. $(\frac{6}{5} \ -\frac{1}{5})$
3. $(\frac{1}{4} \ \frac{1}{3})$
4. $(1 \ 0)$
5. $(\frac{1}{2} \ 0 \ \frac{1}{2})$
6. $(\frac{1}{3} \ \frac{1}{2} \ \frac{1}{6})$
7. $(\frac{1}{8} \ \frac{1}{4} \ \frac{1}{2})$
8. $(\frac{3}{5} \ -\frac{1}{10} \ \frac{1}{2})$

In Exercises 9–16, determine which of the given matrices are transition matrices.

9. $\begin{pmatrix} .4 & .2 \\ .6 & .8 \end{pmatrix}$
10. $\begin{pmatrix} .5 & .2 & .3 \\ .1 & .7 & .2 \end{pmatrix}$
11. $\begin{pmatrix} \frac{1}{4} & \frac{3}{4} \\ \frac{3}{5} & \frac{2}{5} \end{pmatrix}$
12. $\begin{pmatrix} \frac{2}{3} & \frac{1}{3} \\ 0 & 1 \end{pmatrix}$
13. $\begin{pmatrix} \frac{1}{2} & 0 & \frac{1}{2} \\ \frac{3}{4} & \frac{3}{4} & -\frac{1}{2} \\ \frac{1}{3} & \frac{1}{3} & \frac{1}{3} \end{pmatrix}$
14. $\begin{pmatrix} .4 & .2 & .4 \\ .5 & .2 & .3 \\ .3 & .3 & .3 \end{pmatrix}$

15. $\begin{pmatrix} .6 & .1 & .3 \\ .2 & .7 & .3 \\ .1 & 0 & .9 \end{pmatrix}$ 16. $\begin{pmatrix} .4 & .2 & .4 \\ 0 & 1 & 0 \\ .2 & .3 & .5 \end{pmatrix}$

For each of the transition matrices P and initial distribution vectors D in Exercises 17–24, determine the probability of passing from state 1 to state 2 in two trials and the probability of being in each state after two trials.

17. $P = \begin{pmatrix} .7 & .3 \\ .2 & .8 \end{pmatrix}, D = (.6 \;\; .4)$

18. $P = \begin{pmatrix} .5 & .5 \\ .6 & .4 \end{pmatrix}, D = (.3 \;\; .7)$

19. $P = \begin{pmatrix} .9 & .1 \\ .1 & .9 \end{pmatrix}, D = (.6 \;\; .4)$

20. $P = \begin{pmatrix} 1 & 0 \\ .1 & .9 \end{pmatrix}, D = (0 \;\; 1)$

21. $P = \begin{pmatrix} .6 & .2 & .2 \\ .1 & .7 & .2 \\ .1 & .1 & .8 \end{pmatrix}, D = (.4 \;\; .4 \;\; .2)$

22. $P = \begin{pmatrix} 0 & .5 & .5 \\ .5 & 0 & .5 \\ .5 & .5 & 0 \end{pmatrix}, D = (\tfrac{1}{3} \;\; \tfrac{1}{3} \;\; \tfrac{1}{3})$

23. $P = \begin{pmatrix} .5 & 0 & .5 \\ .5 & 0 & .5 \\ 0 & 1 & 0 \end{pmatrix}, D = (.3 \;\; .5 \;\; .2)$

24. $P = \begin{pmatrix} .4 & .3 & .3 \\ .2 & .6 & .2 \\ .1 & .1 & .8 \end{pmatrix}, D = (.8 \;\; .2 \;\; 0)$

25. An insurance company classifies policyholders of its automobile insurance according to the number of claims that have been made against them. The three possible classifications are no claims filed, one claim filed, or two or more claims filed. Analysis of the company's records during the last year shows that of those persons against whom no claims had been filed prior to last year, 92% still had no claims filed against them, 7% now had one claim filed against them, and 1% had two or more claims filed against them. Of those against whom one claim had been filed prior to last year, 85% had no new claims filed against them and 15% had one or more new claims filed against them.

   (a) Under what circumstances can this information be used to create a Markov chain model of the accident rates of the company's policyholders?

   (b) If the information above is used to form a Markov chain, what time period will one trial represent?

   (c) Write the transition matrix for a Markov chain based on the information above.

26. Weather patterns for a certain location show that, if there is precipitation on a given day, then the probability that there will be precipitation on the next day is .6, whereas if there is no precipitation, then the probability that there will be precipitation on the next day is .2. If the weather forecast for Friday calls for a 50% chance of precipitation, what is the probability that there will be no precipitation on Monday?

27. In a certain city labor statistics show that, if someone is employed at the start of a month, then the probability that he or she will be employed at the start of the next month is .95, and if someone is unemployed at the start of a month, then the probability that he or she will be unemployed at the start of the next month is .7. If the January rate of unemployment in this city is 8%, what will the unemployment rates be for February and March?

28. A department store classifies its accounts as being paid or not paid. At the end of May 70% of its accounts were paid and 30% were not. Past data for the store show that an account that is paid at the end of one month will be paid at the end of the next month with a probability of .9, while an account that is not paid at the end of one month will be paid at the end of the next month with a probability of .8. What percentage of unpaid accounts does the store expect at the end of July?

29. Suppose that 60% of the children of agricultural workers become agricultural workers, 30% become blue-collar workers, and 10% become white-collar workers, that 20% of the offspring of blue-collar workers become agricultural workers, 50% become blue-collar workers, and 30% become white-collar workers, and that 10% of the children of white-collar workers become agricultural workers, 30% become blue-collar workers, and 60% become white-collar workers. If 20% of the current generation of men and women are agricultural workers, 50% are blue-collar workers, and 30% are white-collar workers, what percentage of their grandchildren will become workers of each type?

30. If in Exercise 25 the insurance company finds that 90% of its policyholders have no claims against them, 9% have one claim against them, and 1% have two or more claims against them prior to a certain year, what percentage of its policyholders will be expected in each classification two years later if the trend in Exercise 25 continues?

31. In [11] Hunter examined changes in 75 Chicago communities with respect to economic status and family status. Hunter's model is a four-state Markov chain with states

   1. High economic status and high family status
   2. High economic status and low family status
   3. Low economic status and high family status
   4. Low economic status and low family status

   Averaging the changes in status over the decades 1930–1940, 1940–1950, and 1950–1960, Hunter obtains the following transition matrix for changes in status during a decade.

$$\begin{array}{c} \\ 1 \\ 2 \\ 3 \\ 4 \end{array} \begin{array}{c} \begin{matrix} 1 & 2 & 3 & 4 \end{matrix} \\ \begin{pmatrix} .77 & .17 & .06 & 0 \\ .02 & .77 & 0 & .20 \\ .18 & .02 & .74 & .06 \\ 0 & .04 & .19 & .76 \end{pmatrix} \end{array}$$

If in a given year 30% of the communities are in state 1, 30% are in state 2, 20% are in state 3, and 20% are in state 4, what percentage of communities will be of each type two decades later?

8.2 Regular Markov Chains

In Section 8.1 we saw that, if P is the transition matrix and D is the initial distribution vector of a Markov chain, then the entries in the row vector DP^k represent the probability of being in each state after k trials. In many situations it is important to know whether or not the distribution will eventually stabilize, that is, whether or not the vectors DP^k will remain virtually unchanged for sufficiently large values of k.

For instance, in Application 1 we discussed Hoffman's Markov chain model of the age grade system found in the Galla tribes in Ethiopia. Hoffman's reason for formulating this model was to examine the stability of Galla communities in view of the fact that the important administrative, judicial, and priestly offices of the tribes could only be held by members of the highest age grade. (Thus a large proportion of older men in the lowest age grade would indicate a future shortage of men in the highest age grade and a resulting disruption of tribal government.) So in this case a lack of stability in the Markov chain could have necessitated a great change in Galla tribal government.

Application 2 provided a striking illustration of stability in that the distribution of genotypes remained unchanged after only one generation (one trial of the Markov chain). In general, however, stability is not perfectly achieved, but the distributions DP^k become virtually constant (that is, change by arbitrarily small amounts). Such is the case for the city-suburbs problem in Section 8.1, where the vectors DP^k approach $(\frac{1}{3} \; \frac{2}{3})$ as k increases, but DP^k never actually equals $(\frac{1}{3} \; \frac{2}{3})$. (See Table 8.1.)

Table 8.1 *Distribution of Population Between the City and the Suburbs*

Trial number, k	$DP^{k\,a}$	City	Suburbs
1	(.59 .41)	.59	.41
2	(.513 .487)	.513	.487
3	(.4591 .5409)	.4591	.5409
4	(.42137 .57863)	.42137	.57863
5	(.39496 .60504)	.39496	.60504
6	(.37647 .62353)	.37647	.62353
10	(.34369 .65631)	.34369	.65631
15	(.33507 .66493)	.33507	.66493
20	(.33363 .66637)	.33363	.66637
21	(.33354 .66646)	.33354	.66646
22	(.33348 .66652)	.33348	.66652

Proportion of population living in

[a] Entries are rounded to five decimal places.

8.2 Regular Markov Chains

As the entries in Table 8.1 suggest, the distribution after each trial stabilizes slowly in this case. (For accuracy to three decimal places, 22 trials are required.) In such instances it is extremely tedious to determine that the distribution vectors DP^k stabilize by actually computing DP^k for various values of k. Fortunately, there is a large class of Markov chains called regular Markov chains which always stabilize at a vector that can be found by solving a system of linear equations.

regular Markov chain

regular transition matrix

A Markov chain is said to be *regular* if some power of its transition matrix contains no zero entries. In this case the transition matrix is called a *regular transition matrix*. The Markov chains in Application 1 and in the city-suburbs problem are regular, since each entry of the transition matrix is nonzero. Notice, however, that the Markov chain in Application 2 is regular whenever $a \neq 0$ and $b \neq 0$, even though its transition matrix P has zero entries, for in this case the entries of P^2 are all nonzero. On the other hand, the transition matrix

$$P = \begin{pmatrix} 0 & 1 \\ 1 & 0 \end{pmatrix}$$

is not regular, since every power of P contains two zero entries. (Notice that even powers of P equal I_2 and odd powers of P equal P.) In Section 8.3 we shall consider the question of stability for certain nonregular Markov chains.

When we speak of distributions stabilizing, we mean that the vectors DP^k approach a probability vector that is unchanged from one trial to the next, that is, a probability vector X such that $XP = X$. Such a vector is called a *fixed probability vector* (or *steady-state vector*) for P. Since the matrix equation $XP = X$ can be rewritten as

fixed probability vector

$$0 = X - XP = X(I - P)$$

where 0 is a zero row vector, the vector X may be found by solving a system of linear equations. To illustrate this technique, consider the city-suburbs problem in Section 8.1 for which the transition matrix is

$$P = \begin{pmatrix} .8 & .2 \\ .1 & .9 \end{pmatrix}$$

Since this Markov chain has two states, the fixed probability vector X for P will be a row vector having two entries, say

$$X = (x_1 \quad x_2)$$

Thus the equation $X(I - P) = 0$ is

$$(x_1 \quad x_2)\left[\begin{pmatrix} 1 & 0 \\ 0 & 1 \end{pmatrix} - \begin{pmatrix} .8 & .2 \\ .1 & .9 \end{pmatrix}\right] = (0 \quad 0)$$

or

$$(x_1 \quad x_2)\begin{pmatrix} .2 & -.2 \\ -.1 & .1 \end{pmatrix} = (0 \quad 0)$$

Multiplying the left side of this equation and equating the entries with the corresponding entries of the right side give

$$.2x_1 - .1x_2 = 0$$
$$-.2x_1 + .1x_2 = 0$$

a system of two linear equations in two unknowns. It is easily seen that one of these equations is redundant (either equation is -1 times the other), and so this system has infinitely many solutions. However, when we include the equation

$$x_1 + x_2 = 1$$

which is necessary if X is to be a probability vector, the resulting system

$$.2x_1 - .1x_2 = 0$$
$$-.2x_1 + .1x_2 = 0$$
$$x_1 + x_2 = 1$$

will have a unique solution. Using the techniques of Chapter 3, the reader can verify that $x_1 = \frac{1}{3}$ and $x_2 = \frac{2}{3}$.

The following theorem summarizes the important facts about regular Markov chains. Observe that part (c) asserts that the fixed probability vector is independent of the initial distribution vector.

THEOREM 8.3

Let P be a regular transition matrix. Then

(a) P has a unique fixed probability vector X.
(b) As k increases, each row of P^k approaches X.
(c) As k increases, DP^k approaches X irrespective of the initial distribution vector D.

EXAMPLE 3

A small town contains only three supermarkets. During a certain week 40% of the residents shopped at the first store and 30% shopped at each of the others. During the following week a survey of shoppers taken at each of the three supermarkets produced the following data:

1. Of those who had shopped at the first store during the previous week, 60% continued to shop there, 10% switched to the second store, and 30% changed to the third store.
2. Of those who had shopped at the second store during the previous week, 80% continued to shop there, 10% switched to the first store, and 10% switched to the third store.
3. Of those who had shopped at the third store during the previous week, 70% continued to shop there, 10% switched to the first store, and 20% switched to the second store.

On the assumption that the trend indicated by 1–3 continues, the preceding paragraph describes a Markov chain in which the three states are the supermarkets at which an individual may shop. From the data given we observe that the transition matrix P is

	Store used during current week		
Store used during previous week	First store	Second store	Third store
First store	$\begin{pmatrix} .6 $	$ .1 $	$ .3 \end{pmatrix}$
Second store	$.1$	$.8$	$.1$
Third store	$.1$	$.2$	$.7$

and from the second sentence in the example we see that the initial distribution vector is $D = (.40 \quad .30 \quad .30)$. Thus from Theorem 8.2 the current proportions of townspeople using each store are the entries of

$$DP = (.30 \quad .34 \quad .36)$$

and the proportions of townspeople using each store next week are the entries of

$$DP^2 = (.250 \quad .374 \quad .376)$$

Moreover, since P is regular (every entry of P is nonzero), we know from Theorem 8.3 that the distributions DP^k will stabilize as k increases. To determine the eventual proportion of townspeople who will be shopping at each store, we need only determine the fixed probability vector X for P. Let $X = (x_1 \quad x_2 \quad x_3)$ and recall that X is a probability vector that is also a solution of the matrix equation $X(I - P) = 0$. Thus X is a solution of the system of linear equations

$$.4x_1 - .1x_2 - .1x_3 = 0$$
$$-.1x_1 + .2x_2 - .2x_3 = 0$$
$$-.3x_1 - .1x_2 + .3x_3 = 0$$
$$x_1 + x_2 + x_3 = 1$$

The solution of this system of equations is $x_1 = .20$, $x_2 = .45$, and $x_3 = .35$. Hence if the trend indicated by the data continues, eventually 20% of the townspeople will shop at the first store, 45% will shop at the second store, and 35% will shop at the third store each week.

APPLICATION 3

During a recent political campaign in New Zealand the leader of the opposition political party stated that the entire South Island, which comprises 56% of the total land area of New Zealand and has 30% of its total population, may be regarded as a "depressed area" suitable for government subsidies and other development incentives. In [9] Hampton investigates this statement by examining the pattern of location changes made by New Zealand industries during the years 1952–1964. He takes as the states of a Markov chain the following regions in New Zealand:

1. Auckland
2. Hawke's Bay
3. Taranaki
4. Wellington
5. Marlborough
6. Nelson
7. Westland
8. Canterbury
9. Otago
10. Southland

and obtains the transition matrix

$$\begin{array}{c} \\ 1 \\ 2 \\ 3 \\ 4 \\ 5 \\ 6 \\ 7 \\ 8 \\ 9 \\ 10 \end{array} \begin{pmatrix} 1 & 2 & 3 & 4 & 5 & 6 & 7 & 8 & 9 & 10 \\ .6092 & .0403 & .0276 & .1417 & .0065 & .0135 & .0020 & .1238 & .0086 & .0268 \\ .4955 & .0655 & .0298 & .1477 & .0097 & .0222 & .0013 & .1283 & .0439 & .0561 \\ .5350 & .0594 & .0498 & .1312 & .0093 & .0201 & .0020 & .1111 & .0277 & .0542 \\ .5789 & .0386 & .0290 & .1544 & .0069 & .0129 & .0025 & .1363 & .0150 & .0255 \\ .5303 & .0518 & .0313 & .1597 & .0115 & .0197 & .0045 & .1360 & .0117 & .0435 \\ .5266 & .0503 & .0184 & .1534 & .0099 & .0218 & .0019 & .1436 & .0312 & .0429 \\ .6846 & .0249 & .0078 & .1349 & .0073 & .0005 & .0005 & .1363 & .0001 & .0031 \\ .5624 & .0430 & .0334 & .1379 & .0064 & .0143 & .0020 & .1519 & .0244 & .0243 \\ .5499 & .0469 & .0303 & .1425 & .0059 & .0158 & .0011 & .1415 & .0375 & .0286 \\ .5136 & .0584 & .0246 & .1506 & .0093 & .0211 & .0015 & .1261 & .0429 & .0519 \end{pmatrix}$$

At the time when the article was written the distribution of industries among the various regions was

$D = (.423 \ .036 \ .032 \ .214 \ .006 \ .016 \ .006 \ .163 \ .075 \ .030)$

The eventual distribution of industries among the 10 regions is given by the fixed probability vector

$X \approx (.586 \ .043 \ .029 \ .144 \ .007 \ .014 \ .002 \ .130 \ .015 \ .029)$

Thus we see that, if the present trend continues, Canterbury and Otago on South Island and Wellington on North Island will continue to lose industries to Auckland and Hawke's Bay on North Island. In fact, nearly 60% of New Zealand's industries will eventually be located in the Auckland area.

APPLICATION 4

In [4] Bourne examined changes in land usage in the city of Toronto, Canada, for the period 1952–1962. He classified land according to the following 10 uses:

1. Low-density residential (single-family residences and multifamily residences having fewer than six units)

2. High-density residential
3. Office
4. General commercial
5. Automobile commercial
6. Parking
7. Warehousing
8. Industry
9. Transportation
10. Vacant

With these 10 states the following transition matrix[2] was obtained:

Use in 1952

Use in 1962

	1	2	3	4	5	6	7	8	9	10
1	.13	.34	.10	.04	.04	.22	.03	.02	.00	.08
2	.02	.41	.05	.04	.00	.04	.00	.00	.00	.44
3	.00	.07	.43	.05	.01	.28	.14	.00	.00	.02
4	.02	.01	.09	.30	.09	.27	.05	.08	.01	.08
5	.00	.00	.11	.07	.70	.06	.00	.01	.00	.05
6	.08	.05	.14	.08	.12	.39	.04	.00	.01	.09
7	.01	.03	.02	.12	.03	.11	.38	.21	.01	.08
8	.01	.02	.02	.03	.03	.08	.18	.61	.00	.02
9	.01	.18	.14	.04	.10	.39	.03	.03	.08	.00
10	.25	.08	.03	.03	.05	.15	.22	.13	.00	.06

Although the transition matrix P contains zero entries, it is not difficult to see that P^2 does not; hence P is regular. Thus P has a fixed probability vector, which is approximately

(.050 .084 .119 .082 .151 .190 .114 .115 .004 .091)

From this vector we can see that, if the trend indicated by the transition matrix continues, then eventually 19% of the land will be used for parking and 9.1% will be vacant. These percentages suggest that the city government may wish to take action to prevent so much land being used for these two purposes.

Exercises

Which of the transition matrices in Exercises 1–8 are regular?

1. $\begin{pmatrix} .2 & .8 \\ 1 & 0 \end{pmatrix}$

2. $\begin{pmatrix} .7 & .3 \\ 0 & 1 \end{pmatrix}$

3. $\begin{pmatrix} .4 & .6 & 0 \\ .5 & .5 & 0 \\ .3 & .3 & .4 \end{pmatrix}$

4. $\begin{pmatrix} 0 & .5 & .5 \\ .7 & 0 & .3 \\ .2 & .8 & 0 \end{pmatrix}$

[2] Entries of .00 indicate probabilities less than .005.

5. $\begin{pmatrix} .2 & .3 & .5 \\ .4 & .5 & .1 \\ .2 & .2 & .6 \end{pmatrix}$
6. $\begin{pmatrix} 0 & 0 & 1 \\ .3 & .4 & .3 \\ .5 & .5 & 0 \end{pmatrix}$

7. $\begin{pmatrix} .6 & .1 & .2 & .1 \\ 0 & .5 & .3 & .2 \\ 0 & 0 & 1 & 0 \\ .2 & .3 & 0 & .5 \end{pmatrix}$
8. $\begin{pmatrix} .4 & .3 & .1 & .2 \\ 0 & 0 & 1 & 0 \\ .7 & .2 & .1 & 0 \\ .4 & .2 & 0 & .4 \end{pmatrix}$

Determine the fixed probability vector for each of the regular transition matrices P in Exercises 9–16.

9. $\begin{pmatrix} .8 & .2 \\ .3 & .7 \end{pmatrix}$
10. $\begin{pmatrix} .5 & .5 \\ .4 & .6 \end{pmatrix}$

11. $\begin{pmatrix} \frac{3}{4} & \frac{1}{4} \\ \frac{1}{3} & \frac{2}{3} \end{pmatrix}$
12. $\begin{pmatrix} .92 & .08 \\ .20 & .80 \end{pmatrix}$

13. $\begin{pmatrix} 0 & .50 & .50 \\ 0 & .25 & .75 \\ .25 & .25 & .50 \end{pmatrix}$
14. $\begin{pmatrix} .3 & .2 & .5 \\ .3 & .2 & .5 \\ .3 & .2 & .5 \end{pmatrix}$

15. $\begin{pmatrix} .6 & .2 & .2 \\ .1 & .8 & .1 \\ 0 & 1 & 0 \end{pmatrix}$
16. $\begin{pmatrix} .50 & .25 & .25 \\ .25 & .50 & .25 \\ .25 & .25 & .50 \end{pmatrix}$

17. Verify that the fixed probability vector for the transition matrix in Application 1 is approximately (.264 .452 .284). Interpret this fact in the context of the example.

18. A city's water is supplied by a reservoir. Data accumulated over many years show that, if the reservoir is full at the beginning of summer, then the probability is .9 that it will be full at the beginning of the following summer. On the other hand, if the reservoir is not full at the beginning of summer, then the probability is .6 that it will not be full at the beginning of the next summer.

    (a) If the reservoir is not full at the beginning of summer, what is the probability that it will be full at the beginning of the next summer? The summer two years hence?
    (b) If the trend continues, what percentage of the time will the reservoir be full over the long run?

19. A bank teller was observed every 10 minutes. It was found that, if he was busy during one observation, then 80% of the time he was busy during the next observation, while if he was not busy during one observation, then 60% of the time he was busy during the next observation. When the bank first opens, there is a 50% chance that the teller will have a customer during the first 10 minutes.

    (a) What is the probability that the teller will be busy between 30 and 40 minutes after the bank opens?
    (b) If the above trend continues, estimate the percentage of time the teller will be observed to be busy over the course of an eight-hour day.

L ▯ R

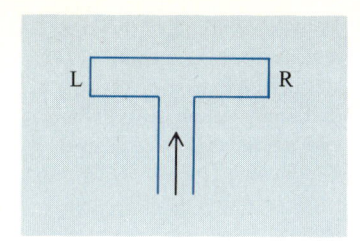

Figure 8.2 *A T maze*

20. Suppose that a rat is placed in a T maze such as that shown in Figure 8.2. If the rat turns to the right, it is given food with probability p, and if it turns to the left, it is given food with probability $1 - p$. Suppose also that while the rat is in the runway (before turning in either direction) a bell rings with probability $\frac{1}{2}$.

    W. K. Estes has proposed a model explaining the conditioning of the rat to the bell. Estes' model makes the following assumptions:

    1. On the first trial the rat is conditioned to go right (response R) with probability $\frac{1}{2}$ and to go left (response L) with probability $\frac{1}{2}$. Prior to each subsequent trial the rat is conditioned to exactly one of the two responses.
    2. If the bell does not ring, the conditioning does not change.
    3. If the bell rings and the rat's response is rewarded with food, the conditioning does not change. Otherwise the rat becomes conditioned to the other response.

    (a) Show that $Pr(R|R) = \frac{1}{2} + p/2$ and $Pr(L|L) = 1 - p/2$, where $Pr(R|R)$ denotes the probability of being conditioned to R on the current trial given that the rat was conditioned to R on the previous trial, and where $Pr(L|L)$ has an analogous meaning.
    (b) Deduce that, if $0 < p < 1$, then Estes' model can be described by a regular Markov chain with transition matrix

    $$P = \begin{matrix} & \begin{matrix} R & \;\;\; L \end{matrix} \\ \begin{matrix} R \\ L \end{matrix} & \begin{pmatrix} \frac{1}{2} + p/2 & \frac{1}{2} - p/2 \\ p/2 & 1 - p/2 \end{pmatrix} \end{matrix}$$

    (c) Compute the fixed probability vector for P and interpret it in the context of this experiment. This type of prediction is called *probability matching*.[3]
    (d) If $p = .8$, compute the probability of obtaining a rewarded response when probability matching is used. Note that, since this probability is less than .8, the probability of a rewarded response would be greater if the rat always gave response R. Hence probability matching leads to nonoptimal behavior.

21. In 1970 a survey of workers in a metropolitan area showed that 20% rode the subway to work, 30% took the bus, and 50% came in automobiles. A follow-up survey two years later showed that 60% of the subway riders in 1970 continued to ride the subway, but that 10% now rode the bus and 30% now used automobiles to get to work. Of the 1970 bus riders, 90% continued to ride the bus and 10% rode the subway in 1972. Finally, 70% of the automobile riders in 1970 continued to come to work by car in 1972, but 10% now rode the subway and 20% now took the bus.

    (a) What percentage of the metropolitan population used each form of transportation to come to work in 1972?
    (b) If the above trend continues, what proportion of the population can eventually be expected to use each form of transportation?

22. A survey in 1970 showed that 40% of American car owners had luxury cars, 50% had intermediate-sized cars, and 10% had compact cars. A second survey in 1975 showed that of the people who had owned luxury cars

---

[3] It has been discovered that rats do not probability-match, whereas fish do. Humans sometimes probability-match.

in 1970, 80% still had luxury cars, but 10% now owned cars of the other two types. Of the people who had owned intermediate-sized cars in 1970, 30% owned luxury cars in 1975, 60% owned intermediate-sized cars in 1975, and 10% owned compact cars in 1975. Finally, of the people who had owned compact cars in 1970, 10% owned intermediate-sized cars in 1975 and 90% continued to own compact cars in 1975.

(a) If the changes from 1970 to 1975 continued, what percentage of Americans owned each type of car in 1980?

(b) If the trend from 1970 to 1975 continues, what proportion of Americans will eventually own cars of each type?

23. In 1930, 10% of the land on a certain island was classified as urban, 60% was used for agriculture, and 30% was unused. A decade later, 80% of the land that had been classified as urban remained urban, while 10% was found to be used for agriculture and 10% was found to be unused. Similarly, of the land used for agriculture in 1930, 80% continued to be used for agriculture a decade later, but 10% had become urban and 10% had become unused. Finally, of the unused land in 1930, 20% had become urban and 20% was being used for agriculture in 1940.

(a) If this trend continued, what percentage of land was used in each way in 1950?

(b) If this trend continues indefinitely, what proportion of the land on the island will eventually be used in each way?

24. An analysis of registered voters in a certain county was made prior to the 1972 presidential election. Of those who considered themselves Democrats in 1968, 60% considered themselves Democrats in 1972, but 20% considered themselves Republicans and 20% considered themselves independents. Of the voters who considered themselves Republicans in 1968, 70% still considered themselves Republicans in 1972, but 10% considered themselves Democrats and 20% considered themselves independents. Finally, of those who considered themselves independents in 1968, 50% considered themselves Democrats, 10% considered themselves Republicans, and 40% considered themselves independents four years later.

(a) If in 1968 50% of the voters in this county considered themselves Democrats, 40% considered themselves Republicans, and 10% considered themselves independents, what were the corresponding percentages in 1972?

(b) If this trend continues, what will be the eventual proportion of voters with each affiliation?

8.3 Absorbing Markov Chains

Consider a simple model (based on [8]) of an accounting system for a department store in which customers are allowed 3 months to pay for each transaction. The store classifies each unpaid transaction as being in its first, second, or third month and as being a bad debt if not paid within 3 months. Let us suppose that the passage of transactions from one of these states to another can be described by a Markov chain. Then there will be five states, which we denote by 1, 2, 3 (corresponding to the first 3 months of an unpaid transaction), B (a bad debt), and C (a closed, that is, paid, account). Suppose that the transition matrix for this Markov chain is

$$P = \begin{array}{c} \\ 1 \\ 2 \\ 3 \\ B \\ C \end{array} \begin{pmatrix} 1 & 2 & 3 & B & C \\ 0 & .5 & 0 & 0 & .5 \\ 0 & 0 & .8 & 0 & .2 \\ 0 & 0 & 0 & .6 & .4 \\ 0 & 0 & 0 & 1 & 0 \\ 0 & 0 & 0 & 0 & 1 \end{pmatrix}$$

and observe that the initial distribution vector is $D = (1 \ 0 \ 0 \ 0 \ 0)$ because all unpaid accounts begin in state 1. This Markov chain is not regular, since the last two rows of P^k for any power k will be the same as the last two rows of P (hence P^k has zero entries). Thus the theory in Section 8.2 cannot be used to determine the eventual proportion of accounts in each state. Fortunately, however, a different technique can be used to examine the long-term behavior of this Markov chain.

Before discussing this technique, let us make a few observations about this Markov chain. First, notice that any transaction that enters either state B or C never leaves that state. Such a state is called an *absorbing state* and is characterized by the fact that the diagonal entry of the transition matrix corresponding to the state in question is 1. For example, the fact that the 4, 4 entry of P is 1 signifies that state B is an absorbing state. Second, observe that it is possible to reach an absorbing state from each of the nonabsorbing states; in fact, in this instance it is possible to reach absorbing state C from each of the nonabsorbing states 1, 2, and 3. These two observations are the requirements for an absorbing Markov chain.

In general, a Markov chain is called *absorbing* if it has one or more absorbing states and if it is possible to pass (in one or more trials) from each nonabsorbing state to an absorbing state. Because of these requirements, in an absorbing Markov chain the probability of eventually reaching an absorbing state is 1.

EXAMPLE 4

Consider the Markov chains having as their transition matrices

$$P_1 = \begin{pmatrix} .5 & .2 & .3 & 0 \\ 0 & 1 & 0 & 0 \\ .2 & 0 & .4 & .4 \\ .1 & 0 & .2 & .7 \end{pmatrix} \quad \text{and} \quad P_2 = \begin{pmatrix} .5 & .2 & .3 & 0 \\ 0 & 1 & 0 & 0 \\ 0 & 0 & .4 & .6 \\ 0 & 0 & .3 & .7 \end{pmatrix}$$

The chain having P_1 as its transition matrix is absorbing, since the second state is an absorbing state and it is possible to pass from each of the other states to the second. Specifically, it is possible to pass from the first state directly to the second state and from either the third or fourth state to the first state and then to the second. On the other hand the Markov chain having P_2 as its transition matrix is not absorbing even though it has one absorbing state (the second), for in this case it is impossible to reach the absorbing state from either the third or fourth state.

In an absorbing Markov chain it is convenient to renumber the states so that the absorbing states occur before the nonabsorbing states. With this relabeling the transition matrix P above becomes

$$\begin{array}{c} \\ B \\ C \\ 1 \\ 2 \\ 3 \end{array} \begin{array}{cccccc} B & C & 1 & 2 & 3 \\ \begin{pmatrix} 1 & 0 & 0 & 0 & 0 \\ 0 & 1 & 0 & 0 & 0 \\ 0 & .5 & 0 & .5 & 0 \\ 0 & .2 & 0 & 0 & .8 \\ .6 & .4 & 0 & 0 & 0 \end{pmatrix} \end{array} \qquad (8.1)$$

canonical form of a transition matrix

This form is called the *canonical form* of the transition matrix. In general, the canonical form of an $n \times n$ transition matrix having m absorbing states $A_1, A_2, \ldots, A_m$ and $n - m$ nonabsorbing states $S_1, S_2, \ldots, S_{n-m}$ can be partitioned as

$$\begin{array}{c} \\ A_1 \\ A_2 \\ \vdots \\ A_m \\ S_1 \\ S_2 \\ \vdots \\ S_{n-m} \end{array} \begin{array}{c} A_1 \ A_2 \cdots A_m \quad S_1 \ S_2 \cdots S_{n-m} \\ \left(\begin{array}{c|c} I & O \\ \hline R & Q \end{array} \right) \end{array} \qquad (8.2)$$

where I is the $m \times m$ identity matrix and O is the $m \times (n - m)$ zero matrix. In (8.1), where $m = 2$ and $n = 5$, the matrices R and Q in (8.2) are

$$R = \begin{pmatrix} 0 & .5 \\ 0 & .2 \\ .6 & .4 \end{pmatrix} \quad \text{and} \quad Q = \begin{pmatrix} 0 & .5 & 0 \\ 0 & 0 & .8 \\ 0 & 0 & 0 \end{pmatrix}$$

Notice that the entries of the $(n - m) \times m$ matrix R are the probabilities of passing from each nonabsorbing state to each absorbing state, and that the entries of the $(n - m) \times (n - m)$ matrix Q are the probabilities of passing between any two nonabsorbing states.

In our example, the department store is interested in knowing what proportion of its transactions will become bad debts and what proportion will eventually be paid. These questions are examples of the following more general questions which can be answered for absorbing Markov chains.

1. If the Markov process begins in a particular nonabsorbing state, what is the expected number of times (trials) it will pass through some specified nonabsorbing state before absorption?
2. If the Markov process begins in a particular nonabsorbing state, what is the expected number of trials before absorption?
3. If the Markov process begins in a particular nonabsorbing state, what is the probability of entering a specified absorbing state?

The answers to all these questions are given in the theorem below. Observe that all the answers involve the matrix $(I - Q)^{-1}$, where Q is as in (8.2); the matrix $(I - Q)^{-1}$ is called the *fundamental matrix* of the Markov chain.

fundamental matrix of an absorbing Markov chain

THEOREM 8.4

Let (8.2) be the canonical form of the transition matrix of an absorbing Markov chain.

(a) If the Markov chain begins in nonabsorbing state S_i, then the expected number of times (trials) the chain passes through nonabsorbing state S_j before absorption is the i, j entry of $(I - Q)^{-1}$.
(b) If the Markov chain begins in nonabsorbing state S_i, then the expected number of trials before absorption is the sum of the entries in row i of $(I - Q)^{-1}$.
(c) If the Markov chain begins in nonabsorbing state S_i, then the probability of being absorbed in absorbing state A_j is the i, j entry of $(I - Q)^{-1}R$.

For our department store example the fundamental matrix is

$$(I - Q)^{-1} = \begin{pmatrix} 1 & -.5 & 0 \\ 0 & 1 & -.8 \\ 0 & 0 & 1 \end{pmatrix}^{-1} = \begin{pmatrix} 1 & .5 & .4 \\ 0 & 1 & .8 \\ 0 & 0 & 1 \end{pmatrix}$$

(The inverse matrix is computed by the method discussed in Section 3.8.) Recall that all transactions begin in the first nonabsorbing state (state 1). Thus by Theorem 8.4(b) we see that the expected number of months (trials) before an account enters either state B or C is $1 + .5 + .4 = 1.9$, the sum of the entries in the first row of $(I - Q)^{-1}$. Likewise from Theorem 8.4(c) we know that the proportion of transactions that will become bad debts (that is, will enter the first absorbing state B) is the 1, 1 entry of $(I - Q)^{-1}R$. Since

$$(I - Q)^{-1}R = \begin{pmatrix} 1 & .5 & .4 \\ 0 & 1 & .8 \\ 0 & 0 & 1 \end{pmatrix} \begin{pmatrix} 0 & .5 \\ 0 & .2 \\ .6 & .4 \end{pmatrix} = \begin{pmatrix} .24 & .76 \\ .48 & .52 \\ .6 & .4 \end{pmatrix}$$

the proportion of bad debts is .24. Similarly, the proportion of transactions that will be paid (that is, will enter the second absorbing state C) is the 1, 2 entry of $(I - Q)^{-1}R$. Note that the other entries of $(I - Q)^{-1}R$ have similar interpretations; for example, the proportion of transactions in state 2 that will become bad debts is .48.

EXAMPLE 5

In [14] Mosimann presents a simple model for the passage of a phosphorus molecule through a pasture ecosystem having four states: soil, grass, cattle, and outside (that is, no longer in the ecosystem). Suppose that the passage of the phosphorus molecule between states forms a Markov chain with transition matrix

$$P = \begin{array}{c} \text{Soil} \\ \text{Grass} \\ \text{Cattle} \\ \text{Outside} \end{array} \begin{pmatrix} \text{Soil} & \text{Grass} & \text{Cattle} & \text{Outside} \\ .5 & .5 & 0 & 0 \\ .1 & .6 & .3 & 0 \\ .6 & 0 & .3 & .1 \\ 0 & 0 & 0 & 1 \end{pmatrix}$$

where each trial of the Markov chain corresponds to one day. Clearly this Markov chain is absorbing, and the outside is the only absorbing state. The canonical form of P is

$$\begin{array}{c} \text{Outside} \\ \text{Soil} \\ \text{Grass} \\ \text{Cattle} \end{array} \begin{pmatrix} \text{Outside} & \text{Soil} & \text{Grass} & \text{Cattle} \\ 1 & 0 & 0 & 0 \\ 0 & .5 & .5 & 0 \\ 0 & .1 & .6 & .3 \\ .1 & .6 & 0 & .3 \end{pmatrix}$$

and therefore

$$R = \begin{pmatrix} 0 \\ 0 \\ .1 \end{pmatrix} \quad \text{and} \quad Q = \begin{pmatrix} .5 & .5 & 0 \\ .1 & .6 & .3 \\ .6 & 0 & .3 \end{pmatrix}$$

Hence

$$I - Q = \begin{pmatrix} .5 & -.5 & 0 \\ -.1 & .4 & -.3 \\ -.6 & 0 & .7 \end{pmatrix}$$

and

$$(I - Q)^{-1} = \begin{pmatrix} \frac{56}{3} & \frac{70}{3} & 10 \\ \frac{50}{3} & \frac{70}{3} & 10 \\ 16 & 20 & 10 \end{pmatrix}$$

Thus from Theorem 8.4(a) we see that, if the phosphorus molecule starts in the soil, it can be expected to spend $\frac{56}{3}$ days in the soil, $\frac{70}{3}$ days in the grass, and 10 days in the cattle before absorption (passing outside the ecosystem). Hence, if the molecule begins in the soil, the total number of days to be expected before absorption is $\frac{56}{3} + \frac{70}{3} + 10 = 52$, which is the sum of the entries of the first row of $(I - Q)^{-1}$.

Notice that in this case

$$(I - Q)^{-1} R = \begin{pmatrix} \frac{56}{3} & \frac{70}{3} & 10 \\ \frac{50}{3} & \frac{70}{3} & 10 \\ 16 & 20 & 10 \end{pmatrix} \begin{pmatrix} 0 \\ 0 \\ .1 \end{pmatrix} = \begin{pmatrix} 1 \\ 1 \\ 1 \end{pmatrix}$$

which from Theorem 8.4(c) indicates that, no matter whether the molecule begins in the soil, grass, or cattle, it will eventually be absorbed on the outside. But this conclusion is obvious, because the outside is the only absorbing state.

Exercises

Determine if the Markov chains having the transition matrices in Exercises 1–8 are absorbing Markov chains. If so, identify all the absorbing states.

1. $\begin{pmatrix} .8 & .2 & 0 \\ 0 & 1 & 0 \\ .3 & 0 & .7 \end{pmatrix}$

2. $\begin{pmatrix} 0 & 0 & 1 \\ 0 & .6 & .4 \\ .5 & .5 & 0 \end{pmatrix}$

3. $\begin{pmatrix} .9 & .1 & 0 \\ .2 & .8 & 0 \\ 0 & 0 & 1 \end{pmatrix}$

4. $\begin{pmatrix} 1 & 0 & 0 & 0 \\ .5 & .5 & 0 & 0 \\ 0 & 0 & 1 & 0 \\ 0 & 0 & .4 & .6 \end{pmatrix}$

5. $\begin{pmatrix} 1 & 0 & 0 & 0 \\ 0 & 0 & 1 & 0 \\ .2 & .4 & .2 & .2 \\ 0 & 0 & 0 & 1 \end{pmatrix}$

6. $\begin{pmatrix} 1 & 0 & 0 & 0 \\ 0 & .8 & 0 & .2 \\ 0 & 0 & 1 & 0 \\ 0 & .3 & 0 & .7 \end{pmatrix}$

7. $\begin{pmatrix} .5 & .2 & 0 & .3 & 0 \\ 0 & 1 & 0 & 0 & 0 \\ 0 & 0 & 1 & 0 & 0 \\ 0 & 0 & 0 & .6 & .4 \\ .1 & 0 & 0 & 0 & .9 \end{pmatrix}$

8. $\begin{pmatrix} .7 & 0 & .3 & 0 & 0 \\ 0 & .6 & .1 & 0 & .3 \\ .2 & 0 & .8 & 0 & 0 \\ .5 & 0 & 0 & .5 & 0 \\ 0 & .1 & 0 & 0 & .9 \end{pmatrix}$

Each of the matrices in Exercises 9–16 is the transition matrix of an absorbing Markov chain. Put each of these matrices in canonical form, identify the matrices R and Q in (8.2), and compute the fundamental matrix $(I - Q)^{-1}$.

9. $\begin{pmatrix} .6 & .2 & .2 \\ .1 & .7 & .2 \\ 0 & 0 & 1 \end{pmatrix}$

10. $\begin{pmatrix} .4 & .5 & .1 \\ 0 & 1 & 0 \\ .5 & 0 & .5 \end{pmatrix}$

11. $\begin{pmatrix} .5 & 0 & .5 \\ 0 & 1 & 0 \\ .1 & .2 & .7 \end{pmatrix}$

12. $\begin{pmatrix} .8 & .1 & 0 & .1 \\ 0 & 1 & 0 & 0 \\ 0 & 0 & 1 & 0 \\ .4 & .1 & .2 & .3 \end{pmatrix}$

13. $\begin{pmatrix} 1 & 0 & 0 & 0 \\ .2 & .5 & .1 & .2 \\ 0 & 0 & 1 & 0 \\ 0 & .5 & .1 & .4 \end{pmatrix}$ 14. $\begin{pmatrix} \frac{1}{2} & \frac{1}{8} & \frac{1}{4} & \frac{1}{8} \\ \frac{1}{2} & \frac{1}{8} & \frac{1}{4} & \frac{1}{8} \\ \frac{1}{2} & \frac{1}{8} & \frac{1}{4} & \frac{1}{8} \\ 0 & 0 & 0 & 1 \end{pmatrix}$

15. $\begin{pmatrix} .1 & .6 & .1 & .2 \\ 0 & 1 & 0 & 0 \\ .4 & 0 & .4 & .2 \\ 0 & 0 & 0 & 1 \end{pmatrix}$ 16. $\begin{pmatrix} .2 & .4 & .1 & .3 \\ .2 & .4 & .1 & .3 \\ .1 & .2 & .3 & .4 \\ 0 & 0 & 0 & 1 \end{pmatrix}$

Use the transition matrices in the corresponding Exercises 9–16 to answer the questions asked in Exercises 17–24.

17. What is the expected number of trials before absorption if the Markov chain begins in the second state?
18. If the Markov chain begins in the third state, what is the expected number of times it will pass through the third state before absorption?
19. If the Markov chain begins in the first state, what is the expected number of times it will pass through the third state before absorption?
20. What is the probability of being absorbed into the third state if the Markov chain begins in the first state?
21. What is the probability of being absorbed into the first state if the Markov chain begins in the second state? In the fourth state?
22. What is the expected number of trials before absorption if the Markov chain begins in the first state? In the second state?
23. If the Markov chain begins in the third state, what is the probability of being absorbed into the second state? Into the fourth state?
24. If the Markov chain begins in the third state, what is the expected number of times it will pass through the second state before absorption?
25. A spokesman for a small industry claims that wastes discharged from a plant into a nearby river are soon swept out into the ocean. Specifically, he states that the probability of a mercury molecule in the river being swept into the ocean in a single day is .98. Assuming that this claim is correct and that mercury does not reenter the river once it has been swept into the ocean, determine the expected time that a mercury molecule discharged from the plant will remain in the river.
26. A hospital trauma unit classifies its patients according to whether they are ambulatory or bedridden at the time of admission. Its data show that within one week after admission, 60% of the ambulatory patients are released, 30% remain ambulatory, and 10% become bedridden. After the same period 10% of the bedridden patients are released, 10% become ambulatory, 70% remain bedridden, and 10% die.

    (a) If a patient is bedridden at the time of admission to the hospital, how long can he or she expect to remain bedridden before being released or dying?
    (b) What is the probability that a patient who is ambulatory at the time of admission will eventually be released?
    (c) What is the probability that a patient who is bedridden at the time of admission will eventually be released?

27. During each semester a certain junior college classifies its past and present students as graduates, sophomores, freshmen, or unenrolled. After examining the academic records of its recent graduates, the school has discovered that from one semester to the next 40% of the sophomores graduate, 20% remain sophomores, and 40% do not enroll, while 80% of the freshmen become sophomores, 10% remain freshmen, and 10% do not enroll. Of the students who are not enrolled during a given semester, 20% enroll as sophomores, 30% enroll as freshmen, and 50% do not enroll for the following semester. What is the expected number of semesters until a freshman graduates?

28. Each play from scrimmage by a particular football team is classified as either a scoring play, a passing play, a running play, or a lost ball. The team finds that, after any passing play, the probability that the next play will be a scoring play, a passing play, a running play, or a lost ball is .3, .2, .4, or .1, respectively. Likewise after any running play the probability is .05, .3, .6, or .05 that the next play will be a scoring play, a passing play, a running play, or a lost ball, respectively.

   (a) If the team begins each ball possession with a running play, what is the expected number of running plays during the ball possession?
   (b) What is the probability of scoring if the team begins each ball possession with a running play?

29. A labor system has four grades (numbered 1–4). Persons in the system can be promoted to higher grades but not to lower grades, and persons reaching the highest grade (grade 4) retain this status forever. At any time prior to reaching grade 4, however, a person may resign. Suppose that within a 10-year period 10% of those in grade 1 resign, 80% are promoted to grade 2, and 10% are promoted to grade 3. Within the same period suppose that 30% of those in grade 2 resign, 60% are promoted to grade 3, and 10% are promoted to grade 4. Finally suppose that of those in grade 3, 40% resign, 40% remain in grade 3, and 20% are promoted to grade 4 within 10 years.

   (a) What is the expected length of time that someone starting in grade 1 can expect to be in grade 2?
   (b) What is the expected length of time before someone beginning in grade 2 resigns or reaches grade 4?
   (c) What is the probability that someone beginning in grade 1 will eventually resign?
   (d) What is the probability that someone starting in grade 2 will eventually reach grade 4?

30. *Gambler's ruin.* Suppose that Tom and Joan play a game of chance in which Tom has a probability p ($0 < p < 1$) of winning \$1 from Joan and a probability $1 - p$ of losing \$1 to Joan. Furthermore, suppose that Tom starts the game with r dollars and Joan starts with s dollars and that both players agree to play until one of them goes broke. This situation can be described by an absorbing Markov chain having $t + 1$ states, where $t = r + s$, namely, the amount of money presently belonging to Tom (that is, 0 dollars, 1 dollar, 2 dollars, $\cdots$, t dollars). Clearly states 0 and t, which correspond to Joan winning and Tom winning, respectively, are the absorbing states in this Markov chain, and the transition matrix has the form

$$\begin{pmatrix} & 0 & 1 & 2 & 3 & 4 & 5 & \cdots & t-3 & t-2 & t-1 & t \\ 0 & 1 & 0 & 0 & 0 & 0 & 0 & \cdots & 0 & 0 & 0 & 0 \\ 1 & q & 0 & p & 0 & 0 & 0 & \cdots & 0 & 0 & 0 & 0 \\ 2 & 0 & q & 0 & p & 0 & 0 & \cdots & 0 & 0 & 0 & 0 \\ 3 & 0 & 0 & q & 0 & p & 0 & \cdots & 0 & 0 & 0 & 0 \\ \vdots & \vdots & \vdots & \vdots & \vdots & \vdots & \vdots & & \vdots & \vdots & \vdots & \vdots \\ t-1 & 0 & 0 & 0 & 0 & 0 & 0 & \cdots & 0 & q & 0 & p \\ t & 0 & 0 & 0 & 0 & 0 & 0 & \cdots & 0 & 0 & 0 & 1 \end{pmatrix}$$

where $q = 1 - p$.

Now suppose that $r = 2$ and $s = 3$; that is, Tom begins with \$2 and Joan with \$3. They agree to play the following game: Tom rolls an ordinary die and wins \$1 from Joan if a 1, 2, 3, or 4 appears and loses \$1 to Joan if a 5 or 6 appears.

(a) Under these circumstances what is the expected number of rolls before the game ends?
(b) How many times can Joan expect to have \$4 before the game ends?
(c) What is the probability of Joan winning?
(d) If Tom starts with \$1 and Joan starts with \$4, what is the probability of Joan winning?

31. Suppose that a rat is released in the maze shown in Figure 8.3. We assume that it will wander through the rooms of the maze until it enters a room containing food (room A or F), at which point it will remain indefinitely in that room. Furthermore, suppose that, when the rat is in a room without food, the likelihood of its leaving the room by each door is the same.

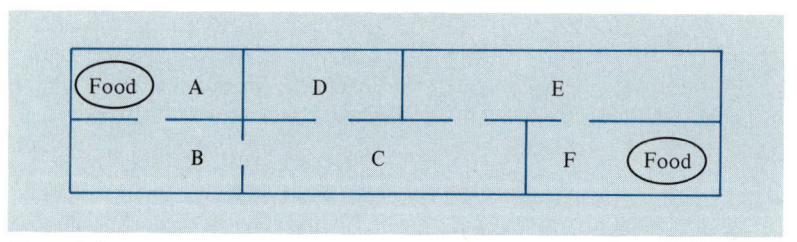

Figure 8.3

(a) If the rat is initially placed in room D, what is the expected number of times it will enter room C before finding food?
(b) If the rat is initially placed in room E, what is the expected number of rooms it will enter before entering either room A or F?
(c) If the rat is initially placed in room C, what is the probability that it will find the food in room A?
(d) If the rat is initially placed in room E, what is the probability that it will find the food in room F?

*8.4 Some Applications Involving Absorbing Markov Chains

In this section we shall discuss two applications that involve absorbing Markov chains, one arising in psychology and one in sociology. When studying complicated mental processes, psychologists and sociologists often seek a model in the absence of an accepted theory. Experiments are then performed, and the results are compared with the predictions of the model. When the experimental results and the predicted results disagree, the model must be modified or abandoned. But when they agree, the model is subjected to further testing to see if it can predict other types of behavior. In the two applications presented here, Markov chain models were able to predict successfully the outcomes of experiments in learning theory and conflict.

Paired-Associate Learning

Paired-associate learning involves the learning of a response corresponding to a specific stimulus. Examples of this type of learning include learning the English translations of words in a foreign language and learning the dates of historical events. To study paired-associate learning, experimenters usually attempt to reduce extraneous factors by using stimuli such as nonsense syllables and responses that are well-known to the subjects of the experiment.

In [5] Bower asked 29 subjects to learn 10 different stimulus-response pairs in which the stimuli were different pairs of consonant letters and the responses were the integers 1 and 2. (Each of these integers was randomly paired with 5 of the stimuli.) On every presentation of a stimulus item, the subject was required to give one of the possible responses, after which he or she was informed whether the response was correct. Each of the 10 stimulus-response pairs was treated as a single experiment, and the order in which the stimulus cards were presented was randomized after every cycle of the stimuli was completed. Subjects were required to continue the experiment until they had finished two consecutive cycles of the stimulus deck without error.

Bower's model involved the following assumptions:

Axiom 1: For each stimulus item the subject is in one of two possible states, C (conditioned to the correct response) or N (not conditioned to the correct response). If the subject is in state C for a particular stimulus item, then the probability of a correct response is 1, whereas if the subject is in state N for a particular item, then the probability of a correct response is g, the reciprocal of the number of response alternatives.[4]

Axiom 2: At the beginning of the experiment the subject is in state N for each stimulus item. Thereafter the probability of a transition from N to C is a constant c ($0 < c \leq 1$), and the probability of a transition from C to C is 1.

Axiom 3: The probability c is independent of the trial number and the outcomes of preceding trials.

Because of the nature of the assumptions in axiom 1, Bower's model is called an *all-or-none* model. Clearly these three axioms permit this

---

[4] In Bower's experiment, there were only two possible responses (1 or 2), hence $g = \frac{1}{2}$.

experiment to be described by an absorbing Markov chain with transition matrix

$$P = \begin{matrix} & C & N \\ C & \\ N & \end{matrix} \begin{pmatrix} 1 & 0 \\ c & 1-c \end{pmatrix}$$

where c is an unknown parameter which must be determined experimentally. It can easily be seen that

$$P^k = \begin{pmatrix} 1 & 0 \\ 1-(1-c)^k & (1-c)^k \end{pmatrix}$$

for any positive integer k. Since the initial distribution vector is $D = (0 \ 1)$, the probability of being in state N after k trials is $(1-c)^k$, the second entry of DP^k. Noting that P is already in canonical form, we see that the matrix Q in (8.2) is $Q = (1-c)$. Thus $I - Q = (c)$, and so $(I - Q)^{-1} = (1/c)$. We see therefore that the expected number of trials before learning occurs (that is, before absorption into state C) is $1/c$.

As a consequence of this model, Bower is able to deduce that the expected number of errors u before a subject learns any stimulus item is $u = (1-g)/c$. Since u can be calculated experimentally, this equation allows us to compute c as $c = (1-g)/u$. For Bower's experiment[5] $u \approx 1.45$ and $g = \frac{1}{2}$; so c, the probability of passing from N to C, is approximately .344.

Conflict and Conformity

In [1] Asch describes experiments designed to measure the degree to which an individual would modify his correct opinion when confronted with the incorrect opinion of a majority. Similar experiments were conducted by Cohen (see [6] and [7]) and analyzed in [13] and [2]. The presentation here follows that in [2].

Subjects in Cohen's experiments were presented with 38 pairs of cards such as those in Figure 8.4 and asked to identify which of comparison lines A, B, or C was the same length as the standard line. (In Figure 8.4 response A is correct.) After some individual practice, each subject was placed as the last member of a group which usually contained six or seven others, all of whom were confederates of the experimenter. On the first two trials (pairs of cards), the confederates gave the correct response, but on the remaining 36 trials the confederates gave the same incorrect response. The object of the experiment was to determine whether the subject would give the correct response or would repeat the answer given by the confederates.

Cohen's experiments involved two types of conflict: "moderate" conflict, where the difference in the length of the line chosen by the confederates and the standard was $1\frac{1}{4}$ inches, and "extreme" conflict,

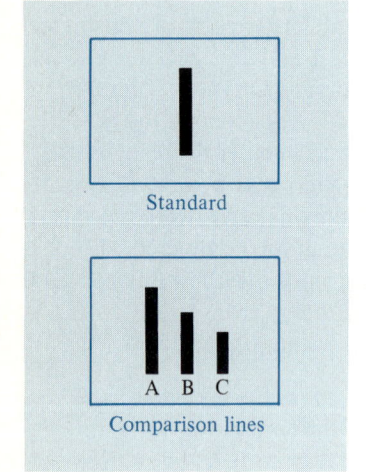

Figure 8.4

Standard

Comparison lines
A B C

---

[5] Because each of the 10 stimulus-response pairs was treated as a single experiment, this model does not take into account the number of such pairs. For another model that better reflects the number of pairs, see Exercise 1.

where the difference was $1\frac{3}{4}$ inches. As expected, the subjects were more likely to disagree with the confederates in the extreme conflict situation where the error was more blatant. We confine our discussion to this case.

Cohen assumed that his subjects were in one of four mental states:

1. Nonconforming
2. Temporarily nonconforming
3. Temporarily conforming
4. Conforming

Because it is impossible to present definitions of these states in theoretical terms, the following operational definitions were used.

1. A subject in the first state will respond correctly (that is, not agree with the confederates) on every subsequent trial.
2. A subject in the second state will respond correctly on the next trial but may or may not respond correctly on a later trial.
3. A subject in the third state will respond incorrectly (that is, will agree with the confederates) on the next trial but may or may not respond incorrectly on a later trial.
4. A subject in the fourth state will respond incorrectly on every subsequent trial.

Thus on the next trial subjects in the first or second state will respond correctly, and those in the third or fourth state will respond incorrectly. Cohen made three assumptions:

(a) Before the start of the experiment each subject is in the second state (temporarily nonconforming).
(b) All the subjects will be absorbed within 38 trials.
(c) It is impossible to pass from the third state directly to the first or to pass from the second state directly to the fourth. (Thus a subject in state 3 must enter state 2 before state 1, and a subject in state 2 must enter state 3 before state 4.)

Of these assumptions (a) and (b) were supported by the data from Cohen's experiments, and (c) is a clarification of the operational definitions of the four states.

Clearly these experiments can be modeled by an absorbing Markov chain having states 1 and 4 as the absorbing states. Unfortunately, there is no precise method for determining on which trial a subject first enters an absorbing state. Nevertheless, it is possible to estimate the entries of the transition matrix P by applying various statistical techniques to Cohen's data, the result being

$$P = \begin{array}{c} \\ 1 \\ 2 \\ 3 \\ 4 \end{array} \begin{array}{c} \begin{array}{cccc} 1 & 2 & 3 & 4 \end{array} \\ \left(\begin{array}{cccc} 1 & 0 & 0 & 0 \\ .07 & .74 & .19 & 0 \\ 0 & .42 & .55 & .03 \\ 0 & 0 & 0 & 1 \end{array} \right) \end{array}$$

(See [2] for details.) The canonical form of P is

$$\begin{array}{c} \\ 1 \\ 4 \\ 2 \\ 3 \end{array} \begin{pmatrix} 1 & 4 & 2 & 3 \\ 1 & 0 & 0 & 0 \\ 0 & 1 & 0 & 0 \\ .07 & 0 & .74 & .19 \\ 0 & .03 & .42 & .55 \end{pmatrix}$$

Hence with the notation of (8.2)

$$R = \begin{pmatrix} .07 & 0 \\ 0 & .03 \end{pmatrix} \quad \text{and} \quad Q = \begin{pmatrix} .74 & .19 \\ .42 & .55 \end{pmatrix}$$

Computing $(I - Q)^{-1}$ and $(I - Q)^{-1}R$ to two-decimal accuracy, we find that

$$(I - Q)^{-1} \approx \begin{array}{c} \\ 2 \\ 3 \end{array} \begin{pmatrix} 2 & 3 \\ 12.10 & 5.11 \\ 11.29 & 6.99 \end{pmatrix}$$

and

$$(I - Q)^{-1}R \approx \begin{array}{c} \\ 2 \\ 3 \end{array} \begin{pmatrix} 1 & 4 \\ .85 & .15 \\ .79 & .21 \end{pmatrix}$$

Thus we see that the expected number of trials before absorption is $12.10 + 5.11 = 17.21$ [the sum of the entries in row 1 of $(I - Q)^{-1}$] and that the probability of absorption into the first state is .85 [the 1, 1 entry of $(I - Q)^{-1}R$].

Exercises

1. The three axioms for an all-or-none model on page 325 are appropriate no matter how many different stimulus items there are. Although Bower's experiment involved 10 different stimulus items, the data were analyzed as though there were 10 experiments involving a single stimulus rather than one experiment involving 10 stimuli. Thus the Bower experiment described in this section used a one-element all-or-none model. More generally, an n-element all-or-none model can be formulated from axioms similar to those for the one-element model. Suppose, for example, that there are two stimulus items for which the subject is either conditioned to the correct response or not conditioned. The two-element all-or-none model for this situation is a three-state Markov chain in which the states 0, 1, and 2 represent the number of stimulus items for which the subject is conditioned to the correct response. For simplicity we assume that on each trial the probability of presenting either stimulus item is .5.
    (a) If (as in axiom 2) the probability of a transition from being not conditioned to being conditioned is c $(0 < c < 1)$, and the probability of a transition from being conditioned to being conditioned is 1, write the transition matrix for this Markov chain.

(b) If a subject starts in state 0 (not conditioned to the correct response for either stimulus), what is the expected number of trials before he or she learns both responses correctly?

2. In Application 2 we discussed the distribution of the genotypes GG, Gg, and gg among the offspring of a population in which the proportion of the three genotypes was known. Consider now an experiment in which an individual of unknown genotype is crossed with an individual known to have genotype GG, one of the offspring is crossed with another individual of genotype GG, and so forth. (This process is called *continued crossing with a dominant* because of the use of the GG genotype.)

   (a) Assuming that a parent of genotype Gg is equally likely to pass the G or g gene to its offspring, determine the transition matrix of the Markov chain that describes the distribution of genotypes between a parent and offspring that occurs during continued crossing with a dominant.
   (b) Determine the number of generations expected until only pure dominants are produced for each possible genotype of the unknown parent.

3. Again in the context of Application 2 let us consider a case of *inbreeding*. Suppose that two individuals are allowed to reproduce, two of their offspring are randomly selected and allowed to reproduce, two of these second-generation offspring are randomly selected and allowed to reproduce, and so forth. (Obviously we must assume that the trait being investigated is independent of sex and that there are many offspring in each mating.) In this case we are concerned with determining whether either the G or g gene will eventually disappear, and it is necessary to know the possible pairs of genotypes that can occur. To simplify the notation, let d (dominant), h (hybrid), and r (recessive) represent the GG, Gg, and gg genotypes, respectively. Then there are six possible pairs of genotypes for the two parents: dd, dh (which is the same as hd), dr (which is the same as rd), hh, hr (which is the same as rh), and rr.

   (a) Assuming that a parent of genotype h is equally likely to pass a G or g gene to its offspring, verify that the probabilities of the various genotype pairs for the offspring are as given in the transition matrix

Parents	dd	dh	dr	hh	hr	rr
dd	1	0	0	0	0	0
dh	$\frac{1}{4}$	$\frac{1}{2}$	0	$\frac{1}{4}$	0	0
dr	0	0	0	1	0	0
hh	$\frac{1}{16}$	$\frac{1}{4}$	$\frac{1}{8}$	$\frac{1}{4}$	$\frac{1}{4}$	$\frac{1}{16}$
hr	0	0	0	$\frac{1}{4}$	$\frac{1}{2}$	$\frac{1}{4}$
rr	0	0	0	0	0	1

   (b) Since the transition matrix in part (a) is the transition matrix of an absorbing Markov chain with absorbing states dd and rr, eventually either the g or G gene will disappear from the population. Determine the expected number of generations until this disappearance occurs if the parents are of the dh pairing and of the dr pairing.

(c) Compute the probability that the g gene will disappear (that is, that all offspring pairs will eventually be dd) for each of the dh, dr, hh, and hr pairings.

4. Consider a psychological experiment in which the subject guesses which pair of letters from the response set {ab, ac, ad, bc, bd, cd} was selected (randomly) by the experimenter. After the subject names any pair of letters, the experimenter tells her how many of the letters are in the pair selected by the experimenter. For example, if the subject guesses ab and the experimenter selected cd, then the subject is told that no letters are correct, whereas if the subject guesses ab and the experimenter selected bd, then the subject is told that one letter is correct. Suppose that the subject is rewarded if she guesses both letters picked by the experimenter, but that she is not allowed further attempts if she fails to guess at least one correct letter. This guessing process can be described as a three-state Markov chain in which the states 0, 1, and 2 correspond to the number of letters correctly guessed by the subject. Assume the following axiom:

On the next attempt a subject in state 1 will randomly name one of the letters in the previous guess and one of the letters not included in the previous guess.

(a) Determine the transition matrix for this Markov chain.
(b) What is the expected number of trials until the subject succeeds or fails?
(c) What is the probability of the subject being rewarded?

5. Repeat Exercise 4 for the response set

{ab, ac, ad, ae, bc, bd, be, cd, ce, de}

6. In [15] Suppes and Ginsberg use a four-state Markov chain to describe a two-element stimulus sampling model of learning. The states of their model are: being conditioned to the first stimulus, not being conditioned to the first stimulus, being conditioned to the second stimulus, and not being conditioned to the second stimulus. If only the number of stimuli to which conditioning has occurred are counted, then the four states can be replaced by the three states 2, 1, and 0, representing the number of stimuli to which conditioning has already occurred. The transition matrix will then have the form

$$\begin{array}{c} \\ 2 \\ 1 \\ 0 \end{array} \begin{pmatrix} 2 & 1 & 0 \\ 1 & 0 & 0 \\ a & 1-a & 0 \\ 0 & b & 1-b \end{pmatrix}$$

where a and b are parameters to be determined experimentally.[6] Determine the expected number of trials required for a subject who is not initially conditioned to either stimulus to become conditioned to both.

7. Experimental evidence has suggested that in simple paired-associate learning experiments subjects learn the correct response immediately after being told the correct association. (This is clearly the case in Bower's experiment where there are only two possible responses and a subject is informed whether his or her response is correct.) However, in the course

---

[6] The model in this form was studied by Theios in [16], which discusses a number of its theoretical predictions.

of responding to other items, a subject may forget the answer to some other item. This evidence has led some psychologists to distinguish between long-term and short-term memory. Other experiments have shown that an incorrect response may inhibit recall of the correct response (as though the subject becomes conditioned to a particular incorrect response).

In [3] Bernbach formulated a four-state absorbing Markov chain which incorporated these ideas. The four states are long-term memory L, short-term memory S, an unconditioned state U, and an error state E in which the subject is temporarily conditioned to an incorrect response. The transition matrix of Bernbach's model is

$$\begin{array}{c} \\ L \\ S \\ U \\ E \end{array} \begin{pmatrix} L & S & U & E \\ 1 & 0 & 0 & 0 \\ a & (1-a)(1-c) & (1-a)c & 0 \\ 0 & [1-b(1-g)](1-c) & c & b(1-g)(1-c) \\ 0 & (1-b)(1-c) & c & b(1-c) \end{pmatrix}$$

where a is the probability of entering L from S, b is the probability of entering E given an incorrect response, c is the probability of forgetting, that is, the probability of entering U from S, U, or E, and g is the probability of guessing correctly while in state U. Suppose that $a = \frac{1}{3}$, $b = \frac{1}{3}$, $c = \frac{1}{4}$, and $g = \frac{1}{2}$.

(a) Compute the fundamental matrix $(I - Q)^{-1}$.
(b) If a subject begins in state U, what is the expected number of times he or she will enter state E before entering state L?
(c) If a subject begins in state U, what is the expected number of trials until he or she will enter state L?

Chapter Review

New Terms

absorbing Markov chain (p. 317)
absorbing state (p. 317)
canonical form (p. 318)
fixed probability vector (p. 309)
fundamental matrix (p. 319)
initial distribution vector (p. 301)

Markov chain (p. 299)
probability vector (p. 301)
regular Markov chain (p. 309)
regular transition matrix (p. 309)
transition matrix (p. 299)

Review Exercises

1. Label the following statements true or false.
   (a) The sum of the entries in each column of a transition matrix must equal 1.
   (b) For a Markov chain with transition matrix P, the i, j entry of P^k represents the probability of moving from state j to state i in k trials.
   (c) If D is the initial distribution vector of a Markov chain with transition matrix P, then the entries of DP^k are the probabilities of being in each state after k trials.

(d) A regular transition matrix is a transition matrix in which each entry is positive.
(e) Every regular transition matrix has a unique fixed probability vector.
(f) If D is the initial distribution vector of a regular Markov chain with transition matrix P, then as k increases the vectors DP^k approach the fixed probability vector for P.
(g) If the row of a transition matrix corresponding to state S contains one entry equal to 1 and the other entries are equal to 0, then state S is an absorbing state.
(h) Any Markov chain having one or more absorbing states is an absorbing Markov chain.
(i) In the canonical form of the transition matrix of an absorbing Markov chain, the absorbing states are listed first.
(j) In an absorbing Markov chain the entry of the fundamental matrix in row i, column j is the probability of being absorbed into state j if the Markov chain begins in state i.

2. Determine whether the following transition matrices are regular, absorbing, or neither. For those that are regular, compute the fixed probability vector, and for those that are absorbing, compute the fundamental matrix.

(a) $\begin{pmatrix} 1 & 0 \\ .2 & .8 \end{pmatrix}$

(b) $\begin{pmatrix} 1 & 0 \\ 0 & 1 \end{pmatrix}$

(c) $\begin{pmatrix} .7 & .3 \\ .4 & .6 \end{pmatrix}$

(d) $\begin{pmatrix} .9 & 0 & .1 \\ .6 & .2 & .2 \\ 0 & .6 & .4 \end{pmatrix}$

(e) $\begin{pmatrix} .8 & 0 & .2 \\ 0 & 1 & 0 \\ .9 & 0 & .1 \end{pmatrix}$

(f) $\begin{pmatrix} .25 & .05 & .7 \\ .5 & .3 & .2 \\ 0 & 0 & 1 \end{pmatrix}$

(g) $\begin{pmatrix} .8 & .2 & 0 \\ .2 & .4 & .4 \\ 0 & .3 & .7 \end{pmatrix}$

(h) $\begin{pmatrix} .4 & 0 & .4 & .2 \\ .1 & .8 & 0 & .1 \\ 0 & 0 & 1 & 0 \\ .2 & 0 & .7 & .1 \end{pmatrix}$

(i) $\begin{pmatrix} .8 & .2 & 0 & 0 \\ .3 & .7 & 0 & 0 \\ 0 & 0 & .9 & .1 \\ 0 & 0 & .4 & .6 \end{pmatrix}$

(j) $\begin{pmatrix} .5 & .1 & .3 & .1 \\ 1 & 0 & 0 & 0 \\ .2 & .1 & .7 & 0 \\ 0 & 0 & 1 & 0 \end{pmatrix}$

(k) $\begin{pmatrix} .2 & .3 & .4 & .1 \\ 0 & 1 & 0 & 0 \\ .2 & .3 & .4 & .1 \\ .1 & .4 & .2 & .3 \end{pmatrix}$

(l) $\begin{pmatrix} .9 & 0 & .1 & 0 \\ .1 & .6 & .1 & .2 \\ .3 & 0 & .7 & 0 \\ 0 & 0 & 0 & 1 \end{pmatrix}$

3. For the absorbing Markov chain having transition matrix
$$P = \begin{pmatrix} .10 & .50 & .10 & .30 \\ 0 & 1 & 0 & 0 \\ .25 & .25 & .25 & .25 \\ .10 & .50 & .10 & .30 \end{pmatrix}$$

determine the expected number of trials that an object beginning in state 1 will be in state 4 before absorption and the expected number of trials before an object beginning in state 3 will be absorbed.

4. For the regular Markov chain with transition matrix

$$P = \begin{pmatrix} .8 & .2 & .0 \\ .3 & .5 & .2 \\ .3 & .3 & .4 \end{pmatrix}$$

and initial distribution vector $D = (.4 \quad .2 \quad .4)$, compute the distribution after two trials and the eventual proportion of objects in each state.

5. For the regular Markov chain with transition matrix

$$P = \begin{pmatrix} .7 & .2 & .1 \\ 0 & .8 & .2 \\ .2 & .2 & .6 \end{pmatrix}$$

and initial distribution vector $D = (.4 \quad .5 \quad .1)$, compute the distribution after three trials and the eventual proportion of objects in each state.

6. For the absorbing Markov chain having transition matrix

$$P = \begin{pmatrix} .3 & .2 & .1 & .1 & .3 \\ 0 & 1 & 0 & 0 & 0 \\ 0 & 0 & 1 & 0 & 0 \\ .2 & .1 & .1 & .4 & .2 \\ .1 & .2 & .4 & .2 & .1 \end{pmatrix}$$

compute the expected number of trials before an object starting in state 1 is absorbed and the probability that an object starting in state 4 will be absorbed into state 3.

7. For the absorbing Markov chain with transition matrix

$$P = \begin{pmatrix} 1 & 0 & 0 & 0 & 0 \\ .1 & .2 & .2 & .1 & .4 \\ 0 & .2 & .2 & .2 & .4 \\ 0 & 0 & 0 & 1 & 0 \\ .4 & .1 & .1 & .2 & .2 \end{pmatrix}$$

compute the expected number of trials that an object beginning in state 2 will be in state 5 before absorption and the probability that an object beginning in state 3 will be absorbed into state 1.

8. For the regular Markov chain with transition matrix

$$P = \begin{pmatrix} .1 & .5 & .4 \\ .1 & .5 & .4 \\ .1 & .3 & .6 \end{pmatrix}$$

and initial distribution vector $D = (.3 \quad .2 \quad .5)$, compute the distribution after two trials and the eventual distribution.

9. A barber can cut one person's hair every 15 minutes. He works alone in his shop and never takes a break when customers are waiting. In order to prevent customers from having to wait for long periods, he does not allow more than two customers to wait for a haircut at the same time.

With this policy he finds that no customer ever leaves his shop without getting a haircut. Suppose that the number of customers arriving at the shop during any 15-minute period has the following distribution:

Number of arrivals	0	1	2	3	4 or more
Probability	.2	.5	.2	.1	0

Assume further that the first arrival during each period occurs at the beginning of the period.

(a) Use the information above to form the transition matrix of a Markov chain in which the states represent the number of customers in the barbershop.

(b) Suppose that when the barber first arrives at the shop in the morning he finds no customers waiting with a probability of .5 and one customer waiting with a probability of .5. What distribution of customers can be expected 30 minutes after the shop opens?

(c) Approximately what distribution of customers can the barber expect after many hours of work?

10. A certain small town uses 100,000 gallons of home heating oil during an average winter. The oil is supplied by two companies, one of which presently has 40% of the market. This company is about to begin a controversial advertising campaign which is predicted to increase the company's share of the market by 20,000 gallons per year with a probability of .7 or to decrease the company's yearly share of the market by 20,000 gallons with a probability of .3. Assume that this advertising campaign is continued until one of the two companies gains the entire heating oil market in the town.

(a) Use the information above to form the transition matrix of a Markov chain in which the states represent the number of gallons of oil (in units of 20,000 gallons) sold by the company beginning the advertising campaign.

(b) How many years are expected to elapse until one company or the other corners the market?

(c) What is the probability that the company using the advertising campaign will eventually corner the market?

References

1. Asch, S. E., *Social Psychology*. Englewood Cliffs, N. J.: Prentice-Hall, 1952.
2. Bartos, Otomar J., *Simple Models of Group Behavior*. New York: Columbia University Press, 1967.
3. Bernbach, H. A., "A Forgetting Model for Paired Associate Learning," *J. Math. Psychol.*, vol. 2 (1965), pp. 128–144.
4. Bourne, Larry S., "Physical Adjustment Process and Land Use Succession: A Conceptual Review and Central City Example," *Econ. Geogr.* vol. 47 (1971), pp. 1–15.
5. Bower, Gordon H., "Application of a Model to Paired-Associate Learning," *Psychometrika*, vol 26, no. 3 (September 1961), pp. 255–280.

6. Cohen, Bernard P., "A Probability Model for Conformity," *Sociometry*, vol. 21 (1958), pp. 69–81.
7. Cohen, Bernard P., *Conflict and Conformity: A Probability Model and Its Application*. Cambridge, Mass.: MIT Press, 1963.
8. Cyert, R. M., H. J. Davidson, and G. L. Thompson, "Estimation of the Allowance for Doubtful Accounts by Markov Chains," *Manage. Sci.*, vol. 8, no. 3 (April 1962), pp. 287–303.
9. Hampton, P., "Regional Economic Development in New Zealand," *J. Reg. Sci.*, vol 8, no. 1 (1968), pp. 41–51.
10. Hardy, G. H., "Mendelian Proportions in a Mixed Population," *Science*, new ser., vol. 28 (1908), pp. 49–50.
11. Hunter, Albert, "Community Change: A Stochastic Analysis of Chicago's Local Communities, 1930–1960," *Am. J. Sociol.*, vol. 79 (January 1974), pp. 923–947.
12. Hoffman, Hans, "Markov Chains in Ethiopia," in *Explorations in Mathematical Anthropology*, Paul Kay, ed. Cambridge, Mass.: MIT Press, 1971.
13. Kemeny, John G. and J. Laurie Snell, *Mathematical Models in the Social Sciences*. New York: Blaisdell, 1962.
14. Mosimann, J., *Elementary Probability for the Biological Sciences*. Englewood Cliffs, N. J.: Prentice-Hall, 1968.
15. Suppes, P. and R. Ginsberg, "A Fundamental Property of All-or-None Models: Binomial Distribution Prior to Conditioning with Application to Concept Formation in Children," *Psychol. Rev.*, vol. 70 (1963), pp. 139–161.
16. Theios, J., "Simple Conditioning as Two-Stage All-or-None Learning," *Psychol. Rev.*, vol. 70 (1963), pp. 403–417.

9

Game Theory

The term "game theory" is unfortunately suggestive of games of chance, which are more appropriately analyzed using the theory of probability. As used in this chapter, "game theory" will refer to the study of games of strategy and will be concerned with determining optimal patterns of behavior for conflict situations in which several alternative actions are available.

Because of its concern with situations involving conflict and competition, game theory has found frequent applications in areas of business and economic competition and, to a lesser degree, in analyzing social conflict. (See, for example, [2], [8], [19], [21], and [23].) In fact, expressions such as "playing the stock market" and "rules of the game" are suggestive of the relationship between games and other competitive situations.

In this chapter we shall be concerned with only a simple type of game involving two individuals or groups in strict competition with each other. In such games cooperation between the competing sides is not permitted. Thus we do not consider an important class of games that allow bargaining among the competitors. Nevertheless, the games we shall discuss will involve many of the basic concepts of the subject needed to analyze more complicated types of games. The reader who wishes to pursue a more advanced treatment of game theory is referred to [13].

9.1 Matrix Games

Throughout this chapter we shall be concerned with competitive situations in which there are two opposing persons or groups who are

two-person zero-sum game

players I and II

payoff

not allowed to cooperate with each other. We assume that the opposing sides make rational decisions and have as their objective maximization of their expected gains or minimization of their expected losses.

Such situations are called *two-person zero-sum games* because anything won by one side must be lost by the other (hence the sum of all winnings minus all losses is zero). The opposing sides in such a game are called *players*, and we refer to one side as *player I* and the other as *player II*. Each player will normally have several alternative actions available. In order to utilize the techniques of game theory, it is necessary to have a numerical value called a *payoff* associated with each pair of alternatives for the two players. More specifically, we let a_{ij} denote the *payoff to player I* that results when player I uses alternative i and player II uses alternative j. Observe that $a_{ij} > 0$ if this pair of alternatives results in a gain for player I, and $a_{ij} < 0$ if this pair of alternatives results in a loss for player I (hence a gain for player II).

To illustrate these ideas, let us consider a simple example.

EXAMPLE 1

In search of a new diversion, two inveterate gamblers named Rowe and Collum have agreed to play the following game. Rowe has the ace and 2 of hearts, and Collum has the ace, 2, and 3 of diamonds. Each player will secretly choose one card, and the two selected cards will be revealed simultaneously. If the sum of the numbers on the cards is even (counting an ace as 1), then Rowe will pay Collum as many dollars as the sum of the two cards. But if the sum of the numbers on the cards is odd, then Collum will pay Rowe as many dollars as the sum of the two cards.

Let us call Rowe player I and Collum player II. In this case player I has two alternatives (choose the ace or choose the 2) and player II has three alternatives (choose the ace, choose the 2, or choose the 3). If Rowe chooses to play the ace and Collum chooses to play the 2, then Collum pays Rowe $3. So the payoff when player I chooses his first alternative (to play the ace) and player II chooses her second alternative (to play the 2) is 3. On the other hand, if Rowe chooses to play the ace and Collum chooses to play the 3, then Rowe pays Collum $4. Since the payoffs are always expressed from the perspective of player I, the payoff in this case is -4.

This game can be completely described by Table 9.1.

Table 9.1 *Alternatives and Payoffs for the Game*

Rowe	Collum Alternative 1 (Play the Ace)	Alternative 2 (Play the 2)	Alternative 3 (Play the 3)
Alternative 1 (play the ace)	-2	3	-4
Alternative 2 (play the 2)	3	-4	5

The 2 × 3 matrix

$$\begin{pmatrix} -2 & 3 & -4 \\ 3 & -4 & 5 \end{pmatrix}$$

in which the i, j entry is the payoff that results when Rowe chooses alternative i and Collum chooses alternative j is called the *payoff matrix* for this game.

payoff matrix

Every two-person zero-sum game can be represented by a payoff matrix as in Example 1. Observe that the alternatives available to player I correspond to the rows of the payoff matrix and the alternatives available to player II correspond to the columns of the payoff matrix. Thus if player I has m alternatives available and player II has n alternatives available, then the payoff matrix will be an $m \times n$ matrix. A game described by such a matrix is called an $m \times n$ *matrix game*.

$m \times n$ matrix game

EXAMPLE 2

In the game of matching pennies, two players secretly place a penny so that either heads or tails is showing. When the coins are revealed, if both coins show heads or both coins show tails, then the first player wins one penny, and if the coins do not match, then the second player wins one penny. In this game each player has two alternatives available: to show heads (alternative 1) or to show tails (alternative 2). So the payoff matrix for the game of matching pennies is

$$\begin{array}{c} & \text{Player II} \\ \text{Player I} & \begin{pmatrix} 1 & -1 \\ -1 & 1 \end{pmatrix} \end{array}$$

EXAMPLE 3

Suppose that two candidates are attempting to win election to the state legislature from a predominately rural district. With two days remaining before the election, each candidate plans to divide his campaigning between the two largest cities in the district. Each candidate intends to spend zero, one, or two days in one city and the balance of the time in the other city. Polls show that, if both candidates spend the same number of days in a city, then they will each receive 50% of the city's vote. But if either candidate spends one more day in a city than his opponent, that candidate will receive 55% of the city's vote; and if either candidate spends two more days in a city than his opponent, that candidate will receive 60% of the city's vote. If the two cities have voting populations of 40,000 and 30,000, what is the payoff matrix for this game?

To determine the payoff matrix, we must first observe that each candidate has three available alternatives.

Alternative 1: Spend zero days in the larger city (and two days in the smaller)
Alternative 2: Spend one day in each city
Alternative 3: Spend two days in the larger city (and zero days in the smaller)

Thus the payoff matrix will be a 3×3 matrix. It is easily seen that, if the entries of the payoff matrix represent votes for player I, then the payoff matrix will be

$$\begin{array}{cccc} & \text{Alternative 1} & \text{Alternative 2} & \text{Alternative 3} \\ \text{Alternative 1} & \begin{pmatrix} 35{,}000 & 34{,}500 & 34{,}000 \\ \text{Alternative 2} & 35{,}500 & 35{,}000 & 34{,}500 \\ \text{Alternative 3} & 36{,}000 & 35{,}500 & 35{,}000 \end{pmatrix} \end{array}$$

For instance, if player I employs alternative 2 and player II uses alternative 1, then the payoff to player I is

$$0.55(40{,}000) + 0.45(30{,}000) = 22{,}000 + 13{,}500 = 35{,}500$$

The techniques of game theory can be used to find optimal strategies for both players. (Procedures for computing optimal strategies will be presented in Sections 9.2–9.4.) We shall now discuss the meaning of the term "optimal strategy."

Consider an $m \times n$ matrix game with payoff matrix $A = (a_{ij})$. A *strategy* for player I is a probability vector[1]

$$X = (x_1 \quad x_2 \quad \cdots \quad x_m)$$

in which x_i represents the probability of using player I's ith alternative (the one corresponding to row i of the payoff matrix).

EXAMPLE 4

For the 3×4 matrix game with payoff matrix

$$A = \begin{pmatrix} 5 & 0 & 3 & -1 \\ -2 & 4 & 1 & 2 \\ 3 & 1 & -2 & 2 \end{pmatrix}$$

$X_1 = (0 \quad 1 \quad 0)$, $X_2 = (\frac{1}{3} \quad \frac{1}{3} \quad \frac{1}{3})$, and $X_3 = (.2 \quad .5 \quad .3)$ are strategies for player I. Strategy X_1 represents the use of alternative 2 (row 2) exclusively; X_2 represents the use of each alternative with equal probability; and X_3 represents the use of alternative 1 with probability .2, the use of alternative 2 with probability .5, and the use of alternative 3 with probability .3.

---

[1] Recall that a probability vector is a vector consisting of nonnegative entries whose sum is 1.

When player I uses strategy X, *the entries of the product matrix XA give the expected value for player I against each alternative available to player II.* In Example 4, for instance, $X_1 A = (-2 \ \ 4 \ \ 1 \ \ 2)$ gives the expected winnings for player I against each of the four alternatives available to player II. Thus if player II uses his first alternative (column 1), player I can expect to lose 2, and if player II uses his second alternative, player I can expect to win 4. Similarly, the jth entry of

$$X_2 A = (2 \ \ \tfrac{5}{3} \ \ \tfrac{2}{3} \ \ 1) \quad \text{and} \quad X_3 A = (0.9 \ \ 2.3 \ \ 0.5 \ \ 1.4)$$

gives the expected winnings for player I when he uses strategies X_2 and X_3 and player II chooses his jth alternative.

Suppose player I uses strategy X. Since player II is assumed to be playing so as to maximize his expected winnings or to minimize his expected losses, he would like to choose the alternative (column) that corresponds to the *smallest* entry in XA. For example, if player I uses strategy X_1 in Example 4, then player II would like to choose alternative 1 so that player I loses 2. This result is clearly better for player II than choosing alternative 2, 3, or 4, which would result in winnings of 4, 1, or 2 for player I.

From player I's perspective this means that the worst payoff that can result when he uses strategy X is the smallest entry of the product matrix XA. Thus it is in player I's interest to choose a strategy X for which the smallest entry of XA is as large as possible.

EXAMPLE 5

In the preceding discussion we saw that

$$X_1 A = (-2 \ \ 4 \ \ 1 \ \ 2) \qquad X_2 A = (2 \ \ \tfrac{5}{3} \ \ \tfrac{2}{3} \ \ 1)$$

and

$$X_3 A = (0.9 \ \ 2.3 \ \ 0.5 \ \ 1.4)$$

Hence the worst payoffs player I can expect if he uses strategies X_1, X_2, and X_3 are -2, $\tfrac{2}{3}$, and 0.5, respectively. Therefore player I will be guaranteed a larger minimum payoff ($\tfrac{2}{3}$) by using X_2 than by using X_1 or X_3.

Similarly, a strategy for player II is a probability vector

$$Y = \begin{pmatrix} y_1 \\ y_2 \\ \vdots \\ y_n \end{pmatrix}$$

in which y_j represents the probability that player II will use his jth alternative (the one corresponding to column j of the payoff matrix). As before, when player II uses strategy Y, the entries of the product matrix

AY represent the expected values for player II against each of the alternatives available to player I. This time, however, since positive entries of the payoff matrix represent losses for player II and negative entries represent gains, *player II is concerned with finding a strategy Y for which the largest entry of AY is as small as possible.*

EXAMPLE 6

Let

$$Y_1 = \begin{pmatrix} 0 \\ 0 \\ 1 \\ 0 \end{pmatrix} \quad Y_2 = \begin{pmatrix} .5 \\ 0 \\ 0 \\ .5 \end{pmatrix} \quad \text{and} \quad Y_3 = \begin{pmatrix} .2 \\ .1 \\ .4 \\ .3 \end{pmatrix}$$

If the payoff matrix A is as in Example 4, then Y_1, Y_2, and Y_3 are strategies for player II and

$$AY_1 = \begin{pmatrix} 3 \\ 1 \\ -2 \end{pmatrix} \quad AY_2 = \begin{pmatrix} 2.0 \\ 0.0 \\ 2.5 \end{pmatrix} \quad \text{and} \quad AY_3 = \begin{pmatrix} 1.9 \\ 1.0 \\ 0.5 \end{pmatrix}$$

So the worse payoffs player II can expect if he uses strategies Y_1, Y_2, and Y_3 are 3, 2.5, and 1.9, respectively. Therefore player II will have a smaller maximum loss when using Y_3 than when using Y_1 or Y_2.

The following result due to John von Neumann provides the mathematical foundation for the theory of two-person zero-sum games.

THEOREM 9.1 *Minimax theorem*

Let A be the payoff matrix for a two-person zero-sum game. There exists a real number v and strategies X^* and Y^* for players I and II, respectively, such that

(a) The smallest entry of X^*A is v.
(b) The largest entry of AY^* is v.

value of a game

optimal strategies

In Theorem 9.1 the number v is unique and is called the *value of the game*. The strategies X^* and Y^*, however, need not be unique. Any strategies X^* and Y^* for players I and II that satisfy conditions (a) and (b) of Theorem 9.1 are called *optimal strategies*. It can be shown that any optimal strategies X^* and Y^* have the following properties:

(a) If X is any other strategy for player I, the smallest entry of X^*A is at least as large as the smallest entry of XA.
(b) If Y is any other strategy for player II, the largest entry of AY^* is at least as small as the largest entry of AY.

Thus X^* and Y^* are the best strategies for players I and II in the sense that they accomplish the objectives of maximizing the minimum expected winnings for one player and minimizing the maximum expected losses for the other.

EXAMPLE 7

For the payoff matrix A in Example 4 the value of the game is $\frac{59}{55}$ and the optimal strategies for players I and II are

$$X^* = (\tfrac{17}{55} \quad \tfrac{28}{55} \quad \tfrac{10}{55}) \quad \text{and} \quad Y^* = \begin{pmatrix} \frac{9}{55} \\ 0 \\ \frac{15}{55} \\ \frac{31}{55} \end{pmatrix}$$

respectively, since

$$X^*A = (\tfrac{59}{55} \quad \tfrac{122}{55} \quad \tfrac{59}{55} \quad \tfrac{59}{55}) \quad \text{and} \quad AY^* = \begin{pmatrix} \frac{59}{55} \\ \frac{59}{55} \\ \frac{59}{55} \end{pmatrix}$$

Notice that the smallest entry of X^*A, which is 59/55 (the value of the game), is larger than the smallest entry of $X_1 A$, $X_2 A$, or $X_3 A$, where X_1, X_2, and X_3 are as defined in Example 4. Likewise the largest entry of AY^*, which is again $\frac{59}{55}$, is smaller than the largest entry of AY_1, AY_2, or AY_3, where Y_1, Y_2, and Y_3 are as defined in Example 6.

EXAMPLE 8

Let

$$A = \begin{pmatrix} 9 & -2 & -6 & 1 \\ -3 & 0 & 6 & 0 \\ -6 & 4 & 0 & 0 \end{pmatrix} \quad X^* = (\tfrac{12}{35} \quad \tfrac{14}{35} \quad \tfrac{9}{35})$$

and

$$Y^* = \begin{pmatrix} \frac{10}{35} \\ \frac{18}{35} \\ \frac{7}{35} \\ 0 \end{pmatrix}$$

Since

$$X^*A = (\tfrac{12}{35} \quad \tfrac{12}{35} \quad \tfrac{12}{35} \quad \tfrac{12}{35}) \quad \text{and} \quad AY^* = \begin{pmatrix} \frac{12}{35} \\ \frac{12}{35} \\ \frac{12}{35} \end{pmatrix}$$

X^* and Y^* are optimal strategies for the game having A as its payoff matrix. The value of this game is $\frac{12}{35}$.

In this game player II has an infinite number of optimal strategies available; some others are

$$\begin{pmatrix} 0 \\ \frac{3}{35} \\ \frac{2}{35} \\ \frac{30}{35} \end{pmatrix}, \begin{pmatrix} \frac{10}{70} \\ \frac{21}{70} \\ \frac{9}{70} \\ \frac{30}{70} \end{pmatrix}, \begin{pmatrix} \frac{10}{105} \\ \frac{24}{105} \\ \frac{11}{105} \\ \frac{60}{105} \end{pmatrix} \text{ and } \begin{pmatrix} \frac{20}{105} \\ \frac{39}{105} \\ \frac{16}{105} \\ \frac{30}{105} \end{pmatrix}$$

If both players use their optimal strategies, the value of a game is the expected value to player I each time the game is played. Thus if the value of a game is positive, player I can expect to be a winner if he uses an optimal strategy. On the other hand, if the value of a game is negative, then player I can expect to be a loser if player II uses an optimal strategy. When the value of a game is zero, each player can expect to break even by using an optimal strategy. Games having a value of zero are called *fair games*.

fair game

EXAMPLE 9

For the game of matching pennies in Example 2,

$$X^* = (.5 \quad .5) \quad \text{and} \quad Y^* = \begin{pmatrix} .5 \\ .5 \end{pmatrix}$$

are optimal strategies and the value of the game is 0. So the game of matching pennies is a fair game.

On the other hand, neither of the games in Example 7 and 8 is fair, since the value of each of these games is nonzero.

Although we are not presently concerned with learning how to compute optimal strategies for a game, there are games in which it is clear that one or more alternatives can never be used in an optimal strategy. Consider, for example, the game with payoff matrix

$$A = \begin{pmatrix} 4 & 4 & -2 \\ -1 & 2 & 3 \\ -2 & 1 & 3 \end{pmatrix}$$

Since player I is interested in obtaining the largest possible payoffs, he should not select an alternative that never gives larger payoffs than some other alternative. For example, in matrix A above, the entries in row 3 are never larger than the corresponding entries in row 2. Thus no matter which column is chosen by player II, player I can do no worse by using row 2 than by using row 3. In this case we say that row 3 is dominated by row 2. In general, row i is said to be *dominated* by row j

dominated row

if the entries in row j are always *greater than or equal to* the corresponding entries in row i.

Similarly, since the entries of the payoff matrix represent payoffs to player I, player II should not select an alternative that never gives smaller payoffs than some other alternative. For instance, in the matrix above, the entries in column 2 are never smaller than the corresponding entries in column 1. Hence no matter which row is chosen by player I, player II can do no worse by using column 1 than by using column 2. In this case we say that column 2 is dominated by column 1. In general, column i is said to be *dominated* by column j if the entries in column j are always *less than or equal to* the corresponding entries in column i.

dominated column

As the previous discussion suggests, the probability of using a dominated row or column is zero in an optimal strategy. Thus dominated rows and columns can be eliminated from the payoff matrix when searching for optimal strategies. In this way we can often reduce the size of the payoff matrix, thereby simplifying the computation of optimal strategies.

EXAMPLE 10

Consider the game having the payoff matrix

$$A = \begin{pmatrix} -1 & 4 & 5 & 3 \\ 3 & -2 & 1 & -3 \\ -1 & 0 & 6 & 2 \\ 2 & 1 & 2 & -4 \end{pmatrix}$$

It is easily seen that A has no dominated rows. Column 3, however, is dominated by column 2. Consequently player II should never use column 3; so we eliminate column 3 from consideration.

$$\begin{pmatrix} -1 & 4 & 5 & 3 \\ 3 & -2 & 1 & -3 \\ -1 & 0 & 6 & 2 \\ 2 & 1 & 2 & -4 \end{pmatrix}$$

A rational player I will also observe that player II should not use column 3 of the payoff matrix. Examining the payoff matrix with column 3 removed, player I will notice that row 3 is dominated by row 1. Consequently player I should never use row 3 of the payoff matrix; so we also eliminate row 3 from consideration.

$$\begin{pmatrix} -1 & 4 & 5 & 3 \\ 3 & -2 & 1 & -3 \\ -1 & 0 & 6 & 2 \\ 2 & 1 & 2 & -4 \end{pmatrix}$$

Player II will similarly conclude that player I should not use row 3 of the payoff matrix. Thus he will reexamine the payoff matrix with row 3 and column 3 removed, and he will see that column 2 is dominated by column 4. So player II should not use column 2. Eliminating column 2 from consideration gives

$$\begin{pmatrix} -1 & 4 & 5 & 3 \\ 3 & -2 & 1 & -3 \\ -1 & 0 & 6 & 2 \\ 2 & 1 & 2 & -4 \end{pmatrix}$$

Player I will also conclude that player II should not use the second column. So he will examine the payoff matrix with columns 2 and 3 and row 3 removed and see that row 4 is dominated by row 2. Hence player I should not use row 4 of the payoff matrix. Eliminating row 4 from consideration gives

$$\begin{pmatrix} -1 & 4 & 5 & 3 \\ 3 & -2 & 1 & -3 \\ -1 & 0 & 6 & 2 \\ 2 & 1 & 2 & -4 \end{pmatrix}$$

No more dominated rows or columns can be eliminated. We therefore conclude that in an optimal strategy player I should use only rows 1 and 2 and player II should use only columns 1 and 4. Thus in computing the optimal strategies for the game with payoff matrix A, we can work with the 2×2 payoff matrix

$$\begin{pmatrix} -1 & 3 \\ 3 & -3 \end{pmatrix}$$

obtained by deleting the dominated rows and columns from A. We shall make use of this technique in Example 14 in Section 9.3.

Exercises

In Exercises 1–10 verify that X and Y are optimal strategies for players I and II in the game with payoff matrix A. What is the value of the game?

1. $A = \begin{pmatrix} 4 & -3 \\ -3 & 2 \end{pmatrix}$, $X = (\frac{5}{12} \ \frac{7}{12})$, $Y = \begin{pmatrix} \frac{5}{12} \\ \frac{7}{12} \end{pmatrix}$

2. $A = \begin{pmatrix} 6 & -7 \\ -2 & 5 \end{pmatrix}$, $X = (.35 \ .65)$, $Y = \begin{pmatrix} .6 \\ .4 \end{pmatrix}$

3. $A = \begin{pmatrix} 3 & -1 \\ -6 & 2 \end{pmatrix}$, $X = (\frac{2}{3} \ \frac{1}{3})$, $Y = \begin{pmatrix} \frac{1}{4} \\ \frac{3}{4} \end{pmatrix}$

4. $A = \begin{pmatrix} 7 & -5 \\ -4 & 4 \end{pmatrix}$, $X = (.4 \ .6)$, $Y = \begin{pmatrix} .45 \\ .55 \end{pmatrix}$

5. $A = \begin{pmatrix} 1 & 2 & -1 \\ -3 & 3 & 5 \end{pmatrix}$, $X = (.8 \ .2)$, $Y = \begin{pmatrix} .6 \\ 0 \\ .4 \end{pmatrix}$

6. $A = \begin{pmatrix} 12 & 5 & -10 \\ -2 & -1 & 2 \end{pmatrix}$, $X = (\frac{1}{6} \; \frac{5}{6})$, $Y = \begin{pmatrix} 0 \\ \frac{2}{3} \\ \frac{1}{3} \end{pmatrix}$

7. $A = \begin{pmatrix} 6 & -3 & 4 \\ 2 & -4 & 3 \\ -4 & 7 & 1 \end{pmatrix}$, $X = (.55 \; 0 \; .45)$, $Y = \begin{pmatrix} .5 \\ .5 \\ 0 \end{pmatrix}$

8. $A = \begin{pmatrix} 2 & -3 & -1 \\ 0 & -5 & 2 \\ -1 & -4 & 6 \end{pmatrix}$, $X = (1 \; 0 \; 0)$, $Y = \begin{pmatrix} 0 \\ 1 \\ 0 \end{pmatrix}$

9. $\begin{pmatrix} 5 & 3 & 2 & 7 \\ 8 & 6 & 4 & 5 \\ 6 & 9 & 2 & 1 \\ 2 & 1 & 3 & 6 \end{pmatrix}$, $X = (0 \; 1 \; 0 \; 0)$, $Y = \begin{pmatrix} 0 \\ 0 \\ 1 \\ 0 \end{pmatrix}$

10. $A = \begin{pmatrix} 4 & 1 & 6 & 1 \\ -5 & 0 & -3 & -2 \\ 6 & -1 & 4 & 0 \\ 2 & 1 & 3 & 1 \end{pmatrix}$, $X = (.3 \; 0 \; 0 \; .7)$, $Y = \begin{pmatrix} 0 \\ .6 \\ 0 \\ .4 \end{pmatrix}$

In Exercises 11–20 identify all dominated rows and columns (if any).

11. $\begin{pmatrix} 4 & 0 & 3 \\ 3 & 5 & 1 \\ -2 & 4 & 0 \end{pmatrix}$
12. $\begin{pmatrix} 2 & 7 & 3 \\ -1 & 2 & 6 \\ 3 & 5 & 4 \end{pmatrix}$

13. $\begin{pmatrix} 4 & 1 & -1 \\ -2 & 7 & 1 \\ 2 & -3 & 3 \end{pmatrix}$
14. $\begin{pmatrix} 1 & -4 & 5 \\ -3 & 3 & -6 \\ 2 & -1 & 8 \end{pmatrix}$

15. $\begin{pmatrix} 4 & -7 & 4 \\ -1 & 1 & -2 \\ -3 & 6 & -5 \end{pmatrix}$
16. $\begin{pmatrix} 3 & -5 & 1 \\ -1 & 6 & -4 \\ -2 & 1 & -1 \end{pmatrix}$

17. $\begin{pmatrix} 4 & 2 & 3 & 2 \\ 3 & 0 & 2 & -1 \\ 1 & 5 & 6 & 1 \end{pmatrix}$
18. $\begin{pmatrix} 1 & 3 & -2 & 5 \\ 2 & -2 & 4 & -3 \\ 0 & 6 & -3 & 4 \end{pmatrix}$

19. $\begin{pmatrix} 0 & -1 & -3 & 4 \\ -3 & -2 & 2 & -3 \\ -4 & -1 & 1 & -3 \\ 1 & 3 & -2 & 2 \end{pmatrix}$
20. $\begin{pmatrix} 4 & 2 & 0 & -1 \\ 5 & -1 & 4 & 3 \\ 2 & 2 & 2 & 4 \\ -3 & -1 & 2 & -2 \end{pmatrix}$

21. Prepare the payoff matrix for the following game. Two players (secretly) place a coin so that either heads or tails is showing. If both coins show heads, then the first player wins 9¢; and if both coins show tails, then the

first player wins 4¢. However, if the coins do not match, then the second player wins 6¢.

22. Suppose that country I intends to send two bombers to attack country II. Only one of the planes, however, will actually carry a bomb; the other plane will carry equipment to assess the damage done by the bomb. Country I can let either the first or the second of the two planes carry the bomb, but the first plane will be more vulnerable than the second in case of attack. Specifically, the probability that the first plane will survive an attack is .4, and the probability that the second plane will survive an attack is .6. Either plane is certain to survive if not attacked. If country II is capable of attacking only one of the two planes, prepare a payoff matrix for this situation in which the entries represent the probability of survival for country I's bomb-carrying plane.

23. *Scissors-paper-stone* is a well-known children's game. The two players simultaneously reveal one of the following: two fingers (representing scissors), an open palm (representing paper), or a fist (representing stone). If both reveal the same object, the game is a draw. Otherwise superiority is established according to the following hierarchy: scissors beats paper, paper beats stone, and stone beats scissors. Prepare a payoff matrix assuming that each victory is worth 1.

24. *Two-finger morra* is a game for two players. Each player shows either one or two fingers while simultaneously guessing aloud how many fingers his opponent will show. If only one player guesses correctly, he wins an amount equal to the sum of the fingers shown by both players; otherwise the game is a draw. Determine the payoff matrix for two-finger morra.

25. Suppose that a military commander has 2 divisions and his enemy has 1. The commander will be promoted one rank for capturing the enemy's headquarters without losing his own and will be demoted one rank if the enemy captures his headquarters. The commander can send 0, 1, or 2 divisions to attack the enemy's headquarters, but the enemy can send 0 or 1 division to attack the commander's headquarters. To capture either headquarters requires a numerical superiority of 1 division. Determine the payoff matrix for this situation.

26. In Exercise 25 suppose that the commander, instead of being promoted or demoted, receives one medal each for capturing the enemy's headquarters, holding his own headquarters, and defeating the enemy division. If both of the commander's divisions are required to defeat the enemy division, what is the payoff matrix in this case?

27. A liberal and a conservative are the leading candidates for their party's nomination for state representative. They have agreed to hold a debate in one of the 12 major cities in their district. Each of the 12 cities lies at the intersection of a north-south and an east-west road as shown in Figure 9.1. Since each candidate is anxious to have the debate scheduled in a city in which her support is as strong as possible, they have agreed on the following method for choosing the location of the debate: The liberal candidate will select an east-west road, and the conservative will select a north-south road; the debate will be held at the city located at the intersection of the two roads that are chosen. In the city located at the intersection of east-west route i and north-south route j the excess of liberals over conservatives (measured in thousands) is approximately $20i - 10j$. Prepare a payoff matrix for this situation.

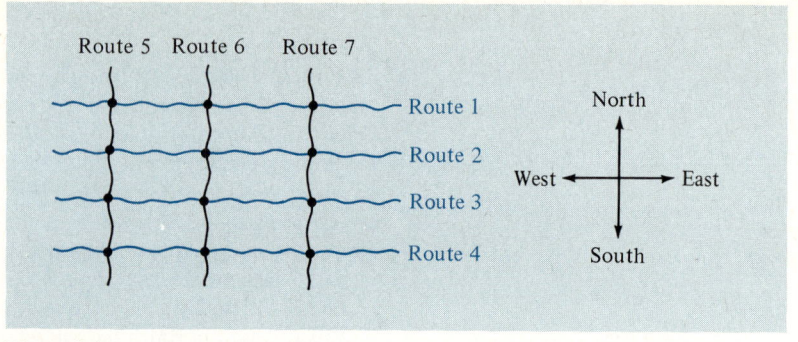

Figure 9.1

28. With 3 days remaining before the primary election, the liberal and conservative candidates in Exercise 27 have decided to divide their campaigning time between the two largest cities in the district. Each candidate intends to spend zero, one, two, or three days in one city and the balance of the time in the other. Polls show that, if both candidates spend the same amount of time in a city, then they will each receive 50% of the city's vote; but if either candidate spends more time in a city than her opponent, then that candidate will increase her share of the vote by 4% for each day she spends in the city beyond the time her opponent spends there. If there are 15,000 voters in one city and 10,000 in the other, prepare a payoff matrix for this situation in which the entries represent votes for the liberal.

29. Two competing department stores intend to build somewhere in the three cities pictured in Figure 9.2. The total business for the department stores is distributed among the cities as follows: 50% in city 1, 30% in city 2, and 20% in city 3. If the two department stores both build in the same city, then department store I, which is larger, will receive 55% of the total business of the three cities. But if the two stores build in different cities, the total business will be divided in the following way: Each city containing a department store will give 80% of its business to the department store located there and 20% to the other, and the city without a department store will give 60% of its business to the department store in the city that is closer and 40% to the other. Prepare a payoff matrix for this situation in which the entries represent the difference between the percentage of business done by department store I and 50%.

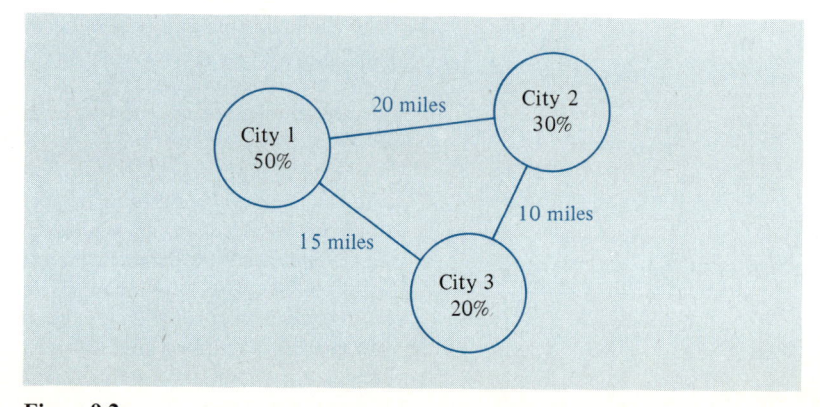

Figure 9.2

9.2 Strictly Determined Games

When the fundamental concepts of game theory were introduced in Section 9.1, we mentioned that the players of a two-person zero-sum game were assumed to play so as to maximize their minimum expected winnings or to minimize their maximum expected losses. In this section we shall see how this assumption dictates the optimal strategies in a particular type of game.

To illustrate the ideas involved, let us consider a two-person zero-sum game with payoff matrix

$$A = \begin{pmatrix} 5 & 3 & 2 & 7 \\ 8 & 6 & 4 & 5 \\ 6 & 9 & 2 & 1 \\ 2 & 1 & 3 & 6 \end{pmatrix}$$

Since all the entries of this matrix are positive, it is clear that the game is biased in favor of player I, that is, that the value of the game is positive. Consequently player I will play so as to maximize his minimum expected winnings, whereas player II will play so as to minimize her maximum expected losses.

If player I chooses his first alternative (row 1), the minimum amount he can expect to win is 2, the smallest entry in row 1. Likewise, the minimum amounts he can win by using alternatives 2, 3, and 4 are 4, 1, and 1, respectively. It is helpful to display these numbers beside the payoff matrix as shown below.

$$\begin{matrix} & & & & & \text{Row minimum} \\ \begin{pmatrix} 5 & 3 & 2 & 7 \\ 8 & 6 & 4 & 5 \\ 6 & 9 & 2 & 1 \\ 2 & 1 & 3 & 6 \end{pmatrix} & & \begin{matrix} 2 \\ 4 \\ 1 \\ 1 \end{matrix} \end{matrix}$$

Thus we see that the maximum of player I's minimum expected winnings is 4, obtained by using row 2.

Let us now consider the payoff matrix from the viewpoint of player II. If player II uses her first alternative (column 1), the maximum amount she can expect to lose is 8, the largest entry in column 1. Similarly, the maximum amounts she can expect to lose by using alternatives 2, 3, and 4 are 9, 4, and 7, respectively. We record these numbers under the payoff matrix as shown below.

$$\begin{matrix} & & & & & & \text{Row minimum} \\ & \begin{pmatrix} 5 & 3 & 2 & 7 \\ 8 & 6 & 4 & 5 \\ 6 & 9 & 2 & 1 \\ 2 & 1 & 3 & 6 \end{pmatrix} & & \begin{matrix} 2 \\ 4 \\ 1 \\ 1 \end{matrix} \\ \text{Column maximum} & 8 \quad 9 \quad 4 \quad 7 & & \end{matrix}$$

strictly determined game

saddle point

Thus the minimum of player II's maximum expected losses is 4, obtained by using column 3.

In this case the largest of the row minima equals the smallest of the column maxima. When this situation occurs, the game is said to be *strictly determined* because player I should always use the row containing the largest of the row minima and play II should always use the column containing the smallest of the column maxima. The common value of the largest of the row minima and the smallest of the column maxima is called a *saddle point* of the payoff matrix. *Thus a saddle point is an entry of the payoff matrix that is both the smallest in its row and the largest in its column.*

We see therefore that 4 (the entry in row 2, column 3) is a saddle point of matrix A above. It follows that player I should always use his second alternative (row 2) and player II should always use her third alternative (column 3). In other words

$$X = (0 \ 1 \ 0 \ 0) \quad \text{and} \quad Y = \begin{pmatrix} 0 \\ 0 \\ 1 \\ 0 \end{pmatrix}$$

are the optimal strategies for players I and II, respectively, and the value of this game is 4.

EXAMPLE 11

To find a saddle point in the payoff matrix

$$\begin{pmatrix} 0 & -1 & 3 & -2 \\ 1 & -7 & 2 & -3 \\ -5 & 8 & -6 & -4 \end{pmatrix}$$

we look for an entry that is the smallest in its row and the largest in its column. Clearly -2, the smallest entry in row 1 and the largest entry in column 4, satisfies these conditions. Thus player I should use row 1 exclusively, and player II should use column 4 exclusively. The value of this game is -2.

EXAMPLE 12

In [10] and [11], Haywood investigates the relationship between the theory of two-person zero-sum games and decision making in times of war. If a military conflict is regarded as a two-person zero-sum game, then the assumptions of game theory amount to maximizing expected gains or minimizing expected losses based on the capabilities of the enemy. The following example is based on [11].

In the World War II Battle of the Bismarck Sea, American intelligence reports indicated that a Japanese troop and supply convoy would be moved from Rabaul to Lae. The convoy could be moved along two possible routes, one north of New Britain and the other south of New Britain. Although the trip would require 3 days along either route, poor visibility was very likely along the northern route and clear weather was likely along the southern route. General Kenney could choose to concentrate most of the American reconnaissance aircraft along either route. Once the convoy was sighted, it could be bombed until its arrival at Lae. Kenney's staff estimated that the number of days of bombing time was as follows:

Kenney's strategy	**Japanese strategy**	
	Use northern route	Use southern route
Watch northern route	2	2
Watch southern route	1	3

It is easily seen that the 2 in row 1, column 1 is a saddle point for this payoff matrix. Hence the best choice for each side was the northern route. These were the choices that were actually made, and the Japanese suffered heavy losses during the bombing. Nevertheless, from the point of view of game theory, the Japanese decision to use the northern route was the correct decision.

When a payoff matrix has a saddle point, neither player can gain by unilaterally using another alternative. In Example 12, for instance, if Kenney had decided to watch the southern route and the Japanese had used the northern route, then the amount of bombing time for Kenney would have been reduced from 2 days to 1 day. Likewise if the Japanese had used the southern route and Kenney had continued to watch the northern route, the Japanese convoy would still have been subjected to 2 days of bombing. Thus when a game has a saddle point, neither player can profit from the knowledge that the other selects the row or column containing the saddle point.

Quite the opposite is true for games without a saddle point, however. Consider, for instance, the 2×2 payoff matrix

$$\begin{pmatrix} 3 & -1 \\ -6 & 2 \end{pmatrix}$$

It is easily seen that this matrix contains no saddle points. In this case either player can profit greatly by knowing which alternative the other plans to use. For example, if player I knows that player II will use column 1, then player I will choose row 1 in order to win 3; and if player I knows that player II will use column 2, then player I will choose row 2 in order to win 2. Similarly player II can profit by knowing which row player I intends to use. So in games without a saddle point it is important for each player to keep his or her choice of alternative secret, whereas no such precaution must be taken when a saddle point exists.

The preceding discussion has shown that, when a payoff matrix has a saddle point, both players should select the alternatives that contain the saddle point. But what happens if a payoff matrix contains two saddle points, say a_{ik} and a_{jl}? If player I selects row i (to try for the first saddle point) and player II selects column l (to try for the second saddle point), then instead of either a_{ik} or a_{jl} the payoff will be a_{il}. Fortunately, in this case both a_{il} and a_{jk} must also be saddle points, and all four saddle points must be equal. Thus no matter which row containing a saddle point is selected by player I and no matter which column containing a saddle point is selected by player II, the payoff will be the same.

EXAMPLE 13

The matrix

$$\begin{pmatrix} 4 & 1 & 6 & 2 & 1 \\ -5 & 0 & -3 & 7 & -2 \\ 6 & -1 & 4 & -2 & 0 \\ 2 & 1 & 3 & 5 & 1 \end{pmatrix}$$

contains four saddle points, all equal to 1. So regardless of whether player I selects row 1 or row 4 and whether player II selects column 2 or column 5, the resulting payoff will be 1.

Exercises

In Exercises 1–20 determine if the given payoff matrices have a saddle point. If so, determine the optimal strategies for each player.

1. $\begin{pmatrix} 2 & -3 & -1 \\ 0 & -5 & 2 \\ -1 & -4 & 6 \end{pmatrix}$
2. $\begin{pmatrix} -5 & 0 & 4 \\ -3 & -1 & 2 \\ 7 & -4 & 5 \end{pmatrix}$

3. $\begin{pmatrix} 2 & 5 & 8 \\ 3 & 1 & 4 \\ 6 & 3 & 7 \end{pmatrix}$
4. $\begin{pmatrix} -2 & 0 & 6 \\ 1 & 2 & 4 \\ 0 & -3 & 1 \end{pmatrix}$

5. $\begin{pmatrix} -3 & 5 & -2 \\ 7 & -1 & -4 \\ 2 & 3 & 0 \end{pmatrix}$
6. $\begin{pmatrix} -2 & 3 & 4 \\ 1 & -6 & 2 \\ 0 & 4 & -3 \end{pmatrix}$

7. $\begin{pmatrix} 3 & -5 & 4 \\ -8 & 6 & 1 \\ 5 & 2 & -9 \end{pmatrix}$
8. $\begin{pmatrix} 1 & 5 & 2 \\ -6 & -3 & 3 \\ 0 & 6 & -4 \end{pmatrix}$

9. $\begin{pmatrix} 2 & 4 & 1 \\ 1 & -2 & 0 \\ 5 & 1 & -3 \\ 3 & -1 & 2 \end{pmatrix}$
10. $\begin{pmatrix} 5 & -1 & -3 \\ -4 & 6 & 1 \\ 3 & -2 & -1 \\ -2 & 1 & 4 \end{pmatrix}$

11. $\begin{pmatrix} 4 & -1 & 1 \\ 2 & 0 & -4 \\ 5 & 2 & 3 \\ -3 & 1 & 2 \end{pmatrix}$ 12. $\begin{pmatrix} 3 & 6 & -9 \\ -6 & 8 & -4 \\ -7 & 3 & 1 \\ 4 & 5 & 7 \end{pmatrix}$

13. $\begin{pmatrix} 2 & 0 & -3 \\ 3 & 6 & 4 \\ -5 & -1 & 7 \\ -1 & 4 & -2 \end{pmatrix}$ 14. $\begin{pmatrix} 2 & -1 & 6 \\ -1 & 1 & -4 \\ -3 & 0 & 2 \\ 4 & 1 & 3 \end{pmatrix}$

15. $\begin{pmatrix} -1 & 5 & -2 \\ -3 & 0 & 4 \\ 1 & -4 & 3 \\ 2 & -3 & -6 \end{pmatrix}$ 16. $\begin{pmatrix} 8 & 7 & 4 \\ 0 & 1 & 3 \\ 2 & 5 & 1 \\ 4 & 3 & 2 \end{pmatrix}$

17. $\begin{pmatrix} 0 & -4 & 3 & -2 \\ 4 & -2 & -6 & 3 \\ 2 & -1 & 0 & 1 \\ -3 & -3 & 1 & 2 \end{pmatrix}$ 18. $\begin{pmatrix} -5 & 0 & 4 & -1 \\ 6 & -1 & -2 & 3 \\ 3 & -2 & 3 & -6 \\ 2 & 0 & 1 & 1 \end{pmatrix}$

19. $\begin{pmatrix} 4 & 3 & 0 & -2 \\ 1 & 0 & -3 & 5 \\ -2 & 2 & 6 & 1 \\ -3 & -1 & -2 & -4 \end{pmatrix}$ 20. $\begin{pmatrix} 1 & -3 & 4 & 2 \\ 2 & 6 & 3 & -5 \\ -4 & 2 & 1 & 3 \\ 5 & 3 & -7 & 2 \end{pmatrix}$

21. Find optimal strategies for the game described in Exercise 27 in Section 9.1.

22. Find optimal strategies for the game described in Exercise 28 in Section 9.1.

9.3 Geometric Solution of 2 × m Matrix Games

In Section 9.2 we learned how to solve matrix games having a saddle point. In this section we shall discuss a method that can be used to solve any matrix game in which at least one of the players has only two undominated alternatives. Since the decision as to which player is called player I is completely arbitrary, we shall assume throughout that player I has only two undominated alternatives.[2]

To illustrate the technique, let us determine the optimal strategies for the game with payoff matrix

$$A = \begin{pmatrix} 8 & 2 & 1 \\ 2 & 6 & 9 \end{pmatrix}$$

Recall that a strategy for player I is a vector

$$X = (x \quad 1 - x)$$

---

[2] Of course, if the roles of players I and II are reversed in a game with payoff matrix $A = (a_{ij})$, then the i,j entry of the new payoff matrix will be $-a_{ji}$.

where $0 \leq x \leq 1$. As we have seen, the expected winnings for player I against the alternatives available to player II are the entries of

$$XA = (8x + 2(1-x) \quad 2x + 6(1-x) \quad 1x + 9(1-x))$$
$$= (6x + 2 \quad -4x + 6 \quad -8x + 9)$$

Moreover, if v is the value of this game, then the optimal strategy for player I is the strategy that maximizes v subject to the condition that the smallest entry of XA is v. Thus the optimal strategy for player I is the strategy X that maximizes v subject to the conditions

$$6x + 2 \geq v \quad -4x + 6 \geq v \quad \text{and} \quad -8x + 9 \geq v$$

Since these inequalities can be rewritten as

$$6x - v \geq -2 \quad 4x + v \leq 6 \quad \text{and} \quad 8x + v \leq 9$$

player I's optimal strategy can be found by solving the following linear programming problem.

Maximize v
Subject to $6x - v \geq -2$
$4x + v \leq 6$
$8x + v \leq 9$
$x \leq 1$
$x \geq 0$

Because this problem contains only two variables, it can be solved by the geometric method described in Section 4.3. The graph of the set of feasible solutions for this problem is shown in Figure 9.3. Notice that, since x is restricted to the interval $0 \leq x \leq 1$, we have used different scales for the horizontal and vertical axes. Also observe that, unlike the problems in Chapter 4, both variables are not required to be nonnegative; consequently the graph of the set of feasible solutions does not lie completely in the first quadrant. The coordinates of each vertex and the corresponding value of the objective function are given below.

Vertex (x, v)	Value of the objective function v
$(0, 2)$	2
$(.4, 4.4)$	4.4 ← Maximum
$(.75, 3)$	3
$(1, 1)$	1

Although the feasible set is unbounded, it is not difficult to see that the maximum value of the objective function is 4.4 and that this value occurs when $x = .4$. Therefore player I's optimal strategy is

$$X = (x \quad 1 - x) = (.4 \quad .6)$$

and the value of this game is $v = 4.4$.

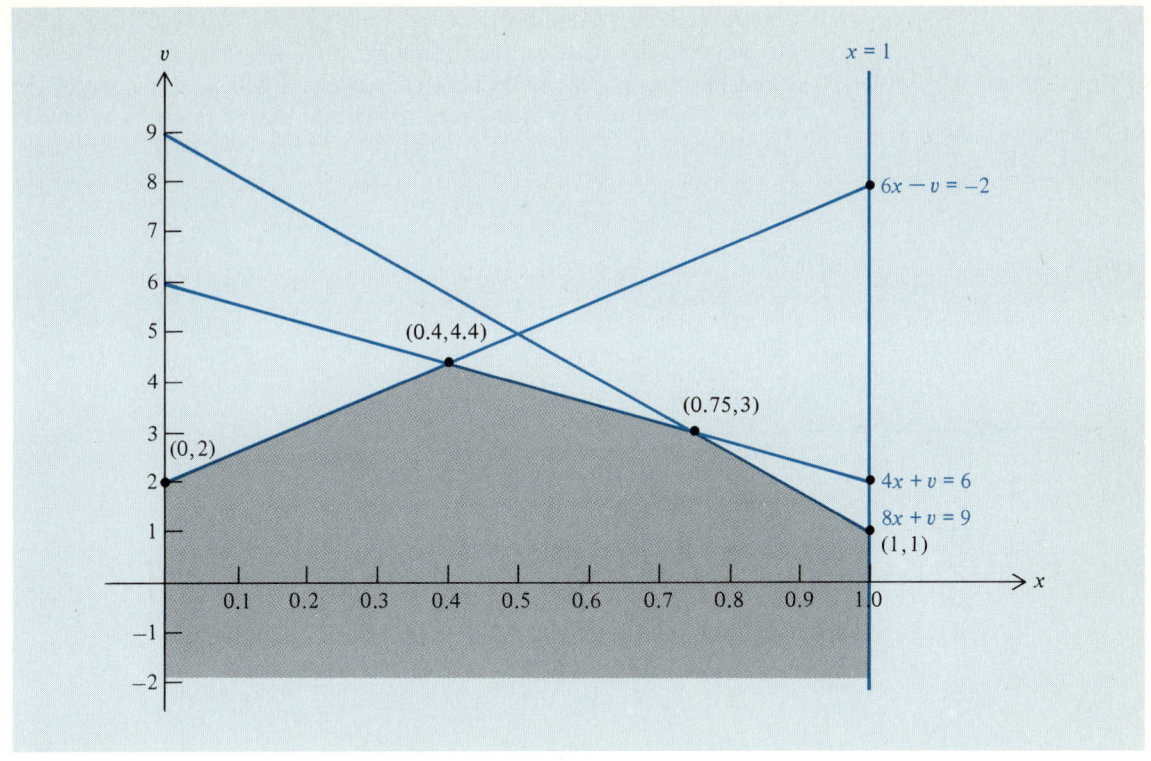

Figure 9.3

The reader should note that, because of the simple form of the objective function, the vertex at which the maximum value occurs can be found by inspection: It is the vertex of the set of feasible solutions that has the largest second coordinate. In other words, the optimum value of the objective function occurs at the "highest" point in the set of feasible solutions.

Since the objective of player II is to limit his losses to the value of the game, he should never use an alternative against which player I's optimal strategy will yield an expectation greater than the value of the game. In the context of our example, this statement means that player II should not use column 3, since the expectation line $8x + v = 9$ corresponding to column 3 does not pass through the vertex of the region of feasible solutions at which v is maximized. Thus player II's optimal strategy is of the form

$$Y = \begin{pmatrix} y \\ 1 - y \\ 0 \end{pmatrix}$$

for some value of y such that $0 \leq y \leq 1$.

Although it is possible to determine the optimal value of y by a method similar to that used in computing the optimal value of x, an easier method is available since we already know the value of the game. If player II uses his optimal strategy, then, no matter which row is used by player I, the expectation for player I will be the value of the game. Therefore, if player I uses row 1 and player II uses strategy Y, we must have

$$8y + 2(1 - y) + 1(0) = 4.4$$

So

$$6y = 2.4$$

and

$$y = .4$$

Therefore

$$Y = \begin{pmatrix} .4 \\ .6 \\ 0 \end{pmatrix}$$

is an optimal strategy for player II. As a check, note that

$$XA = (4.4 \quad 4.4 \quad 5.8) \quad \text{and} \quad AY = \begin{pmatrix} 4.4 \\ 4.4 \end{pmatrix}$$

so that X and Y are optimal strategies from Theorem 9.1.

EXAMPLE 14

To determine the optimal strategies for both players of the game with payoff matrix

$$A = \begin{pmatrix} 5 & -1 & 3 \\ -4 & 6 & -2 \\ -4 & 5 & -3 \end{pmatrix}$$

first observe that row 3 is dominated by row 2, and thus player I will never use his third alternative in an optimal strategy. So optimal strategies for the game with payoff matrix A will correspond to optimal strategies for the game with payoff matrix

$$B = \begin{pmatrix} 5 & -1 & 3 \\ -4 & 6 & -2 \end{pmatrix}$$

obtained by deleting the third row from A.

If player I uses the strategy $X = (x \quad 1 - x)$, then his expectations for each strategy for player II are given by

$$XB = (9x - 4 \quad -7x + 6 \quad 5x - 2)$$

9.3 Geometric Solution of 2 × m Matrix Games

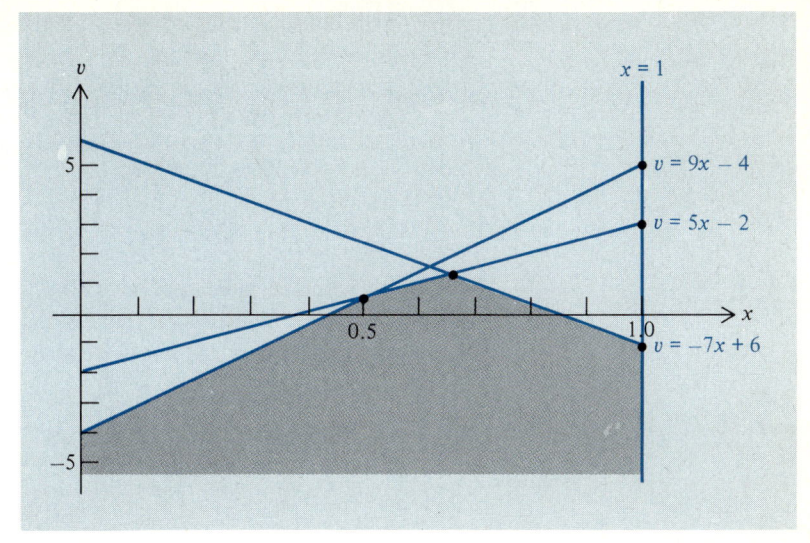

Figure 9.4

So the region of feasible solutions for the linear programming problem that determines player I's optimal strategy is defined by the conditions

$$9x - 4 \geq v$$
$$-7x + 6 \geq v$$
$$5x - 2 \geq v$$
$$x \leq 1$$
$$x \geq 0$$

The graph of this region is shown in Figure 9.4. From this figure it is clear that the vertex at which the maximum of v occurs is the point of intersection of the lines $v = 5x - 2$ and $v = -7x + 6$. Since

$$5x - 2 = -7x + 6$$
$$12x = 8$$
$$x = \tfrac{2}{3}$$

$X = (\tfrac{2}{3} \ \tfrac{1}{3})$ is the optimal strategy for player I. The value of the game can be found by substituting $\tfrac{2}{3}$ for x in either of the expectation lines used to calculate x; so

$$v = 5(\tfrac{2}{3}) - 2 = \tfrac{4}{3}$$

It follows that $X = (\tfrac{2}{3} \ \tfrac{1}{3} \ 0)$ is the optimal strategy for player I in the game with payoff matrix A, and the value of this game is $\tfrac{4}{3}$.

To determine an optimal strategy for player II, we first assign zero probability to any column for which the expectation line does not pass through the vertex of the region of feasible solutions at which v is maximized. Since the line $v = 9x - 4$ in Figure 9.4 does not pass through this vertex, player II should never use his first alternative (column 1 of B). Thus player II's optimal strategy is of the form

$$Y = \begin{pmatrix} 0 \\ y \\ 1-y \end{pmatrix}$$

for some value of y such that $0 \leq y \leq 1$. Because player I's expectation when he uses row 1 will be $\frac{4}{3}$ (the value of the game) if player II uses an optimal strategy, we must have

$$5(0) + (-1)y + 3(1-y) = \tfrac{4}{3}$$

Therefore

$$3 - 4y = \tfrac{4}{3}$$
$$-4y = -\tfrac{5}{3}$$
$$y = \tfrac{5}{12}$$

So in the game with payoff matrix B, an optimal strategy for player II is

$$\begin{pmatrix} 0 \\ \tfrac{5}{12} \\ \tfrac{7}{12} \end{pmatrix}$$

This strategy will also be optimal for player II in the game with payoff matrix A.

It may happen that more than two expectation lines pass through the vertex at which v is maximized. When this situation occurs, player II will have more than one optimal strategy. In this case an optimal strategy for player II can be found by selecting the pair of expectation lines passing through the vertex at which v is maximized that forms part of the boundary of the region of feasible solutions. The following example demonstrates this technique.

EXAMPLE 15

Let us determine optimal strategies for both players of the game with payoff matrix

$$A = \begin{pmatrix} 5 & 2 & -10 \\ -3 & -2 & 2 \end{pmatrix}$$

If player I uses the strategy $X = (x \quad 1 - x)$, his expected winnings against each alternative for player II will be given by

$$XA = (8x - 3 \quad 4x - 2 \quad -12x + 2)$$

9.3 Geometric Solution of 2 × m Matrix Games

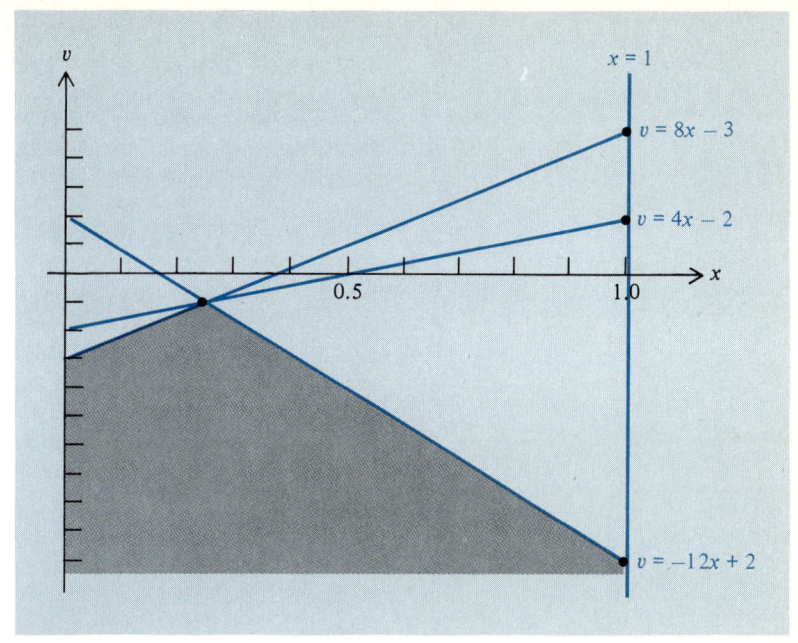

Figure 9.5

Hence the region of feasible solutions for the linear programming problem that determines player I's optimal strategy is defined by the conditions

$$8x - 3 \geq v$$
$$4x - 2 \geq v$$
$$-12x + 2 \geq v$$
$$x \leq 1$$
$$x \geq 0$$

The graph of this region is shown in Figure 9.5; notice that each line passes through the vertex at which v is maximized.

To find the coordinates of this vertex, we may compute the point of intersection of any two of the three expectation lines. Thus

$$8x - 3 = 4x - 2$$
$$4x = 1$$
$$x = \tfrac{1}{4}$$

So $X = (\tfrac{1}{4} \quad \tfrac{3}{4})$ is an optimal strategy for player I, and $8(\tfrac{1}{4}) - 3 = -1$ is the value of the game.

In order to compute an optimal strategy for player II, notice that the two expectation lines passing through the vertex at which v is maximized that form part of the boundary of the region of feasible solutions are

$$v = 8x - 3 \quad \text{and} \quad v = -12x + 2$$

As usual, any column of the payoff matrix corresponding to any line other than these two is assigned a probability of zero. Thus we shall obtain an optimal strategy for player II that has the form

$$\begin{pmatrix} y \\ 0 \\ 1 - y \end{pmatrix}$$

Since player I's expected winnings will be -1 when he uses row 1 against an optimal strategy for player II, we have

$$5y + 2(0) + (-10)(1 - y) = -1$$
$$15y = 9$$
$$y = .6$$

Therefore

$$\begin{pmatrix} .6 \\ 0 \\ .4 \end{pmatrix}$$

is an optimal strategy for player II.

Let us conclude this section with a comment concerning the implementation of an optimal strategy. In Section 9.2 we remarked that, if a payoff matrix does not contain a saddle point, then it is important for each player to keep secret his or her choice of alternative lest the other player exploit this choice. So the safest way for each player to select an alternative is to use a random method. In Example 14, for instance, player I should use row 1 twice as often as row 2 and should never use row 3. One way to select an alternative is to prepare three slips of paper, two containing "row 1" and one containing "row 2." By randomly selecting one of these slips of paper and choosing the row named on the slip, player I can ensure that he is using an optimal strategy and also keeping his choice of alternative secret from his opponent.

Exercises

In Exercises 1–18 compute an optimal strategy for each player and the value of the game having the given payoff matrix.

1. $\begin{pmatrix} 2 & -1 \\ -3 & 4 \end{pmatrix}$ 2. $\begin{pmatrix} 2 & -3 \\ -4 & 6 \end{pmatrix}$

3. $\begin{pmatrix} 5 & -3 \\ -2 & 1 \end{pmatrix}$ 4. $\begin{pmatrix} 3 & -3 \\ -2 & 1 \end{pmatrix}$

5. $\begin{pmatrix} 1 & -2 & -1 \\ -3 & 3 & 5 \end{pmatrix}$ 6. $\begin{pmatrix} 4 & -3 & 5 \\ -2 & 5 & 0 \end{pmatrix}$

7. $\begin{pmatrix} 6 & 2 & 3 \\ 9 & 1 & 4 \end{pmatrix}$ 8. $\begin{pmatrix} 2 & 6 & -4 \\ 0 & -3 & 9 \end{pmatrix}$

9. $\begin{pmatrix} 3 & 0 & 1 \\ -3 & 3 & 1 \end{pmatrix}$ 10. $\begin{pmatrix} 1 & -1 & 0 \\ -3 & 1 & -2 \end{pmatrix}$

11. $\begin{pmatrix} 12 & 5 & -2 \\ -2 & -1 & 8 \end{pmatrix}$ 12. $\begin{pmatrix} -3 & 4 & 9 \\ 2 & 8 & 5 \end{pmatrix}$

13. $\begin{pmatrix} 6 & -3 & 4 \\ 2 & -4 & 3 \\ -4 & 7 & 1 \end{pmatrix}$ 14. $\begin{pmatrix} 2 & -3 & 0 \\ 4 & -1 & 1 \\ -3 & 8 & -2 \end{pmatrix}$

15. $\begin{pmatrix} 5 & 2 & 7 & -3 \\ -1 & 1 & 0 & 1 \end{pmatrix}$ 16. $\begin{pmatrix} 1 & 4 & 0 & 3 \\ -1 & -6 & 8 & 0 \end{pmatrix}$

17. $\begin{pmatrix} -3 & 4 & -1 & 9 \\ 9 & -2 & 5 & -9 \end{pmatrix}$ 18. $\begin{pmatrix} -4 & 2 & 6 & -7 \\ 0 & -2 & -3 & 1 \end{pmatrix}$

19. Find optimal strategies for the game described in Exercise 21 in Section 9.1.

20. Find optimal strategies for the game described in Exercise 22 in Section 9.1. What is the probability that country II will be bombed?

21. Find optimal strategies for the game described in Exercise 29 in Section 9.1.

22. Find optimal strategies for the game described in Exercise 25 in Section 9.1.

9.4 Solution of $m \times n$ Matrix Games

In Section 9.3 we saw that the optimal strategy for player I in a $2 \times m$ matrix game could be found by solving a linear programming problem. In this section we shall see that in any matrix game the optimal strategies for both players can be determined by solving appropriate linear programming problems. Thus for games in which each player has at least three undominated alternatives, determination of the optimal strategies will require use of the simplex method.

Suppose that $A = (a_{ij})$ is the payoff matrix for an $m \times n$ matrix game with value v. We saw in Section 9.2 that an optimal strategy for player II is a probability vector

$$Y = \begin{pmatrix} y_1 \\ y_2 \\ \vdots \\ y_n \end{pmatrix}$$

such that the largest entry of AY is v. Thus an optimal strategy for player II satisfies

$$AY \leq \begin{pmatrix} v \\ v \\ \vdots \\ v \end{pmatrix} \qquad (9.1)$$

Moreover, the value of the game is the smallest number v for which (9.1) holds. Thus the problem of determining player II's optimal strategy and the value of the game can be formulated as follows: Determine the minimum value of v such that (9.1) holds for some probability vector Y.

Likewise player I's optimal strategy is a probability vector

$$X = (x_1 \quad x_2 \quad \cdots \quad x_m)$$

such that

$$XA \geq (v \quad v \quad \cdots \quad v) \qquad (9.2)$$

So the problem of determining player I's optimal strategy and the value of the game can be formulated as follows: Determine the maximum value of v such that (9.2) holds for some probability vector X.

The two preceding paragraphs show that the optimal strategies for players I and II and the value of a game can be found by solving appropriate linear programming problems. In this section the simplex method will be used to compute optimal strategies and the value of any two-person zero-sum game. Fortunately, the two linear programming problems that must be solved to determine the optimal strategies for players I and II are duals of each other. Thus it will be possible to determine optimal strategies for both players simultaneously with only a single application of the simplex method.

To illustrate this procedure, let us find the optimal strategies for both players and the value of the game having the payoff matrix

$$A = \begin{pmatrix} -11 & 9 \\ 1 & 5 \\ 5 & -7 \end{pmatrix} \qquad (9.3)$$

Because of the nature of the inequalities in (9.1) and (9.2), we shall solve for player II's optimal strategy using (9.1) so that the use of artificial variables can be avoided. If v denotes the value of the game, we must solve the problem

Minimize v

Subject to

$$A \begin{pmatrix} y_1 \\ y_2 \end{pmatrix} \leq \begin{pmatrix} v \\ v \\ v \end{pmatrix}$$

when

$$y = \begin{pmatrix} y_1 \\ y_2 \end{pmatrix}$$

is a probability vector. This problem can be written

Minimize v

Subject to
$$-11y_1 + 9y_2 \le v$$
$$y_1 + 5y_2 \le v \qquad (9.4)$$
$$5y_1 - 7y_2 \le v$$

As usual, we must add nonnegative slack variables s_1, s_2, and s_3 to convert the inequalities in (9.4) into equations. Thus we obtain the equations

$$-11y_1 + 9y_2 + s_1 \qquad\qquad = v$$
$$y_1 + 5y_2 \quad + s_2 \qquad = v$$
$$5y_1 - 7y_2 \qquad\quad + s_3 = v$$

Since v is an unknown, let us rewrite these equations with v on the left side of each equation instead of on the right side. The equations now have the form

$$-11y_1 + 9y_2 + s_1 \qquad\qquad - v = 0$$
$$y_1 + 5y_2 \quad + s_2 \qquad - v = 0 \qquad (9.5)$$
$$5y_1 - 7y_2 \qquad\quad + s_3 - v = 0$$

Because (9.4) is a minimization problem, it must be converted into a maximization problem involving the negative of the objective function, and the simplex method will be used to maximize $-v$. Substituting $u = -v$ in (9.5), we obtain the following problem:

Maximize u

Subject to
$$-11y_1 + 9y_2 + s_1 \qquad\qquad + u = 0$$
$$y_1 + 5y_2 \quad + s_2 \qquad + u = 0 \qquad (9.6)$$
$$5y_1 - 7y_2 \qquad\quad + s_3 + u = 0$$
$$s_1 \ge 0, s_2 \ge 0, s_3 \ge 0$$

In (9.6) the objective function u is not expressed in terms of the variables y_1 and y_2. Consequently we shall use one of the constraint equations in (9.6) as the objective function. Suppose that we select the third equation in (9.6) as the objective function; this equation may be written as $-5y_1 + 7y_2 - s_3 = u$. Substituting the left side of this equation into (9.6) produces

Maximize $u = -5y_1 + 7y_2 - s_3$

Subject to
$$-16y_1 + 16y_2 + s_1 \qquad - s_3 = 0$$
$$-4y_1 + 12y_2 \qquad + s_2 - s_3 = 0 \qquad (9.7)$$
$$0 = 0$$
$$s_1 \ge 0, s_2 \ge 0, s_3 \ge 0$$

Clearly the third constraint equation ($0 = 0$) contributes nothing to (9.7) and can be ignored. But we have not yet taken into account that Y must be a probability vector. Because a probability vector is a vector with nonnegative entries that sum to 1, we must include the additional constraints $y_1 \geq 0$, $y_2 \geq 0$, and $y_1 + y_2 = 1$. With these inclusions (9.7) may be written

$$
\begin{aligned}
\text{Maximize} \quad & u = -5y_1 + 7y_2 - s_3 \\
\text{Subject to} \quad & y_1 + y_2 = 1 \\
& -16y_1 + 16y_2 + s_1 \quad\quad - s_3 = 0 \\
& -4y_1 + 12y_2 \quad\quad + s_2 - s_3 = 0 \\
& y_1 \geq 0,\ y_2 \geq 0,\ s_1 \geq 0,\ s_2 \geq 0,\ s_3 \geq 0
\end{aligned} \quad (9.8)
$$

The linear programming problem in (9.8) is the one that must be solved in order to compute the optimal strategy for player II. The simplex tableau for this problem is

$$
\left(\begin{array}{cccccc|c}
1 & 1 & 0 & 0 & 0 & 0 & 1 \\
-16 & 16 & 1 & 0 & -1 & 0 & 0 \\
-4 & 12 & 0 & 1 & -1 & 0 & 0 \\
\hline
5 & -7 & 0 & 0 & 1 & 1 & 0
\end{array}\right)
$$

One additional step is necessary before we are ready to begin the usual simplex algorithm: We must perform a preliminary pivot in order to eliminate the zeros from the last column. By pivoting with the first column as the pivot column and the first row as the pivot row, we obtain the new tableau

$$
\begin{array}{c}
\\ y_1 \\ s_1 \\ s_2 \\ \\
\end{array}
\begin{array}{c}
\begin{array}{cccccc}
y_1 & y_2 & s_1 & s_2 & s_3 & u
\end{array} \\
\left(\begin{array}{cccccc|c}
1 & 1 & 0 & 0 & 0 & 0 & 1 \\
0 & 32 & 1 & 0 & -1 & 0 & 16 \\
0 & 16 & 0 & 1 & -1 & 0 & 4 \\
\hline
0 & -12 & 0 & 0 & 1 & 1 & -5
\end{array}\right)
\end{array} \quad (9.9)
$$

We can now apply the familiar simplex method (as described on page 151 until no negative numbers remain in the bottom row except possibly in the last column. For (9.9) the pivot element is 16, and performing the pivot yields

$$
\begin{array}{c}
\\ y_1 \\ s_1 \\ y_2 \\ \\
\end{array}
\begin{array}{c}
\begin{array}{cccccc}
y_1 & y_2 & s_1 & s_2 & s_3 & u
\end{array} \\
\left(\begin{array}{cccccc|c}
1 & 0 & 0 & -\frac{1}{16} & \frac{1}{16} & 0 & \frac{3}{4} \\
0 & 0 & 1 & -2 & 1 & 0 & 8 \\
0 & 1 & 0 & \frac{1}{16} & -\frac{1}{16} & 0 & \frac{1}{4} \\
\hline
0 & 0 & 0 & \frac{3}{4} & \frac{7}{4} & 1 & -2
\end{array}\right)
\end{array} \quad (9.10)
$$

Since only the last entry of the bottom row is negative, a solution to (9.8) has been found; it is $y_1 = \frac{3}{4}$, $y_2 = \frac{1}{4}$, and $u = -2$. So

$$Y = \begin{pmatrix} y_1 \\ y_2 \end{pmatrix} = \begin{pmatrix} \frac{3}{4} \\ \frac{1}{4} \end{pmatrix}$$

is an optimal strategy for player II, and $v = -u = 2$ is the value of the game. An optimal strategy X for player I is found in the bottom row of (9.10) in the columns corresponding to the slack variables;

thus in this case

$$X = (0 \quad \tfrac{3}{4} \quad \tfrac{1}{4})$$

is an optimal strategy for player I. As a check, observe that

$$XA = (2 \quad 2) \quad \text{and} \quad AY = \begin{pmatrix} -6 \\ 2 \\ 2 \end{pmatrix}$$

so that X and Y satisfy the conditions of Theorem 9.1, hence are optimal strategies.

The procedure used above to obtain optimal strategies for a payoff matrix can be reduced to the following simple steps:

Procedure for solving an $m \times n$ matrix game

Step 1: Adjoin to the payoff matrix a copy of the $m \times m$ identity matrix.

Step 2: If the last row of the matrix resulting from step 1 does not contain the largest entry in the first column, interchange rows so that the largest entry in the first column is in the last row.

Step 3: Adjoin a new first row consisting of n ones followed by m zeros.

Step 4: Adjoin two new columns to the matrix. The next-to-last column should consist of a single zero followed by ones, and the last column should consist of a single one followed by zeros.

Step 5: Subtract the last row from every other row except the first. (These subtractions may be regarded as a pivot using the last row as the pivot row and the next-to-last column as the pivot column).

Step 6: Perform a pivot using the first row as the pivot row and the first column as the pivot column.

Step 7: Use the usual simplex method (as described on page 151) until no negative entries except possibly the last entry remain in the bottom row. An optimal strategy for player II can be read from the final tableau as usual, an optimal strategy for player I is found in the bottom row in the columns corresponding to the slack variables, and the value of the game is the negative of the entry in the last row and last column.

EXAMPLE 16

We shall apply the procedure above to the 3×2 matrix (9.3).

Step 1: Adjoining to matrix A a 3×3 identity matrix gives

$$\begin{pmatrix} -11 & 9 & 1 & 0 & 0 \\ 1 & 5 & 0 & 1 & 0 \\ 5 & -7 & 0 & 0 & 1 \end{pmatrix}$$

Step 2: Since the largest entry of the first column already lies in the last row, no row interchanges are needed for this matrix.

Step 3: To the matrix in step 1 a new first row consisting of two ones followed by three zeros is adjoined. Thus we have

$$\begin{pmatrix} 1 & 1 & 0 & 0 & 0 \\ -11 & 9 & 1 & 0 & 0 \\ 1 & 5 & 0 & 1 & 0 \\ 5 & -7 & 0 & 0 & 1 \end{pmatrix}$$

Step 4: Next we adjoin two new columns as shown below.

$$\begin{pmatrix} 1 & 1 & 0 & 0 & 0 & 0 & 1 \\ -11 & 9 & 1 & 0 & 0 & 1 & 0 \\ 1 & 5 & 0 & 1 & 0 & 1 & 0 \\ 5 & -7 & 0 & 0 & 1 & 1 & 0 \end{pmatrix}$$

Step 5: Subtracting the last row from rows 2 and 3 (or equivalently, pivoting on the 1 in row 4, column 6), we obtain

$$\begin{pmatrix} 1 & 1 & 0 & 0 & 0 & 0 & 1 \\ -16 & 16 & 1 & 0 & -1 & 0 & 0 \\ -4 & 12 & 0 & 1 & -1 & 0 & 0 \\ 5 & -7 & 0 & 0 & 1 & 1 & 0 \end{pmatrix}$$

Step 6: Using column 1 as the pivot column and row 1 as the pivot row, we pivot the tableau above to produce

$$\begin{array}{c} \\ y_1 \\ s_1 \\ s_2 \\ \end{array} \begin{array}{c} y_1 \quad\; y_2 \quad\; s_1 \quad s_2 \quad s_3 \quad\;\; u \\ \left(\begin{array}{ccccc|c} 1 & 1 & 0 & 0 & 0 & 0 \;\;\vert\; 1 \\ 0 & 32 & 1 & 0 & -1 & 0 \;\;\vert\; 16 \\ 0 & 16 & 0 & 1 & -1 & 0 \;\;\vert\; 4 \\ \hline 0 & -12 & 0 & 0 & 1 & 1 \;\;\vert\; -5 \end{array}\right) \end{array}$$

Observe that this is (9.9).

Step 7: Following the usual steps of the simplex method, we perform a pivot with column 2 as the pivot column and row 3 as the pivot row. The result of this pivot is (9.10), from which the optimal strategies

$$Y = \begin{pmatrix} \frac{3}{4} \\ \frac{1}{4} \end{pmatrix} \quad \text{and} \quad X = (0 \;\; \tfrac{3}{4} \;\; \tfrac{1}{4})$$

and the value of the game ($v = 2$) are obtained as before.

EXAMPLE 17

The procedure on page 365 will be used to compute the optimal strategies and the value of the game having the 2 × 3 payoff matrix

$$\begin{pmatrix} 16 & 6 & 1 \\ -2 & 3 & 13 \end{pmatrix}$$

After step 4 of the procedure, we have

$$\begin{pmatrix} 1 & 1 & 1 & 0 & 0 & 0 & 1 \\ -2 & 3 & 13 & 0 & 1 & 1 & 0 \\ 16 & 6 & 1 & 1 & 0 & 1 & 0 \end{pmatrix}$$

Notice that it is necessary to interchange rows 1 and 2 in step 2 so that the last row contains the largest entry in column 1.

In step 5 we subtract row 3 from row 2 (or equivalently, pivot in row 3, column 6) to obtain

$$\begin{pmatrix} 1 & 1 & 1 & 0 & 0 & 0 & 1 \\ -18 & -3 & 12 & -1 & 1 & 0 & 0 \\ 16 & 6 & 1 & 1 & 0 & 1 & 0 \end{pmatrix}$$

In step 6 we pivot in row 1, column 1; the result is the tableau

$$\begin{array}{c c} & \begin{array}{cccccc} y_1 & y_2 & y_3 & s_1 & s_2 & u \end{array} \\ \begin{array}{c} y_1 \\ s_2 \\ \end{array} & \left(\begin{array}{cccccc|c} 1 & 1 & 1 & 0 & 0 & 0 & 1 \\ 0 & 15 & 30 & -1 & 1 & 0 & 18 \\ \hline 0 & -10 & -15 & 1 & 0 & 1 & -16 \end{array} \right) \end{array}$$

Now we continue by applying the simplex method to the tableau above. Performing a pivot with row 2 as the pivot row and column 3 as the pivot column yields

$$\begin{array}{c c} & \begin{array}{cccccc} y_1 & y_2 & y_3 & s_1 & s_2 & u \end{array} \\ \begin{array}{c} y_1 \\ y_3 \\ \end{array} & \left(\begin{array}{cccccc|c} 1 & \frac{1}{2} & 0 & \frac{1}{30} & -\frac{1}{30} & 0 & 0.4 \\ 0 & \frac{1}{2} & 1 & -\frac{1}{30} & \frac{1}{30} & 0 & 0.6 \\ \hline 0 & -\frac{5}{2} & 0 & \frac{1}{2} & \frac{1}{2} & 1 & -7.0 \end{array} \right) \end{array}$$

Next we pivot in row 1, column 2 to obtain

$$\begin{array}{c c} & \begin{array}{cccccc} y_1 & y_2 & y_3 & s_1 & s_2 & u \end{array} \\ \begin{array}{c} y_2 \\ y_3 \\ \end{array} & \left(\begin{array}{cccccc|c} 2 & 1 & 0 & \frac{1}{15} & -\frac{1}{15} & 0 & 0.8 \\ -1 & 0 & 1 & -\frac{1}{15} & \frac{1}{15} & 0 & 0.2 \\ \hline 5 & 0 & 0 & \frac{2}{3} & \frac{1}{3} & 1 & -5.0 \end{array} \right) \end{array}$$

Since the only negative entry in the bottom row of this tableau lies in the last column, a solution has been obtained. Thus

$$Y = \begin{pmatrix} 0 \\ 0.8 \\ 0.2 \end{pmatrix} \quad \text{and} \quad X = (\tfrac{2}{3} \ \tfrac{1}{3})$$

are the optimal strategies for players II and I, and the value of the game is 5.

EXAMPLE 18

We shall compute the optimal strategies and the value of the game having the 3×4 payoff matrix

$$\begin{pmatrix} 5 & 0 & 3 & -1 \\ -2 & 4 & 1 & 2 \\ 3 & 1 & -1 & 3 \end{pmatrix}$$

After step 4 of the procedure on page 365, we have

$$\begin{pmatrix} 1 & 1 & 1 & 1 & 0 & 0 & 0 & 0 & 1 \\ 3 & 1 & -1 & 3 & 0 & 0 & 1 & 1 & 0 \\ -2 & 4 & 1 & 2 & 0 & 1 & 0 & 1 & 0 \\ 5 & 0 & 3 & -1 & 1 & 0 & 0 & 1 & 0 \end{pmatrix}$$

Subtracting row 4 from rows 2 and 3 (or equivalently, pivoting in row 4, column 8) produces

$$\begin{pmatrix} 1 & 1 & 1 & 1 & 0 & 0 & 0 & 0 & 1 \\ -2 & 1 & -4 & 4 & -1 & 0 & 1 & 0 & 0 \\ -7 & 4 & -2 & 3 & -1 & 1 & 0 & 0 & 0 \\ 5 & 0 & 3 & -1 & 1 & 0 & 0 & 1 & 0 \end{pmatrix}$$

Now pivot in row 1, column 1 to obtain

$$\begin{array}{c c} & \begin{array}{ccccccccc} y_1 & y_2 & y_3 & y_4 & s_1 & s_2 & s_3 & u & \end{array} \\ \begin{array}{c} y_1 \\ s_3 \\ s_2 \\ \end{array} & \left(\begin{array}{ccccccc|c} 1 & 1 & 1 & 1 & 0 & 0 & 0 & 0 & 1 \\ 0 & 3 & -2 & 6 & -1 & 0 & 1 & 0 & 2 \\ 0 & 11 & 5 & 10 & -1 & 1 & 0 & 0 & 7 \\ \hline 0 & -5 & -2 & -6 & 1 & 0 & 0 & 1 & -5 \end{array} \right) \end{array}$$

At this point we are ready to begin the usual simplex algorithm. Using row 2 as the pivot row and column 4 as the pivot column produces

$$\begin{array}{c c} & \begin{array}{ccccccccc} y_1 & y_2 & y_3 & y_4 & s_1 & s_2 & s_3 & u & \end{array} \\ \begin{array}{c} y_1 \\ y_4 \\ s_2 \\ \end{array} & \left(\begin{array}{ccccccc|c} 1 & \frac{1}{2} & \frac{4}{3} & 0 & \frac{1}{6} & 0 & -\frac{1}{6} & 0 & \frac{2}{3} \\ 0 & \frac{1}{2} & -\frac{1}{3} & 1 & -\frac{1}{6} & 0 & \frac{1}{6} & 0 & \frac{1}{3} \\ 0 & 6 & \frac{25}{3} & 0 & \frac{2}{3} & 1 & -\frac{5}{3} & 0 & \frac{11}{3} \\ \hline 0 & -2 & -4 & 0 & 0 & 0 & 1 & 1 & -3 \end{array} \right) \end{array}$$

The next pivot will be in row 3, column 3; this pivot yields

$$\begin{array}{c c} & \begin{array}{ccccccccc} y_1 & y_2 & y_3 & y_4 & s_1 & s_2 & s_3 & u & \end{array} \\ \begin{array}{c} y_1 \\ y_4 \\ y_3 \\ \end{array} & \left(\begin{array}{ccccccc|c} 1 & -0.46 & 0 & 0 & 0.06 & -0.16 & 0.1 & 0 & 0.08 \\ 0 & 0.74 & 0 & 1 & -0.14 & 0.04 & 0.1 & 0 & 0.48 \\ 0 & 0.72 & 1 & 0 & 0.08 & 0.12 & -0.2 & 0 & 0.44 \\ \hline 0 & 0.88 & 0 & 0 & 0.32 & 0.48 & 0.2 & 1 & -1.24 \end{array} \right) \end{array}$$

From this tableau we see that the optimal strategies for players II and I are

$$Y = \begin{pmatrix} 0.08 \\ 0 \\ 0.44 \\ 0.48 \end{pmatrix} \quad \text{and} \quad X = (0.32 \quad 0.48 \quad 0.20)$$

and the value of the game is 1.24.

Exercises

In Exercises 1–16 use the simplex method to compute an optimal strategy for each player and the value of the game having the given payoff matrix.

1. $\begin{pmatrix} 4 & -3 \\ -5 & 8 \end{pmatrix}$
2. $\begin{pmatrix} 6 & -4 \\ -3 & 7 \end{pmatrix}$
3. $\begin{pmatrix} 6 & -9 \\ -3 & 12 \end{pmatrix}$
4. $\begin{pmatrix} 9 & -8 \\ -7 & 6 \end{pmatrix}$
5. $\begin{pmatrix} 9 & 57 & 1 \\ -1 & -13 & 11 \end{pmatrix}$
6. $\begin{pmatrix} 4 & 0 & -1 \\ 1 & 2 & 3 \end{pmatrix}$
7. $\begin{pmatrix} -1 & 2 & 3 \\ 6 & -1 & -2 \end{pmatrix}$
8. $\begin{pmatrix} 4 & -2 & -4 \\ -4 & 6 & 2 \end{pmatrix}$
9. $\begin{pmatrix} 2 & 3 & 5 \\ 3 & 1 & 2 \\ 4 & 5 & 2 \end{pmatrix}$
10. $\begin{pmatrix} -3 & 1 & 3 \\ 2 & -4 & 2 \\ 1 & 0 & -1 \end{pmatrix}$
11. $\begin{pmatrix} -1 & -1 & 1 \\ 5 & -4 & 2 \\ -2 & 3 & -5 \end{pmatrix}$
12. $\begin{pmatrix} -2 & 0 & 0 \\ 1 & -3 & 1 \\ 2 & 2 & -4 \end{pmatrix}$
13. $\begin{pmatrix} 1 & 3 & -1 & 0 \\ 2 & 4 & -2 & -1 \\ 0 & -1 & 4 & 3 \end{pmatrix}$
14. $\begin{pmatrix} 4 & -1 & 2 & 1 \\ -2 & 2 & 1 & 1 \\ 6 & 3 & -1 & 0 \end{pmatrix}$
15. $\begin{pmatrix} -1 & 0 & 1 & 2 \\ 3 & -1 & 0 & 2 \\ 2 & 0 & 1 & -1 \\ 0 & 1 & 0 & 0 \end{pmatrix}$
16. $\begin{pmatrix} \frac{1}{3} & 0 & -\frac{1}{3} \\ 0 & \frac{2}{3} & \frac{1}{3} \\ \frac{1}{3} & -\frac{1}{3} & 1 \end{pmatrix}$

17. Find optimal strategies for the game of scissors-paper-stone (described in Exercise 23 in Section 9.1).
18. Find optimal strategies for the game of two-finger morra (described in Exercise 24 in Section 9.1).
19. Compute optimal strategies for the payoff matrix in Example 4 in Section 9.1.
20. Compute optimal strategies for the payoff matrix in Example 8 in Section 9.1.

Chapter Review

New Terms

dominated column (p. 344)
dominated row (p. 343)
fair game (p. 343)
matrix game (p. 338)
optimal strategy (p. 341)
payoff matrix (p. 338)
player I (p. 337)
player II (p. 337)
saddle point (p. 350)
strategy (p. 339)
strictly determined game (p. 350)
two-person zero-sum game (p. 337)
value of a game (p. 341)

Review Exercises

1. Label the following statements true or false.
   (a) The alternatives available to player II correspond to rows of the payoff matrix.
   (b) Entries of a payoff matrix always represent amounts won by player I.
   (c) The value of a game is the minimum amount player I can expect to win by using an optimal strategy.
   (d) If X is an optimal strategy for player I in the game with payoff matrix A, then the largest entry of XA is the value of the game.
   (e) If Y is an optimal strategy for player II in the game with payoff matrix A, then the largest entry of AY is the value of the game.
   (f) Each player has a unique optimal strategy.
   (g) The value of a fair game is zero.
   (h) Row i is dominated by row j if each entry of row j is greater than or equal to the corresponding entry of row i.
   (i) Column i is dominated by column j if each entry of column j is greater than or equal to the corresponding entry of column i.
   (j) A saddle point of a payoff matrix is an entry that is the largest in its row and the smallest in its column.
   (k) Not every game has a saddle point.
   (l) A game may have more than one saddle point.
   (m) When finding optimal strategies graphically, the first coordinate of the vertex at which v is maximized determines player I's optimal strategy.
   (n) When finding optimal strategies using the simplex method, an optimal strategy for player I is found in the last row of the final simplex tableau in the columns corresponding to the slack variables.
   (o) When finding optimal strategies using the simplex method, the entry in the last row and last column of the final simplex tableau is the value of the game.

2. Verify that if
$$X = (.5 \quad .5 \quad 0) \quad Y = \begin{pmatrix} \frac{1}{6} \\ \frac{5}{6} \\ 0 \end{pmatrix} \quad \text{and} \quad A = \begin{pmatrix} 5 & -1 & -2 \\ -5 & 1 & 3 \\ -8 & -6 & 7 \end{pmatrix}$$
then X and Y are optimal strategies for the game with payoff matrix A. What is the value of this game?

3. Identify all the dominated rows and columns (if any) in the following payoff matrices.

(a) $\begin{pmatrix} -3 & 3 & -2 \\ 1 & 0 & 1 \\ 2 & -2 & 5 \end{pmatrix}$ (b) $\begin{pmatrix} 5 & -6 & 0 \\ 2 & 4 & -3 \\ -5 & 1 & 7 \end{pmatrix}$

(c) $\begin{pmatrix} -4 & 3 & 0 & -3 \\ 2 & -3 & 3 & 2 \\ -3 & 6 & -2 & 0 \\ -5 & 2 & -1 & 4 \end{pmatrix}$ (d) $\begin{pmatrix} 0 & -4 & 2 & 1 \\ 4 & -2 & 1 & 2 \\ -5 & 3 & -8 & -7 \\ 3 & -2 & 2 & 3 \end{pmatrix}$

4. Compute optimal strategies for the following payoff matrices using the graphic method.

   (a) $\begin{pmatrix} 10 & 3 & -2 \\ -6 & -1 & 4 \end{pmatrix}$ (b) $\begin{pmatrix} 4 & 6 & -2 \\ -1 & -4 & 8 \end{pmatrix}$

5. Compute optimal strategies and the value of the game having each of the following payoff matrices.

   (a) $\begin{pmatrix} 3 & 5 & 2 \\ 4 & 2 & 6 \\ 1 & 6 & 3 \end{pmatrix}$ (b) $\begin{pmatrix} 4 & -1 & 2 & 1 \\ -2 & 2 & 1 & 1 \\ 6 & 0 & -1 & 1 \end{pmatrix}$

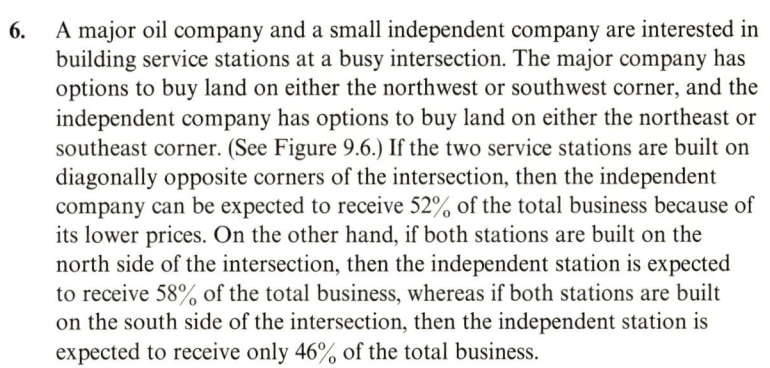

6. A major oil company and a small independent company are interested in building service stations at a busy intersection. The major company has options to buy land on either the northwest or southwest corner, and the independent company has options to buy land on either the northeast or southeast corner. (See Figure 9.6.) If the two service stations are built on diagonally opposite corners of the intersection, then the independent company can be expected to receive 52% of the total business because of its lower prices. On the other hand, if both stations are built on the north side of the intersection, then the independent station is expected to receive 58% of the total business, whereas if both stations are built on the south side of the intersection, then the independent station is expected to receive only 46% of the total business.
   (a) Prepare a payoff matrix for this situation in which the entries represent the amount of business in excess of 50% received by the independent station.
   (b) Where should each company build its service station?

7. Two banks intend to build branches in one of the four suburbs pictured in Figure 9.7. It is estimated that the total business for the banks is distributed as follows: 40% in suburb 1, 20% in suburb 2, 10% in suburb 3, and 30% in suburb 4. If both banks locate in the same suburb, then the larger bank is expected to receive 56% of the total business. Otherwise each suburb containing a bank is expected to give 90% of its business to the bank located there and to give 10% of its business to the other bank, and each suburb not containing a bank is expected to give 80% of its business to whichever bank is closer and 20% of its business to the other.
   (a) Prepare a payoff matrix for this situation in which the entries represent the amount of business in excess of 50% received by the larger bank.
   (b) Find optimal strategies for the larger and smaller banks. What percentage of the total business can the larger bank expect?

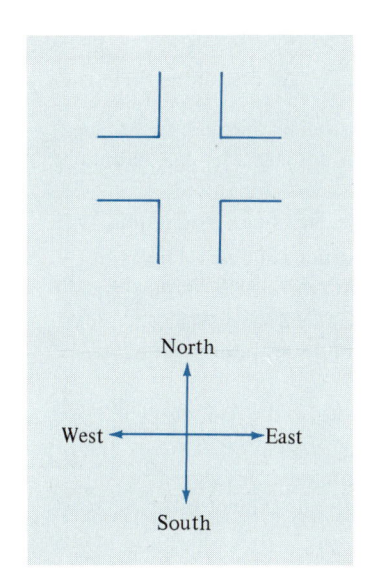

Figure 9.6

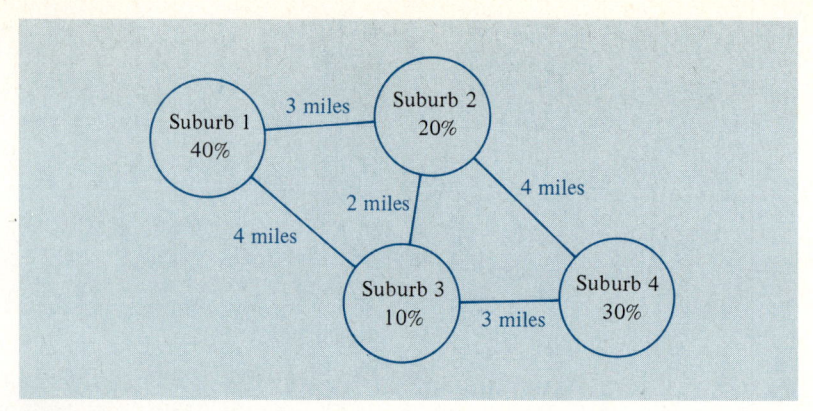

Figure 9.7

References

1. Bennion, Edward G., "Capital Budgeting and Game Theory," *Harv. Bus. Rev.*, vol. 34, no. 6 (November–December 1956), pp. 115–123.
2. Bernard, Jessie, "The Theory of Games of Strategy as a Modern Sociology of Conflict," *Am. J. Sociol.*, vol. 59 (1954), pp. 411–424.
3. Blackett, D. W., "Some Blotto Games," *Nav. Res. Logist. Q.*, vol. 1 (1954), pp. 55–60.
4. Blackwell, David, "Game Theory," in *Operations Research for Management*, J. F. McCloskey and F. N. Trefethen, eds., pp. 238–253. Baltimore: Johns Hopkins Press, 1954.
5. Brams, Steven J., *Game Theory and Politics*. New York: Free Press, 1975.
6. Caywood, T. E. and C. J. Thomas, "Applications of Game Theory in Fighter Versus Bomber Combat," *Oper. Res.*, vol. 3 (1955), pp. 402–411.
7. Davenport, W. C., "Jamaican Fishing: A Game Theory Analysis," *Pap. Carib. Anthropol.*, Yale University Publications in Anthropology, vol. 59 (1960), pp. 3–11.
8. Friedman, Lawrence, "Game-Theory Models in the Allocation of Advertising Expenditures," *Oper. Res.*, vol. 6 (1958), pp. 699–709.
9. Gould, Peter R., "Man Against His Environment: A Game Theoretic Framework," *Ann. Assoc. Am. Geogr.*, vol. 53, no. 3 (September 1963), pp. 290–297.
10. Haywood, O. G., Jr., "Military Decision and the Mathematical Theory of Games," *Air Univ. Q. Rev.*, vol. 4 (1950), pp. 17–30.
11. Haywood, O. G., Jr., "Military Decision and Game Theory," *Oper. Res.*, vol. 2, no. 4 (November 1954), pp. 365–385.
12. Kaufman, Herbert and Gordon M. Becker, "The Empirical Determination of Game-Theoretical Strategies," *J. Exp. Psychol.*, vol. 61, no. 6 (June 1961), pp. 462–468.
13. Luce, R. Duncan and Howard Raiffa, *Games and Decisions*. New York: Wiley, 1957.
14. Luce, R. Duncan and Arnold A. Rogow, "A Game Theoretic Analysis of Congressional Power Distributions for a Stable Two-Party System," *Behav. Sci.*, vol. 1, no. 2 (April 1956), pp. 83–95.

15. McClintock, C. G. and D. M. Messick, "Empirical Approaches to Game Theory and Bargaining: A Bibliography," *Gen. Syst.*, vol. 11 (1966), pp. 229–238.
16. McDonald, John, *Strategy in Poker, Business, and War*. New York: Norton, 1950.
17. Rapoport, Anatol and Albert M. Chammah, "Sex Differences in Factors Contributing to the Level of Cooperation in the Prisoner's Dilemma Game," *J. Pers. Soc. Psychol.*, vol. 2, no. 6 (December 1965), pp. 831–838.
18. Shapley, L. S. and Martin Shubik, "A Method for Evaluating the Distribution of Power in a Committee System," *Am. Polit. Sci. Rev.*, vol. 48, no. 3 (September 1954), pp. 787–792.
19. Shubik, Martin, ed., *Game Theory and Related Approaches to Social Behavior*. New York: Wiley, 1964.
20. Shubik, Martin. *Readings in Game Theory and Political Behavior*. Garden City: Doubleday, 1954.
21. Shubik, Martin, "The Uses of Game Theory in Management," *Manage. Sci.*, vol. 2 (1955), pp. 40–54.
22. Snyder, Richard C., "Game Theory and the Analysis of Political Behavior," in *Research Frontiers in Politics and Government*, pp. 70–103.
23. Von Neumann, John and Oskar Morgenstern, *Theory of Games and Economic Behavior*. Princeton: Princeton University Press, 1947.
24. Williams, J. D., *The Compleat Strategyst*. New York: McGraw-Hill, 1954.

10

The Difference Equation $y_n = ay_{n-1} + b$

In many disciplines it is common to find that certain types of data are available only at regular intervals. For example, the consumer price index is normally reported on a monthly basis, and business inventories are often counted on a quarterly basis. In these situations time may be regarded as a variable that takes on only a discrete set of values; that is, observations of some phenomenon are made only at equally spaced intervals of time.

When time is treated in this manner, it is common to find that at any particular time the value of the phenomenon being observed is related to the value of the same phenomenon at one or more earlier times. This type of a relationship leads to a mathematical model involving difference equations. In this chapter we shall consider exclusively the situation in which the value of a phenomenon at some point in time is related only to the value of the phenomenon at the immediately preceding time. This type of a relationship exists in many important applications, and some of these will be examined in Sections 10.5–10.7. The chapter will begin, however, with a discussion of two important special cases of this relationship—arithmetic and geometric progressions.

10.1 Arithmetic Progressions

In the sequence of numbers

$$3, 7, 11, 15, 19, 23, \cdots$$

each number after the first is 4 greater than its predecessor. More generally, any sequence of numbers in which each number after the first differs from its predecessor by the same amount d is called an *arithmetic progression*, and d is called the *common difference*. Thus the sequence $y_1, y_2, \ldots, y_n, \ldots$ is an arithmetic progression with common difference d if

arithmetic progression
common difference

$$y_n = y_{n-1} + d$$

for all $n > 1$.

EXAMPLE 1

The sequence

$$8, 3, -2, -7, -12, \cdots$$

is an arithmetic progression with common difference -5. On the other hand, the sequence

$$1, 3, 4, 6, 7, \cdots$$

is not an arithmetic progression since there is no common difference between successive terms. (Note, for instance, that $3 - 1 \neq 4 - 3$.)

terms of a sequence

The numbers occurring in a sequence are called the *terms* of the sequence. For the arithmetic progression with first term y_1 and common difference d, it is easy to determine any particular term in the progression. The pattern

$$y_2 = y_1 + d$$
$$y_3 = y_2 + d = (y_1 + d) + d = y_1 + 2d$$
$$y_4 = y_3 + d = (y_1 + 2d) + d = y_1 + 3d$$

suggests the following result.

THEOREM 10.1

In an arithmetic progression $y_1, y_2, \ldots, y_n, \ldots$ with common difference d, the nth term is

$$y_n = y_1 + (n-1)d \qquad (10.1)$$

EXAMPLE 2

We shall determine the sixteenth term in the arithmetic progression $5, 8, 11, 14, 17, \ldots$.

First note that the first term is 5 and the common difference is 3. So applying (10.1) with $y_1 = 5$, $d = 3$, and $n = 16$ gives

$$y_{16} = 5 + (16 - 1)3 = 5 + 45 = 50$$

EXAMPLE 3

The twentieth term in the arithmetic progression 4, −2, −8, −14, −20, ... is

$$y_{20} = y_1 + (20 - 1)d = 4 + (20 - 1)(-6) = 4 - 114 = -110$$

EXAMPLE 4

Membership in the Evergreen Tennis Club cost $50 in 1970 and has increased by $5 each year. To find the membership cost in 1985 if the $5-per-year increase continues, we must determine the sixteenth term of the arithmetic progression with first term $50 and common difference $5. From (10.1) the desired term is

$$y_{16} = y_1 + 15d = \$50 + 15(\$5) = \$125$$

So membership in the club will cost $125 in 1985 if the $5 yearly increase continues.

In certain situations it is necessary to compute the sum of consecutive terms of an arithmetic progression. For example, suppose we would like to compute the sum of the 40 even integers from 4 through 82:

$$4 + 6 + 8 + \cdots + 78 + 80 + 82$$

Notice that the numbers being added are the first 40 terms of the arithmetic progression with first term 4 and common difference 2. Write this sum twice as shown below.

$$\begin{array}{c} 4 + 6 + 8 + \cdots + 78 + 80 + 82 \\ 82 + 80 + 78 + \cdots + 8 + 6 + 4 \end{array}$$

When the pairs of numbers aligned vertically are added, each sum totals 86:

$$\begin{array}{c} 4 + 6 + 8 + \cdots + 78 + 80 + 82 \\ \underline{82 + 80 + 78 + \cdots + 8 + 6 + 4} \\ 86 + 86 + 86 + \cdots + 86 + 86 + 86 \end{array}$$

Since there are 40 sums of 86, the total is $40 \cdot 86 = 3440$. But this total represents twice the desired sum because we added each number twice; so $4 + 6 + 8 + \cdots + 78 + 80 + 82 = \frac{1}{2}(3440) = 1720$.

A similar technique can be used to find the sum of the first n terms of any arithmetic progression. The resulting formula can be written in two forms, as shown below.

THEOREM 10.2

Let $y_1, y_2, \ldots y_n, \ldots$ be an arithmetic progression with common difference d. The sum S_n of the first n terms of this progression is given by

$$S_n = \frac{n}{2}[2y_1 + (n-1)d] \tag{10.2}$$

or equivalently, by

$$S_n = \frac{n}{2}(y_1 + y_n) \tag{10.3}$$

EXAMPLE 5

The sum of the first 30 terms of the arithmetic progression

5, 8, 11, 14, 17, ...

can be found using (10.2) with $y_1 = 5$, $d = 3$, and $n = 30$. The desired sum is therefore

$$S_{30} = \tfrac{30}{2}[2(5) + (30-1)\cdot 3] = 15(97) = 1455$$

Notice that it is more convenient to use (10.2) than (10.3) in this example because the value of the thirtieth term in the progression, y_{30}, is not known.

EXAMPLE 6

Recall from Example 4 that membership in the Evergreen Tennis Club cost $50 in 1970 and has increased by $5 each year. We saw in Example 4 that membership in the club will cost $125 in 1985 if the $5-per-year increase continues.

Let us now determine the total of all the membership fees paid by someone who belongs to the club each year from 1970 to 1985. This amount will be the sum of the first 16 terms of the arithmetic progression with first term $50 and common difference $5. Using (10.3), we have

$$S_{16} = \tfrac{16}{2}(\$50 + \$125) = 8(\$175) = \$1400$$

Observe that in this example it is easier to use (10.3) than (10.2), since the value of y_{16} is known.

EXAMPLE 7

Find the sum of the odd integers from 13 through 89; that is, compute

13 + 15 + ··· + 87 + 89

The desired sum is the sum of consecutive terms of the arithmetic progression with first term 13 and common difference 2. In order to use either (10.2) or (10.3), however, we must first know n, the number of terms being added. Thus we must begin by determining n. Since the nth term of this progression is 89, the value of n can be computed from (10.1) as follows:

$$y_n = y_1 + (n-1)d$$
$$89 = 13 + (n-1) \cdot 2$$
$$76 = (n-1) \cdot 2$$
$$38 = n - 1$$
$$39 = n$$

It is now easy to evaluate $13 + 15 + \cdots + 87 + 89$ using (10.3).

$$S_{39} = \tfrac{39}{2}(13 + 89) = \tfrac{39}{2}(102) = 1989$$

The next example shows a practical situation in which the sum of consecutive terms of an arithmetic progression occurs.

EXAMPLE 8

Suppose that a person borrows $5400 to purchase a car and agrees to repay the loan over a 36-month period by making monthly payments of $150 plus interest charges of 1% of the unpaid balance. What will be the total of all the interest charges paid during the 36-month period?

It is helpful to visualize the interest payments with reference to a time line:

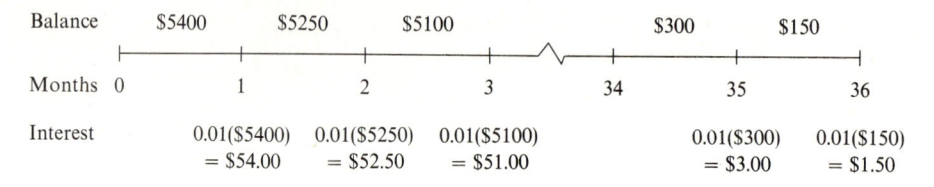

Balance	$5400	$5250	$5100		$300	$150
Months	0	1	2	3 ... 34	35	36
Interest		0.01($5400) = $54.00	0.01($5250) = $52.50	0.01($5100) = $51.00	0.01($300) = $3.00	0.01($150) = $1.50

We see therefore that the total of all the interest charges is

$$\$54.00 + \$52.50 + \$51.00 + \cdots + \$3.00 + \$1.50$$

the sum of the first 36 terms of the arithmetic progression with first term $54.00 and thirty-sixth term $1.50. From (10.3) this sum is

$$S_{36} = \tfrac{36}{2}(\$54.00 + \$1.50) = 18(\$55.50) = \$999$$

Exercises

In Exercises 1–8, determine which of the given sequences are arithmetic progressions. For those that are, determine the common difference and write the next term.

1. 3, 6, 12, 24, 48, ...
2. 1, 7, 13, 19, 25, ...
3. 2, 7, 12, 17, 22, ...
4. 4, 8, 14, 18, 24, ...

5. 10, 6, 2, −2, −6, ...
6. 50, 42, 34, 26, 18, ...
7. 1, −1, 1, −1, 1, ...
8. 160, 80, 40, 20, 10, ...

In Exercises 9–16, find the nth term of the arithmetic progression with first term y_1 and common difference d.

9. $n = 4, y_1 = 8, d = 6$
10. $n = 3, y_1 = -10, d = 5$
11. $n = 7, y_1 = 20, d = -3$
12. $n = 12, y_1 = 30, d = -8$
13. $n = 16, y_1 = 9, d = 4$
14. $n = 20, y_1 = 15, d = 3$
15. $n = 51, y_1 = 7, d = -2$
16. $n = 80, y_1 = 12, d = -6$

In Exercises 17–24, compute the sum of the first n terms of the arithmetic progression with first term y_1 and common difference d.

17. $n = 3, y_1 = 10, d = 9$
18. $n = 8, y_1 = 25, d = 7$
19. $n = 11, y_1 = 100, d = -7$
20. $n = 15, y_1 = 50, d = -4$
21. $n = 18, y_1 = 2, d = 10$
22. $n = 25, y_1 = 5, d = 3$
23. $n = 30, y_1 = 24, d = -\frac{1}{2}$
24. $n = 60, y_1 = 120, d = -\frac{1}{3}$

25. A teaching position offers a beginning salary of $10,500 per year with a guaranteed annual raise of $300 during the next 10 years.
    (a) How much will this job pay during the fifth year?
    (b) What total salary will this job pay during the first 8 years?

26. In 1970 a family membership in a community swimming pool cost $20, but this cost has increased $2 per year since then.
    (a) How much did membership cost in 1980?
    (b) If a family held membership in the pool each year during the period 1970–1980, how much money did it spend on membership fees during this period?

27. A restaurant chain had 24 franchises in 1965 and opened 6 new franchises each year thereafter.
    (a) How many franchises were there in 1977?
    (b) If the chain continues to open 6 new franchises per year, how many franchises will there be in 1990?

28. Suppose that each franchise owner in Exercise 27 pays a $2500 yearly fee.
    (a) How much money was paid for these fees in 1975?
    (b) What was the total amount paid for these fees during the years 1965–1980?

29. Suppose a piece of machinery depreciates by 16% of its original value in the first year, 14.5% of its original value in the second year, 13% of its original value in the third year, and so forth. What percentage of the machinery's original value will be undepreciated after 9 years?

30. If a clock chimes the appropriate number of times every hour and does not chime at other times, how many times per day does it chime?

31. Compute the sum of the first 500 positive integers.

32. Compute the sum of the even integers from 26 through 94.

33. Suppose a person borrows $4800 and agrees to repay the loan over a 24-month period by making monthly payments of $200 plus interest charges of 1% of the unpaid balance. What will be the total of all the interest charges paid?

34. If the loan in Exercise 33 is repaid over a 48-month period by making monthly payments of $100 plus interest charges of 1% of the unpaid balance, what will be the total amount of interest charges paid?

10.2 Geometric Progressions

In Section 10.1 we considered sequences in which each term after the first was obtained by *adding* a common difference d to its predecessor. We shall now discuss sequences in which each term after the first is obtained by *multiplying* its predecessor by a common factor r. Such a sequence is called a *geometric progression*, and r is called the *common ratio*. Thus a sequence $y_1, y_2, \ldots, y_n, \ldots$ is a geometric progression with common ratio r if

$$y_n = r y_{n-1}$$

for all $n > 1$.

EXAMPLE 9

The sequences

(a) $3, 12, 48, 192, 768, \ldots$ (b) $5, -15, 45, -135, 405, \ldots$
(c) $8, 4, 2, 1, \frac{1}{2}, \ldots$

are all geometric progressions. The common ratios are 4 in (a), -3 in (b), and $\frac{1}{2}$ in (c).

On the other hand, the sequence $7, 21, 42, 126, 256, \ldots$ is not a geometric progression because there is no common ratio between successive terms. (Note, for instance, that $\frac{21}{7} \neq \frac{42}{21}$.)

As with arithmetic progressions, it is easy to determine the nth term of a geometric progression with first term y_1 and common ratio r. Noting that

$$y_2 = r y_1$$
$$y_3 = r y_2 = r(r y_1) = r^2 y_1$$
$$y_4 = r y_3 = r(r^2 y_1) = r^3 y_1$$

we are led to the following result.

THEOREM 10.3

In a geometric progression $y_1, y_2, \ldots, y_n, \ldots$ with common ratio r, the nth term is

$$y_n = y_1 r^{n-1} \qquad (10.4)$$

EXAMPLE 10

We shall determine the ninth term of the geometric progression $3, 6, 12, 24, 48, \ldots$. Observe that in this progression the first term is 3 and the common ratio is 2. So applying (10.4) with $y_1 = 3$, $r = 2$, and $n = 9$ gives

$$y_9 = 3 \cdot 2^{9-1} = 3 \cdot 2^8 = 3 \cdot 256 = 768$$

EXAMPLE 11

The tenth term of the geometric progression

$$16, -8, 4, -2, 1, \ldots$$

is

$$y_{10} = y_1 r^{10-1} = 16(-\tfrac{1}{2})^9 = 16(-\tfrac{1}{512}) = -\tfrac{1}{32}$$

EXAMPLE 12

A computer specialist has received a job offering a starting salary of $20,000 with annual increases of 10%. How much will this job pay during the sixth year?

The annual salaries paid by this job form a geometric progression with first term $20,000 and common ratio 1.10. (Notice that a salary increase of 10% corresponds to multiplying the salary by a factor of 110%.) So the salary paid during the sixth year is the sixth term of this sequence. From (10.4) this salary will be

$$y_6 = y_1 r^{6-1} = \$20{,}000(1.10)^5 = \$20{,}000(1.61051)$$
$$= \$32{,}210.20$$

Let us now compute the sum S_n of the first n terms of the geometric progression with first term y_1 and common ratio r. From (10.4) we have

$$S_n = y_1 + y_1 r + y_1 r^2 + \cdots + y_1 r^{n-1}$$

Multiplying both sides by r gives

$$rS_n = \phantom{y_1 +{}} y_1 r + y_1 r^2 + \cdots + y_1 r^{n-1} + y_1 r^n$$

Thus by subtracting the first equality from the second, we obtain

$$rS_n - S_n = y_1 r^n - y_1$$

or

$$(r-1)S_n = y_1(r^n - 1)$$

This equation may be solved for S_n to produce the following result.

THEOREM 10.4

Let $y_1, y_2, \ldots, y_n, \ldots$ be a geometric progression with common ratio $r \neq 1$. The sum of the first n terms of this progression is given by

$$S_n = \frac{y_1(r^n - 1)}{r - 1} \tag{10.5}$$

or equivalently, by

$$S_n = \frac{y_n r - y_1}{r - 1} \tag{10.6}$$

EXAMPLE 13

The sum of the first 8 terms of the geometric progression

$$3, 6, 12, 24, 48, \ldots$$

can be found using (10.5) with $y_1 = 3$, $r = 2$, and $n = 8$. The desired sum is therefore

$$S_8 = \frac{3(2^8 - 1)}{2 - 1} = 3(255) = 765$$

EXAMPLE 14

What total amount will the job described in Example 12 pay during the first 6 years?

Recalling from Example 12 that $y_1 = \$20{,}000$, $r = 1.10$, and $y_6 = \$32{,}210.20$, we see from (10.6) that the desired amount is

$$S_6 = \frac{y_6 r - y_1}{r - 1} = \frac{\$32{,}210.20(1.10) - \$20{,}000}{1.10 - 1}$$

$$= \frac{\$15{,}431.22}{0.10} = \$154{,}312.20$$

It is easily seen that, if $-1 < r < 1$, then the values of r^n approach zero as n increases. Since

$$S_n = \frac{y_1 r^n}{r - 1} - \frac{y_1}{r - 1}$$

sum of the terms of a progression

from (10.5), we see that the values of S_n approach $-y_1/(r - 1) = y_1/(1 - r)$ as n increases. We call this value the *sum of the terms of the progression* and denote it by S_∞. Thus we have the following result.

THEOREM 10.5

If $y_1, y_2, \ldots, y_n, \ldots$ is a geometric progression with common ratio r, then

$$S_\infty = \frac{y_1}{1 - r} \quad \text{if } -1 < r < 1 \tag{10.7}$$

If $r \leq -1$ or $r \geq 1$, then the sum of the terms of the progression does not exist.

EXAMPLE 15

Find the sum of the terms of the geometric progression

$$108, -36, 12, -4, \tfrac{4}{3}, \ldots$$

First note that the common ratio is $r = -\frac{1}{3}$; so the sum of the terms exists. Thus from (10.7)

$$S_\infty = \frac{108}{1-(-\frac{1}{3})} = \frac{108}{\frac{4}{3}} = 81$$

APPLICATION 1

Let us consider a very simplified static model of national income (or gross national product). If government spending or taxation is ignored, then the national income Y is the sum of consumption C plus business investment I. We assume that consumption depends entirely on the incomes people receive and that business investment is independent of consumption or income.

We are concerned with determining the effect of an increase in investment on national income when the economy is stable (in equilibrium). Since $Y = C + I$, it may appear that, if investment increases, then national income will increase by the same amount. But in reality the effect of an increase in investment is more complicated. Suppose that the *marginal propensity to consume* is 0.6; this means that, out of every dollar of additional income, people spend 60% and save the remaining 40%. If investment increases by $30 billion, then this amount will become income to consumers who will spend $18 billion and save $12 billion. This new consumer spending represents $18 billion in new income to the merchants from whom the consumers buy. The merchants in turn spend 60% and save 40% of this $18 billion; so another $10.8 billion is spent and $7.2 billion is saved. This cycle continues, so that the effect of the original $30 billion increase in investment produces a larger increase in national income.

It is easy to see that the total amount of new national income induced by the $30 billion increase in investment is

$$30 + 30(0.6) + 30(0.6)^2 + 30(0.6)^3 + \cdots$$

billion dollars. This value is the sum of the geometric progression with first term 30 and common ratio 0.6. Using (10.7), we see that the sum of this progression is

$$\frac{y_1}{1-r} = \frac{30}{1-0.6} = \frac{30}{0.4} = 75$$

So the $30 billion increase in investment causes a $75 billion increase in national income. This is the so-called multiplier effect.

Exercises

In Exercises 1–8, determine which of the given sequences are geometric progressions. For those that are, determine the common ratio and write the next term.

1. $1, \frac{1}{4}, \frac{1}{16}, \frac{1}{64}, \frac{1}{256}, \ldots$
2. $2, 14, 98, 686, 4802, \ldots$
3. $\frac{1}{3}, \frac{2}{3}, 1, \frac{4}{3}, \frac{5}{3}, \ldots$
4. $3, -5, 7, -9, 11, \ldots$
5. $24, 12, 48, 6, 96, \ldots$
6. $-7, 7, -7, 7, -7, \ldots$
7. $432, -288, 192, -128, \frac{256}{3}, \ldots$
8. $5, -10, 30, -60, 180, \ldots$

In Exercises 9–16, find the nth term of the geometric progression with first term y_1 and common ratio r.

9. $n = 2, y_1 = 24, r = -\frac{1}{2}$
10. $n = 3, y_1 = -3, r = -4$
11. $n = 5, y_1 = 100, r = 1.2$
12. $n = 6, y_1 = 200, r = 1.1$
13. $n = 8, y_1 = 6, r = -1$
14. $n = 10, y_1 = 3, r = -2$
15. $n = 11, y_1 = \frac{1}{8}, r = 2$
16. $n = 9, y_1 = 256, r = \frac{1}{2}$

In Exercises 17–24, compute the sum of the first n terms of the geometric progression with first term y_1 and common ratio r.

17. $n = 2, y_1 = 12, r = 5$
18. $n = 3, y_1 = 8, r = 3$
19. $n = 5, y_1 = 729, r = \frac{1}{3}$
20. $n = 8, y_1 = 64, r = \frac{1}{2}$
21. $n = 9, y_1 = 1000, r = -1.1$
22. $n = 10, y_1 = 500, r = -1.2$
23. $n = 12, y_1 = 7, r = -2$
24. $n = 15, y_1 = 12, r = -3$

In Exercises 25–32 determine if the sum of the terms of the geometric progression $y_1, y_2, \ldots, y_n, \ldots$ exists. If it exists, compute it.

25. $y_n = 8(-1)^{n-1}$
26. $y_n = 2(.1)^{n-1}$
27. $y_n = -4(-\frac{1}{2})^{n-1}$
28. $y_n = 0.3(-4)^{n-1}$
29. $y_n = 12(\frac{1}{3})^{n-1}$
30. $y_n = 0.43(-0.01)^{n-1}$
31. $y_n = 0.2(5^{n-1})$
32. $y_n = 7(2^{n-1})$

33. Use Application 1 to compute the increase in national income resulting from an $11 billion increase in investment if the marginal propensity to consume is 0.45.

34. Use Application 1 to compute the increase in national income resulting from a $6 billion increase in investment if the marginal propensity to consume is 0.8.

35. If an employee earning $12,000 is given a 6% increase in salary each year, what will his or her salary be during the fifteenth year? What will be the total income earned during this 15-year period?

36. Suppose a ball is made of a material that causes it to rebound half the distance it falls.
    (a) What is the total distance the ball will fall if it is released from a height of 12 feet?
    (b) What is the total distance the ball will travel if it is released from a height of 12 feet?

37. Suppose that there are 32 applicants for a particular job. If the company decides to interview each person and then invite half of the applicants for a second interview, and if it continues to invite half of those interviewed at the preceding stage for another interview until only 2 candidates remain, how many interviews will be required to fill the position?

38. An oil field is expected to yield 1 million barrels of oil in its first year, but the yield will diminish in succeeding years. If, after the first year, the field yields only $\frac{1}{4}$ as much oil each year as it did in the previous year, compute the amount of oil yielded after 4 years. What is the total amount of oil the field will yield under these conditions?

39. The Federal Reserve Board determines the percentage of a bank's assets that must be kept on hand to meet withdrawals. Suppose that banks are required to keep 20% of their deposits on hand but are free to loan the remaining 80%. If a deposit of $1000 is made at a given bank, the bank will have $800 of new money available to loan to its customers. This $800 will eventually be deposited in one or more banks, which will then have $640 in new money to loan, and so forth. Compute the total amount of new money the $1000 deposit can generate.
40. If inflation decreases the value of $1.00 by 8% per year, how much will $1.00 be worth 5 years from now?

10.3 Interest

interest *Interest* is a fee paid for borrowing money. Interest is paid not only by individuals, who borrow money for installment purchases, but also by savings institutions and government units, which borrow money by offering savings accounts and issuing bonds. In recent years the rapid increase in interest rates has made it essential for consumers to understand the cost of borrowing money. In this section our knowledge of progressions will be used to develop formulas for computing interest payments.

principal When borrowing money, the amount that is loaned is called the *principal*. The interest charges associated with borrowing are normally
interest rate stated as a percentage called the *interest rate. Unless explicitly stated otherwise, all interest rates in this book will be assumed to be annual rates.*
simple interest The most basic form of interest, called *simple interest*, is computed only on the principal. The amount I of simple interest owed if a principal P is loaned at an annual rate r for t years is given by the formula

$$I = Prt \qquad (10.8)$$

So the total amount (principal plus interest) owed by the borrower is as follows:

Amount due at simple interest

$$A = P(1 + rt) \qquad (10.9)$$

where A = amount due
P = principal
r = annual simple interest rate
t = time in years

EXAMPLE 16

Suppose that an individual borrows $4000 at 10% simple interest. (a) How much will be owed after $2\frac{1}{2}$ years? (b) How much interest will be paid?

(a) The amount due can be computed using (10.9) to be

$$A = \$4000[1 + 0.10(\tfrac{5}{2})] = \$4000(1.25) = \$5000$$

(b) The amount of interest to be paid can be computed using (10.8) to be

$$I = \$4000(0.10)(\tfrac{5}{2}) = \$1000$$

Notice that the interest to be paid is the difference between the amount due and the principal.

EXAMPLE 17

If a consumer borrows $2000 and must repay $2120 in six months, what annual simple interest rate is being charged?

To answer this question, we must use (10.9) to solve for r. Since $A = \$2120$, $P = \$2000$, and $t = \tfrac{1}{2}$, we have the following equation:

$$\$2120 = \$2000\,(1 + r \cdot \tfrac{1}{2})$$
$$1.06 = 1 + r \cdot \tfrac{1}{2}$$
$$0.06 = r \cdot \tfrac{1}{2}$$
$$0.12 = r$$

So the annual simple interest rate is 12%.

Let us note that, if we deposit money in an account paying simple interest and record the value of the account at the end of each year, (10.9) will lead to an arithmetic progression. For if a principal P is deposited at an annual rate r, the value of the account after 1, 2, 3, ... years is $P + Pr$, $P + 2Pr$, $P + 3Pr$, ... This is an arithmetic progression with common difference Pr.

Most transactions involving interest charges do not use simple interest. Instead the interest due at the end of an interest period is added to the principal, and future interest charges are computed based on this larger amount. Thus future interest charges are paid on previously earned interest. In this case the interest is said to have been *compounded*, and this type of interest is called *compound interest*.

compound interest

Suppose, for example, that $2000 is deposited in an account paying 6% interest compounded quarterly. At the end of one quarter the value of the account will be

$$P(1 + rt) = \$2000[1 + (0.06) \cdot \tfrac{1}{4}] = \$2000(1.015) = \$2030$$

from (10.9). The value of the account at the end of the second quarter is found by applying (10.9) to the new principal of $2030. Thus the value of the account after two quarters will be

$$P(1 + rt) = \$2030[1 + (0.06) \cdot \tfrac{1}{4}] = \$2030(1.015) = \$2060.45$$

Likewise at the end of three quarters the value of the account will be

$$P(1 + rt) = \$2060.45(1.015) \approx \$2091.36$$

and at the end of four quarters it will be

$$P(1 + rt) = \$2091.36(1.015) \approx \$2122.73$$

Now let us develop a general formula for the value of a principal P invested at an interest rate of r per period. After 1 period the value will be

$$A_1 = P(1 + r)$$

Likewise, after 2 periods, the value will be

$$A_2 = A_1(1 + r) = P(1 + r)^2$$

Similar reasoning shows that after 3 periods the value will be

$$A_3 = A_2(1 + r) = P(1 + r)^3$$

Since the values $A_1, A_2, A_3, \ldots$ form a geometric progression with common ratio $1 + r$, Theorem 10.3 yields the following formula.

Amount due at compound interest

$$A = P(1 + r)^n \tag{10.10}$$

where A = amount due
P = principal
r = interest rate per period
n = number of periods

EXAMPLE 18

How much will $1000 be worth if it is invested for six years in an account paying 8% interest compounded quarterly?

Notice that the 8% interest rate is an annual rate; thus the rate per quarter is $8\% \div 4 = 2\%$. So the answer to the question can be found using (10.10) with $P = \$1000$, $r = 0.02$, and $n = 24$:

$$A = \$1000(1.02)^{24} \approx \$1000(1.60844) = \$1608.44$$

(The value of $(1.02)^{24}$ can be found by using a calculator or a compound interest table such as Table 2 in the appendix.)

It is instructive to consider the effect of compounding interest with different interest periods. Suppose, for example, that a principal of $1000 is invested for 5 years in a savings account paying 6% interest. The value of this account and the interest earned for various compounding frequencies are shown below.

Interest compounded	Value after five years ($)	Interest earned ($)
Not at all (simple interest)	1300.00	300.00
Annually	1338.23	338.23
Semiannually	1343.92	343.92
Quarterly	1346.86	346.86
Monthly	1348.85	348.85
Daily	1349.83	349.83

From this table we see that, the more frequently the interest is compounded, the larger the amount of interest earned. As the frequency of compounding increases, however, the amount of additional interest becomes less and less.

Even though we used the same annual interest rate of 6% in performing the computations above, the frequency of compounding changed the amount of interest earned. Thus there is an effective difference between 6% simple interest and 6% compound interest. The annual rate of simple interest that is equivalent to a particular compound rate is called the *effective rate* of interest. In this context the stated rate of interest is referred to as the *nominal rate*. So the effective rate of interest is the actual amount of interest (in dollars) earned by investing $1.00 at the nominal rate for one year.

effective rate
nominal rate

EXAMPLE 19

Find the effective rate of interest for a nominal rate of 6% compounded (a) semiannually and (b) quarterly.

(a) The value (in dollars) of an account in which $1.00 is invested at 6% interest compounded semiannually for one year is

$$\$1.00(1 + \tfrac{0.06}{2})^2 = \$1.0609$$

from (10.10). So the amount of interest earned during the year is $0.0609, hence the effective rate is 0.0609 or 6.09%.

(b) The value (in dollars) of $1.00 invested at 6% interest compounded quarterly for one year is

$$\$1.00(1 + \tfrac{0.06}{4})^4 \approx \$1.0614$$

Hence the effective rate is 0.0614 or 6.14%.

In (10.10) it is possible to solve for any one of the variables A, P, r, and n if the other three are known. The following example demonstrates one possibility.

EXAMPLE 20

What annual rate of interest must be paid in order for a principal to double in 8 years when compounded quarterly?

To answer this question, we must solve (10.10) for r when $A = 2P$ and $n = 32$.

$$2P = P(1 + r)^{32}$$
$$2 = (1 + r)^{32}$$
$$2^{1/32} = 1 + r$$
$$2^{1/32} - 1 = r$$

Therefore $r \approx 1.0219 - 1 = 0.0219$. Since r is the rate per quarter, the desired annual rate is $4r \approx 0.0876$.

Many applications involving compound interest require knowing how much money must be invested today at a specified interest rate in order to accumulate a certain amount of money A in the future. This type of problem requires solving (10.10) for P; in this case P is called the *present value* of A.

present value

Present value of a future amount

$$P = A(1 + r)^{-n} \tag{10.11}$$

where P = present value

A = future amount

r = interest rate per period

n = number of periods

Values of $(1 + r)^{-n}$ can be found either with a calculator or with a table of present values such as Table 3 in the appendix.

EXAMPLE 21

How much money should be deposited at 8% interest compounded quarterly in order for a family to accumulate $10,000 in five years for a child's college education?

The answer to this question is the present value of $10,000 invested for five years at 8% interest compounded quarterly. Using (10.11), we see that this value is

$$P = \$10{,}000(1 + \tfrac{0.08}{4})^{-20} = \$10{,}000(1.02)^{-20}$$
$$\approx \$10{,}000(0.672971) = \$6729.71$$

Exercises

In Exercises 1–4, compute the amount of simple interest earned if a principal P is deposited at an annual rate r for t years.

1. $P = \$5000, r = 7\%, t = 1\tfrac{1}{2}$
2. $P = \$1200, r = 8\%, t = 3$
3. $P = \$40{,}000, r = 8\%, t = 6$
4. $P = \$2000, r = 9\%, t = \tfrac{1}{2}$

In Exercises 5–8, compute the amount due after t years if a principal P is deposited in an account paying simple interest at an annual rate r.

5. $P = \$900, r = 5\%, t = 4$
6. $P = \$2400, r = 6\%, t = 8$
7. $P = \$3000, r = 8\%, t = 5$
8. $P = \$5000, r = 9\%, t = 2$

In Exercises 9–12, compute the amount due at compound interest when a principal P is deposited for m years in an account paying interest compounded quarterly at an annual rate i.

9. $P = \$6000, m = 5, i = 4\%$
10. $P = \$800, m = 2, i = 6\%$
11. $P = \$300, m = 1\tfrac{1}{2}, i = 5\%$
12. $P = \$400, m = 2\tfrac{1}{2}, i = 8\%$

In Exercises 13–16 compute the present value of an amount A invested for m years in an account paying interest compounded semiannually at an annual rate i.

13. $A = \$1000, m = 3, i = 5\%$
14. $A = \$500, m = 8, i = 4\%$
15. $A = \$3000, m = 1, i = 6\%$
16. $A = \$2000, m = 2, i = 3\%$

In Exercises 17–20, compute the effective rate of interest for a nominal rate i under the given conditions.

17. $i = 6\%$, compounded monthly
18. $i = 8\%$, compounded semiannually
19. $i = 7\%$, compounded quarterly
20. $i = 8\%$, compounded quarterly
21. If $10,000 is deposited in a six-month savings certificate paying 9% simple interest, how much interest will be earned in six months?
22. If $3000 is borrowed at 12% simple interest, how much will be due in $1\frac{1}{2}$ years?
23. If money can be invested at 6% interest compounded quarterly, how much should be deposited in order to have $10,000 for college expenses in eight years?
24. Suppose that an executive deposits $20,000 in an account paying 8% interest compounded quarterly. How much money will be available to the executive at retirement 25 years later?
25. If you have $500 to invest for 2 years, which option is better: 6% interest compounded semiannually or $6\frac{1}{4}\%$ simple interest?
26. A certain credit card company charges simple interest at an annual rate of 18%. How much must be charged now so that the amount owed in six months will be $100?
27. A bank loaned $500 and collected $620 in payment 18 months later. What annual rate of simple interest did it charge?
28. What annual rate of simple interest is equivalent to a rate of 9% compounded monthly?
29. If $600 is borrowed at an annual simple interest rate of 12%, what amount will be due three months later?
30. If money can be invested at 7% interest compounded quarterly, how much should be paid for a note that will be worth $5000 in six years?
31. What annual rate of simple interest is equivalent to a rate of 18% compounded monthly?
32. If $1200 is borrowed at 9% simple interest for four months, how much interest will be charged?
33. How much should be paid for a note that will pay $2000 in 3 years if simple interest is charged at a rate of 10%?
34. An item costing $50 was charged at a department store. Three months later the store issued a bill for $52. What annual rate of simple interest was it charging?
35. What annual rate of interest must be paid in order for a principal to double in 10 years when compounded quarterly?
36. What annual rate of interest must be paid in order for a principal to triple in 10 years when compounded monthly?
37. Suppose that an insurance company offers a policyholder the option of collecting $1000 now or $1125 in two years. If money can be invested at 6% interest compounded quarterly, which option is better for the policyholder?
38. How long will it take for money to double if it is invested at 18% simple interest?

39. At what annual rate must inflation continue so that a dollar will lose half its value in 10 years?

40. A company with current sales of $3 billion is predicting sales of $4.1 billion in 3 years. What annual rate of increase in sales is this company expecting?

10.4 First-Order Linear Difference Equations

In Sections 10.1 and 10.2 we were concerned with progressions in which the nth term was related to the preceding term by an equation of the form

$$y_n = y_{n-1} + d \quad \text{or} \quad y_n = ry_{n-1}$$

first-order linear difference equation

Both these equations are special cases of the *first-order linear difference equation*

$$y_n = ay_{n-1} + b \tag{10.12}$$

where a and b are constants. (The arithmetic progression corresponds to the case $a = 1$ and $b = d$, and the geometric progression corresponds to the case $a = r$ and $b = 0$.)

solution

A *solution* of (10.12) is a sequence $y_1, y_2, y_3, \ldots$ in which successive terms satisfy the relation $y_n = ay_{n-1} + b$. When a and b are given, a solution of (10.12) is completely determined if its first term is known. For example, the first 5 terms of the sequence that satisfies the difference equation $y_n = 2y_{n-1} - 3$ and has first term 4 are

$$y_1 = 4$$
$$y_2 = 2y_1 - 3 = 2(4) - 3 = 5$$
$$y_3 = 2y_2 - 3 = 2(5) - 3 = 7$$
$$y_4 = 2y_3 - 3 = 2(7) - 3 = 11$$
$$y_5 = 2y_4 - 3 = 2(11) - 3 = 19$$

Recall that we were able to obtain a formula that expressed the nth term of an arithmetic or a geometric progression in terms of the first term. A similar formula can be developed for solutions of (10.12). If y_1 is the first term of a solution to (10.12), then

$$y_2 = ay_1 + b$$
$$y_3 = ay_2 + b = a(ay_1 + b) + b = a^2 y_1 + b(1 + a)$$

and

$$y_4 = ay_3 + b = a[a^2 y_1 + b(1 + a)] + b$$
$$= a^3 y_1 + a(1 + a)b + b = a^3 y_1 + b(1 + a + a^2)$$

It is not difficult to see that the nth term of the solution will be

$$y_n = a^{n-1} y_1 + b(1 + a + a^2 + \cdots + a^{n-2})$$

Since $1 + a + a^2 + \cdots + a^{n-2} = (1 - a^{n-1})/(1 - a)$ from Theorem 10.4, we are led to the following result.

THEOREM 10.6

If $y_1, y_2, \ldots, y_n, \ldots$ is a solution of $y_n = ay_{n-1} + b$, then for all positive integers n

$$y_n = \begin{cases} \left(y_1 - \dfrac{b}{1-a}\right)a^{n-1} + \dfrac{b}{1-a} & \text{if } a \neq 1 \\ y_1 + (n-1)b & \text{if } a = 1 \end{cases} \qquad (10.13)$$

Notice that, if $a = 1$ and $b = d$ in (10.12), so that we have an arithmetic progression with common difference d, (10.13) reduces to $y_n = y_1 + (n-1)d$; this is the solution found previously in (10.1). Likewise, if $a = r$ and $b = 0$ in (10.12), so that we have a geometric progression with common ratio r, the solution given by (10.13) is $y_n = y_1 r^{n-1}$, which is the one found previously in (10.4).

EXAMPLE 22

Find the nth term of the solution to the difference equation $y_n = 3y_{n-1} + 2$ that has first term y_1.

Using (10.13) with $a = 3$ and $b = 2$, we see that

$$y_n = \left(y_1 - \frac{2}{1-3}\right)\cdot 3^{n-1} + \frac{2}{1-3} = (y_1 + 1)\cdot 3^{n-1} - 1$$

EXAMPLE 23

Find the twelfth term of the solution of $y_n = \frac{1}{2}y_{n-1} - 4$ that has first term 7.

Substituting the values $a = \frac{1}{2}$, $b = -4$, $n = 12$, and $y_1 = 7$ into (10.13), we see that the twelfth term of the solution is

$$y_{12} = \left[7 - \frac{(-4)}{1 - \frac{1}{2}}\right]\left(\frac{1}{2}\right)^{11} + \frac{(-4)}{1 - \frac{1}{2}}$$

$$= 15\left(\frac{1}{2048}\right) - 8 = -\frac{16{,}369}{2048}$$

The difference equation (10.12) can be used to describe situations in which the value of a variable quantity is related to its value at some preceding time. The next two examples demonstrate how this equation arises in connection with financial matters. Other applications of this type are presented in Section 10.5.

EXAMPLE 24

If an accounting position pays a starting salary of $15,000 and offers yearly salary increases of $300 plus a 6% cost-of-living increase, how much will this job pay during the fifth year?

Let y_n denote the salary in dollars that this job will pay during the nth year. Because the salary in year n equals the previous year's salary plus $300 plus 6% of the previous year's salary, we have the equation

$$y_n = y_{n-1} + 300 + 0.06 y_{n-1} = (1.06) y_{n-1} + 300$$

Since we are interested in knowing the salary paid during the fifth year, we must determine y_5. Substituting $a = 1.06$, $b = 300$, $n = 5$, and $y_1 = 15{,}000$ into (10.13) yields

$$y_5 = \left[15{,}000 - \frac{300}{1 - (1.06)} \right] (1.06)^4 + \frac{300}{1 - (1.06)}$$

$$= (20{,}000)(1.06)^4 - 5000 \approx 20{,}249.54$$

Hence this job will pay $20,249.54 during the fifth year.

EXAMPLE 25

Suppose that a home buyer has a $50,000 mortgage at an annual interest rate of 9%. Interest is to be charged monthly on the unpaid balance of the mortgage. If the buyer makes payments of $500 per month to repay the loan, what will be the unpaid balance during the 120th month of the mortgage?

Let y_n denote the unpaid balance in dollars during the nth month of the mortgage. Since the unpaid balance during month n equals the unpaid balance during the previous month plus interest charges on this amount (at the monthly rate of $0.09/12 = 0.0075$) minus one payment, we obtain the equation

$$y_n = y_{n-1} + 0.0075 y_{n-1} - 500 = (1.0075) y_{n-1} - 500$$

We must determine the 120th term of the solution of this equation that has $y_1 = 50{,}000$. From (10.13) we have

$$y_{120} = \left[50{,}000 - \frac{(-500)}{1 - 1.0075} \right] (1.0075)^{119} + \frac{(-500)}{1 - 1.0075}$$

$$\approx (-16{,}666.67)(2.433109) + 66{,}666.67 \approx 26{,}114.85$$

So during the 120th month of the mortgage the unpaid balance will be $26,114.85.

APPLICATION 2

In [13] Metzler uses difference equations to obtain a mathematical model of inventory cycles. We shall describe here a special case of Metzler's model.

Our objective will be to describe the value of the inventory of a particular item at regular intervals. Let y_n denote the value of the inventory of this item at the beginning of the nth time period, s_n denote the value of the items produced for sale in time period

n, and t_n denote the total income of the business during period n. We assume that during each time period the business receives a constant net return v_0 that is independent of its production of the item in question. Since the total income produced during period $n - 1$ is the sum of the value of the items produced for sale and the constant net return, we have

$$t_{n-1} = s_{n-1} + v_0 \tag{10.14}$$

The value of the items to be produced during period n is to be determined at the beginning of the period based on sales during the preceding period. We assume that the value of the items produced for sale in period n equals the value of the units sold during the preceding period. Furthermore, we assume that the value of the units sold during any period is a fixed fraction a of the total income of the period. (The constant a is the marginal propensity to consume for the current period's consumption with respect to the previous period's income.) Thus the value of the units actually sold in period $n - 2$ is at_{n-2}, and

$$s_{n-1} = at_{n-2} \tag{10.15}$$

Clearly the value of the inventory at the beginning of period n equals the value of the inventory at the beginning of period $n - 1$ plus the value of the units produced for sale in period $n - 1$ less the value of the units sold during this period. Symbolically,

$$y_n = y_{n-1} + s_{n-1} - at_{n-1} \tag{10.16}$$

It can be shown using (10.14)–(10.16) that

$$y_n - ay_{n-1} = y_{n-1} - ay_{n-2}$$

Hence the quantity $y_n - ay_{n-1}$ is a constant b, and

$$y_n = ay_{n-1} + b$$

So the value of the inventory at the beginning of the nth period is given by (10.13).

Since $0 < a < 1$, it is easy to see from (10.13) that the values of y_n approach $b/(1 - a)$. To illustrate this situation, suppose that $a = \frac{1}{2}, b = \$1000$, and $y_1 = \$4000$. Then the values of the inventory at the start of periods $1, 2, 3, 4, 5, \ldots, n, \ldots$ are

$\$4000, \$3000, \$2500, \$2250, \$2125, \ldots,$
$\$2000(\frac{1}{2})^{n-1} + \$2000, \ldots$

These values approach $2000 as in Figure 10.1.

It follows similarly from (10.14) and (10.15) that

$$t_{n-1} = at_{n-2} + v_0$$

Hence the business's income also satisfies a first-order linear difference equation, and it can be shown that the total income of the business approaches the value $v_0/(1 - a)$.

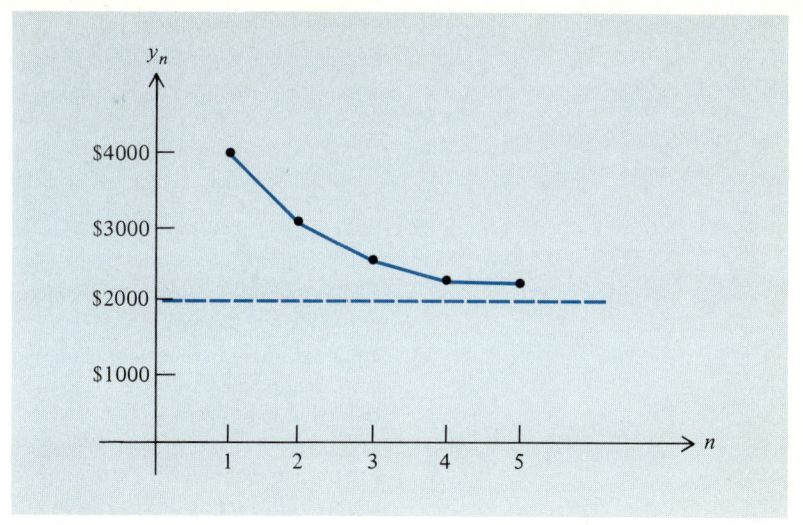

Figure 10.1

In Figure 10.1 we graphed the first five terms of the solution to $y_n = \frac{1}{2}y_{n-1} + \$1000$ that has first term $y_1 = \$4000$. Notice that in Figure 10.1 the horizontal axis represents time, which has been divided into discrete periods numbered 1, 2, 3, and so forth. In the context of this application, it is meaningful to describe the level of inventory for any positive value of n even though the values of y_n are defined only when n is a positive integer. Consequently, in Figure 10.1 we plotted the points $(1, y_1)$, $(2, y_2)$, $(3, y_3)$, $(4, y_4)$, and $(5, y_5)$ and joined consecutive points by a line segment. This practice is quite common in applications of difference equations in other disciplines, and so it will be used throughout this chapter.

Exercises

In Exercises 1–10 compute the first five terms of the solution to the given difference equation that has y_1 as its first term.

1. $y_n = -3y_{n-1},\ y_1 = 8$
2. $y_n = 7y_{n-1},\ y_1 = -4$
3. $y_n = y_{n-1} - 6,\ y_1 = 0$
4. $y_n = -2y_{n-1} + 1,\ y_1 = 3$
5. $y_n = 2y_{n-1} - 1,\ y_1 = -5$
6. $y_n = 3y_{n-1} - 1,\ y_1 = 0$
7. $y_n = -y_{n-1} + 2,\ y_1 = 4$
8. $y_n = y_{n-1} - 2,\ y_1 = 5$
9. $y_n = -4y_{n-1} - 7,\ y_1 = -2$
10. $y_n = -2y_{n-1} - 4,\ y_1 = -3$

In Exercises 11–20 express the general term y_n in the solution of the given difference equation in terms of the first term y_1.

11. $y_n = 5y_{n-1}$
12. $y_n = y_{n-1} - 3$
13. $y_n = -2y_{n-1} + 1$
14. $y_n = 2y_{n-1} + 5$
15. $y_n = y_{n-1} + 6$
16. $y_n = -3y_{n-1} + 2$
17. $y_n = -2y_{n-1} - 4$
18. $y_n = -y_{n-1}$
19. $y_n = 3y_{n-1} - \frac{1}{3}$
20. $y_n = 5y_{n-1} + \frac{1}{2}$

In Exercises 21–30, compute the sixth term of the solution to the given difference equation that has y_1 as its first term.

21. $y_n = -y_{n-1} + 4, y_1 = 5$
22. $y_n = 3y_{n-1} + 6, y_1 = -3$
23. $y_n = \frac{1}{2}y_{n-1} - 8, y_1 = 12$
24. $y_n = -3y_{n-1} + 9, y_1 = 1$
25. $y_n = 2y_{n-1} + 6, y_1 = -1$
26. $y_n = \frac{1}{3}y_{n-1} - 4, y_1 = 7$
27. $y_n = 0.2y_{n-1} - 4, y_1 = -2$
28. $y_n = -4y_{n-1} + 2, y_1 = -1$
29. $y_n = -y_{n-1} - 3, y_1 = 4$
30. $y_n = 2y_{n-1} + 1, y_1 = 6$

31. Suppose that a job offers a starting salary of $20,000 with yearly increases of $500 plus an 8% cost-of-living increase. How much will this job pay during the eighth year?

32. Suppose that a job offers a starting salary of $16,000 with yearly increases of $400 plus a 5% cost-of-living increase. How much will this job pay during the sixth year?

33. A home buyer has borrowed $60,000 at an annual rate of 9%. Interest is to be charged monthly on the unpaid balance of the mortgage. If payments of $600 are made each month to repay the loan, what is the unpaid balance of the mortgage during the 180th month?

34. A home buyer has borrowed $40,000 at an annual rate of 9%. Interest is to be charged monthly on the unpaid balance of the mortgage. If payments of $400 are made each month to repay the loan, what is the unpaid balance of the mortgage during the 60th month?

35. A certain type of cell separates into two identical cells every hour. If there are initially 100 of these cells, how many will there be by the 24th hour?

36. During the Middle Ages certain crafts such as carpentry were learned by becoming apprenticed to a master craftsman. Suppose that each master carpenter can train $\frac{1}{2}$ an apprentice to become a master every year and that $\frac{1}{20}$ master carpenters stop working every year. If there are 10 master carpenters during the first year, how many will there be during the tenth year assuming that there is no shortage of available apprentices?

37. A simplified model of a country's gross national product can be obtained by assuming that the gross national product for any year equals the gross national product for the previous year plus an amount proportional to the country's investment during the previous year. Suppose that a country has an initial gross national product of $200 billion and that the amount proportional to the investment remains constant at $10 billion per year. What will this country's gross national product be for the twentieth year?

38. Suppose that a fair die is rolled. Let y_n denote the expected number of rolls before some outcome (a 1, 2, 3, 4, 5, or 6) occurs on n consecutive rolls.

   (a) Determine y_1.
   (b) What is the expected number of times the same outcome must occur on $n - 1$ consecutive rolls before the next roll produces n consecutive outcomes?
   (c) Write a difference equation involving y_n based on part (b).
   (d) Solve the difference equation in part (c).
   (e) How many rolls of the die should be expected before the same outcome occurs on 5 consecutive rolls?

10.5 Annuities

Most life insurance companies have whole life policies structured so that the policyholder makes annual payments of a fixed amount for a period of 20 or 30 years, after which time the sum of all of the payments is available to the policyholder either as a lump sum or in the form of regular payments for the remainder of his or her life. Such a set of payments at equal intervals of time is called an *annuity*. We shall consider here only *simple annuities*, those for which the interest period coincides with the interval between successive payments.

annuity
simple annuities

Suppose that at the beginning of each interest period an amount p is deposited in an account paying compound interest at a rate of r per period. The value of this account at some future time is called the *future value of the annuity*. To obtain a formula for the future value of the annuity, let y_n denote the value of the account after n payments. Clearly the value of the account after n payments equals the value after $n-1$ payments plus the interest earned during the preceding period plus the regular periodic payment. Symbolically, this relationship may be expressed as the difference equation

future value of an annuity

$$y_n = y_{n-1} + ry_{n-1} + p = (1+r)y_{n-1} + p$$

Since $y_1 = p$, (10.13) yields

$$y_1 = \left[p - \frac{p}{1-(1+r)}\right](1+r)^{n-1} + \frac{p}{1-(1+r)}$$

$$= \left(p + \frac{p}{r}\right)(1+r)^{n-1} - \frac{p}{r}$$

$$= \frac{p}{r}(r+1)(1+r)^{n-1} - \frac{p}{r}$$

$$= \frac{p[(1+r)^n - 1]}{r}$$

Thus we have the following formula.

Future value of an annuity

$$S = \frac{p[(1+r)^n - 1]}{r} \tag{10.17}$$

where S = value of the annuity after the last payment
p = amount of the periodic payment
r = interest rate per period
n = number of payments

(Payments are made at the start of each interest period.)

The expression $[(1 + r)^n - 1]/r$ in (10.17) is usually denoted $s_{\overline{n}|r}$; with this notation (10.17) becomes

$$S = ps_{\overline{n}|r}$$

Tables containing the values of $s_{\overline{n}|r}$ for common values of n and r have been prepared. A short table of this type can be found in Table 4 of the appendix; for a more complete table, see [17].

EXAMPLE 26

Suppose that $100 is deposited at the start of each quarter into an account compounding interest quarterly at an annual rate of 6%. Since the interest rate per period is $0.06/4 = 0.015$, the value of this annuity after 20 payments will be

$$S = \frac{\$100[(1.015)^{20} - 1]}{0.015} \approx \$100(23.1237) = \$2312.37$$

sinking fund

Businesses are frequently faced with the problem of accumulating capital to meet future expenses. An account established to accumulate funds for such a purpose is called a *sinking fund*. If equal periodic payments are to be made into a sinking fund to accumulate a given amount of money, the size of the periodic payment can be determined by solving (10.17) for p. The resulting formula is

Amount of sinking fund payment

$$p = \frac{rS}{(1 + r)^n - 1} \qquad (10.18)$$

or equivalently,

$$p = \frac{S}{s_{\overline{n}|r}}$$

where p = amount of the periodic payment
S = amount of money to be accumulated after the last payment
r = interest rate per period
n = number of payments

(Payments are made at the start of each interest period.)

EXAMPLE 27

In three years, a business will need to replace a piece of machinery costing $10,000. To raise this money, management has decided to create a sinking fund to accumulate the necessary capital. If equal monthly payments are to be made into an account paying 6%

interest compounded monthly, what should the size of each payment be?

This question can be answered by using (10.18) with $S = \$10,000$, $r = 0.06/12 = 0.005$, and $n = 36$. So the monthly payment should be

$$p = \frac{0.005(\$10,000)}{(1.005)^{36} - 1} \approx \frac{\$50}{(1.19668) - 1} \approx \$254.22$$

In problems involving the future value of an annuity, we are concerned with an amount of money at some *future* time. A related, though different, type of problem is concerned with an amount of money at the *present* time. Suppose that beginning with the next interest period we would like to withdraw equal amounts at the start of each interest period from an account paying compound interest at the rate of r per period. The amount of money that must be deposited now so that nothing remains after the last withdrawal is called the

present value of an annuity   *present value of the annuity.*

To obtain a formula for the present value of an annuity, let p denote the amount of each withdrawal and y_n denote the amount remaining in the account after the nth withdrawal. Clearly the amount remaining after withdrawal n equals the amount remaining after withdrawal $n-1$ plus interest minus the regular withdrawal. So y_n satisfies the difference equation

$$y_n = y_{n-1} + ry_{n-1} - p = (1+r)y_n - p$$

Moreover, if A is the amount originally deposited, then

$$y_1 = (1+r)A - p$$

Hence from (10.13)

$$y_n = \left[(1+r)A - p - \frac{(-p)}{1-(1+r)}\right](1+r)^{n-1} + \frac{(-p)}{1-(1+r)}$$

$$= (1+r)^n A - p(1+r)^{n-1} - \frac{p}{r}(1+r)^{n-1} + \frac{p}{r}$$

$$= (1+r)^n A - \frac{pr(1+r)^{n-1} + p(1+r)^{n-1} - p}{r}$$

$$= (1+r)^n A - \frac{p(1+r)^{n-1}(r+1) - p}{r}$$

Thus

$$y_n = (1+r)^n A - \frac{p[(1+r)^n - 1]}{r} \qquad (10.19)$$

Comparing (10.19) with (10.10) and (10.17), we see that the amount remaining in the account after n withdrawals equals the value of the amount originally deposited plus interest for n periods minus the future value of an annuity having regular payments of p.

The present value of the annuity is the value of A for which y_n equals zero in (10.19). Setting $y_n = 0$, we have

$$0 = (1+r)^n A - \frac{p[(1+r)^n - 1]}{r}$$

So

$$A = \frac{p[(1+r)^n - 1]}{r(1+r)^n}$$

Dividing the numerator and denominator by $(1+r)^n$, we can rewrite the formula above as follows:

Present value of an annuity

$$A = \frac{p[1 - (1+r)^{-n}]}{r} \tag{10.20}$$

where $A =$ present value of the annuity

$p =$ amount of the periodic payment

$r =$ interest rate per period

$n =$ number of payments

(Payments are made at the end of each interest period.)

The expression $[1 - (1+r)^{-n}]/r$ in (10.20) is usually denoted $a_{\overline{n}|r}$; with this notation (10.20) becomes

$$A = p a_{\overline{n}|r}$$

As with $s_{\overline{n}|r}$, tables evaluating $a_{\overline{n}|r}$ have been prepared for common values of n and r. A short table of this type can be found in Table 5 of the appendix; a more complete table can be found in [17].

EXAMPLE 28

A beginning college student will have to make semiannual tuition payments for the next four years. How much must be deposited in an account paying 6% interest compounded semiannually so that six months from now the student can begin withdrawing $1000 every six months for four years?

The amount A that must be deposited is the present value of an annuity paying $1000 at 6% interest compounded semiannually for four years. Evaluating (10.20) with $p = \$1000$, $r = 0.06/2 = 0.03$, and $n = 8$, we have

$$A = \frac{\$1000[1 - (1.03)^{-8}]}{0.03} \approx \$1000(7.01969) = \$7019.69$$

amortization

When mortgaging a house, a sum of money is borrowed and repaid by a sequence of equal periodic (usually monthly) payments. These payments must repay not only the amount of the original loan but also the accumulated interest on the loan. Such a method of repaying a debt is called *amortization*.

In problems concerning amortization we usually are interested in determining the size of the payment p necessary to repay a debt of A in a certain time, say n periods. This value can be found by solving (10.20) for p; the result is the following formula.

Amortization

$$p = \frac{rA}{1 - (1+r)^{-n}} \tag{10.21}$$

or equivalently,

$$p = \frac{A}{a_{\overline{n}|r}}$$

where p = amount of the periodic payment

A = amount of the loan

r = interest rate per period

n = number of payments

(Payments are made at the end of each interest period.)

EXAMPLE 29

Suppose that $40,000 is borrowed to purchase a house, that interest is to be charged monthly at an annual rate of 9%, and that the debt is to be repaid in 25 years by equal monthly payments. Using (10.21) with $r = 0.09/12 = 0.0075$, and $n = 300$, we see that the size of the monthly payment must be

$$p = \frac{\$40{,}000(0.0075)}{1 - (1.0075)^{-300}} \approx \frac{\$300}{0.89371} \approx \$335.68$$

Exercises

In Exercises 1–4, compute the future value of an annuity after n payments if p is the amount of the periodic payment and r is the interest rate per period.

1. $n = 12, p = \$200, r = 2\%$
2. $n = 18, p = \$500, r = 3\%$
3. $n = 36, p = \$100, r = 0.5\%$
4. $n = 25, p = \$1000, r = 7\%$

In Exercises 5–8, compute the amount of the sinking fund payment needed to accumulate an amount S in n payments if interest is paid at the rate of r per period.

5. $S = \$5000, n = 16, r = 1.5\%$
6. $S = \$10{,}000, n = 10, r = 3\%$
7. $S = \$8000, n = 36, r = 0.5\%$
8. $S = \$2000, n = 8, r = 2\%$

In Exercises 9–12, compute the present value of an annuity if n payments of an amount p are to be made and r is the interest rate per period.

9. $n = 48, p = \$200, r = 0.5\%$
10. $n = 10, p = \$12{,}000, r = 7\%$
11. $n = 20, p = \$3000, r = 2\%$
12. $n = 24, p = \$500, r = 1.5\%$

In Exercises 13–16, compute the size of the payment necessary to amortize an amount A in n payments if r is the interest rate per period.

13. $A = \$6000, n = 36, r = 1\%$
14. $A = \$10{,}000, n = 60, r = 0.75\%$
15. $A = \$500, n = 12, r = 1.5\%$
16. $A = \$2000, n = 8, r = 2\%$

17. How much money should parents deposit at 6% interest compounded quarterly so that beginning in three months their child can withdraw $1000 every three months for the next four years?

18. What amount of money should be paid every six months into an account paying 8% interest compounded semiannually in order to accumulate $5000 in three years?

19. A newly married couple has decided to deposit $300 each month into an account paying 6% interest compounded monthly. In three years they would like to use the money in this account for a down payment on a house. How much money will there be?

20. In order to purchase a new car, a buyer borrowed $4800 and agreed to repay the loan in 36 equal monthly payments. If interest is charged at a monthly rate of 1%, how much should each payment be?

21. A vacationer traveling to Europe charged a $500 airline ticket to a credit card charging monthly interest of $1\frac{1}{2}\%$. If the vacationer would like to repay the loan in six equal monthly payments, how much should each payment be?

22. A life insurance policy calls for quarterly payments of $150 to be made for 25 years. When the last payment is made, the insured may elect to receive as a lump sum payment an amount equal to all the payments plus interest compounded quarterly at an annual rate of 8%. How much will this lump sum payment be?

23. In 3 years a company would like to purchase a minicomputer costing $40,000. To raise this money, the company has decided to make quarterly payments into an account paying 7% interest compounded quarterly. How much should each payment be?

24. An oil well is expected to yield monthly profits of $4000 for 5 years. If money can be invested at 9% interest compounded monthly, how much is this well worth now?

25. Bob and Linda are considering the purchase of a house costing $60,000. They intend to make a $15,000 down payment and to repay the balance over a 25-year period by making equal monthly payments. If interest is charged at the annual rate of 9%, how much should each payment be?

26. The parents of a newborn child have decided to begin setting aside money for their child's college education. How much should they deposit every three months into an account paying 6% interest compounded quarterly in order to have $8000 available in 18 years?

27. If monthly deposits of $20 are made into a Christmas Club account paying 6% interest compounded monthly, how much money will be available after the twelfth deposit?

28. Several state lotteries offer a "million dollar" prize that pays $50,000 per year for 20 years. If money can be invested at the rate of 10% compounded annually, how much must the lottery deposit now in order to pay a "million dollar" prize for which the first payment will be made 1 year from now?

29. A company is deciding whether to replace a piece of machinery now or to keep the machinery for another three years. If the machinery is replaced now, the cost of replacement will be $2800 but there will be no additional expenses during the three-year period since the machinery will come with a three-year warranty. On the other hand, if the machinery is not replaced, the company can expect to make semiannual repairs costing $500. If money can be deposited at 6% interest compounded semiannually, which option is cheaper for the company?

30. Karen has $3000 in a savings account paying 5% interest compounded quarterly. Beginning with the next interest period, she has decided to make quarterly deposits of $600 into this account. How much money will be in this account after four years?

31. A local government has issued bonds that will be worth $50,000 in five years. How much money must it deposit each month into an account paying 6% interest compounded monthly in order to have the necessary money available to pay off these bonds?

32. Suppose that a down payment of $2000 is made to purchase a car costing $6000. The remaining money will be borrowed and repaid with 36 equal monthly payments. If interest is charged at the monthly rate of 1%, how much will the interest charges be on this loan?

*10.6 Economic Applications

The use of difference equations in economics to formulate dynamic models is widespread. In fact, J. R. Hicks has called the division of time into discrete periods "period analysis" and prefers this approach to that in which time is treated as continuous. (See the mathematical appendix in [11].) Not surprisingly, most of the economic models that use difference equations involve more complicated equations than the simple first-order linear equation we are considering. (See, for instance, [1], [15], [16], and [19].) In this section, however, two classical models will be discussed that require only the use of this simple equation, one describing the relation between supply and demand when adjustment of supply to changes in price is not instantaneous, and the other describing the growth of national income in an expanding economy.

Supply, Demand, and Market Equilibrium

In Section 2.3 we discussed the problem of determining the equilibrium price, supply, and demand when the supply and demand functions were static (not dependent on time). The supply function shows how production should be scheduled in relation to the prevailing price. But since production takes time, the adjustment of supply to the prevailing price is often delayed.

We shall now consider a model for determining equilibrium when the adjustment of supply to the prevailing price takes place after a time lag. This situation often occurs in connection with agricultural production. For example, farmers decide how much of a particular crop to plant based upon the current price. If the price is low, they will plant less of the crop than previously, and the following year's supply will be smaller. Because of the smaller supply, demand may exceed supply, in which case the price will rise. If the price rises, farmers will plant more of the crop for the coming year. This decision will result in a larger supply. If this larger supply exceeds the demand, then the price will fall, causing the cycle to repeat.

Let S_n, D_n, and p_n be the supply, demand, and price of a product (measured in appropriate units) during period n. For convenience we choose the length of a period to equal the production time of the product under consideration. Furthermore, as in Section 2.3, we assume that the supply and demand are linear functions of the price and that the demand D_n is a decreasing function of current price p_n whereas the supply is an increasing function of p_{n-1}, the price during the preceding period. Thus

$$D_n = ap_n + b \tag{10.22}$$

and

$$S_n = cp_{n-1} + d \tag{10.23}$$

where $a < 0$ and $c > 0$. We assume that the price during period n adjusts instantaneously so that transactions during period n occur at the price for which $D_n = S_n$. Then from (10.22) and (10.23) we have

$$ap_n + b = cp_{n-1} + d$$

an equation that can be solved for p_n to give

$$p_n = \frac{c}{a} p_{n-1} + \frac{d-b}{a}$$

From (10.13) the solution of this difference equation satisfying the condition that the initial price is p_1 has the form

$$p_n = \left(p_1 - \frac{d-b}{a-c} \right) \left(\frac{c}{a} \right)^{n-1} + \frac{d-b}{a-c} \tag{10.24}$$

equilibrium price
equilibrium supply and demand

As in Section 2.3, the price at which supply equals demand is called the *equilibrium price*, and the values of the supply and demand functions at the equilibrium price are called the *equilibrium supply* and *equilibrium demand*. Equating the demand $D = ap + b$ and the supply $S = cp + d$ and solving for p shows that the equilibrium price is

$$p_0 = \frac{d-b}{a-c}$$

Thus the equilibrium supply and demand are $ap_0 + b = cp_0 + d$. We now determine the conditions under which the price sequence $p_1, p_2, p_3, \ldots,$ approaches the equilibrium price p_0.

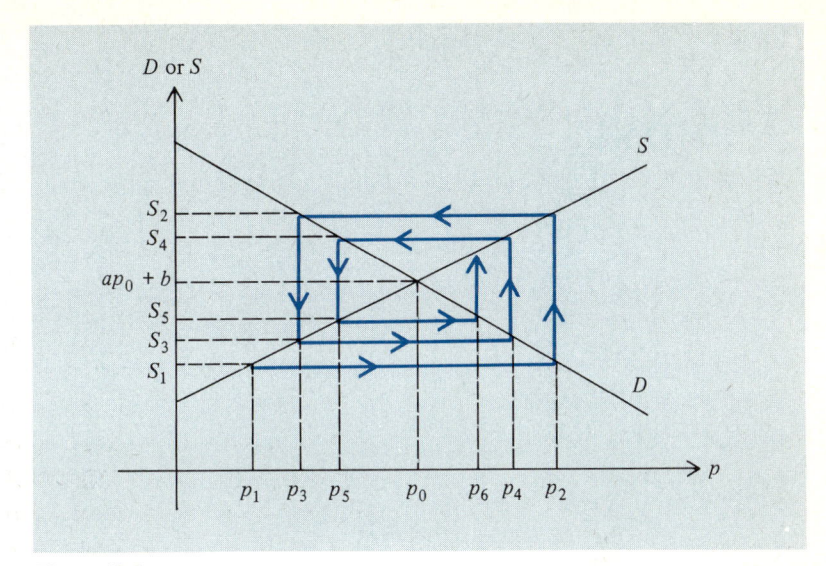

Figure 10.2

In the trivial case where $p_1 = p_0$ [that is, $p_1 - (d-b)/(a-c) = 0$], (10.24) is the constant sequence $p_0, p_0, p_0, \ldots$. Thus the price remains fixed at the equilibrium price, and the supply and demand remain fixed at their equilibrium values. In this case the supply and demand are in equilibrium, and so no change in the price, supply, or demand occurs.

Since $a < 0$ and $c > 0$, we see that $c/a < 0$. We shall consider next the more interesting case where $-1 < c/a < 0$. Suppose for the sake of discussion that p_1 is less than the equilibrium price p_0, that is, that the original price is too low. Then during period 1 the demand exceeds supply. (See Figure 10.2.) This shortage of the product forces the price to rise to the level p_2 (the first coordinate of the point at which the horizontal line $y = S_1$ crosses the demand curve). During period 2 the suppliers will react to the high price level by producing a greater amount S_2 of the product. Hence the supply during period 2 exceeds the demand, and the price falls to a new level p_3 which is the first coordinate of the point at which the horizontal line $y = S_2$ crosses the demand curve. During period 3 the suppliers will react to the low price level by producing a smaller amount S_3 of the product. Hence the demand will exceed the supply in period 4, and the price will rise to a new level p_4 greater than p_3 but less than p_2. This cyclic pattern continues to repeat as the values of p approach the equilibrium value p_0 and the supply and demand approach their equilibrium value $ap_0 + b = cp_0 + d$. The name "cobweb model" has been given to this model because of the behavior depicted in Figure 10.2. (For a history of the cobweb model, see [8].) In the other two cases ($c/a = -1$ and $c/a < -1$) the price, hence the supply and demand, does not approach its equilibrium value. If $c/a = -1$, the price alternates between p_1 and p_2 (Figure 10.3), and if $c/a < -1$, the magnitude of the difference between p_n and the equilibrium price increases with each period (Figure 10.4).

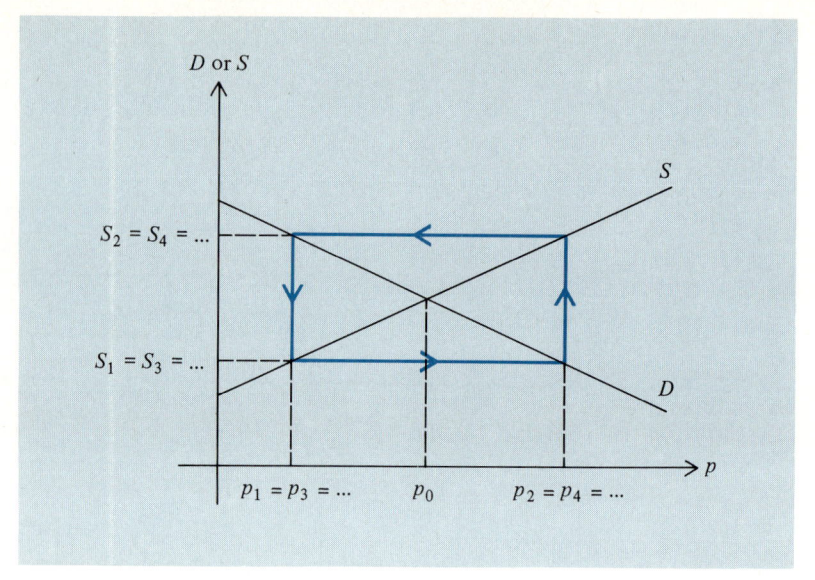

Figure 10.3

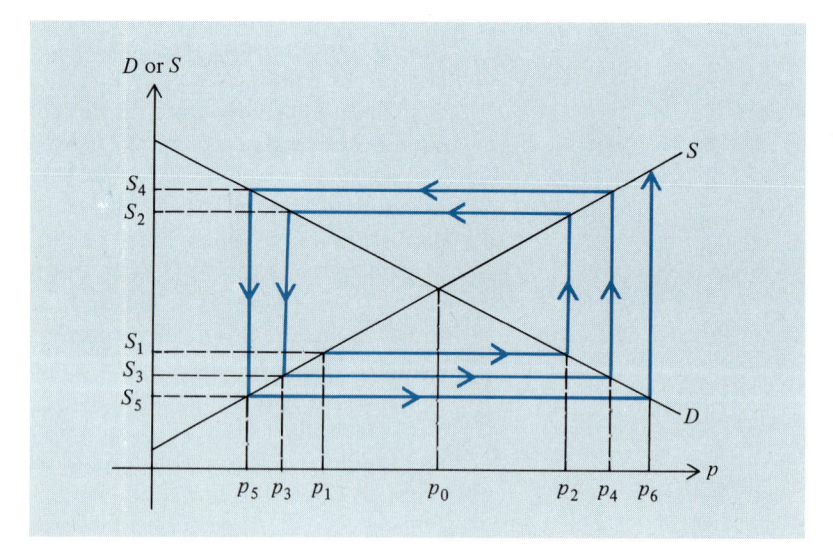

Figure 10.4

Growth of National Income

Perhaps the most widely known model for the growth of national income in an expanding economy was formulated by Harrod in 1939. (See [10].) Specifically, Harrod determined how the national income must grow in order for the actual rate of investment to equal the rate of investment desired by entrepreneurs. In this case income is said to grow at the *warranted rate*.

Harrod's model involves two basic assumptions. The first is that during any time period the net saving is a constant proportion of the income during the period. Since the proportion of actual saving will differ from the proportion of intended saving as income changes,[1] this assumption is plausible only if we assume that the actual and intended saving and the actual and intended income are equal. The second basic assumption is that the amount of intended investment is a constant proportion of the difference in income during the current period as compared to the previous period. This assumption is a particular form of the *acceleration principle* which states that the demand for investment depends upon the rate of change in income.

Letting Y_n, S_n, and I_n denote the income, saving, and investment during period n, we can express these two assumptions in the form

$$S_n = bY_n \tag{10.25}$$

and

$$I_n = a(Y_n - Y_{n-1}) \tag{10.26}$$

where a and b are constants such that $a \geq 0$ and $0 \leq b < 1$. Now, by definition, the actual amounts of saving and investment are equal (since both equal the income minus consumption). Hence

$$S_n = I_n$$

and from (10.25) and (10.26) we have

$$bY_n = a(Y_n - Y_{n-1})$$

This equation may be written in the form

$$Y_n = \frac{a}{a-b} Y_{n-1}$$

and thus the warranted income during period n is

$$Y_n = \left(\frac{a}{a-b}\right)^{n-1} Y_1 \tag{10.27}$$

from (10.4). Also, since investment equals saving, we have

$$I_n = bY_n = b\left(\frac{a}{a-b}\right)^{n-1} Y_1$$

from (10.25).

Exercises

In Exercises 1–14, determine the equilibrium price for (10.22) and (10.23) and graph (10.24) under the given conditions. Also determine if the price sequence $p_1, p_2, \ldots$ approaches the equilibrium price.

1. $p_1 = 8$, $a = -5$, $b = 100$, $c = 4$, $d = 10$
2. $p_1 = 6$, $a = -2$, $b = 200$, $c = 2$, $d = 20$

---

[1] For example, saving $1 million of an anticipated income of $4 million represents an intended saving of 25%; but if income actually is $5 million, then the $1 million becomes an actual saving of only 20%.

3. $p_1 = 12$, $a = -4$, $b = 124$, $c = 6$, $d = 4$
4. $p_1 = 15$, $a = -3$, $b = 250$, $c = 6$, $d = 10$

In Exercises 5–10, graph (10.27) under the given conditions.

5. $a = 0.6$, $b = 0.3$
6. $a = 0.3$, $b = 0.6$
7. $a = 0.4$, $b = 0$
8. $a = 0.2$, $b = -0.2$
9. $a = 0.2$, $b = 0.3$
10. $a = 0.2$, $b = 0.6$

11. In the Harrod model determine the economic condition that will guarantee that income will remain constant.

12. In the Harrod model, instead of assuming that saving is a constant proportion of the income of the present period as in (10.25), suppose that saving is a constant proportion b of the anticipated income of the next period. (Recall that the anticipated income is assumed to equal the actual income.) If investment during period n satisfies (10.26), show that income satisfies the second-order equation

$$Y_{n+1} = \frac{a}{b} Y_n - \frac{a}{b} Y_{n-1}$$

13. Qualitatively describe the behavior of (10.27) if $b > a$. (This unusual possibility is of little significance and can be avoided by modifying the model as in Exercise 14.)

14. In the Harrod model, instead of (10.25), assume that saving is a constant proportion b of the income of the preceding period.
    (a) If investment during period n satisfies (10.26), determine the warranted rate of growth of income.
    (b) Qualitatively describe the solutions in part (a) when both a and b are positive.

15. Generalize the Harrod model by replacing (10.26) by

$$I_n = a(Y_n - Y_{n-1}) + uY_n + v$$

where u and v are constants. (Such an investment demand can account for a constant government investment and a domestic demand for imports that is proportional to income.)
    (a) Determine the difference equation describing Y_n.
    (b) Solve the equation obtained in part (a).

16. Let Y_n, C_n, and I_n denote the national income, consumption, and investment, respectively, during period n. These quantities are related by the basic equation

$$Y_n = C_n + I_n$$

Suppose that in any period consumption is a linear function of income, say

$$C_n = mY_n + b$$

where $0 < m < 1$ and $b \geq 0$. Assume furthermore that the amount of increase in income during any period is a fixed proportion of the investment during the previous period, that is,

$$Y_n - Y_{n-1} = aI_{n-1}$$

(a) Show that income satisfies the difference equation

$$Y_n = (1 + a - am)Y_{n-1} - ab$$

and that investment satisfies the difference equation

$$I_n = (1 + a - am)I_{n-1}$$

(b) Solve the two difference equations in part (a).
(c) Determine C_n and I_n if $Y_1 = b/(1-m)$ in part (b).

17. The effect of spending by individuals employed in public works jobs is investigated by Kahn in [12]. Suppose the government spends an amount I on public works during some initial period and that the marginal and average propensity to consume is c. Kahn states that those who receive income from public works jobs will spend cI during the next period and that this spending will in turn induce further spending in later periods.

   (a) Write a difference equation describing the spending S_n during period n.
   (b) Solve the difference equation in part (a).
   (c) Compute the total spending during all future periods generated by the initial government spending.

18. In [11] Hicks constructs a nonlinear difference equation for modeling the trade cycle. This equation is constructed from several first-order linear equations. For example, consumption is assumed to be a linear function of the income of the previous period; that is,

$$C_n = mY_{n-1} + b$$

where m and b are constants. When there is an excess of capital (as might accompany a slowing of business activity), equipment and inventories will not be replaced as they are used and the resulting net investment will be negative. If this net investment remains constant, then $I_n = -w$ for some $w > 0$.

   (a) Use these equations and $Y_n = C_n + I_n$ to formulate a first-order linear difference equation involving Y_n.
   (b) Solve the equation in part (a).

*10.7 Mathematical Models of Learning

In Section 8.4 we introduced the Bower all-or-none model of learning, which predicted that a subject would always become conditioned to (learn) the correct response to a given stimulus. An entirely different prediction results from a linear model, which is based upon the assumption that learning is gradual and never complete.

We shall consider first the simplest case of a linear model and then discuss a generalization due to Bush and Mosteller. Let p_n denote the probability of making a correct response on trial n of an experiment. Then the probability of an incorrect response on trial n is $q_n = 1 - p_n$. In our first case we assume that the probability of an incorrect response decreases by a constant factor on each trial, that is, that

$$q_n = cq_{n-1}$$

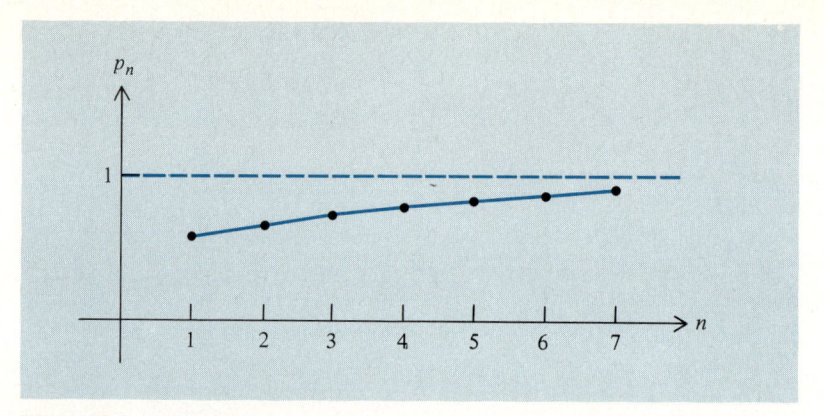

Figure 10.5 *A learning curve*

for some constant c ($0 < c < 1$). Then (10.4) shows that

$$q_n = q_1 c^{n-1}$$

So

$$p_n = 1 - q_n = 1 - q_1 c^{n-1}$$

In this model both q_1 and c are parameters that must be determined experimentally. Plotting p_n gives the well-known learning curve shown in Figure 10.5.

In [5] Bush and Mosteller propose a generalization of the simple model just discussed for the type of learning called *instrumental conditioning* or *operant behavior*. They regard an experiment as a chain of events beginning with perception of a stimulus, followed by performance of some response (traversing a runway, pressing a lever, and so forth), and concluding with some environmental act (presenting food or water, giving an electric shock, sounding a buzzer, and so forth). It is assumed that there is some motivation or drive that causes the subject to perform a response.

Let p_n denote the probability that the desired response will be performed during some definite time interval following the nth presentation of the stimulus. The probability of evoking the desired response on trial n is assumed to be related to p_{n-1} by the first-order linear difference equation

$$p_n = a p_{n-1} + b \tag{10.28}$$

where a and b are constants. Letting $c = 1 - a - b$, we can rewrite this equation as

$$p_n = p_{n-1} + b(1 - p_{n-1}) - c p_{n-1} \tag{10.29}$$

Since the probability that the desired response occurs on trial $n - 1$ is p_{n-1}, $1 - p_{n-1}$ represents the maximum possible increase and $-p_{n-1}$ represents the maximum possible decrease in the level of conditioning

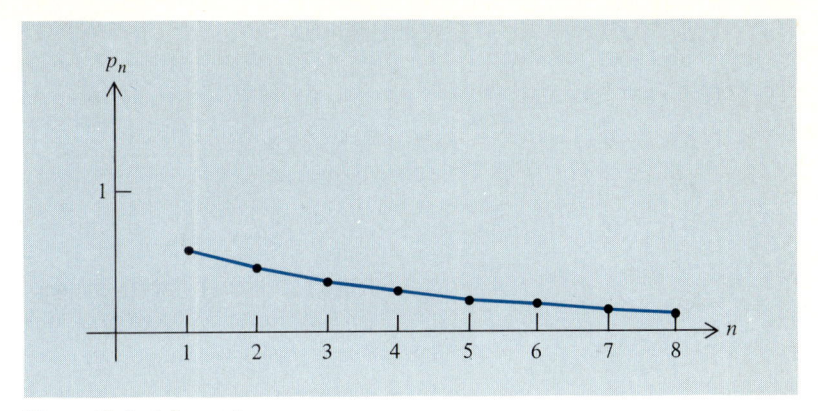

Figure 10.6 *A forgetting curve*

on the next trial.[2] Hence the parameters b and c in (10.29) may be regarded as measuring the positive and negative factors in the environmental acts that occur at the end of the trial. Clearly $0 \le b \le 1$ and $0 \le c \le 1$. Noting that $b = 0$ if $a = 1$, we see from (10.13) that the solution of (10.28) is

$$p_n = \begin{cases} \left(p_1 - \dfrac{b}{1-a}\right) a^{n-1} + \dfrac{b}{1-a} & \text{if } a \ne 1 \\ p_1 & \text{if } a = 1 \end{cases}$$

or with the notation of (10.29)

$$p_n = \begin{cases} \left(p_1 - \dfrac{b}{b+c}\right)(1 - b - c)^{n-1} + \dfrac{b}{b+c} & \text{if } b \ne 0 \text{ or } c \ne 0 \\ p_1 & \text{if } b = c = 0 \end{cases} \quad (10.30)$$

Observe that this model predicts that there will be no change in behavior if there is neither reward nor punishment (that is, if $b = c = 0$). If there is reward but no punishment ($b > 0$ and $c = 0$), then the sequence $p_1, p_2, \ldots$ is an increasing sequence approaching 1; hence conditioning occurs in the manner of Figure 10.5. On the other hand, if there is punishment but no reward ($b = 0$ and $c > 0$), then the sequence $p_1, p_2, \ldots$ is a decreasing sequence approaching 0. In this case we obtain the forgetting (extinction) curve shown in Figure 10.6. If the probabilities of reward and punishment are equal ($b = c$), then the sequence $p_1, p_2, \ldots$ approaches .5, so that eventually the desired response will occur in half the trials. Finally, in the general case where $b > 0$ and $c > 0$, the sequence $p_1, p_2, \ldots$ approaches $b/(b + c)$. Thus this model predicts that the proportion of trials on which the desired response occurs will eventually equal the proportion of all the rewarded and punished responses that are positively reinforced.

---

[2] For this reason (10.29) is often called the *gain-loss form* of (10.28).

Exercises

In Exercises 1–10, graph the solutions of (10.29) under the given conditions.

1. $b = .5, c = .5, p_1 = .5$
2. $b = .2, c = .2, p_1 = .8$
3. $b = .6, c = .2, p_1 = .5$
4. $b = .6, c = .4, p_1 = .8$
5. $b = .2, c = .4, p_1 = .5$
6. $b = .3, c = .6, p_1 = .5$
7. $b = 0, c = .5, p_1 = .5$
8. $b = .4, c = 0, p_1 = .5$
9. $b = .3, c = .3, p_1 = .2$
10. $b = .3, c = .2, p_1 = .2$

In Exercises 11–16, use (10.30) to compute the value that the sequence $p_1, p_2, \ldots$ approaches under the given conditions.

11. $b = .5, c = .5$
12. $b = 0, c = 0$
13. $b = 0, c = .6$
14. $b = .3, c = .5$
15. $b = .6, c = .2$
16. $b = .8, c = 0$

17. If $b = 1$ and $c = 0$ in (10.29), show that for any value of p_1 the solution of (10.29) is a sequence such that $p_n = 1$ for all $n \geq 1$. Interpret this result in the context of the Bush-Mosteller model.

18. If $b = 0$ and $c = 1$ in (10.29), show that for any value of p_1 the solution of (10.29) is a sequence such that $p_n = 0$ for all $n \geq 1$. Interpret this result in the context of the Bush-Mosteller model.

19. Suppose that in the Bush-Mosteller model the positive reinforcing factor is alternately present and absent, for example, $b > 0$ on odd-numbered trials and $b = 0$ on even-numbered trials. Then

$$p_{n+1} = \begin{cases} p_n + b(1 - p_n) - cp_n & \text{if } n \text{ is even} \\ p_n - cp_n & \text{if } n \text{ is odd} \end{cases}$$

(a) Show that for any n

$$p_{2n+2} = p_{2n} + b'(1 - p_{2n}) - c'p_{2n}$$

where $b' = b(1 - c)$ and $c' = 1 - (1 - c)^2$.

(b) Letting $y_n = p_{2n}$, we can write the relationship in part (a) as

$$y_{n+1} = y_n + b'(1 - y_n) - c'y_n$$

Solve this difference equation.

(c) If $1 - b' - c' \neq \pm 1$, what value does the sequence $y_1, y_2, \ldots$ in part (b) approach?

20. In [18] a simple exponential model is proposed to approximate the relative frequency of participation among members of small problem-solving groups. If p_n denotes the estimated percentage of the number of acts of participation by the nth most active member of the group (exclusive of the leader), Stephan and Mishler find that p_n satisfies the difference equation $p_n = rp_{n-1}$. Solve this difference equation. (The data used by Stephan and Mishler yield empirical values of $r \approx 0.52$ and $p_1 = 234/(k + 4)$, where k is the number of persons in the group.)

21. Ettlinger, in [7], studies Thurstone's empirical equation for learning in order to obtain a set of dynamic laws of learning. One such law is expressed by the difference equation

$$R(y_n - y_{n-1}) + y_{n-1} = L$$

where y_n denotes the level of attainment (as measured by the number of successful acts per unit time) during period n, L is a constant measuring the maximum limit of attainment per period, and R is a constant. Solve this difference equation and determine the value the sequence $y_1, y_2, \ldots$ approaches when $R > 0$.

22. In [2] Ammons attempts to lay a partial foundation for the theory of motor learning with regard to reminiscence and spaced practice. He obtains the difference equation

$$A_n = (A_{n-1} + I)(1 - p)$$

where A_n denotes the amount of temporary work decrement at the end of the nth trial cycle, I is a constant increment, and p is the proportion of the work decrement dissipated. Solve this difference equation.

23. The principal assumption of the theory of stimulus variability in learning is that the rate of learning a given response depends upon the rate of sampling the stimuli to which the response becomes conditioned. In [4] Burke, Estes, and Hellyer investigate this assumption and obtain the difference equation

$$y_n = (1 - \theta)y_{n-1} + \theta\pi$$

where y_n denotes the average proportion of stimulus elements related to a specific response at the start of the nth trial, θ denotes the probability of sampling an element of the stimulus set, and π is a constant. Solve this equation.

24. Restle [14] regards a trial of discrimination learning as a set of cues to which conditioning occurs. With this interpretation a conditioned cue is one the subject knows how to use in order to obtain a reward. If y_n denotes the probability that a particular cue has been conditioned at the start of the nth trial, Restle obtains the difference equation

$$y_n = y_{n-1} + \theta(1 - y_{n-1})$$

where θ is the proportion of unconditioned cues that become conditioned on any given trial. Solve this equation. Compare the results of Exercises 23 and 24.

Chapter Review

New Terms

amortization (p. 401)
annuity (p. 397)
arithmetic progression (p. 375)
common difference (p. 375)
common ratio (p. 380)
compound interest (p. 386)
effective rate of interest (p. 388)
first-order linear difference
    equation (p. 391)
future value of an annuity (p. 397)
geometric progression (p. 380)
interest (p. 385)

nominal rate of interest (p. 388)
present value (p. 389)
present value of an annuity (p. 399)
principal (p. 385)
simple annuity (p. 397)
simple interest (p. 385)
sinking fund (p. 398)
solution of a difference equation
    (p. 391)
sum of the terms of a geometric
    progression (p. 382)
terms of a sequence (p. 375)

Review Exercises

1. Label the following statements true or false.
   (a) The nth term of the arithmetic progression with first term y_1 and common difference d is $y_1 + nd$.
   (b) The sum of the first n terms of the arithmetic progression with first term y_1 and common difference d is $\frac{1}{2}n[2y_1 + (n-1)d]$.
   (c) The nth term of the geometric progression with first term y_1 and common ratio r is $y_1 r^n$.
   (d) The sum of the terms of a geometric progression exists whenever the common ratio r satisfies $-1 \leq r \leq 1$.
   (e) If the sum of the terms of the geometric progression with first term y_1 and common ratio r exists, it is $y_1/(1-r)$.
   (f) If a principal P is borrowed for t years at an annual simple interest rate r, the amount of interest owed is $P(1 + rt)$.
   (g) If a principal P is deposited in an account paying compound interest at the rate of r per period, the value of the account after n periods will be $P(1 + r)^n$.
   (h) The present value of A compounded for n periods at an interest rate of r per period is $A(1 + r)^{-n}$.
   (i) The effective rate of interest is the annual simple interest rate that is equivalent to a particular compound interest rate.
   (j) In a simple annuity the interest period must coincide with the interval between successive payments.
   (k) A sinking fund is the repayment of a loan and interest by a sequence of equal periodic payments.
   (l) The present value of an annuity is the sum of the present values of all the payments of the annuity.

2. Determine the twentieth term of the arithmetic progression $3, -1, -5, -9, \ldots$.

3. Compute the sum of the first 30 terms of the arithmetic progression $-12, -9, -6, -3, \ldots$.

4. Determine the tenth term of the geometric progression $6, -12, 24, -48, \ldots$.

5. Compute the sum of the first 20 terms of the geometric progression $-32, 16, -8, 4, \ldots$.

6. Compute the sum of the terms of the geometric progression $192, 48, 12, 3, \ldots$.

7. If $6000 is deposited in an account paying 7% simple interest, what will the value of the account be after 3 years?

8. If $2000 is deposited in an account that compounds interest quarterly at an annual rate of 8%, what will the value of the account be after six years?

9. Compute the present value of $10,000 compounded semiannually for 10 years at an annual interest rate of 6%.

10. Write the first five terms of the solution of the difference equation $y_n = 3y_{n-1} - 5$ that has first term 1.

11. Use (10.13) to evaluate the twentieth term of the solution of the difference equation $y_n = 1.025 y_{n-1} + 50$ that has first term 1000.

12. A $5000 automobile loan, borrowed at a monthly rate of 1% interest, is to be repaid by a sequence of 36 equal monthly payments. How much should each payment be?

13. If payments of $300 are made each month into an account compounding interest monthly at an annual rate of 6%, what amount of money will be in this account after five years?
14. What amount of money should be deposited now in an account paying 5% interest compounded quarterly in order to withdraw $500 every three months for four years starting three months from now?
15. How much money should a company deposit each month in an account paying 9% interest compounded monthly in order to have $20,000 available after two years?
16. A manufacturer bought a large piece of machinery for $24,000. If its book value decreases by $1200 each year, what will the book value of the machinery be during the twelfth year?
17. A company with a $30,000 advertising budget in 1975 intends to increase this budget at the rate of 2% per year.
    (a) What will this company's advertising budget be for the tenth year (1984)?
    (b) How much will this company spend on advertising during the period 1975–1984?

References

1. Allen, R. G. D., *Mathematical Economics*, 2nd ed. London: Macmillan, 1966.
2. Ammons, Robert B., "Acquisition of Motor Skill: I. Quantitative Analysis and Theoretical Formulation," *Psychol. Rev.*, vol. 54 (1947), pp. 263–281.
3. Baumol, William J., *Economic Dynamics*, 3rd ed. New York: Macmillan, 1970.
4. Burke, C. J., W. K. Estes, and S. Hellyer, "Rate of Verbal Conditioning in Relation to Stimulus Variability," *J. Exp. Psychol.*, vol. 48, no. 3 (September 1954), pp. 153–161.
5. Bush, Robert R. and Frederick Mosteller, "A Mathematical Model for Simple Learning," *Psychol. Rev.*, vol. 58, no. 5 (September 1951), pp. 313–323.
6. Champernowne, D. G., "Model of Income Distribution," *Econ. J.*, vol. 63 (June 1953), pp. 318–351.
7. Ettlinger, J. H., "A Curve of Growth to Represent the Learning Process," *J. Exp. Psychol.*, vol. 9 (1926), pp. 409–414.
8. Ezekiel, Mordecai, "The Cobweb Theorem," *Q. J. Econ.*, vol. 52 (1938), pp. 255–280.
9. Goldberg, Samuel, *Introduction to Differences Equations*. New York: Wiley, 1958.
10. Harrod, Roy F., "An Essay in Dynamic Theory," *Econ. J.*, vol. 49 (March 1939), pp. 14–33.
11. Hicks, J. R., *The Trade Cycle*. London: Oxford University Press, 1950.
12. Kahn, R. F., "The Relation of Home Investment to Unemployment," *Econ. J.*, vol. 41 (1931), pp. 173–198.
13. Metzler, L. A., "The Nature and Stability of Inventory Cycles," *Rev. Econ. Stat.*, vol. 23 (1941), pp. 113–129.

14. Restle, Frank, "A Theory of Discrimination Learning," *Psychol. Rev.*, vol. 62, no. 1 (January 1955), pp. 11–19.
15. Samuelson, Paul A., *Foundations of Economic Analysis.* Cambridge, Mass.: Harvard University Press, 1947.
16. Samuelson, Paul A., "Interactions Between the Multiplier Analysis and the Principle of Acceleration," *Rev. Econ. Stat.*, vol. 21 (1939), pp. 75–78.
17. Selby, Samuel M., ed., *Handbook of Tables for Mathematics*, 4th ed. Cleveland: Chemical Rubber, 1970.
18. Stephan, Frederick F. and Elliot G. Mishler, "The Distribution of Participation in Small Groups: An Exponential Approximation," *Am. Sociol. Rev.*, vol. 17, no. 5 (October 1952), pp. 598–608.
19. Tinbergen, J., *Statistical Testing of Business Cycle Theories.* Geneva: League of Nations, 1939.

11

Graph Theory

In previous chapters the word "graph" was used in connection with functions. Recall, for example, that by plotting the points (x, y) that satisfy $y = f(x)$ we obtain the graph of the function f.

In this chapter, however, we shall be concerned with a different meaning of the word "graph." In this context a graph may be regarded as a set of points together with curves joining some of the points. There are many occasions when this type of graph may be used to represent a situation of interest; for instance, the points may represent people and the curves may represent kinship relationships, or the points may represent cities and the curves may represent roads. These types of diagrams occur in many disciplines and are called by such names as family trees, road networks, circuit diagrams, organizational structures, communication networks, and sociograms.

Since its invention by the great Swiss mathematician Leonhard Euler (1707–1783) in order to solve the Königsberg bridge problem, graph theory has been associated with applications in physics and chemistry. More recently, graph theory has also proved useful in the social, life, and management sciences. (See, for example, [1], [6], [7], [9], [12], [24], and [27].) Sections 11.1 and 11.2 discuss the basic concepts of graph theory used in these applications, and a few specific types of applications are presented in Sections 11.3 and 11.4.

11.1 Graphs and Their Representations

In [24] Shaw, Rothschild, and Strickland investigate the effects of three different communication patterns on the performance of four-member teams attempting to solve a problem concerning interpersonal relations. The three patterns they consider can be distinguished by the number of members of the team who are capable of communicating directly with all the others. In the first pattern (called the *star*) only one member can communicate directly with all the others, in the second pattern (called the *slash*) two members can communicate directly with all the others, and in the third pattern (called the *comcon*) each member can communicate directly with all the others. These three patterns can be visualized as in Figure 11.1, where a dot corresponds to a team member and a line joins two dots if the corresponding teammates can communicate directly.

The mathematical structure represented by the patterns in Figure 11.1 is called a graph. By a *graph* we mean a nonempty set $V = \{v_1, v_2, \ldots, v_p\}$ of elements called *vertices* together with a set E of unordered pairs $v_i v_j$ of distinct vertices called *edges*. In this notation the edge $v_i v_j$ is regarded as being the same as the edge $v_j v_i$. Graphs may be represented by drawing dots for each of the vertices and by connecting two dots whenever the corresponding pair of vertices form an edge.

graph
vertices
edges

EXAMPLE 1

The graph in which $V = \{v_1, v_2, v_3, v_4\}$ and $E = \{v_1 v_2, v_1 v_3, v_1 v_4\}$ may be represented as in Figure 11.2. This graph is the star pattern shown in Figure 11.1.

EXAMPLE 2

The comcon pattern in Figure 11.1 is a representation of the graph in which $V = \{v_1, v_2, v_3, v_4\}$ and $E = \{v_1 v_2, v_1 v_3, v_1 v_4, v_2 v_3, v_2 v_4, v_3 v_4\}$.

The same graph may have different representations. For example, the graph in Example 2 may be represented as in Figure 11.3 or as in Figure 11.4. Notice, in particular, that the representation of two edges may intersect at a point that is not a vertex (as in Figure 11.3). Since it is easy to construct the set of vertices and the set of edges from any representation of a graph, it is customary to refer to a representation of a graph as being the graph itself.

adjacent vertices
degree of a vertex

Two vertices v_i and v_j are called *adjacent* if $v_i v_j$ is an edge. The *degree* of a vertex is the number of vertices adjacent to it. Thus in the graph shown in Figure 11.5, v_1 is adjacent to v_2, v_3, and v_4 only, hence the degree of v_1 is 3. Likewise v_7 is adjacent to v_3, v_6, v_8, and v_9 only, hence the degree of v_7 is 4.

Since each edge of a graph joins exactly two vertices, the following result is immediate.

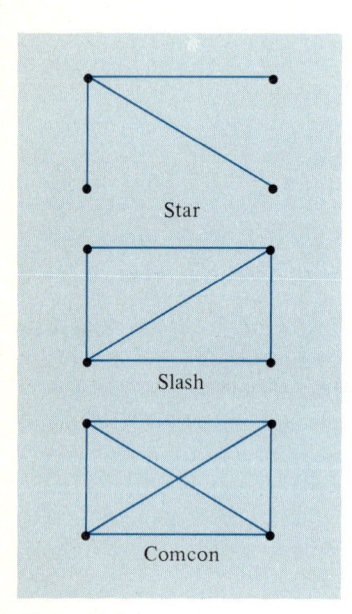

Star

Slash

Comcon

Figure 11.1

Figure 11.2

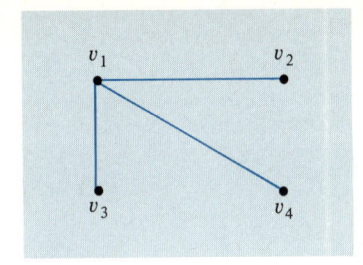

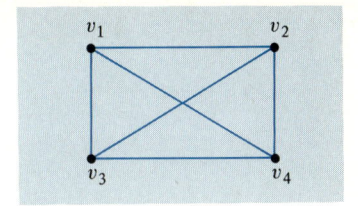

Figure 11.3

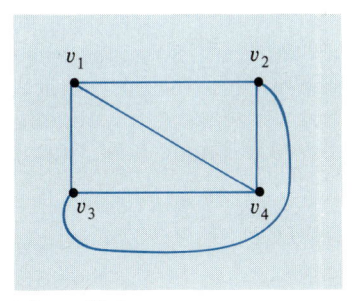

Figure 11.4

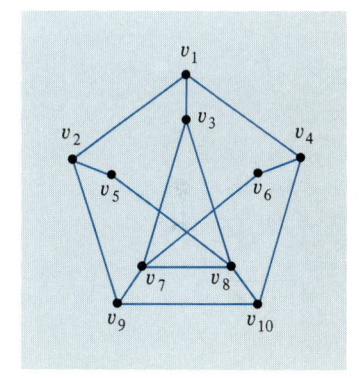

Figure 11.5

THEOREM 11.1

The sum of the degrees of all the vertices in a graph equals twice the number of edges. In particular, the sum of the degrees of all the vertices must be an even number.

Graphs are useful as models in the study of symmetric relationships. For example, the following social relationships can be represented by graphs: being acquainted, residing in the same neighborhood, belonging to the same organization, and having the same socioeconomic status. The following example is of this type.

EXAMPLE 3

Among a set of seven people, is it possible that everyone knows exactly four of the others? Is it possible that everyone knows exactly three of the others?

To answer these questions, we shall regard the persons as vertices of a graph and consider two vertices to be adjacent if the corresponding persons are acquainted. Thus the condition that everyone knows exactly four of the others means that the degree of

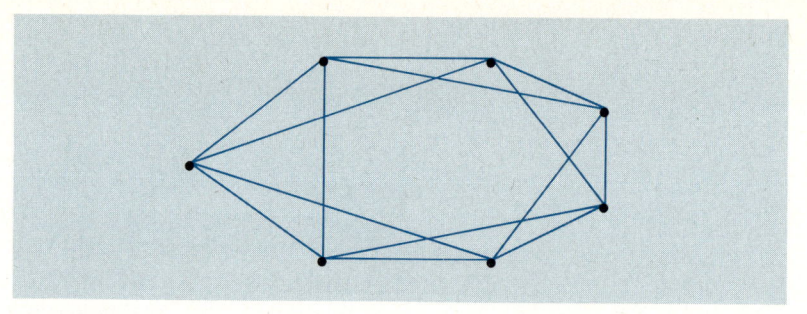

Figure 11.6

each vertex is 4. So it is possible for everyone to know exactly four of the others if there is a graph with seven vertices in which each vertex has degree 4. It is not difficult to construct such a graph; one is shown in Figure 11.6. Thus the first question has an affirmative answer.

Likewise it is possible for each of the seven to know exactly three of the others only if there is a graph with seven vertices in which each vertex has degree 3. But the sum of the degrees of all the vertices in such a graph would be 21, in contradiction to Theorem 11.1. Therefore it is impossible for everyone to know exactly three of the others.

planar graph

We have seen that in a representation of a graph it is possible for two edges to intersect at a point that is not a vertex. A *planar graph* is a graph having the property that some representation of it can be drawn so that no edges intersect except at vertices. Thus, for example, the graph in Figure 11.3 is a planar graph since it may be redrawn as in Figure 11.4 so that no edges intersect except at vertices.

The *three houses and three utilities problem* is a well-known recreational problem involving planar graphs. It asks if the three houses (labeled h_1, h_2, and h_3) shown in Figure 11.7 can be connected directly to each of the three utilities (labeled u_1, u_2, u_3) in such a way that none of the lines or pipes cross. In the terminology of graph theory this problem is equivalent to determining if the graph in Figure 11.8 is planar.

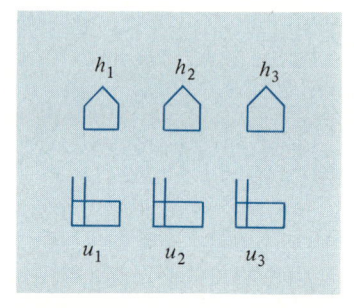

Figure 11.7

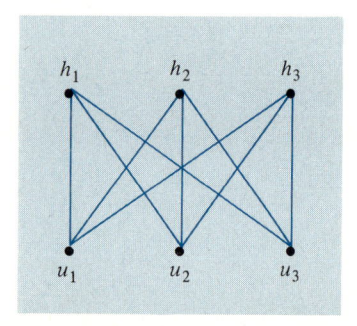

Figure 11.8

11.1 Graphs and Their Representations 421

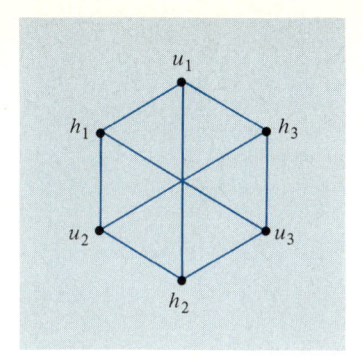

Figure 11.9

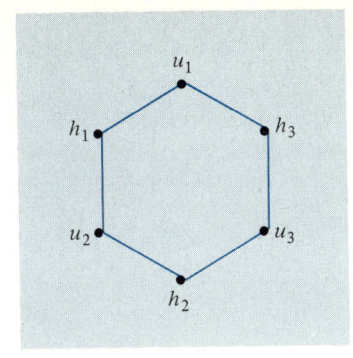

Figure 11.10

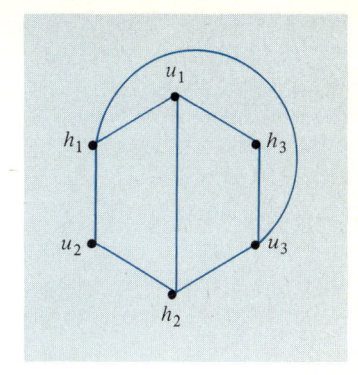

Figure 11.11

hexagonal graph

Note that the graph in Figure 11.8 is another representation of the *hexagonal graph*, shown in Figure 11.9. We can see easily that the hexagonal graph is not planar by the following reasoning. In any representation of the hexagonal graph it must be possible to pass through the vertices u_1, h_1, u_2, h_2, u_3, h_3, and u_1 by traveling along edges as in Figure 11.10. There is an edge h_2u_1 of the hexagonal graph that can be drawn either inside or outside the hexagon in Figure 11.10; let us draw it on the inside as in Figure 11.11. (The argument is similar if it is drawn on the outside.) If the graph is to be planar, then the edge h_1u_3 must be drawn on the outside (as in Figure 11.11) because h_2u_1 prevents it from being drawn on the inside. But then the edge h_3u_2 must intersect either h_2u_1 (if it is drawn on the inside of the hexagon) or h_1u_3 (if it is drawn on the outside). So the hexagonal graph is not planar, hence the three houses and three utilities problem has no solution.[1]

EXAMPLE 4

pentagonal graph

By reasoning as above, we can show that the *pentagonal graph* shown in Figure 11.12 is also not planar.

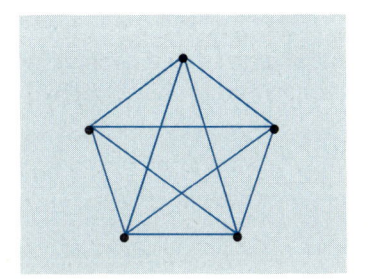

Figure 11.12

We have seen that the hexagonal graph in Figure 11.9 and the pentagonal graph in Figure 11.12 are not planar. Surprisingly, the only graphs that are not planar are ones that in some sense contain a copy of the hexagonal or pentagonal graph. To make this statement precise, we must consider two operations that may be used to change a graph by including or deleting vertices of degree 2.

If we start with a graph G, we may form a new graph by inserting new vertices anywhere along an edge of G. For example, we may insert a new vertex v_7 on the edge v_1v_3 in Figure 11.13 to obtain the new graph shown in Figure 11.14. After this insertion, the edge v_1v_3 in Figure 11.13

---

[1] If however, we make the more realistic assumption that the problem is three-dimensional instead of two-dimensional, so that lines or pipes may be constructed over or under other lines or pipes, then a solution can be easily obtained.

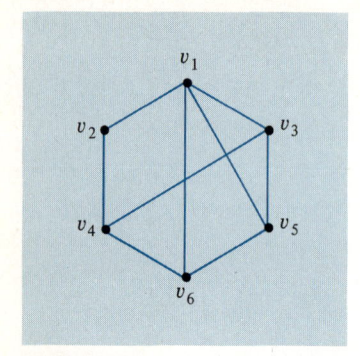

Figure 11.13

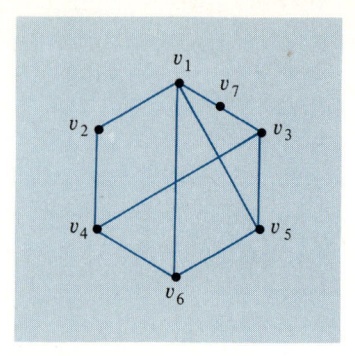

Figure 11.14

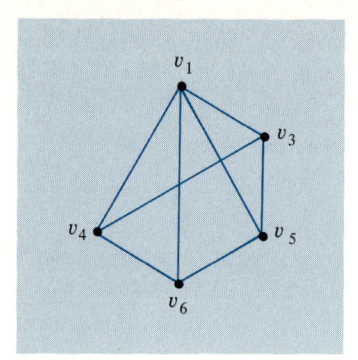

Figure 11.15

is replaced by the two edges v_1v_7 and v_7v_3 in Figure 11.14. Each vertex inserted in this manner is a vertex of degree 2. Conversely, a new graph can be formed by deleting any vertex of degree 2 through the reverse process: If u is a vertex of degree 2 with edges uv_i and uv_j, remove the vertex u and replace the edges uv_i and uv_j by v_iv_j. In this way the graph in Figure 11.14 can be changed into the graph in Figure 11.15 by deleting v_2 and v_7. This operation of deleting vertices of degree 2 will be called *contracting* the graph. With this terminology we can now characterize all planar graphs.

contracting a graph

THEOREM 11.2

A graph is a planar graph precisely when it does not contain within it any graph that can be contracted to the hexagonal graph or the pentagonal graph.

EXAMPLE 5

The graph shown in Figure 11.16 is not planar, since it contains a graph within it (in color) that can be contracted to the hexagonal graph. (See Figure 11.17.)

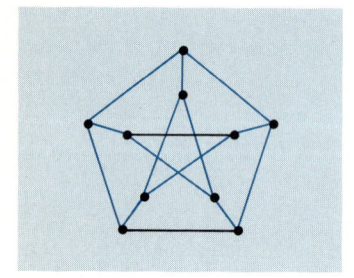

Figure 11.16

Exercises

In Exercises 1–4, construct a representation of each graph from the given set of vertices V and the given set of edges E.

1. $V = \{v_1, v_2, v_3, v_4\}$ and $E = \{v_1v_3, v_2v_3, v_2v_4, v_3v_4\}$
2. $V = \{v_1, v_2, v_3, v_4, v_5\}$ and $E = \{v_1v_3, v_1v_4, v_2v_3, v_2v_5, v_3v_4, v_3v_5\}$
3. $V = \{v_1, v_2, v_3, v_4, v_5\}$ and $E = \{v_1v_2, v_1v_3, v_1v_4, v_2v_3, v_2v_5, v_3v_4, v_3v_5, v_4v_5\}$
4. $V = \{v_1, v_2, v_3, v_4, v_5\}$ and $E = \{v_1v_2, v_1v_4, v_1v_5, v_2v_3, v_2v_5, v_3v_4, v_3v_5\}$

In Exercises 5–8, determine which vertices are adjacent to v_1 and compute the degree of each vertex. Then verify the conclusion of Theorem 11.1.

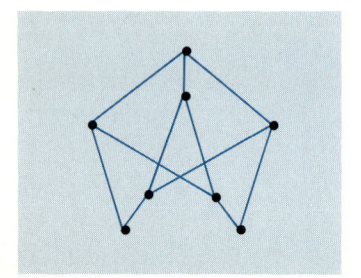

Figure 11.17

5. [graph with vertices v_1, v_2, v_3, v_4]

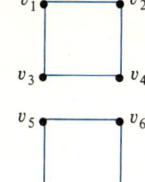

6. [graph with vertices $v_1, v_2, v_3, v_4, v_5, v_6, v_7, v_8$ forming two squares]

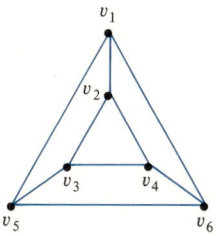

7. [graph with vertices $v_1, v_2, v_3, v_4, v_5, v_6$]

8. [graph with vertices $v_1, v_2, v_3, v_4, v_5, v_6$]

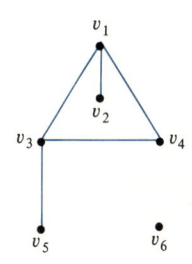

In Exercises 9–14, give an example of a graph satisfying the given conditions. If no such example exists, explain why.

9. A graph containing no vertices of even degree
10. A graph containing no vertices of odd degree
11. A graph containing exactly one vertex of even degree
12. A graph containing exactly one vertex of odd degree
13. A graph containing four vertices, three of degree 1 and one of degree 3
14. A graph containing four vertices, two of degree 1 and two of degree 3

In Exercises 15–20, determine if the given graphs are planar. If so, draw a representation having no edges intersecting except at vertices.

15. [star graph with vertices v_1, v_2, v_3, v_4, v_5]

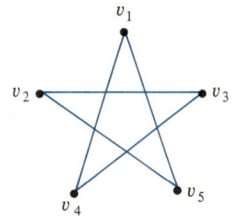

16. [graph with vertices v_1, v_2, v_3, v_4, v_5]

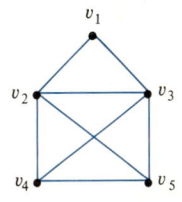

17. [graph with vertices $v_1, v_2, v_3, v_4, v_5, v_6, v_7, v_8$]

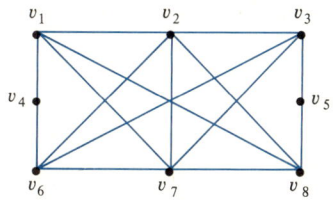

18. [graph with vertices $v_1, v_2, v_3, v_4, v_5, v_6, v_7, v_8$]

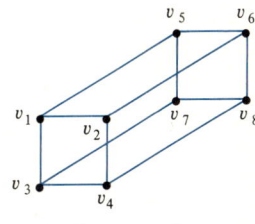

19. [bipartite graph with vertices $v_1, v_2, v_3, v_4, v_5, v_6$]

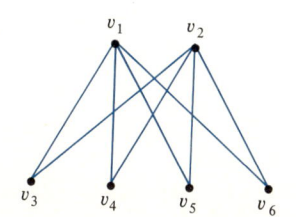

20. [graph with vertices $v_1, v_2, v_3, v_4, v_5, v_6$]

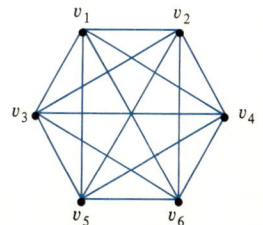

21. Among a set of five people, is it possible that everyone knows
    (a) Exactly two of the others?
    (b) Exactly three of the others?

22. Represent the following acquaintances by a graph in which the vertices represent the six people and an edge is drawn between vertices wherever the corresponding persons are acquainted:

    Andy knows Curtis and Don.
    Barbara knows Don, Ellen, and Frank.
    Curtis knows Andy, Don, and Frank.
    Don knows Andy, Barbara, and Curtis.
    Ellen knows Barbara.
    Frank knows Barbara and Curtis.

23. Below are the boards of directors of five companies. Represent each company by the vertex of a graph and join two vertices by an edge wherever the corresponding companies' boards of directors interlock (that is, have a common member).

    Company 1: Gonzalez, Jones, Martin, Smith, Stein, Washington
    Company 2: Allen, Black, Burke, Griffith, Johnson
    Company 3: Goldberg, Gonzalez, Green, Murray, Walker, White
    Company 4: Allen, Gilmore, Martin, Silver, Winters
    Company 5: Black, Castor, Jenkins, Peterson, Schmidt, Winters

24. In a modified round-robin tennis tournament, each of the eight players opposed three others. Represent each player by the vertex of a graph and join two vertices wherever the corresponding players opposed each other.

    Ashe played Dibbs, Gottfried, and McEnroe.
    Connors played Gerulaitis, Solomon, and Tanner.
    Dibbs played Ashe, McEnroe, and Solomon.
    Gerulaitis played Connors, Gottfried, and Tanner.
    Gottfried played Ashe, Gerulaitis, and Solomon.
    McEnroe played Ashe, Dibbs, and Tanner.
    Solomon played Connors, Dibbs, and Gottfried.
    Tanner played Connors, Gerulaitis, and McEnroe.

complete graph

25. A graph is called *complete* if every pair of vertices is adjacent. How many edges are there in the complete graph with n vertices?

11.2 Paths and Circuits

Many applications of graph theory involve finding a route along the edges of a graph satisfying certain conditions. In this section we shall investigate several problems of this type; another will be discussed in Section 11.4.

If we think of a graph as a road map in which the vertices represent cities and the edges represent roads, then we can begin a trip at some city u, travel along a road uv_1 to another city v_1, then along another road v_1v_2 to city v_2, and so forth. Such a set of n ($n \geq 1$) edges $uv_1, v_1v_2, \ldots,$ *edge progression* $v_{n-1}v$ in which consecutive edges (roads) share a common vertex (city) is called an *edge progression of length n* from u to v. Observe that once

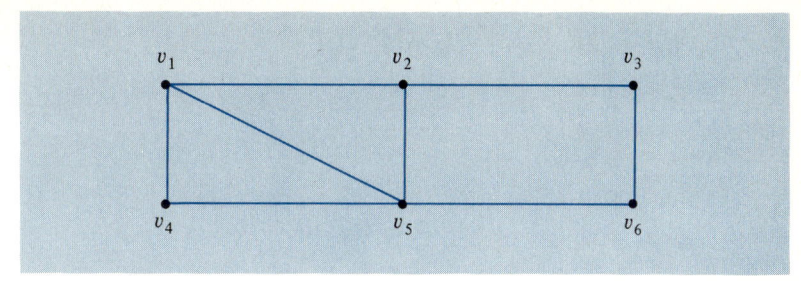

Figure 11.18

the consecutive vertices (cities) in the edge progression are known, then the corresponding edges (roads) are obvious. Consequently we denote the edge progression above by $uv_1v_2\ldots v_{n-1}v$, that is, by listing its successive vertices.

In an edge progression both vertices and edges may be repeated. For example, in Figure 11.18, $v_5v_1v_5v_2v_3v_6v_5v_4$ is an edge progression of length 7 from v_5 to v_4. An edge progression of length n containing no repeated edges is called a *path* of length n. The edge progression above is not a path because the edge v_5v_1 is repeated; however, $v_5v_2v_3v_6v_5v_4$ is a path of length 5 from v_5 to v_4. Notice that vertices, unlike edges, may be repeated in a path.

path

connected graph

components of a graph

A graph in which there is a path from one vertex to every other vertex is called *connected*. The graph in Figure 11.18 is connected, whereas that in Figure 11.19 is not connected. The latter consists of four separated parts called *components*, each of which (considered by itself) is connected. For most purposes in graph theory it is possible to assume that a graph is connected, for otherwise each connected component can be examined separately.

Recall that a graph is completely determined by its vertices and a knowledge of which vertices are adjacent. This information can be conveyed by a matrix in the following way: If G is a graph with vertices $v_1, v_2, \ldots, v_p$, associate with G the $p \times p$ matrix $A = (a_{ij})$ in which $a_{ij} = 1$ if there is an edge joining v_i and v_j and $a_{ij} = 0$ otherwise. The matrix A is called the *adjacency matrix* of G and is an incidence matrix in the sense of Section 3.4. Thus the results stated there are true for adjacency matrices; in particular, the i, j entry of A^n represents the number

adjacency matrix

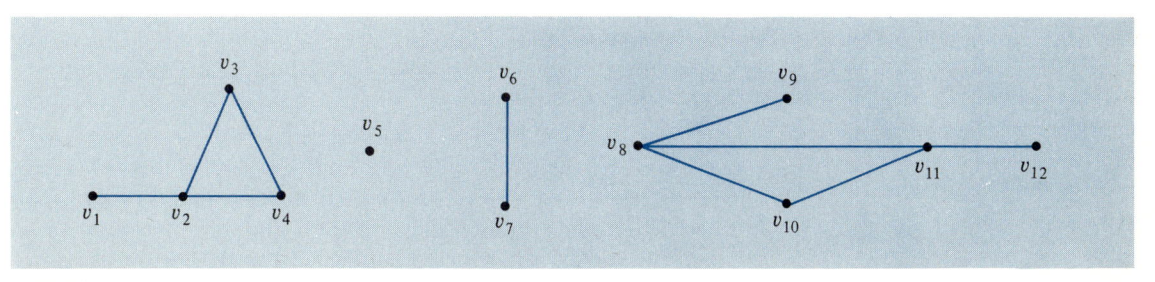

Figure 11.19

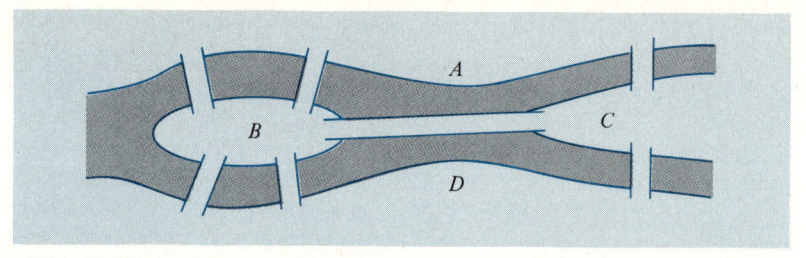

Figure 11.20

of edge progressions of length n from v_i to v_j. Although there are computational advantages in formulating a graph as a matrix, this destroys the visual aspect of the graph. Consequently, we will not pursue this approach further.

Many practical situations involving graphs require traversing all the edges or vertices of a graph exactly once. In fact, graph theory was invented to solve such a problem, the *Königsberg bridge problem*. The city of Königsberg (now called Kaliningrad, USSR) in East Prussia is located along both banks and on two islands of the river Pregel. Seven bridges connected the four regions as shown in Figure 11.20. The townspeople amused themselves with the problem of finding a continuous route across all seven bridges that did not cross any bridge more than once.

This problem was solved by Leonhard Euler, who was not only able to show that it was impossible to cross the Königsberg bridges in this manner but actually determined the precise conditions under which such a route exists. He began by representing the four parts of Königsberg by dots and joining each pair of dots as many times as the number of bridges joining the corresponding parts of the city. The resulting diagram, shown in Figure 11.21, is a *multigraph*, a generalized graph in which more than one edge may join the same pair of vertices.

multigraph

Euler noted that, in order to be able to find a path that includes each edge of a multigraph exactly once, the multigraph must first be connected. In addition, except for the first and last vertices in the path, every other vertex must be of even degree since each entry into a vertex by one edge and exit by another edge requires two different edges at the vertex. Since the four vertices in Figure 11.21 are all of odd degree, Euler concluded that there was no way of crossing all seven bridges exactly once. More interestingly, he also proved that, if the two conditions above are satisfied, then there is a path in a multigraph that includes each edge exactly once.

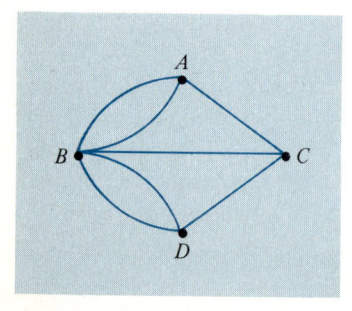

Figure 11.21

THEOREM 11.3

There is a path including each edge of a multigraph exactly once precisely when it is connected and has either no vertices of odd degree or exactly two vertices of odd degree. Furthermore, if there are no vertices of odd degree, then such a path must begin and end at the same vertex; otherwise, if there are two vertices of odd degree, then such a path must begin at one of these vertices and end at the other.

EXAMPLE 6

There is no path including each edge of the graph in Figure 11.22 exactly once, since there are four vertices (v_1, v_3, v_5, and v_6) of odd degree. On the other hand, the graph in Figure 11.23 contains only two vertices (v_1 and v_6) of odd degree. Hence from Theorem 11.3 there is a path including each edge of this graph exactly once, and any such path must begin at either v_1 or v_6 and end at the other. One path of this type is $v_1 v_2 v_6 v_4 v_1 v_3 v_2 v_5 v_4 v_3 v_5 v_6$.

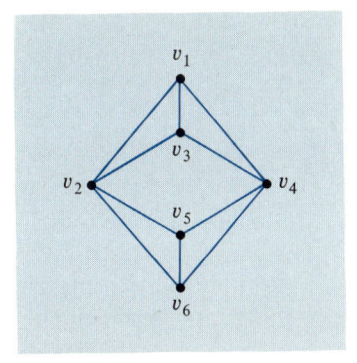

Figure 11.22

EXAMPLE 7

Figure 11.24 shows the territory in which a letter carrier must deliver mail. She is responsible for both sides of Center Street, Second Avenue, and Third Avenue, but only one side of First Avenue, Fourth Avenue, North Street, and South Street. Because of the heavy traffic along these streets, it is impossible to cross back and forth to deliver to houses on both sides of a street. Consequently it is necessary to walk along Center Street, Second Avenue, and Third Avenue at least twice, once on each side. Is it possible for the letter carrier to park her truck, deliver mail throughout this territory, and return to the truck without walking along any side of a street more than once?

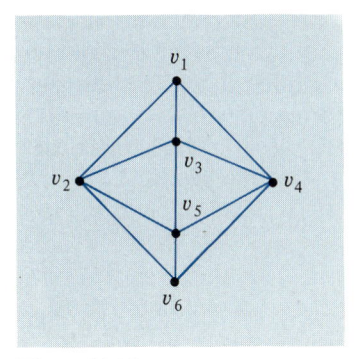

Figure 11.23

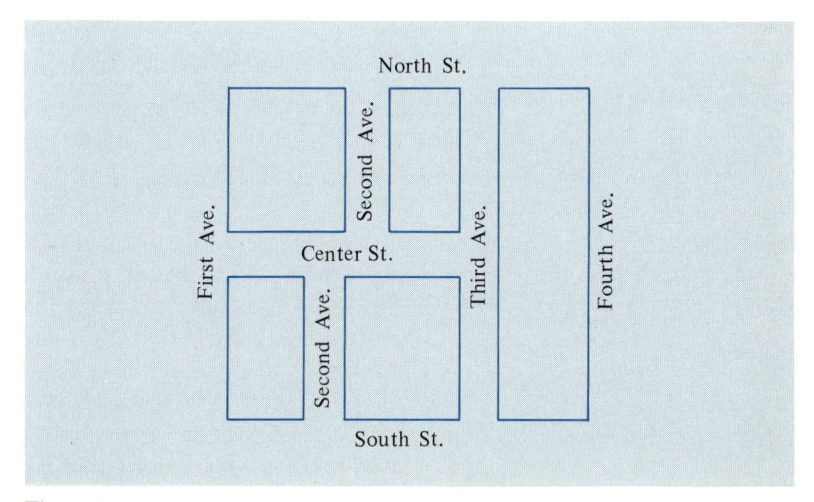

Figure 11.24

428 *Chapter 11 Graph Theory*

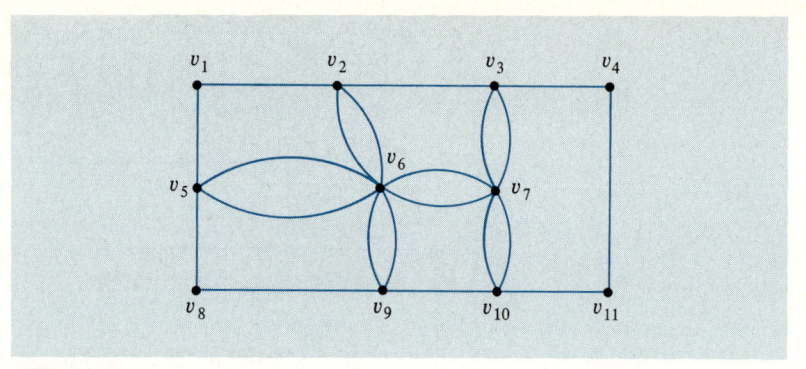

Figure 11.25

To answer this question, let us form a multigraph in which each vertex represents an intersection of two streets served by the letter carrier and in which each edge corresponds to one side of a street between two intersections. One such representation of the letter carrier's territory is shown in Figure 11.25. Our problem can now be formulated as follows: Is there a path through the multigraph that begins and ends at the same vertex and includes each edge exactly once? Since each vertex is of even degree, Theorem 11.3 guarantees the existence of such a path. Moreover, the letter carrier can begin delivering anywhere and end at the same place. One possible path is

$$v_1 v_2 v_3 v_4 v_{11} v_{10} v_7 v_3 v_7 v_6 v_7 v_{10} v_9 v_6 v_2 v_6 v_5 v_6 v_9 v_8 v_5 v_1$$

In Examples 6 and 7 we were concerned with finding a path that includes each edge of a graph or multigraph exactly once. A different problem that arises in certain types of applications is to find a path that includes each *vertex* exactly once. Unfortunately, characterizing graphs that have such a path is an unsolved problem. Thus, in general, determining the existence of such a path requires examining each case individually.

EXAMPLE 8

A sales representative living in Indianapolis must visit clients in the other nine cities shown in Figure 11.26. He would like to plan his trip using interstate roads so that he passes through each city exactly once before returning home. If the interstate roads that pass through these cities are as in Figure 11.26, is such a trip possible?

Observe that, if the sales representative is to visit each city exactly once, then he will use only two of the roads passing through each city, one when entering the city and the other when leaving. In addition, he must visit either Terre Haute or Gary first and the

11.2 Paths and Circuits 429

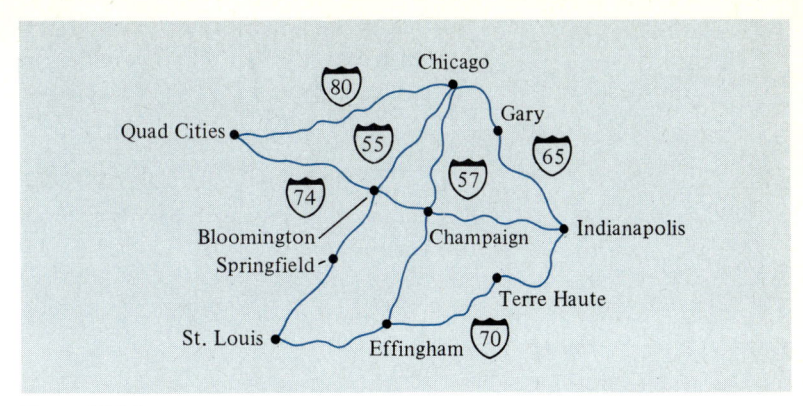

Figure 11.26

other last (immediately before returning to Indianapolis). Thus the road from Champaign to Indianapolis cannot be used.

Let us try to construct a route satisfying the required conditions. If Gary is the first city visited, then Chicago must be visited second. From Chicago the representative must travel to the Quad Cities, for, if this road is not used, then the only way to enter and leave the Quad Cities would be through Bloomington. After leaving the Quad Cities, the next stop must be Bloomington. But it is now easy to see that there is no route to Terre Haute through Champaign and St. Louis that does not pass through either Bloomington or Effingham at least twice. So the sales representative will not be able to visit each city exactly once.

If, however, it is not necessary to visit Terre Haute, then such a trip can be made through the remaining cities. One possible route is Indianapolis, Gary, Chicago, the Quad Cities, Bloomington, Springfield, St. Louis, Effingham, Champaign, and Indianapolis.

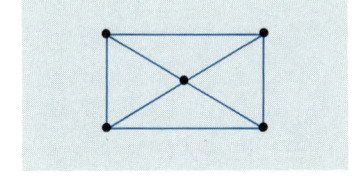

Figure 11.27

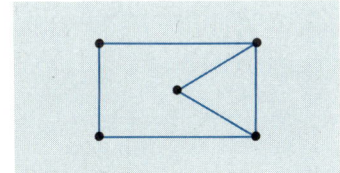

Figure 11.28

Although there is no characterization of graphs having a path including each vertex exactly once, the following result guarantees the existence of such a path in certain graphs.

THEOREM 11.4

Let G be a graph containing p vertices, where $p \geq 3$. If each vertex of G has degree at least $\frac{1}{2}p$, then there exists a path in G that includes each vertex exactly once.

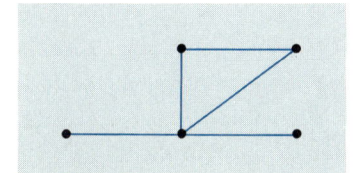

Figure 11.29

It follows from Theorem 11.4 that the graph in Figure 11.27 has a path including each vertex exactly once, for the graph has five vertices, each with a degree of at least 3. On the other hand, Theorem 11.4 gives no information about the graphs in Figures 11.28 and 11.29 because some vertex is of degree less than $\frac{1}{2}p = 2.5$. The reader should verify that in the graph shown in Figure 11.28 there is a path including each vertex exactly once, but that in the graph shown in Figure 11.29 no such path exists.

Exercises

For the graph pictured below, determine if the edge progressions given in Exercises 1–4 are paths.

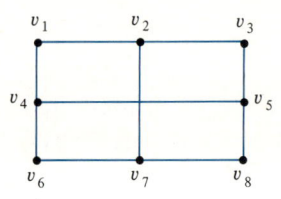

1. $v_1v_2v_7v_8v_5$
2. $v_3v_5v_4v_1v_2v_3v_5v_8v_7$
3. $v_2v_7v_8v_5v_4v_6v_7v_2v_1$
4. $v_1v_2v_3v_5v_4v_6v_7v_2$

In Exercises 5–16, determine if there is a path through the given graph or multigraph that includes each edge exactly once. If such a path exists, find one.

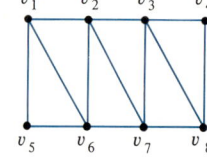

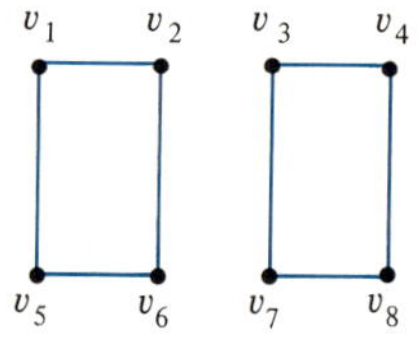

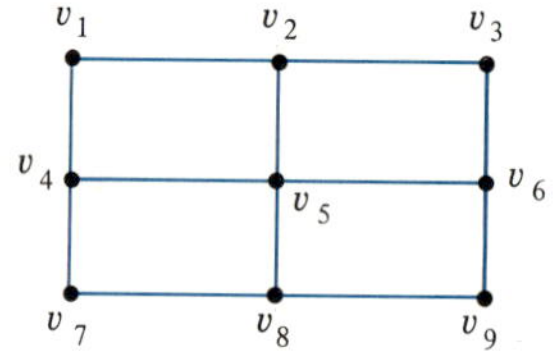

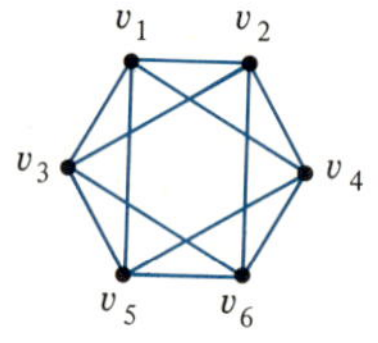

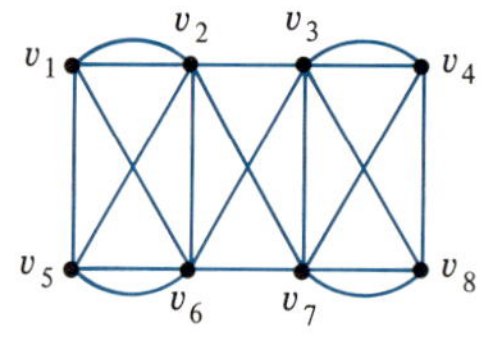

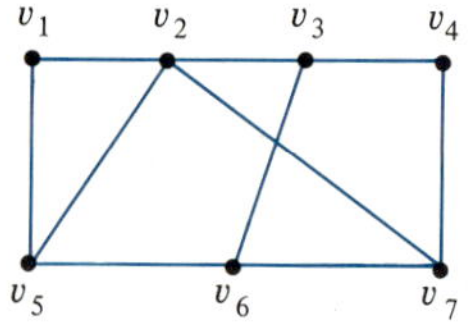

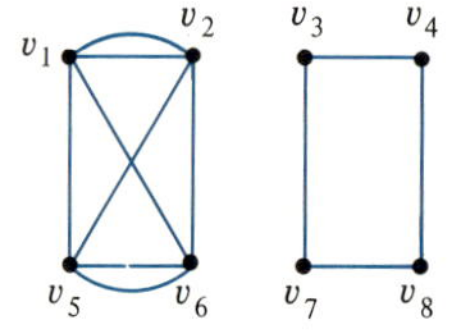

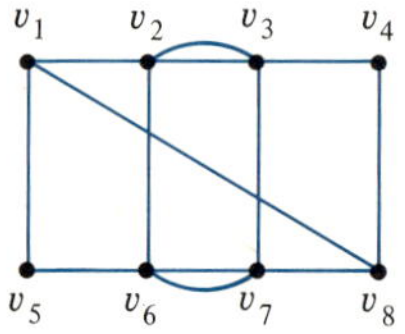

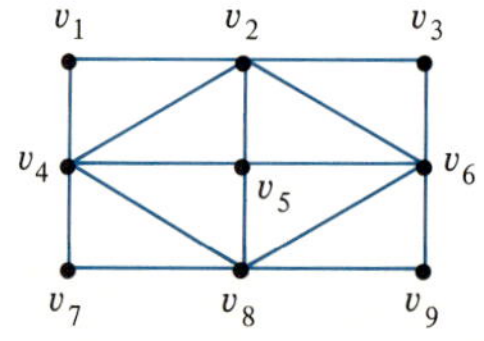

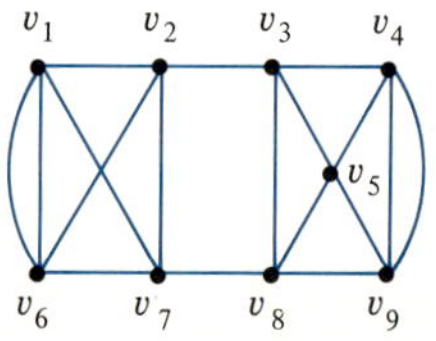

15. **16.**

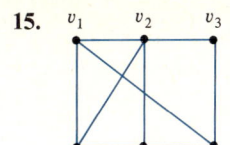

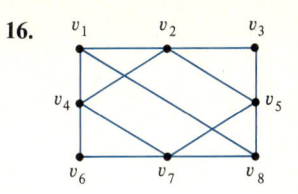

In Exercises 17–28, determine if there is a path through the given graph that includes each vertex exactly once. If such a path exists, find one.

17. **18.**

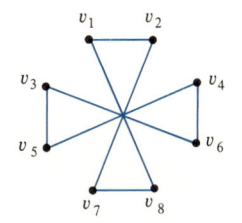

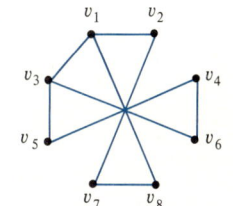

19. 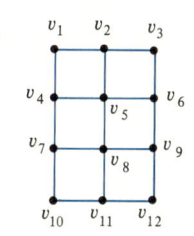 **20.**

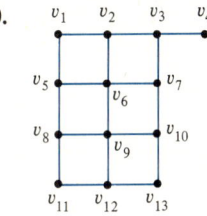

21. 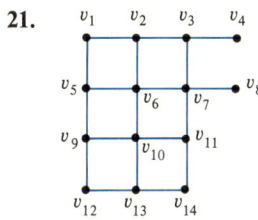 **22.**

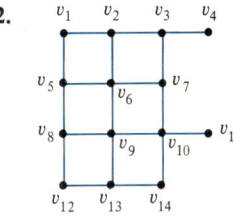

23. 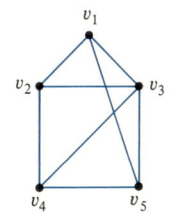 **24.**

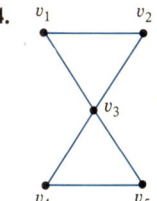

25. 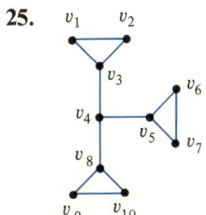 **26.**

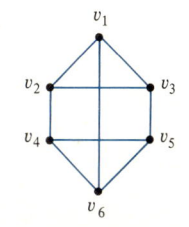

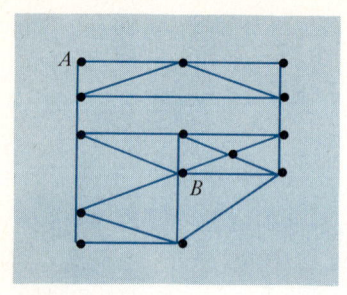

432 Chapter 11 Graph Theory

Figure 11.30

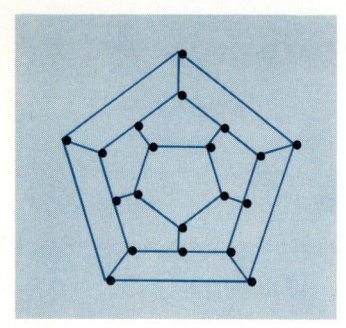

Figure 11.31

27.

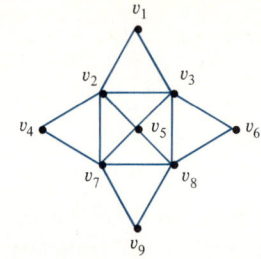

28.

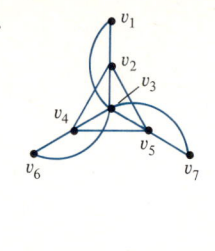

29. The graph in Figure 11.30 depicts certain towns and the roads joining them. A highway crew must drive along each of the roads to check for potholes. Will the crew be able to start from and return to town A without traveling along any road more than once? What if the crew must start from and return to town B?

30. In 1859 the famous Irish mathematician William Rowan Hamilton (1805–1865) marketed a puzzle in the shape of a regular dodecahedron (a solid figure with twelve sides, each in the shape of a regular pentagon). Each corner was labeled with the name of an important city, and the object of the puzzle was to find a route along the edges of the dodecahedron that begins and ends at the same city and includes every other city exactly once. Find such a path (called a *Hamiltonian circuit*) for the graph in Figure 11.31, which is a planar representation of Hamilton's dodecahedron.

31. A saleswoman living in Chicago would like to visit clients in each of the cities shown in Figure 11.32. Is it possible for her to visit each city exactly once before returning home, using only the interstate roads shown in the figure?

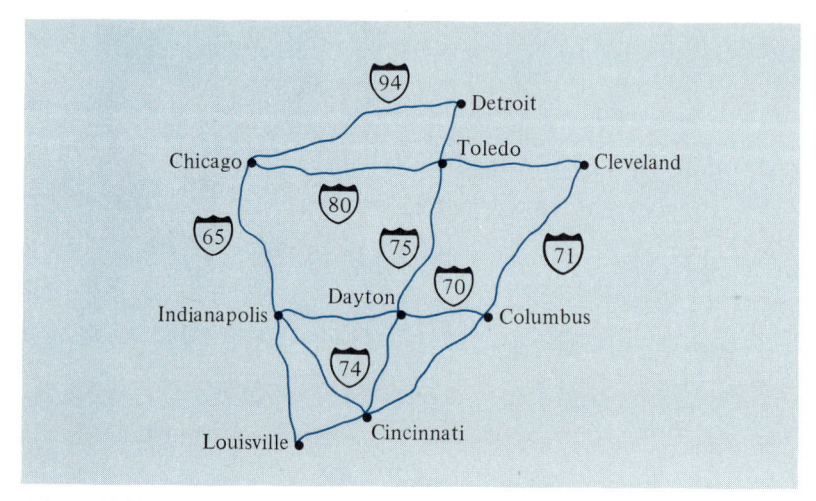

Figure 11.32

32. Figure 11.33 shows the floor plan of the House of Horrors at an amusement park.

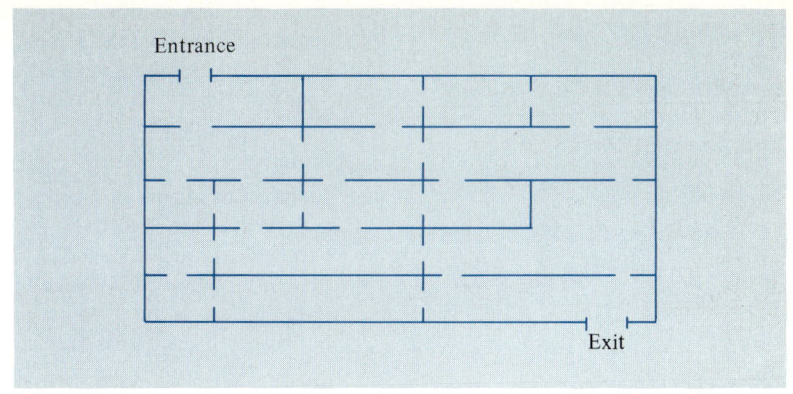

Figure 11.33

(a) Represent this figure by a multigraph in which the vertices denote rooms and two vertices are adjacent precisely where there is a door between the corresponding rooms.
(b) The doors at the House of Horrors are designed to shut and lock automatically as someone passes through them. Assuming that someone will eventually be able to leave any room as long as all the doors in that room are not locked, determine whether or not someone might become trapped inside the House of Horrors.

33. A letter carrier must deliver mail to both sides of the streets shown in Figure 11.34.

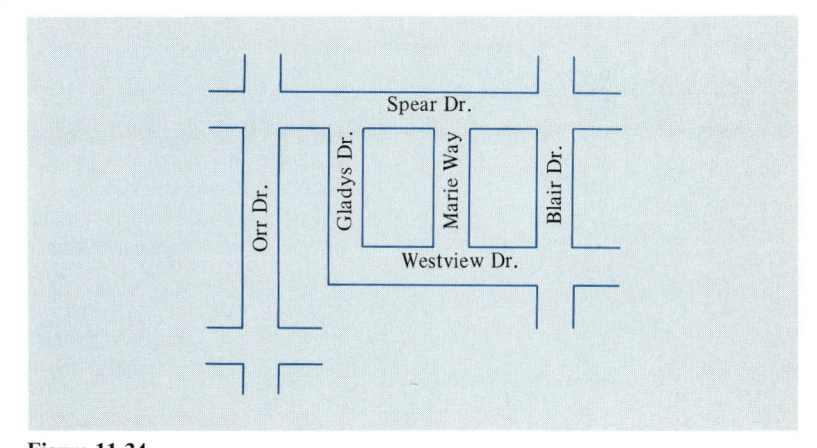

Figure 11.34

(a) Represent this figure by a multigraph in which a vertex denotes an intersection and an edge denotes one side of a street.
(b) Determine a route for delivering the mail that does not require the letter carrier to walk along the same side of any street more than once.

434 Chapter 11 Graph Theory

34. After Interstate 72 is completed between Champaign and Springfield, will it be possible for the sales representative in Example 8 to travel through each city in Figure 11.26 exactly once before returning to Indianapolis?

35. Figure 11.35 shows the pattern of streets in a particular residential neighborhood.
    (a) Represent this figure by a graph in which vertices denote intersections and edges denote streets.
    (b) A truck driver delivers bundles of newspapers to each of the intersections in Figure 11.35, where they are picked up by carriers for home delivery. Is there a route beginning and ending at intersection A that passes through each intersection exactly once?

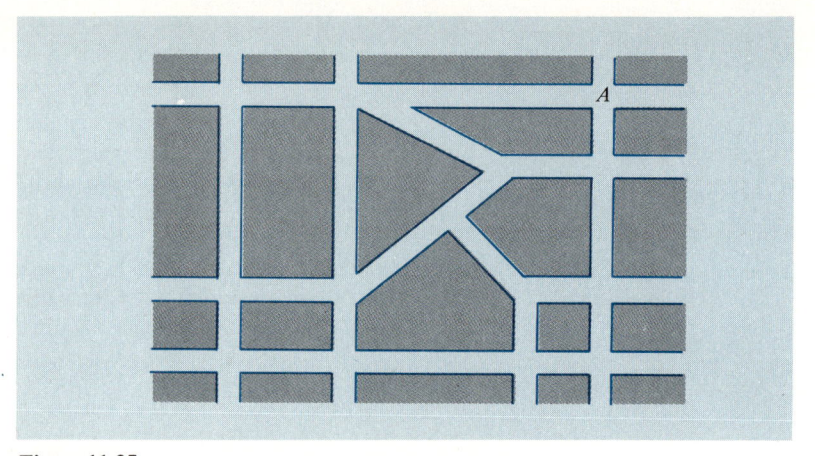

Figure 11.35

36. Figure 11.36 shows the floor plan for an office suite.
    (a) Represent this figure by a graph in which vertices denote rooms and edges denote doors between rooms.
    (b) Is it possible for a security guard to enter the suite from the hall and enter each room exactly once before returning to the hall?

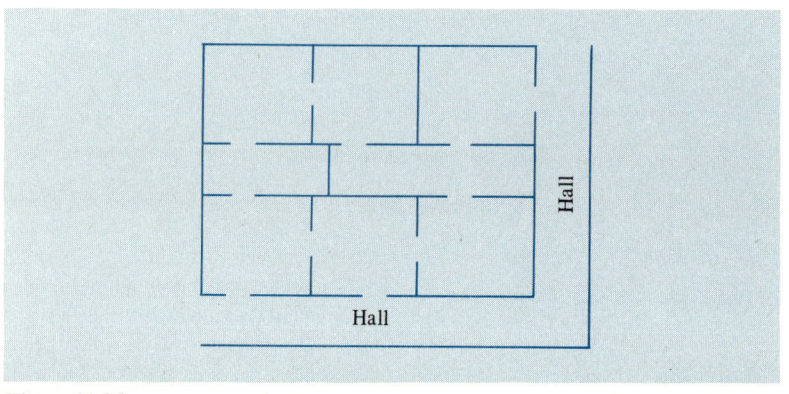

Figure 11.36

37. A well-known puzzle requires drawing the envelope shown below without retracing any line or lifting the pencil from the paper. Find a solution to this puzzle.

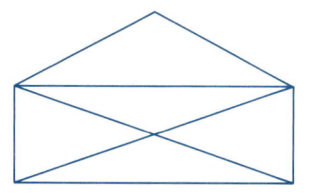

38. Figure 11.37 is a map of Eastern Europe.
    (a) Represent this map by a graph in which vertices denote countries and an edge between vertices denotes that the corresponding countries share a common border.
    (b) A political scientist studying customs procedures would like to cross the border between each pair of adjacent countries. Will it be possible to do this without crossing any border more than once?

Figure 11.37

11.3 Coloring Problems

Efficient scheduling of complex operations often results in considerable savings of money, time, or personnel. For many years the federal government and most large corporations have utilized mathematical models to plan their operations. More recently, local governments have begun using models to schedule urban operations more efficiently. In this way New York City has recently cut the cost of such municipal services as garbage collection and street sweeping by $10 million annually. (See [2] and [26].)

Figure 11.38

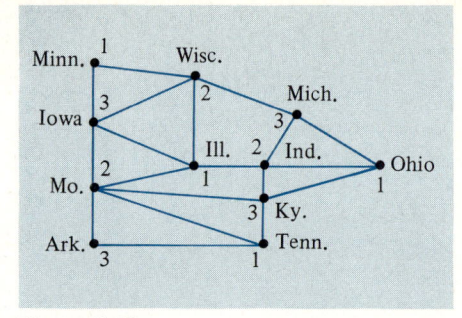

Figure 11.39

In this section we shall discuss a graphical model that is useful in determining the minimal number of time periods needed to schedule several activities, some of which may occur simultaneously. Surprisingly, this model is the same as that used to determine the minimum number of colors required to color a map so that no two adjacent regions are the same color. In order to better understand the necessary terminology, the latter problem will be considered first.

Figure 11.38 shows a portion of a map of the United States. Using a minimum number of colors, we would like to color each state in such a way that no two contiguous states are the same color. The map in Figure 11.38 can be converted to a graph by placing a vertex within each state and connecting two vertices whenever the corresponding states are adjacent. This graph is shown in Figure 11.39.

n-coloring

By an *n-coloring* of a graph we mean an assignment of *n* colors to the vertices of the graph, one color per vertex, in such a way that adjacent vertices are assigned different colors. Figure 11.39 shows a three-coloring of the graph in which the colors are denoted by the numbers 1, 2, and 3. It is easily seen that this graph has no two-coloring, and so the fewest number of colors with which it can be colored is three.

Examples of graphs that cannot be colored with fewer than four colors are easily constructed. (The simplest such example is shown in Figure 11.40.) For over 125 years mathematicians attempted to prove that four colors were enough to color any planar graph. This result was finally established in 1976 by dividing the problem into nearly 2000 cases and analyzing the possible colorings in each case with the aid of a computer.

In view of the difficulty of establishing this result, it is not surprising that there is no known formula for determining the fewest number of colors needed to color an arbitrary graph. However, in the case of a complete graph (a graph in which every pair of vertices is adjacent), every vertex requires a different color. (See, for example, Figure 11.40.) In other cases a graph can be colored using no more colors than the largest degree of any vertex. We state these facts formally as our next result.

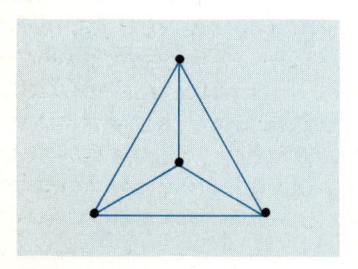

Figure 11.40

11.3 Coloring Problems   437

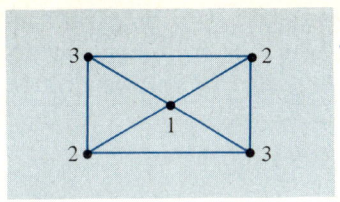

Figure 11.41

THEOREM 11.5

(a) If G is a complete graph with n vertices, then G has an n-coloring. Moreover, G cannot be colored with fewer than n colors.

(b) If G is not a complete graph and no vertex of G is of degree exceeding n, then G has an n-coloring.

Observe that Theorem 11.5(b) asserts only that the graph can be colored with n colors: Fewer colors may suffice. For example, the graph in Figure 11.41 can be three-colored even though it has a vertex of degree 4.

Theorem 11.5 suggests a useful rule for constructing an n-coloring: *Begin by assigning color(s) to the vertices of the greatest degree.* Note that when constructing an n-coloring we can safely ignore any vertex of degree less than n because, after all the other vertices are colored, there will always be at least one color not used on some adjacent vertex.

EXAMPLE 9

Determine the fewest number of colors required to color the graph in Figure 11.42.

First, notice that vertices B, D, E, and G are of degree 4 and that vertices A, C, F, and H are of degree 2. Thus we begin by coloring B, D, E, and G. It is easy to see that four colors are required to color these vertices. (In fact, this conclusion follows from Theorem 11.5(a), since B, D, E, and G and the edges joining them form a complete graph.) Once vertices B, D, E, and G are colored, it is easy to color A, C, F, and H. One possibility is shown in Figure 11.43.

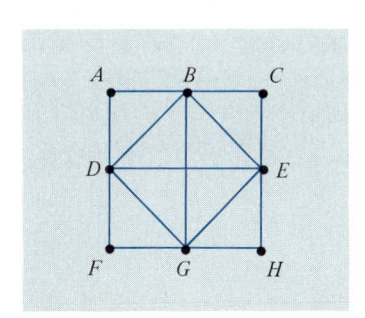

Figure 11.42

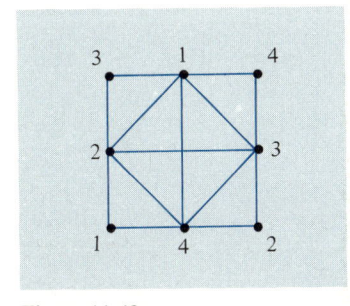

Figure 11.43

Let us now consider a simple scheduling problem. Suppose the mathematics department of a small college would like to schedule 16 one-hour classes beginning at 8:00, 9:00, 10:00, and 11:00, preferably 4 classes each hour. The classes to be offered are:

Three sections of finite mathematics (FM)
One section of trigonometry (T)
Three sections of FORTRAN (F)
Three sections of calculus (C)
Two sections of intermediate calculus (IC)
One section of geometry (G)
One section of differential equations (DE)
One section of abstract algebra (AA)
One section of linear algebra (LA)

In order to allow the maximum opportunity for students to take courses in which they are interested, the department does not want to schedule more than one section of the same course at the same time. Furthermore, in order to allow students to enroll in more than one mathematics course, the department does not want to schedule the following course combinations at the same hour:

(a) Trigonometry and calculus
(b) Trigonometry and FORTRAN
(c) FORTRAN and differential equations
(d) Intermediate calculus and differential equations
(e) Differential equations, abstract algebra, and linear algebra
(f) Abstract algebra, linear algebra, and geometry
(g) Finite mathematics and linear algebra

Although scheduling the classes under these conditions seems to be quite complicated, it can be converted to a simple graph-coloring problem by representing each of the 16 classes as the vertex of a graph. If we can obtain a four-coloring of the resulting graph such that vertices of the same color correspond to courses that may be taught at the same hour, then we will have determined a satisfactory scheduling. Notice that, in order for vertices of the same color to correspond to courses that may be taught at the same time, it is necessary to connect two vertices by an edge whenever the corresponding courses *cannot* be taught at the same hour. The graph formed in this way is shown in Figure 11.44. One possible four-coloring of this graph using each of the colors an equal number of times is shown in Figure 11.45.

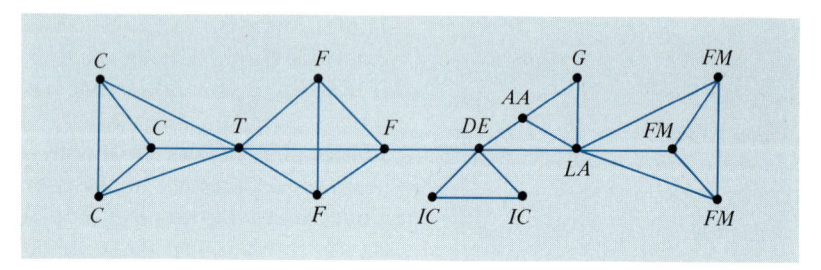

Figure 11.44

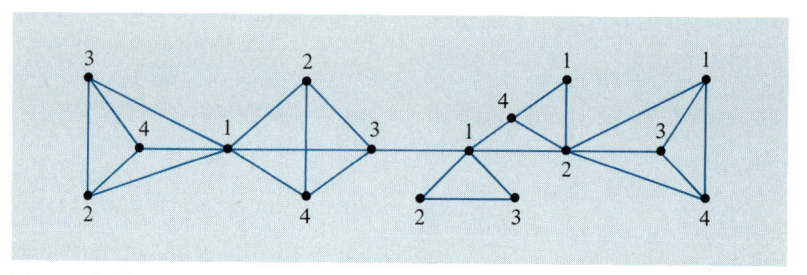

Figure 11.45

Hence an acceptable scheduling is:

8:00
Trigonometry
Differential equations
Geometry
Finite mathematics

9:00
Calculus
FORTRAN
Intermediate calculus
Linear algebra

10:00
Calculus
FORTRAN
Intermediate calculus
Finite mathematics

11:00
Calculus
FORTRAN
Abstract algebra
Finite mathematics

EXAMPLE 10

Suppose that New York City is considering seven new routes for garbage trucks that will visit 12 heavily used locations as listed below.

Route A: The Empire State Building, Madison Square Garden, the New York Stock Exchange, and Grand Central Station
Route B: Lincoln Center, the Bronx Zoo, Columbia University, and Yankee Stadium
Route C: The Statue of Liberty, Lincoln Center, Yankee Stadium, and Grand Central Station
Route D: The New York Public Library, Madison Square Garden, the New York Stock Exchange, and Grand Central Station
Route E: The Brooklyn Botanic Garden, Shea Stadium, the Bronx Zoo, and Madison Square Garden
Route F: Columbia University, the Empire State Building, Yankee Stadium, and the Bronx Zoo
Route G: Shea Stadium, the New York Public Library, the Statue of Liberty, and the Brooklyn Botanic Garden

Is it possible to schedule these routes on Monday, Tuesday, and Wednesday in such a way that no location is visited twice on the same day?

To answer this question, we shall formulate it as a coloring problem. Form a graph by letting a vertex represent one of the seven routes and connect two vertices whenever the corresponding routes service a common location. Then a solution to the scheduling problem can be found provided that there is a three-coloring of this graph. Figure 11.46 shows such a coloring; hence one solution of the original problem is to schedule routes C and E on Monday, routes A, B, and G on Tuesday, and routes D and F on Wednesday.

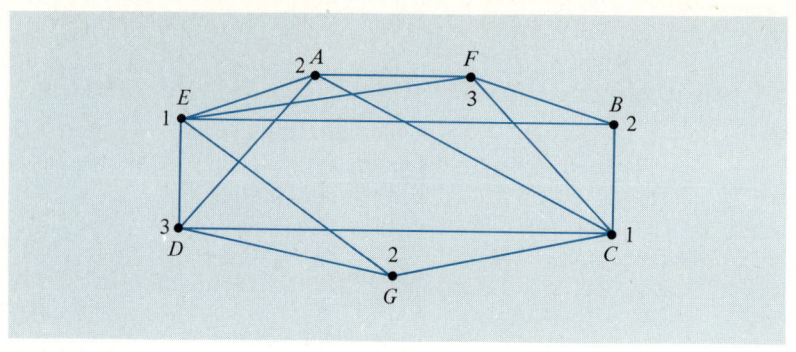

Figure 11.46

Exercises

In Exercises 1–12, color the given graph with the fewest colors possible.

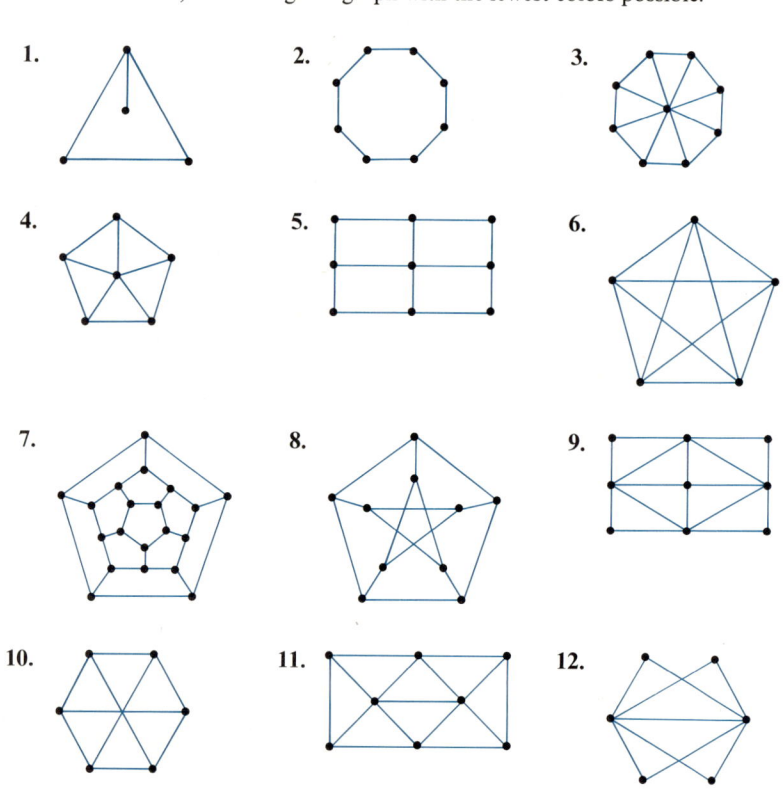

1.

2.

3.

4.

5.

6.

7.

8.

9.

10.

11.

12.

13. Represent the map in Figure 11.47 by a graph in which the vertices denote countries and two vertices are adjacent precisely where the corresponding countries share a common border. Then color the graph using the fewest possible colors.

Figure 11.47

14. Represent the map in Figure 11.48 by a graph in which the vertices denote countries and two vertices are adjacent precisely where the corresponding countries share a common border. Then color the graph using the fewest possible colors.

Figure 11.48

15. A bus company has begun sight-seeing tours of Baltimore. The six tours visit the sites named below.

   Tour A: The Baltimore Museum of Art, Walters Art Gallery, the Peabody Conservatory, and Edgar Allan Poe's birthplace

Tour B: The Constellation, the Flag House, the Shot Tower, and Fort McHenry

Tour C: City Hall, the Shot Tower, Edgar Allan Poe's birthplace, and Walters Art Gallery

Tour D: Memorial Stadium, Johns Hopkins University, the Baltimore Museum of Art, and the Druid Park Zoo

Tour E: Memorial Stadium, the Druid Park Zoo, and the Baltimore Streetcar Museum

Tour F: The Constellation, Fort McHenry, and the Baltimore Streetcar Museum

Construct a graph representing these tours as in Example 10 and use it to decide how to schedule the tours using the fewest number of days without visiting any site more than once per day.

16. Twin City Tours has designed seven sight-seeing tours of Bloomington-Normal. The sites visited by each tour are described below.

Tour A: Illinois State University, Illinois Wesleyan University, State Farm Insurance Corporate Headquarters, and the Illinois Agricultural Association

Tour B: The Adlai Stevenson Grave, the David Davis Mansion, and the Bloomington-Normal Airport

Tour C: The Bloomington Post Office, the Bloomington-Normal Airport, and the Illinois Agricultural Association

Tour D: Illinois State University, State Farm Insurance Corporate Headquarters, and Doug Collins' Locker

Tour E: Illinois State University, Illinois Wesleyan University, Doug Collins' Locker, Vanden Eyndens' Garden, and the Miller Park Zoo

Tour F: The Bloomington Post Office, the Bloomington-Normal Airport, and the Phares O'Daffer Equipment Center

Tour G: Vanden Eyndens' Garden, the Phares O'Daffer Equipment Center, and the Miller Park Zoo

Construct a graph representing these tours as in Example 10 and use it to decide how to schedule the tours using the fewest number of days without visiting any site more than once per day.

17. The mathematics department of a university schedules most of its advanced courses on a "to be arranged" basis in order to allow its graduate students more flexibility in choosing courses. The enrollment for this semester's "to be arranged" classes is shown below.

Abstract algebra: Beverly, David, Judy, and Mike
Complex analysis: Bob, David, Debbie, Lei, and Matt
Differential geometry: Debbie, Ho-Ling, Jim, and Judy
Linear algebra: Beverly, Mike, Paul, and Shirley
Real analysis: Ho-Ling, Jim, Ken, Matt, and Shirley
Sampling theory: Bob, Ken, Lei, and Paul

Construct a graph representing these courses and use it to decide how to schedule the courses at the fewest number of times without scheduling any student for two courses meeting at the same time.

18. Much to the dismay of the faculty, the Mathematics Department chairperson has called for six one-hour committee meetings on a Saturday. The composition of the committees is shown below.

   Committee A: Berk, Dossey, Friedberg
   Committee B: Berk, Brown, Parr, Trojanowski
   Committee C: Hathway, Insel, Tucker
   Committee D: Banks, Dossey, Hershberger, Retzer
   Committee E: Friedberg, Insel, Seltzer, Smith
   Committee F: Gilmore, Hershberger, Retzer

   Naturally the faculty wants to finish the meetings as quickly as possible. Represent these committees by a graph and use it to schedule the committee meetings so that all the meetings can be held in the shortest possible time.

19. A hotel has five meeting rooms of various sizes, which it uses when hosting conventions. Five conventions have inquired about the availability of certain rooms during either week of a particular two-week period: The first convention wants to use the gold and silver rooms; the second convention wants to use the gold and green rooms; the third convention wants to use the pink and blue rooms; the fourth convention wants to use the blue and green rooms; and the fifth convention wants to use the pink and silver rooms. Construct a graph to help schedule these conventions. Can the hotel accommodate all five conventions by proper scheduling?

20. The morning session of a management seminar is to be devoted to the subjects of accounting and marketing. Six one-hour lectures must be scheduled at the hours of 9, 10, and 11 o'clock. The speakers and their topics are:

    Andrews, Barber, and Dougherty—marketing
    Calhoun, Edwards, and Fine—accounting

    No two speakers lecturing on the same subject are to be scheduled at the same hour. In addition, Andrews wants to hear Fine's lecture, Edwards wants to hear both Andrews and Dougherty, and Calhoun wants to hear Andrews. Construct a graph to help schedule these speakers. Is it possible to schedule the speakers so that all the conditions above are satisfied?

21. Several observatories are interested in conducting six experiments. Each experiment will begin and end on a specific day, but each experiment will need to be repeated for several years. Experiment A runs from January 1 to June 1; experiment B runs from March 15 to June 30; experiment C runs from May 15 to August 30; experiment D runs from August 1 through February 1; experiment E runs from September 15 to October 15; and experiment F runs from October 1 to January 15. Because of the complexity of each experiment, no observatory is capable of conducting more than one experiment at a time. Construct a graph to help with the scheduling of these experiments. What is the fewest number of observatories required to conduct all six experiments?

22. In order to keep peace on a cub scout trip, the scoutmaster has decided not to allow any two boys who do not get along together to ride in the same car. The pairs of scouts who do not get along together are Alex and Byron, Alex and Greg, Byron and Dan, Byron and Frank, Carl and

Earl, Carl and Frank, Carl and Harry, Dan and Greg, and Earl and Greg. Construct a graph to help determine the seating arrangements for the trip. What is the fewest number of cars needed? Is it possible to use the fewest number of cars without requiring more than four boys in any one car?

11.4 Digraphs

In our discussion of the Königsberg bridge problem in Section 11.2 we encountered the mathematical structure called a multigraph, which, although similar to a graph, is not a graph. There are other situations where different types of structures are more appropriate as mathematical models than are graphs or multigraphs. Suppose, for example, that a city wishes to clean each side of the seven streets shown in Figure 11.24 with a mechanical street sweeper. The street sweeper must take into account several factors that were irrelevant to the letter carrier in Example 7, the most important of which is the direction of traffic flow along one-way streets. In this context we need a structure that associates a direction with each edge.

digraph
vertices
arcs

A *digraph* (or *directed graph*) is a nonempty set $V = \{v_1, v_2, \ldots, v_p\}$ of elements called *vertices* together with a set E of ordered pairs of distinct vertices called *arcs* (or *directed edges*).[2] We denote the arc (v_i, v_j) as v_iv_j and say that v_iv_j is an arc *from v_i to v_j*. Notice that for arcs, unlike edges, $v_iv_j \neq v_jv_i$. As was true for graphs, digraphs may be represented by drawing dots for each vertex and by connecting the dots corresponding to v_i and v_j with a curve containing an arrowhead pointing toward v_j whenever v_iv_j is an arc. Observe that, if v_iv_j is an arc, then v_jv_i need not be an arc. If, however, both are arcs, then we connect the dots corresponding to v_i and v_j by two nonintersecting curves and insert an arrowhead on each arc, one arrowhead pointing toward v_i and the other toward v_j.

EXAMPLE 11

Ecologists use digraphs to depict the food web of an ecological system. (See [21].) A *food web* is a digraph in which the vertices correspond to the various types of plant or animal life in a region and an arc joins vertices u and v if u preys on v. Figure 11.49 shows the food web of an ecological system including wolves, skunks, insects, plants, rodents, bears, and deer.

EXAMPLE 12

In [13] Hart uses digraphs to analyze the patterns of cooperation and conflict among European nations during the decade 1870–

---

[2] The word "edge" is not used in reference to digraphs.

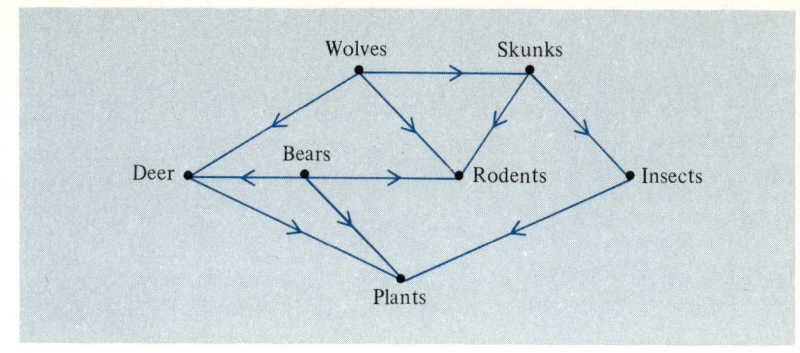

Figure 11.49

1879. One such digraph for the year 1875 is shown in Figure 11.50, where solid lines denote cooperation and dashed lines denote conflict.

Actually the graph shown in Figure 11.50 is an example of a signed digraph, a digraph in which each arc is assigned a positive or negative sign. In the case of Figure 11.50, solid lines and dashed lines are used instead of positive and negative signs.

EXAMPLE 13

Maruyama, in [18], uses the signed digraph in Figure 11.51 to depict the causal relationships among various factors involving health and population in an urban area. Here a positive sign along arc uv means that an increase in u causes an increase in v, whereas a negative sign along arc uv means that an increase in u causes a decrease in v.

Whereas graphs are appropriate as models for symmetric relationships, digraphs are useful as models for asymmetric relationships. The three preceding examples are all of this type.

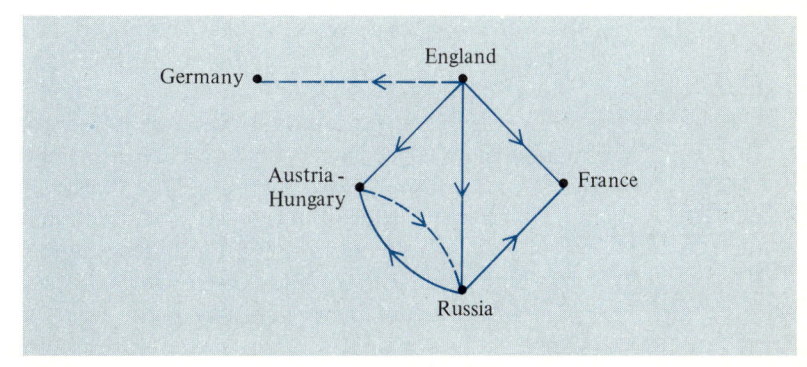

Figure 11.50

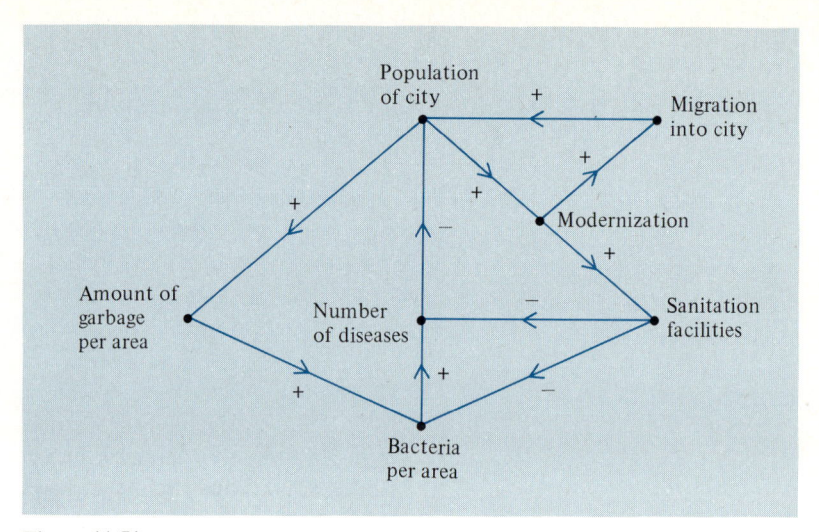

Figure 11.51

Organization theory (an area of mathematical sociology concerned with the status of an individual within an organization) provides another situation in which digraphs can be used as models. Organizational structures are easily pictured with digraphs by drawing an arc from u to v whenever v is a direct subordinate of u. For example, let us consider a small research project involving a funding agent (FA), a project director (PD), two principal researchers (PR1 and PR2), a research assistant (RA), a laboratory technician (LT), an executive secretary (ES), and a clerk-typist (CT). Suppose the funding agent directly supervises the project director, the project director directly supervises both principal researchers, the research assistant, and the executive secretary, each principal researcher supervises the research assistant and the laboratory technician, the research assistant supervises the laboratory technician and the clerk-typist, and the executive secretary supervises the clerk-typist. Then the organizational structure of this project can be depicted by the digraph in Figure 11.52.

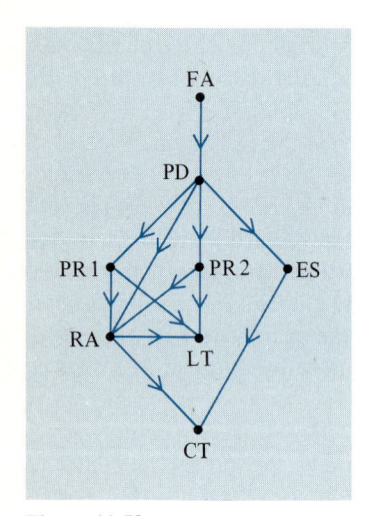

Figure 11.52

Because the arcs in a digraph are directed from one vertex to another, most of the graph-theoretic concepts introduced in previous sections require slight modifications. In a digraph the *indegree* of a vertex v_j is the number of arcs $v_i v_j$ directed to v_j, and the *outdegree* of v_j is the number of arcs $v_j v_k$ directed from v_j. Most of the other basic concepts for graphs can be modified for digraphs by replacing the word "edge" by the word "arc." For instance, an *arc progression of length n* from u to v is a set of n ($n \geq 1$) arcs $uv_1, v_1 v_2, \ldots, v_{n-1} v$ in which each arc leads from the vertex at which the previous arc ends. As with edge progressions, the arc progression above will be denoted by $uv_1 v_2 \ldots v_{n-1} v$. Likewise, a *(directed) path* in a digraph is an arc progression containing no repeated arcs.

In [10] Harary proposed a simple numerical measure of the status of each person in an organizational structure. In order to introduce this

indegree
outdegree

arc progression

path

11.4 Digraphs **447**

measure, some additional terminology is required. A vertex v in a digraph is said to be *reachable* from a vertex u if there is a path from u to v. If v is reachable from u, the *distance* from u to v is the length of the shortest path from u to v; otherwise, if v is not reachable from u, the distance from u to v is undefined. The *status* $s(u)$ of a vertex u is then defined to be the sum of the distances from u to each reachable vertex. Thus the more subordinates an individual has, the higher is the individual's status within the organization.

reachable vertex
distance

status

EXAMPLE 14

In Figure 11.52, CT is reachable from ES by a path of length 1; so the distance from ES to CT is 1. Since no other vertex is reachable from ES, $s(\text{ES}) = 1$. Likewise the distance from PR2 to CT is 2, and the distance from PR2 to both RA and LT is 1. Thus $s(\text{PR2}) = 2 + 1 + 1 = 4$.

Similar computations show that $s(\text{CT}) = 0$, $s(\text{LT}) = 0$, $s(\text{RA}) = 2$, $s(\text{PR1}) = 4$, $s(\text{PD}) = 8$, and $s(\text{FA}) = 15$.

We shall conclude this section by discussing the digraph corresponding to a dominance relation. Recall from Section 3.4 that a dominance relation is one in which, for any pair of persons i and j, either i dominates j or j dominates i (but not both). If we represent each person i by a vertex v_i and draw an arc from v_i to v_j whenever person i dominates person j, the resulting digraph has the property that between any pair of its vertices there is exactly one arc. Any digraph having this property is called a *tournament* (or *dominance digraph*). We have already seen in Section 3.4 that any person who directly dominates the greatest number of people must dominate everyone within at most two stages. In graph-theoretic terms this result may be reformulated as follows: *In a tournament the distance from a vertex having the largest outdegree to every other vertex is 1 or 2.*

tournament

The term "tournament" is used to describe this type of digraph because such a structure results when an arc is drawn from the winner to the loser in every match of a round-robin athletic competition.[3] In this context the *score* of a team or an individual, that is, the number of matches won, is the outdegree of the corresponding vertex in the digraph. The competitors can then be ranked according to their scores. In a tournament with vertices $v_1, v_2, \ldots, v_p$, the p-tuple of nonnegative integers $(s_1, s_2, \ldots, s_p)$ such that s_i is the score of v_i is called a *score sequence*.

score

score sequence

Consider, for example, a round-robin tennis competition with five players. Suppose that Ashe (A) beat Gottfried and McEnroe; Connors (C) beat Ashe, Gottfried, and McEnroe; Gottfried (G) beat McEnroe

---

[3] In a round-robin competition, as opposed to the more common elimination competition, each team or individual plays every other.

448 Chapter 11 Graph Theory

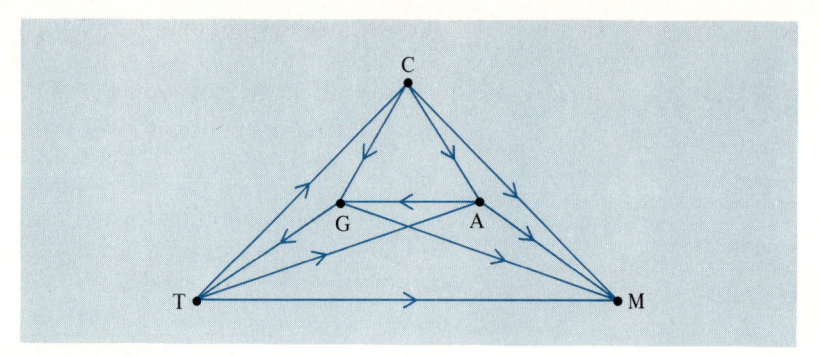

Figure 11.53

and Tanner; McEnroe (M) beat nobody; and Tanner (T) beat Ashe, Connors, and McEnroe. The tournament corresponding to this competition is shown in Figure 11.53. The score of each player is as follows: 2 for Ashe, 3 for Connors, 2 for Gottfried, 0 for McEnroe, and 3 for Tanner. The corresponding score sequence for this digraph is (2, 3, 2, 0, 3).

In a dominance relation it is natural to expect that, if person i dominates person j and person j dominates person k, then person i dominates person k. Such a set of vertices in a tournament is called a *transitive triple*. In Figure 11.53 vertices A, G, and M form a transitive triple, since Ashe beat Gottfried, Gottfried beat McEnroe, and Ashe beat McEnroe. In any athletic competition, however, upsets are likely to occur. Thus although Tanner beat Connors and Connors beat Gottfried, Gottfried beat Tanner. A set of three vertices that does not form a transitive triple is called a *cyclic triple*; hence T, C, and G form a cyclic triple in Figure 11.53.

transitive triple

cyclic triple

EXAMPLE 15

In the tournament shown in Figure 11.53 there are eight transitive triples ({A, G, M}, {C, A, G}, {C, A, M}, {C, G, M}, {G, T, M}, {T, A, M}, {T, C, A}, and {T, C, M}) and two cyclic triples ({A, G, T} and {C, G, T}).

Tournaments arise in connection with the method of paired comparisons, an important experimental technique in psychology and sociology in which a subject is presented with every possible pair of objects from a given set and asked which object from each pair is preferred. (See [16].) For example, an experimenter may have 6 colors that she presents two at a time to a subject who is asked to indicate which color in each pair is more relaxing. If all 15 pairs of colors are presented to the subject, the digraph corresponding to this relation is a tournament. In this case the number of cyclic triples is a measure of the inconsistency of the subject: The fewer the number of cyclic triples, the greater the consistency.

It is of importance, therefore, to know the number of cyclic triples in a tournament. Fortunately, it is possible to determine this number if a score sequence for the tournament is known. Observe first that the total number of triples (either transitive or cyclic) in a tournament having p vertices is the number of combinations of p vertices taken 3 at a time, which is $C(p, 3) = \frac{1}{6}p(p-1)(p-2)$. Next notice that every pair of arcs leading from a vertex determines a transitive triple. Thus if s_i is the score of vertex v_i, then there are $C(s_i, 2) = \frac{1}{2}s_i(s_i - 1)$ transitive triples in which v_i dominates both the other vertices. If we consider all the vertices in the tournament, we see that the total number n of transitive triples is

$$n = \tfrac{1}{2}s_1(s_1 - 1) + \tfrac{1}{2}s_2(s_2 - 1) + \cdots + \tfrac{1}{2}s_p(s_p - 1) \tag{11.1}$$

where $(s_1, s_2, \ldots, s_p)$ is a score sequence for the tournament. Hence the number of cyclic triples is

$$C(p, 3) - n = \tfrac{1}{6}p(p-1)(p-2) - n \tag{11.2}$$

EXAMPLE 16

For the tournament in Figure 11.53 with score sequence $(2, 3, 2, 0, 3)$, the number of transitive triples given by (11.1) is

$$\tfrac{1}{2}(2)(1) + \tfrac{1}{2}(3)(2) + \tfrac{1}{2}(2)(1) + \tfrac{1}{2}(0)(-1) + \tfrac{1}{2}(3)(2) = 8$$

Hence the number of cyclic triples given by (11.2) is

$$C(5, 3) - 8 = 10 - 8 = 2$$

These figures agree with those obtained in Example 15.

It can be shown that the expected proportion of cyclic triples in a tournament with three or more vertices is $\frac{1}{4}$. More interestingly, the maximum proportion of cyclic triples is

$$\begin{aligned} &\frac{1}{4} + \frac{3}{4p - 8} \quad &\text{if } p \text{ is odd} \\ &\frac{1}{4} + \frac{3}{4p - 4} \quad &\text{if } p \text{ is even} \end{aligned} \tag{11.3}$$

This means that, for large values of p, the maximum proportion of cyclic triples is nearly the same as the proportion of cyclic triples expected by chance. So in an experiment using the method of paired comparisons, a subject who deliberately attempts to be as inconsistent as possible will produce nearly the same proportion of cyclic triples as a subject who behaves randomly.

Exercises

In Exercises 1–8, use Figure 11.53 to compute the given distance.

1. From T to M
2. From A to C
3. From G to A
4. From C to A
5. From A to G
6. From M to A
7. From M to T
8. From A to M

In Exercises 9–14, compute the status of each vertex in the given graph.

9.

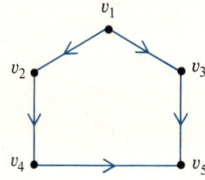

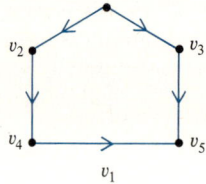

10.

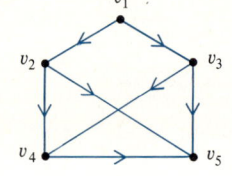

11.

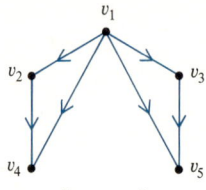

12.

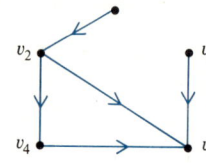

13.

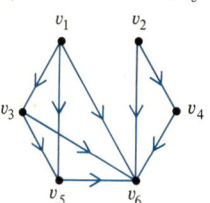

14.

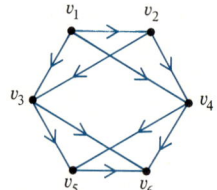

In Exercises 15–20, determine the score sequence, the number of transitive triples, and the number of cyclic triples for the given tournament.

15.

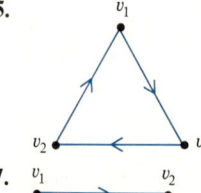

16.

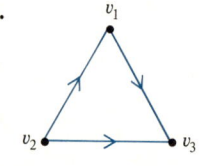

17.

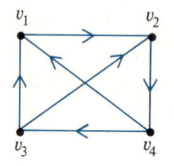

18.

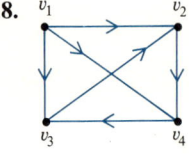

19.

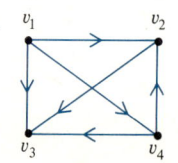

20.

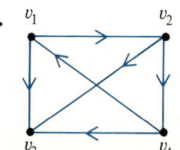

21. Construct a digraph depicting the following relationships.

    Al likes Barbara.
    Barbara likes Al and Ellen.
    Cathy likes Duncan.
    Duncan likes Cathy and Fred.
    Ellen likes Barbara.
    Fred likes Al, Duncan, and Ellen.
    Gloria likes Henry.
    Henry likes Gloria.

22. The spread of rumors by the teenagers in a certain neighborhood was studied, and the following results were obtained.

    Alice tells rumors to Bill, Darla, and Frances.
    Bill tells rumors to Earl.
    Clint tells rumors to Bill, George, and Hanna.
    Darla tells rumors to Alice and Frances.
    Earl tells rumors to Bill and George.
    Frances never repeats rumors.
    George tells rumors to Clint, Earl, and Hanna.
    Hanna tells rumors to all the boys.

    Construct a digraph representing the patterns for spreading a rumor among these teenagers.

23. In a certain corporation, the president directly supervises three vice-presidents, each of whom has different responsibilities. The first vice-president supervises the chief accountant and the director of computer operations; the second vice-president supervises the plant manager; and the third vice-president supervises the director of marketing and the sales manager.

    Represent this organizational structure by a digraph and compute the status of each member.

24. At a particular college, the provost and the director of student services report directly to the president. The director of admissions and records reports to both the provost and the director of student services. The director of the health service reports only to the director of student services. Both deans report directly to the provost, and the director of academic advising reports to both deans and the director of student services.

    Represent this organizational structure by a digraph and compute the status of each member.

25. A psychology major and her date stopped at an ice cream parlor. When her date was unable to decide what flavor of ice cream to choose, the psychology major decided to use the method of paired comparisons to help arrive at a decision. She found that her date preferred peach to fudge ripple, vanilla, and chocolate; preferred fudge ripple to cherry vanilla, vanilla, and chocolate; preferred cherry vanilla to peach, vanilla, and chocolate; and preferred chocolate to vanilla.

    (a) Construct a digraph representing these preferences.
    (b) Determine a score sequence for the digraph in part (a).
    (c) Determine the number of transitive and cyclic triples in the digraph.
    (d) What type of ice cream cone did the psychology major's date select?

26. In the Olympic Games, basketball teams play a round-robin competition from which the finalists are selected. Suppose the following results occurred in round-robin play: Brazil beat Russia and Yugoslavia; Cuba beat Brazil; Russia beat Cuba and Yugoslavia; the United States beat Brazil, Cuba, and Russia; and Yugoslavia beat Cuba and the United States.

    (a) Represent the outcomes of these games by a digraph.
    (b) Determine a score sequence for the digraph in part (a).
    (c) Determine the number of transitive and cyclic triples in the digraph.

27. Three candidates (Adams, Baker, and Carroll) are seeking the office of mayor in a small town. Reliable polls show that 40% of the voters prefer Adams, and virtually all of these have Carroll as their second choice; 35% of the voters prefer Baker, and virtually all of these have Carroll as their second choice; 25% of the voters prefer Carroll, and virtually all of these have Baker as their second choice.

    (a) Construct a tournament in which the vertices represent the three candidates and an arc uv signifies that more voters prefer candidate u to candidate v in a *two-way* race between u and v.
    (b) Interpret the results of part (a).

28. Answer the following questions about Exercise 27.

    (a) Who will become mayor if the town has a three-way race and the person receiving a plurality of the votes cast is named the winner?
    (b) Who will become mayor if the town has a three-way race and a majority of the votes cast is required for election? (If no candidate receives a majority, a runoff will be held between the two candidates receiving the largest number of votes.)

29. A street sweeper must clean *both* sides of the streets shown in Figure 11.24. Unlike the letter carrier in Example 7, however, the street sweeper must take into account the direction of traffic on one-way streets. Suppose that First Avenue is one-way from North Street to South Street, Fourth Avenue is one-way from South Street to North Street, South Street is one-way from First Avenue to Fourth Avenue, and North Street is one-way from Fourth Avenue to First Avenue.

    (a) Construct a directed multigraph in which vertices denote intersections and arcs denote sides of the streets to be cleaned.
    (b) Find a path through the directed multigraph in part (a) that will allow the street sweeper to clean each side of the street exactly once.

30. Every tournament contains a (directed) path passing through each vertex exactly once.

    (a) Find such a path in the tournament shown in Figure 11.54.
    (b) Can you find such a path that is consistent with a score sequence for the tournament, that is, a path in which no arc leads from a vertex with a lower score to a vertex with a higher score?

31. Draw a signed digraph as in Example 13 depicting causal relationships among the following factors: energy use, energy capacity, energy price, number of factories, number of jobs, population, and quality of the environment.

32. Draw a signed digraph depicting causal relationships among the following factors relating to a college student with a job: hours worked, study time,

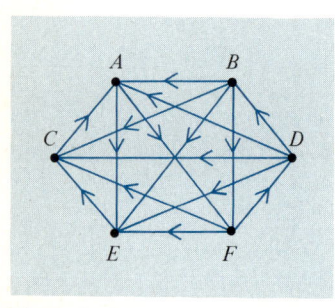

Figure 11.54

recreation time, grade point average, job offers after graduation, standard of living, and spending money.

33. How many arcs are there in a tournament with p vertices?
34. In a tournament, what does the sum of the indegrees of all the vertices equal? What does the sum of all the outdegrees equal?

Chapter Review

New Terms

adjacency matrix (p. 425)
adjacent vertices (p. 418)
arc (p. 444)
arc progression (p. 446)
complete graph (p. 424)
components (p. 425)
connected graph (p. 425)
contracting a graph (p. 422)
cyclic triple (p. 448)
degree of a vertex (p. 418)
digraph (p. 444)
distance between vertices (p. 447)
edge (p. 418)
edge progression (p. 424)
graph (p. 418)
hexagonal graph (p. 421)

indegree (p. 446)
multigraph (p. 426)
n-coloring of a graph (p. 436)
outdegree (p. 446)
path (p. 425)
pentagonal graph (p. 421)
planar graph (p. 420)
reachable vertex (p. 447)
score sequence for a tournament (p. 447)
status of a vertex in a digraph (p. 447)
tournament (p. 447)
transitive triple (p. 448)
vertex (p. 418)

Review Exercises

1. Label each of the following statements true or false.
   (a) Every graph has a unique representation.
   (b) The sum of the degrees of all the vertices in a graph equals the number of edges.
   (c) A graph in which two edges intersect at a point other than a vertex is not planar.
   (d) The pentagonal and hexagonal graphs are not planar.
   (e) A path contains no repeated vertices.
   (f) A path contains no repeated edges.
   (g) If there is a path from one vertex to every other vertex, then the graph is connected.
   (h) A graphlike structure in which more than one edge joins a pair of vertices is called a digraph.
   (i) When there are either no vertices or exactly two vertices of odd degree in a graph, the graph contains a path including each vertex of the graph exactly once.
   (j) In any coloring of a graph, adjacent vertices always have different colors.
   (k) If a graph has no vertices of degree exceeding n, then it can be n-colored.

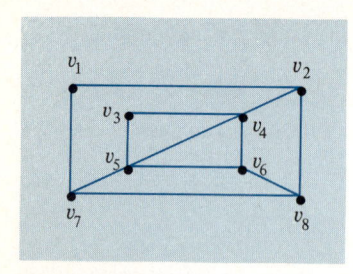

Figure 11.55

(l) The status of a vertex in a digraph equals the sum of the distances from the vertex to every reachable vertex.

(m) A tournament is a digraph in which every pair of vertices is joined by an arc.

2. Compute the degree of each of the vertices in the graph shown in Figure 11.55.

3. Determine whether the graphs in Figure 11.56 are planar or not.

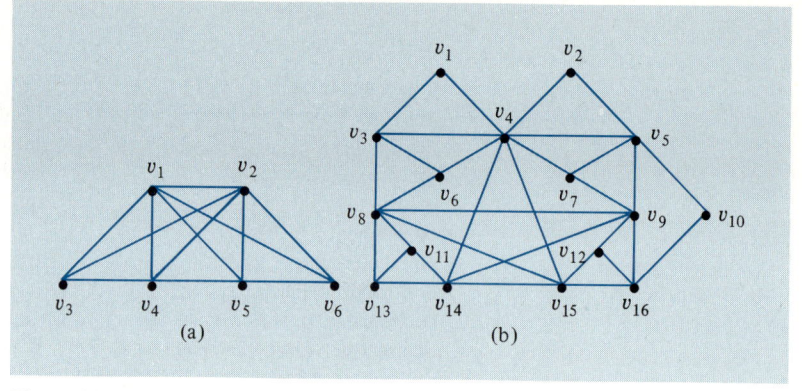

Figure 11.56

4. For each of the graphs in Figure 11.57, determine if there is a path including each edge exactly once or a path including each vertex exactly once. If such paths exist, give examples.

5. Ten departments wishing to hold departmental meetings have requested use of the large conference room at the times indicated below.

Sales, 8:00–10:30
Personnel, 8:00–11:30
Budgeting, 10:00–11:30 and 1:30–2:30
Engineering, 9:00–10:00 and 12:30–1:30
Data Processing, 11:00–12:00 and 1:00–2:00
Quality Control, 1:00–3:00
Payroll, 2:00–3:00
Maintenance, 2:30–4:00
Accounts Receivable, 3:00–4:00
Accounts Payable, 3:00–4:00

If each department wants to complete its meeting in a single day, schedule the use of the conference room so that all the meetings can be held in the fewest number of days.

6. A bus company operates seven sight-seeing tours of Chicago. The sites visited on each tour are named below.

Tour A: The Field Museum of Natural History and the Museum of Science and Industry
Tour B: McCormick Place, Wrigley Field, and the Museum of Science and Industry
Tour C: The Loop, Wrigley Field, and the Lincoln Park Zoo
Tour D: The Loop, Sears Tower, and McCormick Place

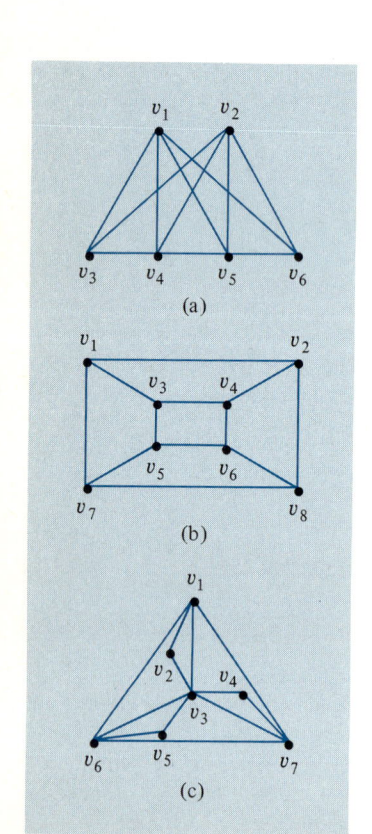

Figure 11.57

Tour E: Orchestra Hall, the Chicago Opera House, and the Art Institute of Chicago

Tour F: Union Stockyards, McCormick Place, and the Art Institute of Chicago

Schedule the tours on the fewest number of days without visiting any site more than once per day.

7. The president of a small bank directly supervises two vice-presidents. The vice-president in charge of operations directly supervises the loan officer and the bank manager, whereas the vice-president in charge of finances supervises only the loan officer. Both the loan officer and the bank manager supervise the head teller, but the bank manager also supervises the executive secretary and the receptionist. The head teller supervises the two tellers.

Represent this organizational structure by means of a digraph and compute the status of each employee of the bank.

8. In the local children's football league, the outcome of the season's games was as follows: the Giants beat the Bears; the Bears beat the Cardinals, Dolphins, and Eagles; the Cardinals beat the Giants and the Dolphins; the Dolphins beat the Giants; the Eagles beat the Giants, Cardinals, and Dolphins; and the Falcons beat each of the other teams.

Represent the outcomes of these games as a tournament and determine a score sequence for this tournament. Then determine the number of transitive and cyclic triples in the tournament.

9. Among three married couples, Angela knows the ages of Bill, Evelyn, and Forest; Bill knows the ages of Angela and Dick; Courtney knows Dick's age; Dick knows the ages of Bill and Courtney; Evelyn knows the ages of Angela, Bill, Dick, and Forest; and Forest knows the ages of Bill, Dick, and Evelyn.

Represent this situation by a digraph and compute the indegree and outdegree of each vertex.

10. On one of its bottling machines, a drug company fills and labels seven different bottles (A, B, C, D, E, F, and G) each day. After finishing with any bottle, the machine must be adjusted before another type of bottle can be processed. The number of minutes required to convert the machine from one type of bottle to another is shown below.

		Convert to						
		A	B	C	D	E	F	G
Convert from	A	—	9	15	8	11	13	17
	B	13	—	14	16	14	10	18
	C	8	13	—	13	9	14	15
	D	14	10	13	—	15	11	13
	E	15	9	16	17	—	13	12
	F	16	15	14	15	16	—	14
	G	13	8	9	14	9	13	—

(a) Is there some sequence in which the bottles can be processed so that none of the conversion times exceeds 10 minutes?

(b) Is there some sequence in which the bottles can be processed so that none of the conversion times exceeds 12 minutes?

References

1. Axelrod, Robert, ed., *Structure of Decision*. Princeton: Princeton University Press, 1976.
2. Beltrami, E. J. and L. D. Bodin, "Networks and Vehicle Routing for Municipal Waste Collection," *Networks*, vol. 4 (1973), pp. 65–94.
3. Busacker, Robert G. and Thomas L. Saaty, *Finite Graphs and Networks: An Introduction with Applications*. New York: McGraw-Hill, 1965.
4. Cartwright, Dorwin and Frank Harary, "Structural Balance: A Generalization of Heider's Theory," *Psychol. Rev.*, vol. 63, no. 5 (September 1956), pp. 277–293.
5. Chartrand, Gary, *Graphs as Mathematical Models*. Boston: Prindle, Weber and Schmidt, 1977.
6. Doreian, Patrick, "Interaction under Conditions of Crisis: Applications of Graph Theory to International Relations," *Peace Res. Soc. (Int.) Pap.*, vol. 11 (1969), pp. 89–107.
7. Guetzkow, Harold and Herbert A. Simon, "The Impact of Certain Communication Nets upon Organization and Performance in Task-Oriented Groups," *Manage. Sci.*, vol. 1, nos. 3–4 (April–July 1955), pp. 233–250.
8. Harary, Frank, "A Graph Theoretic Approach to Similarity Relations," *Psychometrika*, vol. 29, no. 2 (June 1964), pp. 143–151.
9. Harary, Frank, "Graph Theoretic Methods in the Management Sciences," *Manage. Sci.*, vol. 5, no. 4 (July 1959), pp. 387–403.
10. Harary, Frank, "Status and Contrastatus," *Sociometry*, vol. 22 (1959), pp. 23–43.
11. Harary, Frank and Ian C. Ross, "The Number of Complete Cycles in a Communication Network," *J. Soc. Psychol.*, vol. 40 (1954), pp. 329–332.
12. Hart, Jeffrey, "Structures of Influence and Cooperation-Conflict," *Int. Interact.*, vol. 1 (1974), pp. 141–162.
13. Hart, Jeffrey, "Symmetry and Polarization in the European International System, 1870–1879: A Methodological Study," *J. Peace Res.*, vol. 11 (1974), pp. 229–244.
14. Healy, Brian and Arthur Stein, "The Balance of Power in International History: Theory and Reality," *J. Conflict Resolut.*, vol. 17, no. 1 (March 1973), pp. 33–61.
15. Hutchinson, Joan P. and Herbert S. Wilf, "On Eulerian Circuits and Words with Prescribed Adjacency Patterns," *J. Combinatorial Theor.*, ser. A, vol. 18 (1975), pp. 80–87.
16. Kendall, M. G. and B. Babington Smith, "On the Method of Paired Comparisons," *Biometrika*, vol. 31 (1940), pp. 324–345.
17. Leavitt, Harold J., "Some Effects of Certain Communication Patterns on Group Performance," *J. Abnorm. Soc. Psychol.*, vol. 46 (1951), pp. 38–50.
18. Maruyama, Magoroh, "The Second Cybernetics: Deviation-Amplifying Mutual Causal Processes," *Am. Sci.*, vol. 51, no. 2 (June 1963), pp. 164–179.
19. Ore, Oystein, *Graphs and Their Uses*. New York: Random House, 1963.
20. Parthasarathy, K. R., "Enumeration of Paths in Digraphs," *Psychometrika*, vol. 29, no. 2 (June 1964), pp. 153–165.

21. Roberts, Fred S., *Discrete Mathematical Models*. Englewood Cliffs, N.J.: Prentice-Hall, 1976.
22. Roberts, Fred S., "On Nontransitive Indifference," *J. Math. Psychol.*, vol. 7 (1970), pp. 243–258.
23. Saaty, Thomas L., "A Model for the Control of Arms," *Oper. Res.*, vol. 12 (September–October 1964), pp. 586–609.
24. Shaw, Marvin E., Gerard H. Rothschild, and John F. Strickland, "Decision Processes in Communication Nets," *J. Abnorm. Soc. Psychol.*, vol. 54, no. 3 (May 1957), pp. 323–330.
25. Stoffers, Karl E., "Scheduling of Traffic Lights—A New Approach," *Transp. Res.*, vol. 2 (1968), pp. 199–234.
26. Tucker, A. and L. Bodin, "A Model for Municipal Street Sweeping Operations," in *Case Studies in Applied Mathematics*, Hayward, Calif.: Committee on the Undergraduate Program in Mathematics, 1976, pp. 107–150.
27. Zajonc, Robert B. and Eugene Burnstein, "The Learning of Balanced and Unbalanced Social Structures," *J. Pers.*, vol. 33, no. 2 (June 1965), pp. 153–163.

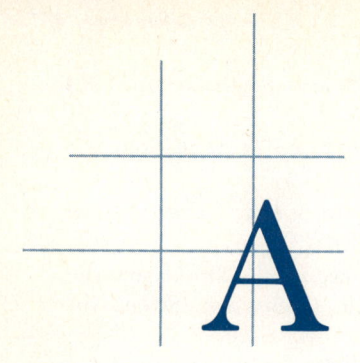

Appendix

Table 1 *Areas Under the Standard Normal Distribution*
Table 2 *Compound Interest*
Table 3 *Present Value of a Dollar*
Table 4 *Amount of an Annuity*
Table 5 *Present Value of an Annuity*

Table 1 *Areas Under the Standard Normal Distribution*[a]

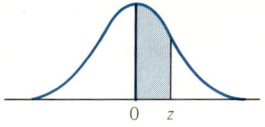

z	.00	.01	.02	.03	.04	.05	.06	.07	.08	.09
0.0	.0000	.0040	.0080	.0120	.0160	.0199	.0239	.0279	.0319	.0359
0.1	.0398	.0438	.0478	.0517	.0557	.0596	.0636	.0675	.0714	.0753
0.2	.0793	.0832	.0871	.0910	.0948	.0987	.1026	.1064	.1103	.1141
0.3	.1179	.1217	.1255	.1293	.1331	.1368	.1406	.1443	.1480	.1517
0.4	.1554	.1591	.1628	.1664	.1700	.1736	.1772	.1808	.1844	.1879
0.5	.1915	.1950	.1985	.2019	.2054	.2088	.2123	.2157	.2190	.2224
0.6	.2257	.2291	.2324	.2357	.2389	.2422	.2454	.2486	.2517	.2549
0.7	.2580	.2611	.2642	.2673	.2703	.2734	.2764	.2794	.2823	.2852
0.8	.2881	.2910	.2939	.2967	.2995	.3023	.3051	.3078	.3106	.3133
0.9	.3159	.3186	.3212	.3238	.3264	.3289	.3315	.3340	.3365	.3389
1.0	.3413	.3438	.3461	.3485	.3508	.3531	.3554	.3577	.3599	.3621
1.1	.3642	.3665	.3686	.3708	.3729	.3749	.3770	.3790	.3810	.3830
1.2	.3849	.3869	.3888	.3907	.3925	.3944	.3962	.3980	.3997	.4015
1.3	.4032	.4049	.4066	.4082	.4099	.4115	.4131	.4147	.4162	.4177
1.4	.4192	.4207	.4222	.4236	.4251	.4265	.4279	.4292	.4306	.4319
1.5	.4332	.4345	.4357	.4370	.4382	.4394	.4406	.4418	.4429	.4441
1.6	.4452	.4463	.4474	.4484	.4495	.4505	.4515	.4525	.4535	.4545
1.7	.4554	.4564	.4573	.4582	.4591	.4599	.4608	.4616	.4625	.4633
1.8	.4641	.4649	.4656	.4664	.4671	.4678	.4686	.4693	.4699	.4706
1.9	.4713	.4719	.4726	.4732	.4738	.4744	.4750	.4756	.4761	.4767
2.0	.4772	.4778	.4783	.4788	.4793	.4798	.4803	.4808	.4812	.4817
2.1	.4821	.4826	.4830	.4834	.4838	.4842	.4846	.4850	.4854	.4857
2.2	.4861	.4864	.4868	.4871	.4875	.4878	.4881	.4884	.4887	.4890
2.3	.4893	.4896	.4898	.4901	.4904	.4906	.4909	.4911	.4913	.4916
2.4	.4918	.4920	.4922	.4925	.4927	.4929	.4931	.4932	.4934	.4936
2.5	.4938	.4940	.4941	.4943	.4945	.4946	.4948	.4949	.4951	.4952
2.6	.4953	.4955	.4956	.4957	.4959	.4960	.4961	.4962	.4963	.4964
2.7	.4965	.4966	.4967	.4968	.4969	.4970	.4971	.4972	.4973	.4974
2.8	.4974	.4975	.4976	.4977	.4977	.4978	.4979	.4979	.4980	.4981
2.9	.4981	.4982	.4982	.4983	.4984	.4984	.4985	.4985	.4986	.4986
3.0	.4987	.4987	.4987	.4988	.4988	.4989	.4989	.4989	.4990	.4990
3.1	.4990	.4991	.4991	.4991	.4992	.4992	.4992	.4992	.4993	.4993
3.2	.4993	.4993	.4994	.4994	.4994	.4994	.4994	.4995	.4995	.4995
3.3	.4995	.4995	.4996	.4996	.4996	.4996	.4996	.4996	.4996	.4997
3.4	.4997	.4997	.4997	.4997	.4997	.4997	.4997	.4997	.4998	.4998
3.5	.4998	.4998	.4998	.4998	.4998	.4998	.4998	.4998	.4998	.4998
3.6	.4998	.4999	.4999	.4999	.4999	.4999	.4999	.4999	.4999	.4999
3.7	.4999	.4999	.4999	.4999	.4999	.4999	.4999	.4999	.4999	.4999
3.8	.4999	.4999	.4999	.4999	.4999	.4999	.4999	.5000	.5000	.5000

[a] The table gives the shaded area shown in the figure at the top.

Table 2 *Compound Interest*[a] $\qquad (1+r)^n$

n	$\frac{1}{4}\%$	$\frac{1}{2}\%$	$\frac{3}{4}\%$	1%	$1\frac{1}{4}\%$
1	1.002500	1.005000	1.007500	1.010000	1.012500
2	1.005006	1.010025	1.015056	1.020100	1.025156
3	1.007519	1.015075	1.022669	1.030301	1.037971
4	1.010038	1.020151	1.030339	1.040604	1.050945
5	1.012563	1.025251	1.038067	1.051010	1.064082
6	1.015094	1.030378	1.045852	1.061520	1.077383
7	1.017632	1.035529	1.053696	1.072135	1.090850
8	1.020176	1.040707	1.061599	1.082857	1.104486
9	1.022726	1.045911	1.069561	1.093685	1.118292
10	1.025283	1.051140	1.077583	1.104622	1.132271
11	1.027846	1.056396	1.085664	1.115668	1.146424
12	1.030416	1.061678	1.093807	1.126825	1.160755
13	1.032922	1.066986	1.102010	1.138093	1.175264
14	1.035574	1.072321	1.110276	1.149474	1.189955
15	1.038163	1.077683	1.118603	1.160969	1.204829
16	1.040759	1.083071	1.126992	1.172579	1.219890
17	1.043361	1.088487	1.135445	1.184304	1.235138
18	1.045969	1.093929	1.143960	1.196147	1.250577
19	1.048584	1.099399	1.152540	1.208109	1.266210
20	1.051205	1.104896	1.161134	1.220190	1.282037
21	1.053833	1.110420	1.169893	1.232392	1.298063
22	1.056468	1.115972	1.178667	1.244716	1.314288
23	1.059109	1.121552	1.187507	1.257163	1.330717
24	1.061757	1.127160	1.196414	1.269735	1.347351
25	1.064411	1.132796	1.205387	1.282432	1.364193
26	1.067072	1.138460	1.214427	1.295256	1.381245
27	1.069740	1.144152	1.223535	1.308209	1.398511
28	1.072414	1.149873	1.232712	1.321291	1.415992
29	1.075096	1.155622	1.241957	1.334504	1.433692
30	1.077783	1.161400	1.251272	1.347849	1.451613
31	1.080478	1.167207	1.260656	1.361327	1.469758
32	1.083179	1.173043	1.270111	1.374941	1.488130
33	1.085887	1.178908	1.279637	1.388690	1.506732
34	1.088602	1.184803	1.289234	1.402577	1.525566
35	1.091323	1.190727	1.298904	1.416603	1.544636
36	1.094051	1.196681	1.308645	1.430769	1.563944
37	1.096786	1.202664	1.318460	1.445076	1.583493
38	1.099528	1.208677	1.328349	1.459527	1.603287
39	1.102277	1.214721	1.338311	1.474122	1.623328
40	1.105033	1.220794	1.348349	1.488864	1.643619
41	1.107796	1.226898	1.358461	1.503752	1.664165
42	1.110565	1.233033	1.368650	1.518790	1.684967
43	1.113341	1.239198	1.378915	1.533978	1.706029
44	1.116125	1.245394	1.389256	1.549318	1.727354
45	1.118915	1.251621	1.399676	1.564811	1.748946
46	1.121712	1.257879	1.410173	1.580459	1.770808
47	1.124517	1.264168	1.420750	1.596263	1.792943
48	1.127328	1.270489	1.431405	1.612226	1.815355
49	1.130146	1.270842	1.442141	1.628348	1.818047
50	1.132972	1.283226	1.452957	1.644632	1.861022

[a] r = rate of interest per payment period; n = number of payment periods

Table 2 (Continued)

n	$\frac{1}{4}\%$	$\frac{1}{2}\%$	$\frac{3}{4}\%$	1%	$1\frac{1}{4}\%$
51	1.135804	1.289642	1.463854	1.661078	1.884285
52	1.138644	1.296090	1.474833	1.677688	1.907839
53	1.141490	1.302571	1.485894	1.694466	1.931687
54	1.144344	1.309083	1.497038	1.711410	1.955833
55	1.147205	1.315629	1.508266	1.728525	1.980281
56	1.150073	1.322207	1.519578	1.745810	2.005034
57	1.152948	1.328818	1.530975	1.763268	2.030097
58	1.155830	1.335462	1.542457	1.780901	2.059473
59	1.158720	1.342139	1.554026	1.798770	2.081167
60	1.161617	1.348850	1.565681	1.816697	2.107181
61	1.164521	1.355594	1.577424	1.834864	2.133521
62	1.167432	1.362372	1.589254	1.853212	2.160190
63	1.170351	1.365184	1.601174	1.871744	2.187192
64	1.173277	1.376030	1.613182	1.890462	2.214532
65	1.176210	1.382910	1.625281	1.905366	2.242214
66	1.179150	1.389825	1.637471	1.928460	2.270242
67	1.182098	1.396774	1.649752	1.947745	2.298620
68	1.185053	1.403758	1.662125	1.967222	2.327352
69	1.188016	1.410777	1.674591	1.986894	2.356444
70	1.190986	1.417831	1.687151	2.006763	2.385900
71	1.193963	1.424920	1.699804	2.026831	2.415724
72	1.196948	1.432044	1.712553	2.047099	2.445920
73	1.199941	1.439205	1.725397	2.067570	2.476494
74	1.202941	1.446401	1.738337	2.088246	2.507450
75	1.205948	1.453633	1.751375	2.109128	2.538793
76	1.208963	1.460901	1.764510	2.130220	2.570528
77	1.211985	1.468205	1.777744	2.151522	2.602660
78	1.215015	1.475546	1.791077	2.173037	2.635193
79	1.218053	1.482924	1.804510	2.194767	2.668133
80	1.221098	1.490339	1.818044	2.216715	2.701485
81	1.224151	1.497790	1.831679	2.238882	2.735253
82	1.227211	1.505279	1.845417	2.261271	2.769444
83	1.230279	1.512806	1.859257	2.283884	2.804062
84	1.233355	1.520370	1.873202	2.306723	2.839113
85	1.236438	1.527972	1.887251	2.329790	2.874602
86	1.239529	1.535611	1.901405	2.353088	2.910534
87	1.242628	1.543289	1.915666	2.376619	2.946916
88	1.245735	1.551006	1.930033	2.400385	2.983752
89	1.248849	1.558761	1.944509	2.424389	3.021049
90	1.251971	1.566555	1.959092	2.448633	3.058812
91	1.255101	1.574387	1.973786	2.473119	3.097048
92	1.258239	1.582259	1.988589	2.497850	3.135761
93	1.261384	1.590171	2.003503	2.522829	3.174958
94	1.264538	1.598122	2.018530	2.548057	3.214645
95	1.267699	1.606112	2.033669	2.573537	3.254828
96	1.270868	1.614143	2.048921	2.599273	3.295513
97	1.274046	1.622213	2.064288	2.625266	3.336707
98	1.277231	1.630325	2.079770	2.651518	3.378416
99	1.280424	1.638476	2.095368	2.678033	3.420646
100	1.283625	1.646669	2.111084	2.704814	3.463404

Table 2 (*Continued*)

n	$1\frac{1}{2}\%$	$1\frac{3}{4}\%$	2%	$2\frac{1}{2}\%$	3%
1	1.015000	1.017500	1.020000	1.025000	1.030000
2	1.030225	1.035306	1.040400	1.050625	1.060900
3	1.045678	1.053424	1.061208	1.076891	1.092727
4	1.061364	1.071859	1.082432	1.103813	1.125509
5	1.077284	1.090617	1.104081	1.131408	1.159274
6	1.093443	1.109702	1.126162	1.159693	1.194052
7	1.109845	1.129122	1.148686	1.188686	1.229874
8	1.126493	1.148882	1.171659	1.218403	1.266770
9	1.143390	1.168987	1.195093	1.248863	1.304773
10	1.160541	1.189444	1.218994	1.280085	1.343916
11	1.177949	1.210260	1.243374	1.312087	1.384234
12	1.195618	1.231439	1.268242	1.344889	1.425761
13	1.213552	1.252989	1.293607	1.378511	1.468534
14	1.231756	1.274917	1.319479	1.412974	1.512590
15	1.250232	1.297228	1.345868	1.448298	1.557967
16	1.268986	1.319929	1.372786	1.484506	1.604706
17	1.288020	1.343028	1.400241	1.521618	1.652848
18	1.307341	1.366531	1.428246	1.559659	1.702433
19	1.326951	1.390445	1.456811	1.598650	1.753506
20	1.346855	1.414778	1.485947	1.638616	1.806111
21	1.367058	1.439537	1.515666	1.679582	1.860295
22	1.387564	1.464729	1.545980	1.721571	1.916103
23	1.408377	1.490361	1.576899	1.764611	1.973586
24	1.429503	1.516443	1.608437	1.808726	2.032794
25	1.450945	1.542981	1.640606	1.853944	2.093778
26	1.472710	1.569983	1.673418	1.900293	2.156591
27	1.494800	1.597457	1.706886	1.947800	2.221289
28	1.517222	1.625413	1.741024	1.996495	2.287928
29	1.539981	1.653858	1.775845	2.046407	2.356565
30	1.563080	1.682800	1.811362	2.097568	2.427262
31	1.586526	1.712249	1.847589	2.150007	2.500080
32	1.610324	1.742213	1.884541	2.203757	2.575083
33	1.634479	1.772702	1.922231	2.258851	2.652335
34	1.658996	1.803724	1.960676	2.315322	2.731905
35	1.683881	1.835290	1.999889	2.373205	2.813862
36	1.709140	1.867407	2.039887	2.432535	2.898278
37	1.734777	1.900087	2.080685	2.493349	2.985227
38	1.760798	1.933338	2.122299	2.555682	2.074783
39	1.787210	1.967172	2.164745	2.619574	3.167027
40	1.814018	2.001597	2.208040	2.685064	3.262038
41	1.841229	2.036625	2.252200	2.752190	3.359899
42	1.868847	2.072266	2.297244	2.820995	3.460696
43	1.896880	2.108531	2.343189	2.891520	3.564517
44	1.925333	2.145430	2.390053	2.963808	3.671452
45	1.954213	2.182975	2.437854	3.037902	3.781596
46	1.983526	2.221177	2.486611	3.113851	3.895044
47	2.013279	2.260048	2.536343	3.191697	4.011895
48	2.043478	2.299599	2.587070	3.271489	4.132252
49	2.074130	2.329842	2.638812	3.353277	4.256219
50	2.105242	2.380789	2.691588	3.437109	4.381906

Table 2 (Continued)

n	$1\frac{1}{2}\%$	$1\frac{3}{4}\%$	2%	$2\frac{1}{2}\%$	3%
51	2.136821	2.422453	2.745420	3.523036	4.515423
52	2.168873	2.464846	2.800328	3.611112	4.650886
53	2.201406	2.507980	2.856335	3.701390	4.790412
54	2.234428	2.551870	2.913461	3.793925	4.934125
55	2.267944	2.596528	2.971731	3.888773	5.082148
56	2.301963	2.641967	3.031165	3.985992	5.234613
57	2.336493	2.688201	3.091788	4.085642	5.391651
58	2.371540	2.735245	3.153624	4.187783	5.553401
59	2.407113	2.783112	3.216697	4.292478	5.720003
60	2.443220	2.831816	3.281031	4.399790	5.891603
61	2.479868	2.881373	3.346651	4.509784	6.068351
62	2.517066	2.931797	3.413584	4.622529	6.250402
63	2.554822	2.983103	3.481856	4.738092	6.437914
64	2.593144	3.035308	3.551493	4.856544	6.631051
65	2.632042	3.088426	3.622523	4.977958	6.829982
66	2.671522	3.142473	3.694973	5.102407	7.034882
67	2.711595	3.197466	3.768873	5.229967	7.245928
68	2.752269	3.253422	3.844250	5.360716	7.463306
69	2.793553	3.310357	3.921135	5.494734	7.687205
70	2.835456	3.368288	3.999558	5.632103	7.917822
71	2.877988	3.427233	4.079549	5.772905	8.155356
72	2.921158	3.487210	4.161140	5.917228	8.400017
73	2.964975	3.548236	4.244363	6.065158	8.652017
74	3.009450	3.610330	4.329250	6.216787	8.911578
75	3.054592	3.673511	4.415835	6.372207	9.178925
76	3.100411	3.737797	4.504152	6.531512	9.454293
77	3.146917	3.803209	4.594235	6.694800	9.737922
78	3.194120	3.869765	4.686120	6.862170	10.030060
79	3.242032	3.937486	4.779842	7.033724	10.330961
80	3.290663	4.006392	4.875439	7.209567	10.640890
81	3.340023	4.076504	4.972948	7.389806	10.960117
82	3.390123	4.147842	5.072407	7.574552	11.288920
83	3.440975	4.220430	5.173855	7.763915	11.627588
84	3.492590	4.294287	5.277332	7.958013	11.976416
85	3.544978	4.369437	5.382878	8.156964	12.335708
86	3.598153	4.445902	5.490536	8.360888	12.705779
87	3.652125	4.523706	5.600347	8.569910	13.086953
88	3.706907	4.602870	5.712354	8.784158	13.479561
89	3.762511	4.683421	5.826601	9.003762	13.883948
90	3.818948	4.765380	5.943133	9.228856	14.300466
91	3.876233	4.848775	6.061995	9.459577	14.729480
92	3.934376	4.933628	6.183235	9.696066	15.171365
93	3.993392	5.019967	6.306900	9.938468	15.626506
94	4.053293	5.107816	6.433038	10.186930	16.095301
95	4.114092	5.197203	6.561699	10.441603	16.578160
96	4.175804	5.288154	6.692933	10.702643	17.075505
97	4.238441	5.380697	6.826791	10.970209	17.587770
98	4.302017	5.474859	6.963327	11.244464	18.115403
99	4.366547	5.570669	7.102594	11.525576	18.658865
100	4.432046	5.668156	7.244645	11.813715	19.218631

Table 3 *Present Value of a Dollar*[a] $(1 + r)^{-n}$

n	$\tfrac{1}{4}\%$	$\tfrac{1}{2}\%$	$\tfrac{3}{4}\%$	1%	$1\tfrac{1}{4}\%$
1	0.997506	0.995025	0.992556	0.990099	0.987654
2	0.995019	0.990075	0.985167	0.980296	0.975461
3	0.992537	0.985149	0.977833	0.970590	0.963418
4	0.990062	0.980248	0.970554	0.960980	0.951524
5	0.987593	0.975371	0.963329	0.951466	0.939777
6	0.985130	0.970518	0.956158	0.942045	0.928175
7	0.982674	0.965690	0.949040	0.932718	0.916716
8	0.980223	0.960885	0.941975	0.923483	0.905398
9	0.977779	0.956105	0.934963	0.914340	0.894221
10	0.975340	0.951348	0.928003	0.905287	0.883181
11	0.972908	0.946615	0.921095	0.896324	0.872277
12	0.970482	0.941905	0.914238	0.887449	0.861509
13	0.968062	0.937219	0.907432	0.878663	0.850873
14	0.965648	0.932556	0.900677	0.869963	0.840368
15	0.963240	0.927917	0.893973	0.861349	0.829993
16	0.960837	0.923300	0.887318	0.852821	0.819746
17	0.958441	0.918707	0.880712	0.844377	0.809626
18	0.956051	0.914136	0.874156	0.836017	0.799631
19	0.953667	0.909588	0.867649	0.827740	0.789759
20	0.951289	0.905063	0.861190	0.819544	0.780009
21	0.948917	0.900560	0.854779	0.811430	0.770379
22	0.946550	0.896080	0.848416	0.803396	0.760868
23	0.944190	0.891622	0.842100	0.795442	0.751475
24	0.941835	0.887186	0.835831	0.787566	0.742197
25	0.939486	0.882772	0.829609	0.779768	0.733034
26	0.937144	0.878380	0.823434	0.772048	0.723984
27	0.934806	0.874010	0.817304	0.764404	0.715046
28	0.932475	0.869662	0.811220	0.756836	0.706219
29	0.930150	0.865335	0.805181	0.749342	0.697500
30	0.927830	0.861030	0.799187	0.741923	0.688889
31	0.925517	0.856746	0.793238	0.734577	0.680384
32	0.923209	0.852484	0.787333	0.727304	0.671984
33	0.920906	0.848242	0.781472	0.720103	0.663688
34	0.918610	0.844022	0.775654	0.712973	0.655494
35	0.916319	0.839823	0.769880	0.705914	0.647402
36	0.914034	0.835645	0.764149	0.698925	0.639409
37	0.911754	0.831487	0.758461	0.692005	0.631515
38	0.909481	0.827351	0.752814	0.685153	0.623719
39	0.907213	0.823235	0.747210	0.678370	0.616019
40	0.904950	0.819139	0.741648	0.671653	0.608413
41	0.902694	0.815064	0.736127	0.665003	0.600902
42	0.900443	0.811008	0.730647	0.658419	0.593484
43	0.898197	0.806974	0.725208	0.651900	0.586157
44	0.895957	0.802959	0.719810	0.645445	0.578920
45	0.893723	0.798964	0.714451	0.639055	0.571773
46	0.891494	0.794989	0.709133	0.632728	0.564714
47	0.889271	0.791034	0.703854	0.626463	0.557742
48	0.887053	0.787098	0.698614	0.620260	0.550857
49	0.884841	0.783182	0.693414	0.614119	0.544056
50	0.882635	0.779286	0.688252	0.608039	0.537339

[a] r = rate of interest per payment period; n = number of payment periods

Table 3 (*Continued*)

n	$\frac{1}{4}\%$	$\frac{1}{2}\%$	$\frac{3}{4}\%$	1%	$1\frac{1}{4}\%$
51	0.880434	0.775409	0.683128	0.602019	0.530705
52	0.878238	0.771551	0.678043	0.596058	0.524153
53	0.876048	0.767713	0.672995	0.590157	0.517682
54	0.873863	0.763893	0.667986	0.584313	0.511291
55	0.871684	0.760093	0.663013	0.578528	0.504979
56	0.869510	0.756311	0.658077	0.572800	0.498745
57	0.867342	0.752548	0.653179	0.567129	0.492587
58	0.865179	0.748804	0.648316	0.561514	0.486506
59	0.863021	0.745079	0.643490	0.555954	0.480500
60	0.860869	0.741372	0.638700	0.550450	0.474568
61	0.858722	0.737684	0.633945	0.545000	0.468709
62	0.856581	0.734014	0.629226	0.539604	0.462922
63	0.854445	0.730362	0.624542	0.534261	0.457207
64	0.852314	0.726728	0.619893	0.528971	0.451563
65	0.850189	0.723113	0.615278	0.523734	0.455988
66	0.848068	0.719515	0.610698	0.518548	0.440482
67	0.845953	0.715935	0.606152	0.513414	0.435044
68	0.843844	0.712374	0.601639	0.508331	0.429673
69	0.841740	0.708829	0.597161	0.503298	0.424368
70	0.839640	0.705303	0.592715	0.498315	0.419129
71	0.837547	0.701794	0.588303	0.493381	0.413955
72	0.835458	0.698302	0.583924	0.488496	0.408844
73	0.833374	0.694828	0.579577	0.483660	0.403797
74	0.831296	0.691371	0.575262	0.478871	0.398811
75	0.829233	0.687932	0.570980	0.474130	0.393888
76	0.827155	0.684509	0.566730	0.469435	0.389025
77	0.825093	0.681104	0.562511	0.464787	0.384222
78	0.823035	0.677715	0.558323	0.460185	0.379479
79	0.820983	0.674343	0.554167	0.455629	0.374794
80	0.818935	0.670988	0.550042	0.451118	0.370167
81	0.816893	0.667650	0.545947	0.446651	0.365597
82	0.814856	0.664329	0.541883	0.442229	0.361083
83	0.812824	0.661023	0.537849	0.437851	0.356625
84	0.810797	0.657735	0.533845	0.433515	0.352223
85	0.808775	0.654462	0.529871	0.429223	0.347874
86	0.806758	0.651206	0.525927	0.424974	0.343580
87	0.804746	0.647967	0.522012	0.420766	0.339338
88	0.802739	0.644743	0.518126	0.416600	0.335148
89	0.800737	0.641535	0.514269	0.412475	0.331011
90	0.798741	0.638343	0.510440	0.408391	0.326924
91	0.796749	0.635168	0.506641	0.404348	0.322888
92	0.794762	0.632008	0.502869	0.400344	0.318902
93	0.792780	0.628863	0.499126	0.396380	0.314965
94	0.790803	0.625735	0.495410	0.392456	0.311076
95	0.788831	0.622622	0.491722	0.388570	0.307236
96	0.786864	0.619524	0.488062	0.384723	0.303443
97	0.784901	0.616442	0.484429	0.380914	0.299697
98	0.782944	0.613375	0.480822	0.377142	0.295997
99	0.780991	0.610323	0.477243	0.373408	0.292342
100	0.779044	0.607287	0.473690	0.369711	0.288733

Table 3 (*Continued*)

n	$1\frac{1}{2}\%$	$1\frac{3}{4}\%$	2%	$2\frac{1}{2}\%$	3%
1	0.985222	0.982801	0.980392	0.975610	0.970874
2	0.970662	0.965898	0.961169	0.951814	0.942596
3	0.956317	0.949285	0.942322	0.928599	0.915142
4	0.942184	0.932959	0.923845	0.905951	0.888487
5	0.928260	0.916913	0.905731	0.883854	0.862609
6	0.914542	0.901143	0.887971	0.862297	0.837484
7	0.901027	0.885644	0.870560	0.841265	0.813092
8	0.887711	0.870412	0.853490	0.820747	0.789409
9	0.874592	0.855441	0.836755	0.800728	0.766417
10	0.861667	0.840729	0.820348	0.781198	0.744094
11	0.848933	0.826269	0.804263	0.762145	0.722421
12	0.836387	0.812058	0.788493	0.743556	0.701380
13	0.824027	0.798091	0.773033	0.725420	0.680951
14	0.811849	0.784365	0.757875	0.707727	0.661118
15	0.799852	0.770875	0.743015	0.690466	0.641862
16	0.788031	0.757616	0.728446	0.673625	0.623167
17	0.776385	0.744586	0.714163	0.657195	0.605016
18	0.764912	0.731780	0.700159	0.641166	0.587395
19	0.753607	0.719194	0.686431	0.625528	0.570286
20	0.742470	0.706825	0.672971	0.610271	0.553676
21	0.731498	0.694668	0.659776	0.595386	0.537549
22	0.720688	0.682720	0.646839	0.580865	0.521893
23	0.710037	0.670978	0.634156	0.566697	0.506692
24	0.699544	0.659438	0.621722	0.552875	0.491934
25	0.689206	0.648096	0.609531	0.539391	0.477606
26	0.679021	0.636950	0.597579	0.526235	0.463695
27	0.668986	0.625995	0.585862	0.513400	0.450189
28	0.659099	0.615228	0.574375	0.500878	0.437077
29	0.649359	0.604647	0.563112	0.488661	0.424346
30	0.639762	0.594248	0.552071	0.476743	0.411987
31	0.630308	0.584027	0.541246	0.465115	0.399987
32	0.620993	0.573982	0.530633	0.453771	0.388337
33	0.611816	0.564111	0.520229	0.442703	0.377026
34	0.602774	0.554408	0.510028	0.431905	0.366045
35	0.593866	0.544873	0.500028	0.421371	0.355383
36	0.585090	0.535502	0.490223	0.411094	0.345032
37	0.576443	0.526292	0.480611	0.401067	0.334983
38	0.567924	0.517240	0.471187	0.391285	0.325226
39	0.559531	0.508344	0.461948	0.381741	0.315754
40	0.551262	0.499601	0.452890	0.372431	0.306557
41	0.543116	0.491008	0.444010	0.363347	0.297628
42	0.535089	0.482563	0.435304	0.354485	0.288959
43	0.527182	0.474264	0.426769	0.345839	0.280543
44	0.519391	0.466107	0.418401	0.337404	0.272372
45	0.511715	0.458090	0.410197	0.329174	0.264439
46	0.504153	0.450212	0.402154	0.321146	0.256737
47	0.496702	0.442469	0.394268	0.313313	0.249259
48	0.489362	0.434858	0.386538	0.305671	0.241999
49	0.482130	0.427379	0.378958	0.298216	0.234950
50	0.475005	0.420029	0.371528	0.290942	0.228107

Table 3 (*Continued*)

n	$1\frac{1}{2}\%$	$1\frac{3}{4}\%$	2%	$2\frac{1}{2}\%$	3%
51	0.467985	0.412805	0.364243	0.283846	0.221463
52	0.461069	0.405705	0.357101	0.276923	0.215013
53	0.454255	0.398727	0.350099	0.270169	0.208750
54	0.447542	0.391869	0.343234	0.263579	0.202670
55	0.440928	0.385130	0.336504	0.257151	0.196767
56	0.434412	0.378506	0.329906	0.250879	0.191036
57	0.427992	0.371996	0.323437	0.244760	0.185472
58	0.421667	0.365598	0.317095	0.238790	0.180070
59	0.415435	0.359310	0.310878	0.232966	0.174825
60	0.409296	0.353130	0.304782	0.227284	0.169733
61	0.403247	0.347057	0.298806	0.221740	0.164789
62	0.397288	0.341088	0.292947	0.216332	0.159990
63	0.391417	0.335221	0.287203	0.211055	0.155330
64	0.385632	0.329456	0.281572	0.205908	0.150806
65	0.379933	0.323790	0.276051	0.200886	0.146413
66	0.374318	0.318221	0.270638	0.195986	0.142149
67	0.368787	0.312748	0.265331	0.191206	0.138009
68	0.363337	0.307369	0.260129	0.186542	0.133989
69	0.357967	0.302082	0.255028	0.181992	0.130086
70	0.352677	0.296887	0.250028	0.177554	0.126297
71	0.347365	0.291781	0.245125	0.173223	0.122619
72	0.342330	0.286762	0.240319	0.168998	0.119047
73	0.337271	0.281830	0.235607	0.164876	0.115580
74	0.332287	0.276983	0.230987	0.160855	0.112214
75	0.327376	0.272219	0.226458	0.156931	0.108945
76	0.322538	0.267537	0.222017	0.153104	0.105772
77	0.317771	0.262936	0.217664	0.149370	0.102691
78	0.313075	0.258414	0.213396	0.145726	0.099700
79	0.308449	0.253969	0.209212	0.142172	0.096796
80	0.303890	0.249601	0.205110	0.138705	0.093977
81	0.299399	0.245308	0.201088	0.135322	0.091240
82	0.294975	0.241089	0.197145	0.132021	0.088582
83	0.290615	0.236943	0.193279	0.128801	0.086002
84	0.286321	0.232868	0.189490	0.125660	0.083497
85	0.282089	0.228862	0.185774	0.122595	0.081065
86	0.277920	0.224926	0.182132	0.119605	0.078704
87	0.273813	0.221058	0.178560	0.116687	0.076412
88	0.269767	0.217256	0.175059	0.113841	0.074186
89	0.265780	0.213519	0.171627	0.111065	0.072026
90	0.261852	0.209847	0.168261	0.108356	0.069928
91	0.257982	0.206238	0.164962	0.105713	0.067891
92	0.254170	0.202691	0.161728	0.103135	0.065914
93	0.250414	0.199205	0.158557	0.100619	0.063994
94	0.246713	0.195778	0.155448	0.098165	0.062130
95	0.243067	0.192411	0.152400	0.095771	0.060320
96	0.239475	0.189102	0.149411	0.093435	0.058563
97	0.235936	0.185850	0.146482	0.091156	0.056858
98	0.232449	0.182653	0.143610	0.088933	0.055202
99	0.229014	0.179512	0.140794	0.086764	0.053594
100	0.225629	0.176424	0.138033	0.084647	0.052033

Table 4 *Amount of an Annuity*[a] $s_{\overline{n}|r}$

n	1/4%	1/2%	3/4%	1%	1 1/4%
1	1.000000	1.000000	1.000000	1.000000	1.000000
2	2.002499	2.005000	2.007500	2.010000	2.012500
3	3.007505	3.015025	3.022556	3.030100	3.037656
4	4.015023	4.030100	4.045225	4.060401	4.075627
5	5.025060	5.050251	5.075564	5.101005	5.126572
6	6.037623	6.075502	6.113631	6.152015	6.190654
7	7.052717	7.105880	7.159483	7.213535	7.268037
8	8.070347	8.141409	8.213179	8.285670	8.358888
9	9.090523	9.182116	9.274778	9.368527	9.463374
10	10.113249	10.228027	10.344339	10.462212	10.581666
11	11.138532	11.279167	11.421921	11.566834	11.713936
12	12.166377	12.335563	12.507586	12.682502	12.860361
13	13.196793	13.397241	13.601393	13.809327	14.021115
14	14.229784	14.464227	14.703403	14.947421	15.196379
15	15.265359	15.536549	15.813679	16.096895	16.386334
16	16.303521	16.614231	16.932281	17.257864	17.591163
17	17.344280	17.697302	18.059273	18.430442	18.811052
18	18.387640	18.785789	19.194717	19.614747	20.046190
19	19.433609	19.879718	20.338678	20.810894	21.296767
20	20.482192	20.979116	21.491218	22.019003	22.562977
21	21.533398	22.084012	22.652402	23.239193	23.845014
22	22.587230	23.194432	23.822295	24.471585	25.143077
23	23.643699	24.310404	25.000962	25.716301	26.457365
24	24.702807	25.431957	26.188469	26.973463	27.788082
25	25.764564	26.559116	27.384883	28.243198	29.135433
26	26.828975	27.691912	28.590269	29.525630	30.499626
27	27.896046	28.830372	29.804696	30.820886	31.880871
28	28.965785	29.974524	31.028231	32.129095	33.279382
29	30.038200	31.124396	32.260943	33.450386	34.695374
30	31.113295	32.280018	33.502900	34.784890	36.129066
31	32.191078	33.441419	34.754172	36.132739	37.580679
32	33.271555	34.608626	36.014828	37.494066	39.050438
33	34.354734	35.781669	37.284939	38.869006	40.538568
34	35.440620	36.960577	38.564576	40.257696	42.045300
35	36.529221	38.145380	39.853810	41.660273	43.670866
36	37.620543	39.336107	41.152714	43.076876	45.115502
37	38.714594	40.532788	42.461359	44.507645	46.679446
38	39.811380	41.735452	43.779819	45.992721	48.262939
39	40.910909	42.944129	45.108168	47.412248	49.866225
40	42.013185	44.158850	46.446479	48.886371	51.489553
41	43.118218	45.379644	47.794828	50.375234	53.133172
42	44.226012	46.606543	49.153289	51.878987	54.797337
43	45.336577	47.839575	50.521938	53.397776	56.482304
44	46.449918	49.078773	51.900853	54.931754	58.188332
45	47.566043	50.324167	53.290109	56.481072	59.915686
46	48.684957	51.575788	54.689785	58.045882	61.664632
47	49.806669	52.833667	56.099958	59.626341	63.435440
48	50.931185	54.097835	57.520707	61.222604	65.228383
49	52.058514	55.368324	58.952113	62.834830	67.043738
50	53.188659	56.645166	60.384253	64.463178	68.881786

[a] r = interest rate per payment period; n = number of payment periods

Table 4 (*Continued*)

n	¼%	½%	¾%	1%	1¼%
51	54.321630	57.928392	61.847210	66.107810	70.742806
52	55.457433	59.218034	63.311064	67.768888	72.627092
53	56.596077	60.514125	64.785897	69.446577	74.534930
54	57.737566	61.816695	66.271791	71.141043	76.466616
55	58.881910	63.125778	67.768830	72.852453	78.422449
56	60.029113	64.441408	69.277096	74.580977	80.402730
57	61.179186	65.763614	70.796674	76.326787	82.407764
58	62.332134	67.092433	72.327649	78.090055	84.437861
59	63.487963	68.427895	73.870107	79.870956	86.493334
60	64.646682	69.770034	75.424132	81.669665	88.574500
61	65.808299	71.118885	76.989813	83.486361	90.681681
62	66.972818	72.474479	78.567236	85.321225	92.815202
63	68.140251	73.836852	80.156491	87.174437	94.975392
64	69.310600	75.206036	81.757665	89.046181	97.162584
65	70.483877	76.582066	83.370847	90.936643	99.377116
66	71.660086	77.964977	84.996128	92.846010	101.619330
67	72.839236	79.354802	86.633599	94.779970	103.889572
68	74.021333	80.751576	88.283351	96.722214	106.188191
69	75.206386	82.155334	89.945476	98.689436	108.515543
70	76.394402	83.566111	91.620067	100.676380	110.871988
71	77.585387	84.983941	93.307217	102.683094	113.257887
72	78.779350	86.408861	95.007022	104.709924	115.673611
73	79.976298	87.840905	96.719574	106.757024	118.119531
74	81.176238	89.280110	98.444971	108.824594	120.596025
75	82.379178	90.726511	100.183308	110.912840	123.103475
76	83.585124	92.180143	101.934683	113.021968	125.642268
77	84.794088	93.641044	103.699193	115.152188	128.212797
78	86.006071	95.109249	105.476936	117.303709	130.815456
79	87.221088	96.584796	107.268014	119.476747	133.450649
80	88.439139	98.067720	109.072523	121.671514	136.118782
81	89.660237	99.558058	110.890567	123.888229	138.820267
82	90.884387	101.055849	112.722246	126.127111	141.555520
83	92.111597	102.561128	114.567663	128.388382	144.324964
84	93.341875	104.073934	116.426920	130.672266	147.129026
85	94.575230	105.594304	118.300123	132.978988	149.968138
86	95.811667	107.122275	120.187373	135.308778	152.842740
87	97.051197	108.657887	122.088778	137.661866	155.753274
88	98.293823	110.201176	124.004444	140.038484	158.700190
89	99.539557	111.752182	125.934477	142.438869	161.683942
90	100.788406	113.310943	127.878986	144.863258	164.704991
91	102.040376	114.877498	129.838078	147.311890	167.763803
92	103.295475	116.451885	131.811864	149.785009	170.860850
93	104.553715	118.034145	133.800453	152.282859	173.996611
94	105.815098	119.624315	135.803956	154.805687	177.171568
95	107.079636	121.222438	137.822486	157.353744	180.386213
96	108.347334	122.828550	139.856154	159.927281	183.641040
97	109.618202	124.442693	141.905075	162.526554	186.936553
98	110.892247	126.064906	143.969368	165.151819	190.273260
99	112.169477	127.695231	146.049133	167.803338	193.651675
100	113.449899	129.333707	148.144501	170.481370	197.072322

Table 4 (*Continued*)

n	$1\frac{1}{2}\%$	$1\frac{3}{4}\%$	2%	$2\frac{1}{2}\%$	3%
1	1.000000	1.000000	1.000000	1.000000	1.000000
2	2.015000	2.017500	2.020000	2.025000	2.030000
3	3.045225	3.052806	3.060400	3.075625	3.090900
4	4.090903	4.106230	4.121608	4.152515	4.183627
5	5.152267	5.178089	5.204040	5.256328	5.309136
6	6.229551	6.268706	6.308121	6.387737	6.468410
7	7.322994	7.378408	7.434283	7.547430	7.662462
8	8.432839	8.507530	8.582969	8.736116	8.892336
9	9.559332	9.656412	9.754628	9.954518	10.159106
10	10.702722	10.825399	10.949720	11.203381	11.463879
11	11.863262	12.014844	12.168715	12.483466	12.807795
12	13.941211	13.225103	13.412089	13.795552	14.192029
13	14.236830	14.456542	14.680331	15.140441	15.617790
14	15.450382	15.709532	15.973937	16.518952	17.086324
15	16.682138	16.984449	17.293416	17.931926	18.598913
16	17.932370	18.281676	18.639284	19.380224	20.156881
17	19.201355	19.601606	20.012070	20.864730	21.761587
18	20.489376	20.944634	21.412311	22.386348	23.414435
19	21.796716	22.311165	22.840558	23.946006	25.116868
20	23.123667	23.701610	24.297369	25.544656	26.870374
21	24.470522	25.116388	25.783316	27.183273	28.676485
22	25.837580	26.555925	27.298982	28.862855	30.536780
23	27.225143	28.020654	28.844962	30.584426	32.452883
24	28.633521	29.511015	30.421861	32.349036	34.426469
25	30.063024	31.027458	32.030298	34.157762	36.459263
26	31.513969	32.570438	33.670904	36.011706	38.553041
27	32.986678	34.140421	35.344322	37.911999	40.709632
28	34.481478	35.737878	37.051208	39.859799	42.930921
29	35.998701	37.363291	38.792232	41.856294	45.218849
30	37.538681	39.017148	40.568077	43.902701	47.575414
31	39.101761	40.699948	42.379438	46.000268	50.002677
32	40.688288	42.412197	44.227027	48.150275	52.502757
33	42.298612	44.154411	46.111568	50.354032	55.077840
34	43.933091	45.927113	48.033799	52.612883	57.730175
35	45.592088	47.730837	49.994475	54.928205	60.462080
36	47.275969	49.566127	51.994364	57.301409	63.275942
37	48.985109	51.433534	54.034251	59.733945	66.174221
38	50.719885	53.333621	56.114936	62.227293	69.159447
39	52.480683	55.266959	58.237235	64.782976	72.234231
40	54.267894	57.234131	60.401979	67.402550	75.401258
41	56.081912	59.235728	62.610019	70.087614	78.663295
42	57.923141	61.272353	64.862219	72.839804	82.023194
43	59.791988	63.344619	67.159464	75.660799	85.483890
44	61.688868	65.453150	69.502653	78.552318	89.048406
45	63.614201	67.598580	71.892706	81.516126	92.719858
46	65.568414	69.781555	74.330560	84.554030	96.501454
47	67.551940	72.002732	76.817171	87.667880	100.396498
48	69.565219	74.262780	79.353514	90.859577	104.408392
49	71.608698	76.562378	81.940584	94.131066	108.540644
50	73.682828	78.902220	84.579396	97.484343	112.796863

Table 4 (*Continued*)

n	1½%	1¾%	2%	2½%	3%
51	75.788070	81.283009	87.270984	100.921451	117.180769
52	77.924891	83.705461	90.016403	104.444487	121.696192
53	80.093765	86.170307	92.816731	108.055599	126.347078
54	82.295171	88.678287	95.673065	111.756989	131.137490
55	84.529599	91.230157	98.586527	115.550914	136.071615
56	86.797543	93.826684	101.558257	119.439686	141.153763
57	89.099506	96.468651	104.589422	123.425679	146.388376
58	91.435998	99.156852	107.681210	127.511320	151.780027
59	93.807539	101.892097	110.834834	131.699103	157.333428
60	96.214651	104.675209	114.051531	135.991581	163.053431
61	98.657871	107.507025	117.332562	140.391370	168.945034
62	101.137739	110.388398	120.679212	144.901154	175.013384
63	103.654805	113.320195	124.092797	149.523683	181.263786
64	106.209628	116.303298	127.574652	154.261775	187.701699
65	108.802772	119.338605	131.126145	159.118319	194.332750
66	111.434813	122.427031	134.748668	164.096277	201.162733
67	114.106336	125.569504	138.443642	169.198684	208.197614
68	116.817931	128.766970	142.212514	174.428650	215.443543
69	119.570200	132.020392	146.056764	179.789366	222.906849
70	122.363753	135.330748	149.977899	185.284100	230.594054
71	125.199209	138.699037	153.977457	190.916203	238.511875
72	128.077197	142.126269	158.057006	196.689107	246.667232
73	130.998355	145.613479	162.218146	202.606335	255.067249
74	133.963330	149.161715	166.462508	208.671493	263.719266
75	136.972780	152.772045	170.791759	214.888280	272.630844
76	140.027372	156.445555	175.207593	221.260487	281.809769
77	143.127783	160.183352	179.711746	227.791999	291.264062
78	146.274699	163.986561	184.305980	234.486799	301.001983
79	149.468820	167.856326	188.992100	241.348968	311.032043
80	152.710852	171.793811	193.771941	248.382692	321.363004
81	156.001515	175.800202	198.647380	255.592259	332.003894
82	159.341538	179.876706	203.620327	262.982065	342.964010
83	162.731661	184.024548	208.692734	270.556617	354.252930
84	166.172636	188.244977	213.866588	278.320532	365.880518
85	169.665225	192.539264	219.143920	286.278545	377.856933
86	173.210204	196.908701	224.526798	294.435508	390.192641
87	176.808356	201.354604	230.017333	302.796396	402.898420
88	180.460482	205.878308	235.617680	311.366305	415.985373
89	184.167389	210.481179	241.330033	320.150463	429.464934
90	187.929900	215.164599	247.156633	329.154224	443.348881
91	191.748848	219.929980	253.099766	338.383079	457.649348
92	195.625081	224.778753	259.161761	347.842656	472.378828
93	199.559458	229.712382	265.344996	357.538722	487.550192
94	203.552850	234.732348	271.651895	367.477190	503.176698
95	207.606142	239.840165	278.084933	377.664119	519.271998
96	211.720234	245.037367	284.646631	388.105722	535.850158
97	215.896038	250.325521	291.339564	398.808365	552.925662
98	220.134478	255.706217	298.166354	409.778573	570.513433
99	224.436456	261.181070	305.129682	421.023038	588.628835
100	228.003043	266.751744	312.232215	432.548612	607.287700

Table 5 *Present Value of an Annuity*[a] $a_{\overline{n}|r}$

n	$\frac{1}{4}\%$	$\frac{1}{2}\%$	$\frac{3}{4}\%$	1%	$1\frac{1}{4}\%$
1	0.997506	0.995025	0.992556	0.990099	0.987654
2	1.992524	1.985099	1.977723	1.970395	1.963115
3	2.985061	2.970248	2.955556	2.940985	2.926534
4	3.975123	3.950496	3.926110	3.901965	3.878058
5	4.962716	4.925867	4.889439	4.853431	4.817835
6	5.947846	5.896385	5.845597	5.795476	5.746010
7	6.930519	6.862074	6.794637	6.728194	6.662725
8	7.910741	7.822960	7.736613	7.651677	7.568124
9	8.888520	8.779064	8.671576	8.566017	8.462344
10	9.863860	9.730412	9.599579	9.471304	9.345525
11	10.836767	10.677027	10.520674	10.367628	10.217803
12	11.807249	11.618933	11.434912	11.255077	11.079311
13	12.775310	12.556152	12.342345	12.133740	11.930184
14	13.740957	13.488708	13.243022	13.003702	12.770552
15	14.704197	14.416626	14.136994	13.865052	13.600545
16	15.665033	15.339926	15.024312	14.717873	14.420291
17	16.623475	16.258633	15.905024	15.562251	15.229918
18	17.579525	17.172769	16.779180	16.398268	16.029548
19	18.533192	18.082357	17.646829	17.226008	16.819307
20	19.484480	18.987420	18.508019	18.045552	17.599315
21	20.433396	19.887980	19.362798	18.856982	18.369694
22	21.379946	20.784060	20.211214	19.660379	19.130562
23	22.324136	21.675682	21.053314	20.455820	19.882036
24	23.265970	22.562867	21.889145	21.243386	20.624233
25	24.205456	23.445639	22.718754	22.023155	21.357268
26	25.142599	24.324019	23.542188	22.795203	22.081252
27	26.077405	25.198029	24.359492	23.559607	22.796298
28	27.009879	26.067691	25.170711	24.316442	23.502517
29	27.940030	26.933025	25.975892	25.065784	24.200016
30	28.867859	27.794055	26.775079	25.807707	24.888905
31	29.793376	28.650802	27.568317	26.542284	25.569289
32	30.716584	29.503285	28.355649	27.269588	26.241273
33	31.637490	30.351527	29.137121	27.989691	26.904961
34	32.556099	31.195550	29.912775	28.702665	27.560455
35	33.472417	32.035373	30.682655	29.408579	28.207857
36	34.386451	32.871018	31.446804	30.107504	28.847266
37	35.298205	33.702505	32.205264	30.799509	29.478781
38	36.207685	34.529856	32.958079	31.484662	30.102500
39	37.114898	35.353091	33.705289	32.163032	30.718518
40	38.019848	36.172230	34.446937	32.834685	31.326932
41	38.922541	36.987293	35.183064	33.499688	31.927834
42	39.822983	37.798302	35.913711	34.158107	32.521317
43	40.721180	38.605275	36.638919	34.810007	33.107474
44	41.617136	39.408234	37.358729	35.455452	33.686394
45	42.510859	40.207198	38.073180	36.094507	34.258167
46	43.402353	41.002187	38.782312	36.727235	34.822881
47	44.291624	41.793221	39.486166	37.353698	35.380623
48	45.178676	42.580320	40.184780	37.973958	35.931479
49	46.063518	43.363502	40.878194	38.588077	36.475535
50	46.946152	44.142788	41.566445	39.196116	37.012874

[a] r = interest rate per payment period; n = number of payment periods

Table 5 (*Continued*)

n	$\frac{1}{4}\%$	$\frac{1}{2}\%$	$\frac{3}{4}\%$	1%	$1\frac{1}{4}\%$
51	47.826585	44.918198	42.249573	39.798135	37.543579
52	48.704822	45.689749	42.927616	40.394193	38.067733
53	49.580870	46.457462	43.600612	40.984349	38.585415
54	50.454732	47.221355	44.268597	41.568663	39.096706
55	51.326417	47.981447	44.931610	42.147191	39.601685
56	52.195926	48.737759	45.589687	42.719991	40.100430
57	53.063268	49.490307	46.242866	43.287120	40.593017
58	53.928446	50.239112	46.891182	43.848633	41.079523
59	54.791466	50.984191	47.534672	44.404587	41.560023
60	55.652335	51.725563	48.173372	44.955037	42.034590
61	56.511058	52.463247	48.807317	45.500037	42.503299
62	57.367637	53.197261	49.436542	46.039640	42.966221
63	58.222083	53.927623	50.061085	46.573901	43.423428
64	59.074396	54.654351	50.680977	47.102872	43.874991
65	59.924584	55.377464	51.296255	47.626606	44.320978
66	60.772652	56.096979	51.906953	48.145155	44.761460
67	61.618605	56.812914	52.513105	48.658569	45.196504
68	62.462449	57.525288	53.114744	49.166900	45.626177
69	63.304188	58.234117	53.711905	49.670198	46.050545
70	64.143828	58.939420	54.304620	50.168513	46.469674
71	64.981375	59.641214	54.892923	50.661894	46.883629
72	65.816832	60.339517	55.476847	51.150390	47.292473
73	66.650206	61.034345	56.056424	51.634049	47.696269
74	67.481502	61.725716	56.631686	52.112920	48.095081
75	68.310725	62.413648	57.202666	52.587050	48.488969
76	69.137879	63.098157	57.769395	53.056485	48.877994
77	69.962972	63.779261	58.331906	53.521272	49.262216
78	70.786006	64.456976	58.890229	53.981457	49.641695
79	71.606989	65.131320	59.444396	54.437087	50.016488
80	72.425923	65.802308	59.994438	54.888205	50.386655
81	73.242816	66.469958	60.540385	55.334856	50.752252
82	74.057672	67.134287	61.082268	55.777085	51.113335
83	74.870495	67.795311	61.620117	56.214936	51.469961
84	75.681291	68.453045	62.153962	56.648451	51.822184
85	76.490066	69.107508	62.683834	57.077674	52.170058
86	77.296823	69.758714	63.209760	57.502648	52.513637
87	78.101570	70.406681	63.731772	57.923414	52.852975
88	78.904308	71.051424	64.249898	58.340014	53.188124
89	79.705045	71.692959	64.764167	58.752489	53.519134
90	80.503785	72.331303	65.274607	59.160880	53.846059
91	81.300533	72.966470	65.781248	59.565228	54.168947
92	82.095294	73.598478	66.284117	59.965572	54.487849
93	82.888075	74.227341	66.783242	60.361952	54.802813
94	83.678877	74.853076	67.278652	60.754408	55.113890
95	84.467708	75.475697	67.770375	61.142978	55.421126
96	85.254571	76.095221	68.258436	61.527701	55.724569
97	86.039472	76.711663	68.742865	61.908615	56.024265
98	86.822415	77.325038	69.223687	62.285758	56.320262
99	87.603406	77.935361	69.700930	62.659166	56.612604
100	88.382449	78.542648	70.174620	63.028877	56.901338

Table 5 (*Continued*)

n	$1\frac{1}{2}\%$	$1\frac{3}{4}\%$	2%	$2\frac{1}{2}\%$	3%
1	0.985222	0.982801	0.980392	0.975610	0.970874
2	1.955883	1.948699	1.941561	1.927424	1.913470
3	2.912200	2.897984	2.883883	2.856024	2.828611
4	3.854385	3.830942	3.807729	3.761974	3.717098
5	4.782645	4.747855	4.713459	4.645828	4.579707
6	5.697187	5.648997	5.601431	5.508125	5.417191
7	6.598214	6.534641	6.471991	6.349390	6.230283
8	7.485925	7.405053	7.325481	7.170137	7.019692
9	8.360517	8.260494	8.162236	7.970865	7.786109
10	9.222184	9.101223	8.982585	8.752064	8.530203
11	10.071118	9.927492	9.786848	9.514208	9.252624
12	10.907505	10.739549	10.575341	10.257764	9.954004
13	11.731532	11.537641	11.348373	10.983185	10.634955
14	12.543381	12.322005	12.106248	11.690912	11.296073
15	13.343233	13.092880	12.849263	12.381377	11.937935
16	14.131264	13.850496	13.577709	13.055002	12.561102
17	14.907649	14.595082	14.291871	13.712197	13.166118
18	15.672561	15.326862	14.992031	14.353363	13.753513
19	16.426168	16.046056	15.678462	14.978891	14.323799
20	17.168639	16.752881	16.351433	15.589162	14.877475
21	17.900137	17.447549	17.011209	16.184548	15.415024
22	18.620824	18.130269	17.658048	16.765413	15.936916
23	19.330861	18.801247	18.292204	17.332110	16.443608
24	20.030405	19.460685	18.913925	17.884985	16.935542
25	20.719611	20.108781	19.523456	18.424376	17.413147
26	21.398632	20.745731	20.121035	18.950611	17.876842
27	22.067617	21.371726	20.706897	19.464010	18.327031
28	22.726717	21.986854	21.281272	19.964888	18.764108
29	23.376076	22.591601	21.844384	20.453549	19.188454
30	24.015838	23.185849	22.396455	20.930292	19.600441
31	24.646146	23.769876	22.937701	21.395407	20.000428
32	25.267139	24.343858	23.468334	21.849177	20.388765
33	25.878954	24.907969	23.988563	22.291880	20.765792
34	26.481728	25.462377	24.498591	22.723786	21.131836
35	27.075595	26.007250	24.998619	23.145157	21.487220
36	27.660684	26.542752	25.488842	23.556251	21.832252
37	28.237127	27.069044	25.969453	23.957318	22.167235
38	28.805052	27.586284	26.440640	24.348603	22.492461
39	29.364583	28.094628	26.902588	24.730344	22.808215
40	29.915845	28.594229	27.355478	25.102775	23.114772
41	30.458961	29.085237	27.799489	25.466121	23.412400
42	30.994050	29.567801	28.234793	25.820606	23.701359
43	31.521232	30.042064	28.661562	26.166445	23.981902
44	32.040622	30.508171	29.079962	26.503849	24.254274
45	32.552337	30.966262	29.490159	26.833023	24.518712
46	33.056490	31.416473	29.892313	27.154169	24.775449
47	33.553192	31.858942	30.286581	27.467482	25.024708
48	34.042554	32.293800	30.673119	27.773153	25.266706
49	34.524683	32.721180	31.052077	28.071369	25.501657
50	34.999688	33.141209	31.423605	28.362311	25.729764

Table 5 (*Continued*)

n	$1\frac{1}{2}\%$	$1\frac{3}{4}\%$	2%	$2\frac{1}{2}\%$	3%
51	35.467673	33.554013	31.787848	28.646157	25.951227
52	35.928742	33.959718	32.144949	28.923080	26.166240
53	36.382997	34.358445	32.495048	29.193249	26.374990
54	36.830539	34.750315	32.838282	29.456828	26.577660
55	37.271467	35.135445	33.174787	29.713979	26.774427
56	37.705879	35.513950	33.504693	29.964857	26.965464
57	38.133871	35.885946	33.828130	30.209617	27.150935
58	38.555537	36.251544	34.145226	30.448407	27.331005
59	38.970973	36.610854	34.456104	30.681372	27.505830
60	39.380269	36.963985	34.760886	30.908656	27.675564
61	39.783516	37.311041	35.059692	31.130396	27.840353
62	40.180804	37.652129	35.352639	31.346728	28.000343
63	40.572221	37.987351	35.639842	31.557783	28.155672
64	40.957853	38.316806	35.921414	31.763691	28.306478
65	41.337786	38.640596	36.197465	31.964577	28.452891
66	41.712105	38.958817	36.468103	32.160562	28.595040
67	42.080891	39.271564	36.733434	32.351768	28.733049
68	42.444228	39.578933	36.993563	32.538311	28.867038
69	42.802195	39.881015	37.248591	32.720303	28.997124
70	43.154872	40.177902	37.498619	32.897857	29.123421
71	43.502337	40.469682	37.743744	33.071080	29.246040
72	43.844667	40.756445	37.984062	33.240078	29.365087
73	44.181938	41.038275	38.219669	33.404954	29.480667
74	44.514224	41.315258	38.450656	33.565809	29.592881
75	44.841600	41.587477	38.677114	33.722740	29.701826
76	45.164138	41.855014	38.899131	33.875844	29.807598
77	45.481910	42.117950	39.116795	34.025214	29.910290
78	45.794985	42.376364	39.330191	34.170940	30.009990
79	46.103433	42.630333	39.539403	34.313112	30.106786
80	46.407323	42.879934	39.744513	34.451817	30.200763
81	46.706723	43.125242	39.945601	34.587138	30.292003
82	47.001697	43.366331	40.142746	34.719159	30.380586
83	47.292313	43.603274	40.336025	34.847960	30.466588
84	47.578633	43.836142	40.525515	34.973620	30.550085
85	47.860722	44.065004	40.711289	35.096214	30.631151
86	48.138643	44.289930	40.893421	35.215819	30.709855
87	48.412456	44.510988	41.071981	35.332506	30.786267
88	48.682222	44.728244	41.247040	35.446348	30.860454
89	48.948002	44.941763	41.418667	35.557412	30.932479
90	49.209854	45.151610	41.586929	35.665768	31.002407
91	49.467837	45.357847	41.751891	35.771481	31.070298
92	49.722007	45.560538	41.913618	35.874616	31.136212
93	49.972421	45.759742	42.072175	35.975235	31.200206
94	50.219134	45.955521	42.227622	36.073400	31.262336
95	50.462201	46.147932	42.380022	36.169171	31.322656
96	50.701675	46.337034	42.529433	36.262605	31.381219
97	50.937611	46.522883	42.675915	36.353761	31.438077
98	51.170060	46.705537	42.819524	36.442694	31.493279
99	51.399074	46.885048	42.960318	36.529458	31.546872
100	51.624704	47.061472	43.098351	36.614105	31.598905

Answers to Odd-Numbered Exercises

Chapter 2

Section 2.1

1. u is independent; v is dependent. 3. -13 5. 17 7. 4
9. -7 11. 0 13. $\sqrt{5}$ 15. 3 17. $2\sqrt{3}$
19. $12a - 48$ 21. $2a - 48$ 23. $12a - 72$ 25. $24a - 60$
27. $6a$ 29. $-6a + 24$ 31. 1 33. -2 35. -6
37. -7 39. 5 41. -3 43. -21 45. 2
47. $A = (4, -2)$ 49. $B = (0, -6)$ 51. $C = (-7, -3)$
53. $D = (8, 1)$ 55. $E = (5, 0)$ 57. $F = (-2, 6)$

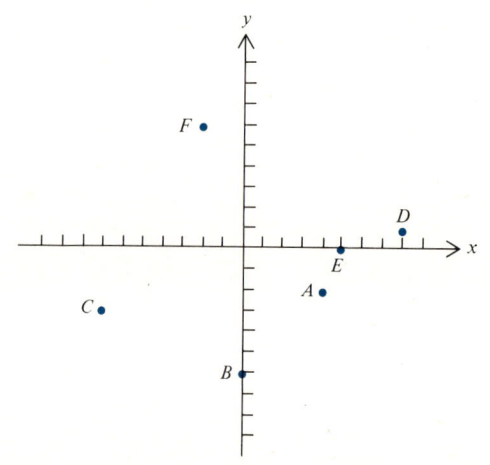

59. x intercept 6; y intercept -30

61. x intercepts -2 and 2; y intercept -4
63. No x intercept; y intercept 4
65. No x intercept; y intercept 1

67.

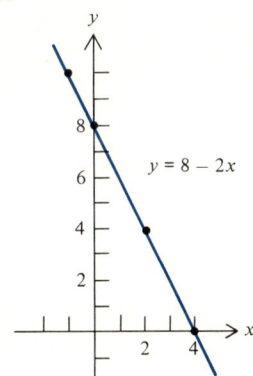

69.

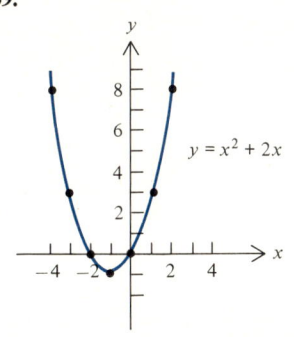

71.

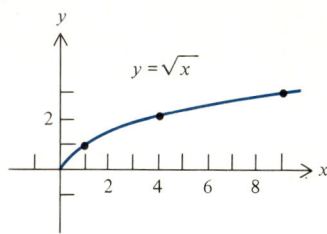

73.

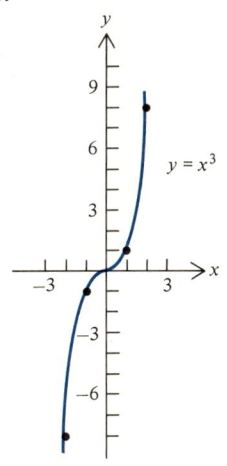

75.

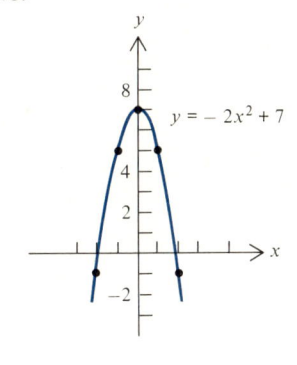

77.

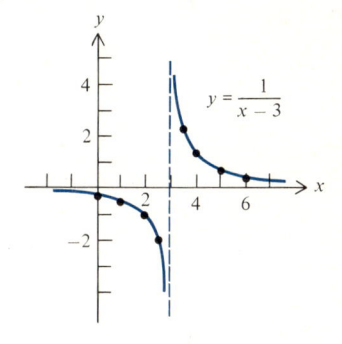

79. The minimum occurs at $x = 50$.

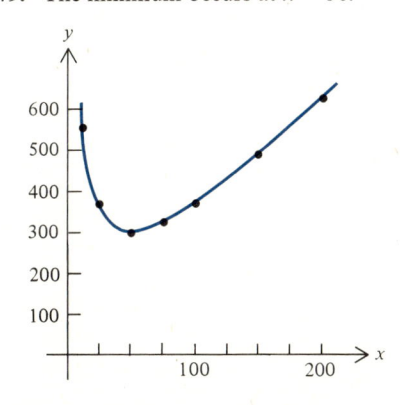

81. The minimum occurs at $x = 1200$.

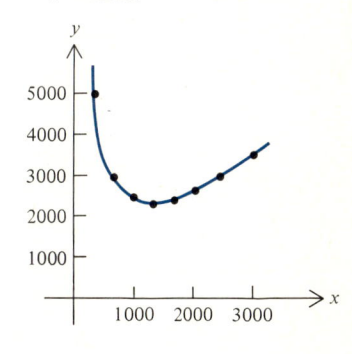

Section 2.2

1. Is a line 3. Is not a line 5. Is a line 7. Is a line

9. [graph of $3x - 4y = 24$]

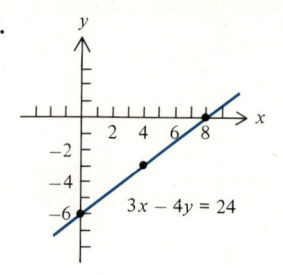

11. [graph of $y = 5x - 6$]

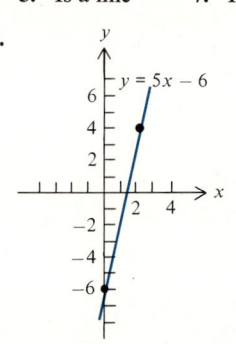

13. [graph of $x = -7$]

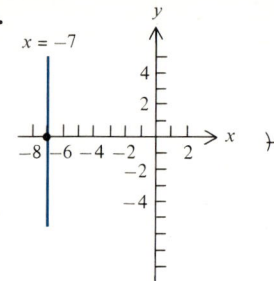

15. [graph of $y = -4x$]

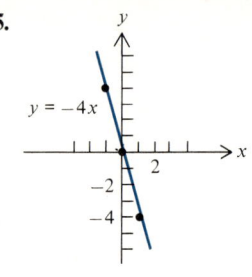

17. $y = 0;\ x = -3$ 19. $y = -3;\ x = -8$ 21. $y = 5;\ x = 7$
23. $y = -2;\ x = 4$ 25. $y = 6;\ x = -2$ 27. $y = 4;\ x = 0$
29. -3 31. -2.5 33. 4 35. $\frac{1}{4}$ 37. $y = -2x - 7$
39. $y = 3x - 19$ 41. $y = -4x + 34$ 43. $y = x - 1$
45. $y = 2x - 5$ 47. $y = \frac{2}{3}x + \frac{10}{3}$ 49. $y = x + 2$
51. $y = 4x - 21$ 53. Slope -6; y intercept 4
55. Slope 0; y intercept 7 57. Slope $-\frac{3}{2}$; y intercept -2
59. Slope $\frac{5}{3}$; y intercept $-\frac{8}{3}$ 61. $y = 4x - 13$ 63. $y = -6x - 7$
65. $x = 2$ 67. $2x + 5y = -22$ 69. $x + 4y = -1$
71. $x - 6y = -32$ 73. $y = 5$ 75. $5x - 2y = 3$
77. The second option is less expensive.

Section 2.3

1. $p = 6;\ D(6) = 1500$ 3. $p = 7.50;\ D(7.50) = 750$
5. $p = 7;\ D(7) = 800$ 7. $p = 13.40;\ D(13.40) = 1288$
9. $p = 5;\ D(5) = 2000$ 11. $p = 8;\ D(8) = 720$
13. $p = 7.40;\ D(7.40) = 760$ 15. $p = 11.20;\ D(11.20) = 1904$
17. Before: $p = 4.80$ and $D(4.80) = 1056$; after: $p = 5$ and $D(5) = 1000$
19. Before: $p = 2.40$ and $D(2.40) = 1512$; after: $p = 2.50$ and $D(2.50) = 1500$
21. (a) $p = 10.40;\ D(10.40) = 880$ (b) $p = 10;\ D(10) = 800$
23. $R(x) = 7x;\ C(x) = 4x + 830$ 25. $R(x) = 8x;\ C(x) = 6x + 1250$

Answers to Odd-Numbered Exercises 479

27. $R(x) = 9.50x$; $C(x) = 7.80x + 1600$
29. $R(x) = 5.80x$; $C(x) = 4x + 1125$ **31.** $2100; $7 **33.** $3200; $3
35. $1700; $5 **37.** $2700; $12
39. The break-even quantity is 900.

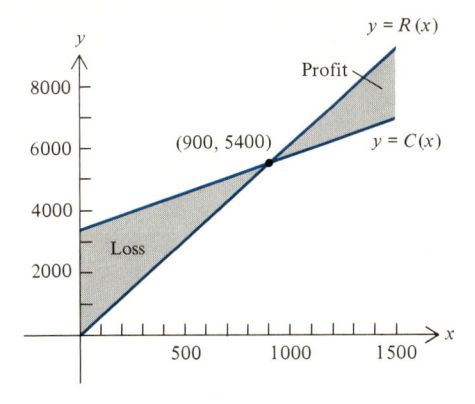

41. The break-even quantity is 1200.

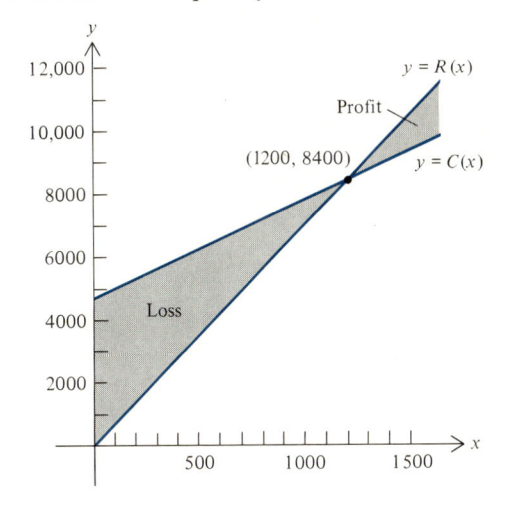

43. The break-even quantity is 1600.

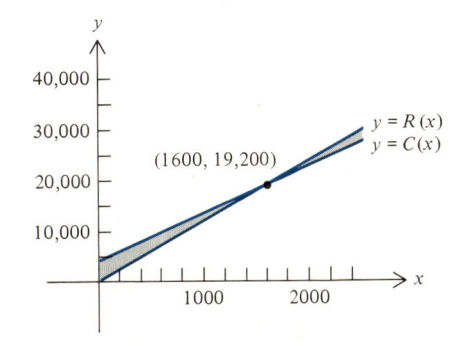

45. The break-even quantity is 600.

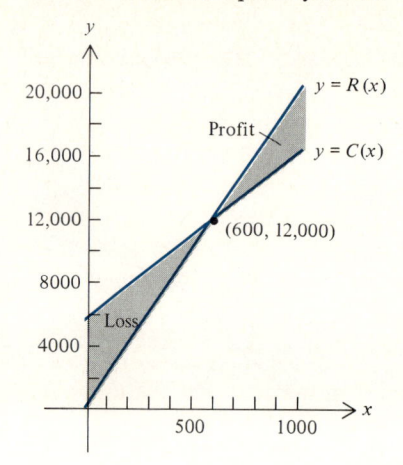

47. (a) $R(x) = 12x$; $C(x) = 8x + 4400$; $P(x) = 4x - 4400$
(b) 1100 (c) 2000 (d) 2200

49. (a) $R(x) = 4.50x$; $C(x) = 3x + 1800$; $P(x) = 1.50x - 1800$
(b) 1200 (c) 4000 (d) 900

51. (a) Option 1 (b) Option 2 (c) 1200

Section 2.4

1. $S(c) = 1.42c$ **3.** $S(c) = 1.30c$ **5.** $S(c) = 1.45c$
7. $S(c) = 1.27c$ **9.** $R(x) = 7.50x$ **11.** $R(x) = 5x$
13. $R(x) = 3.25x$ **15.** $R(x) = 5.90x$ **17.** $2600   **19.** $3200
21. $800   **23.** $11,600
25. (a) ($2,400,000, $3.20) (b) Option (i) (c) Option (ii)
27. (a) ($80,000, $0.80)
(b)

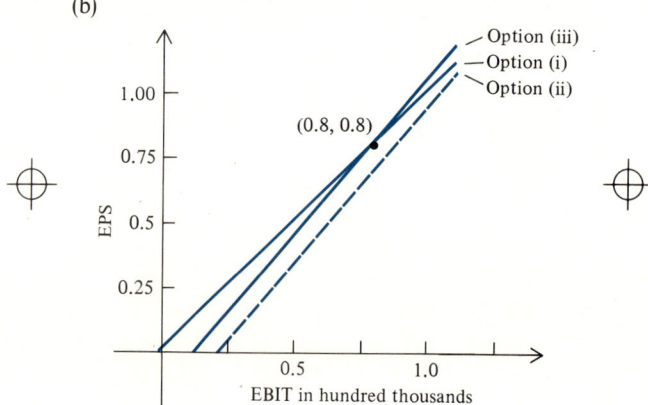

(c) Option (i)
(d) Option (iii)

29. (a) ($5,000,000, $4.00)
(b) Option (i)
(c) Option (ii)

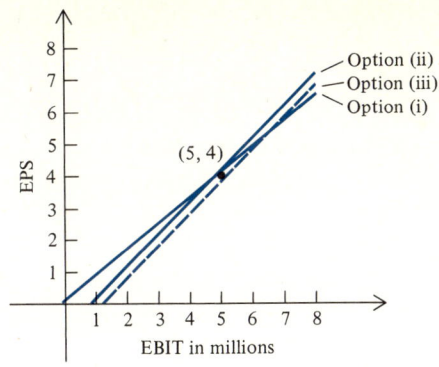

31. Option (i): $y = \frac{5}{6}x$; option (ii): $y = x - 0.64$; option (iii): $y = x - 0.40$

Review Exercises

1. (a) False (b) False (c) True (d) True (e) False
   (f) True (g) False (h) True (i) True (j) False
   (k) True

2. (a) x intercept 8; y intercept -4 (b) No x intercept; y intercept 7
   (c) x intercept -3; y intercept $\sqrt{3}$ (d) x intercept 0; y intercept 0
   (e) x intercepts -2 and 2; y intercept -8
   (f) x intercepts -3 and 1; y intercept 3

3. (a) 13 (b) 33 (c) $2a^2 + 1$ (d) $3a - 2$
   (e) $6a + 10$ (f) $8a^2 + 24a + 19$ (g) $18a^2 - 12a + 3$
   (h) $a - 17$

4. (a) (b) 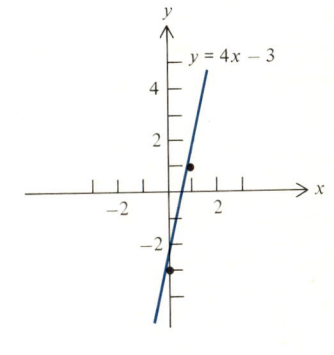 (c) 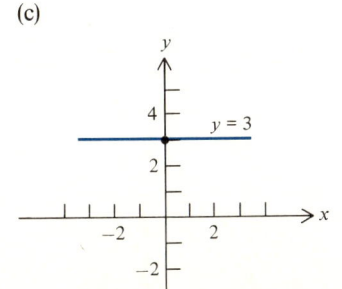 (d)

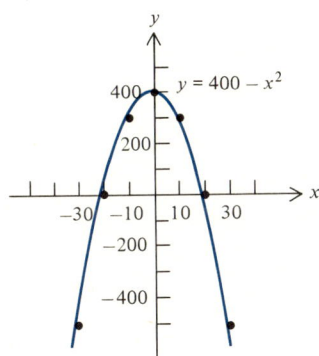

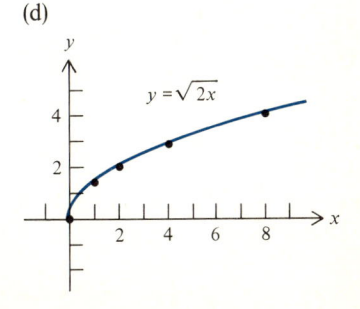

5. (a) $\frac{3}{8}$ (b) 0 (c) 2 (d) $-\frac{4}{5}$
6. (a) $y = 4x - 23$ (b) $y = -2x + 6$ (c) $y = -3x + 6$
(d) $y = 5x + 7$
7. (a) $x = -2$ (b) $y = -4x + 17$ (c) $y = 3x + 2$
(d) $y = 7$
8. (a) $p = 35; D(35) = 1470$ (b) $p = 5.60; D(5.60) = 1680$
(c) $p = 12; D(12) = 1440$ (d) $p = 17.10; D(17.10) = 5643$
9. (a) $p = 36; D(36) = 1440$ (b) $p = 5.84; D(5.84) = 1632$
(c) $p = 11.80; D(11.80) = 1476$ (d) $p = 18; D(18) = 5400$
10. Fixed cost: $2400; variable cost per unit: $6
11. (a) The break-even quantity is 900.

(b) The break-even quantity is 1200.
(c) The break-even quantity is 1130.
(d) The break-even quantity is 950.
12. (a) $R(x) = 10x$
$C(x) = 6x + 6000$
$P(x) = 4x - 6000$

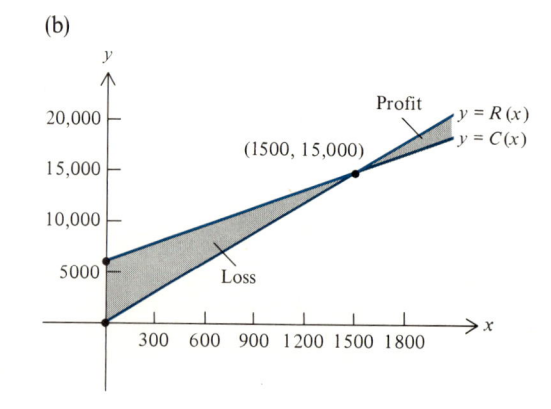

(b)

(c) 1500 (d) 2250
13. (a) $800 (b) $5300
14. (a) ($50,000, $1.00) (b) Option (i) (c) Option (iii)

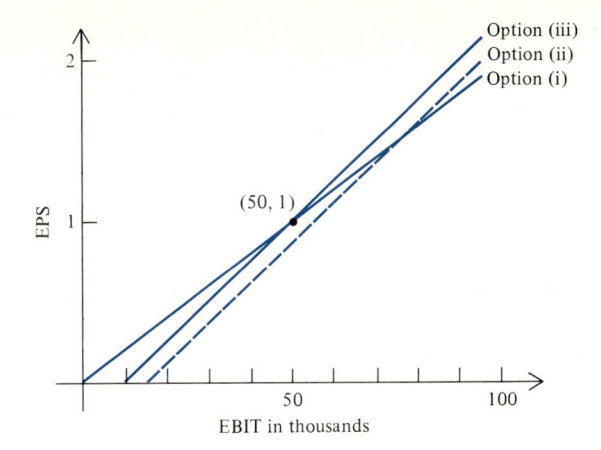

Chapter 3

Section 3.1

1. 3×4 **3.** 2×3 **5.** 5×4 **7.** 3×2 **9.** 2×2, square
11. 1, 2, and -3 **13.** 3 and 6 **15.** 5, 0, -5, and 3
17. 4 and 4 **19.** 3 and 1 **21.** $x = 3; y = 4; z = 3$ **23.** mn

25. $\begin{pmatrix} 3 & 4 & 5 & 6 & 7 \\ 5 & 6 & 7 & 8 & 9 \\ 7 & 8 & 9 & 10 & 11 \\ 9 & 10 & 11 & 12 & 13 \\ 11 & 12 & 13 & 14 & 15 \end{pmatrix}$

27. $(1), (-1), (3), (2), (1 \ \ -1), (3 \ \ 2),$

$\begin{pmatrix} 1 \\ 3 \end{pmatrix}, \begin{pmatrix} -1 \\ 2 \end{pmatrix}, \begin{pmatrix} 1 & -1 \\ 3 & 2 \end{pmatrix}$

29. $(3), (-4), (2), (1), (5), (-1), (3 \ \ -4), (3 \ \ 2), (-4 \ \ 2), (1 \ \ 5), (1 \ \ -1),$
$(5 \ \ -1), (3 \ \ -4 \ \ 2), (1 \ \ 5 \ \ -1),$

$\begin{pmatrix} 3 \\ 1 \end{pmatrix}, \begin{pmatrix} -4 \\ 5 \end{pmatrix}, \begin{pmatrix} 2 \\ -1 \end{pmatrix}, \begin{pmatrix} 3 & -4 \\ 1 & 5 \end{pmatrix}, \begin{pmatrix} 3 & 2 \\ 1 & -1 \end{pmatrix}, \begin{pmatrix} -4 & 2 \\ 5 & -1 \end{pmatrix}, \begin{pmatrix} 3 & -4 & 2 \\ 1 & 5 & -1 \end{pmatrix}$

31.

	Vitamin A	Thiamine	Riboflavin	Niacin
Potatoes	20	0.08	0.05	1.0
Spinach	8,100	0.07	0.14	0.5
Carrots	11,000	0.06	0.05	0.6
Lima beans	280	0.18	0.10	1.3

33.

	Potatoes	Spinach	Carrots	Lima beans
Protein	2.1	3.0	1.1	7.6
Fat	0.7	0.3	0.2	0.5
Carbohydrates	13.0	3.6	9.7	19.8

Section 3.2

1. $2A = \begin{pmatrix} 6 & -4 \\ 2 & 2 \end{pmatrix}$; $(-3)B = \begin{pmatrix} 6 & -15 \\ 0 & -9 \end{pmatrix}$; $A + B = \begin{pmatrix} 1 & 3 \\ 1 & 4 \end{pmatrix}$;

   $A - B = \begin{pmatrix} 5 & -7 \\ 1 & -2 \end{pmatrix}$; $4A - 2B = \begin{pmatrix} 16 & -18 \\ 4 & -2 \end{pmatrix}$

3. $2A = \begin{pmatrix} -8 & 2 \\ 4 & 6 \\ 0 & -2 \end{pmatrix}$; $(-3)B = \begin{pmatrix} -6 & 12 \\ -3 & 6 \\ -9 & 3 \end{pmatrix}$; $A + B = \begin{pmatrix} -2 & -3 \\ 3 & 1 \\ 3 & -2 \end{pmatrix}$;

   $A - B = \begin{pmatrix} -6 & 5 \\ 1 & 5 \\ -3 & 0 \end{pmatrix}$; $4A - 2B = \begin{pmatrix} -20 & 12 \\ 6 & 16 \\ -6 & -2 \end{pmatrix}$

5. $5A = \begin{pmatrix} -10 & 5 \\ 0 & 15 \end{pmatrix}$; $(-1)B = \begin{pmatrix} -5 & 0 \\ -2 & 1 \end{pmatrix}$; $A + B = \begin{pmatrix} 3 & 1 \\ 2 & 2 \end{pmatrix}$;

   $A - B = \begin{pmatrix} -7 & 1 \\ -2 & 4 \end{pmatrix}$; $3A + 2B = \begin{pmatrix} 4 & 3 \\ 4 & 7 \end{pmatrix}$

7. $5A = \begin{pmatrix} 5 & 0 \\ -10 & 15 \\ 0 & -5 \end{pmatrix}$; $(-1)B = \begin{pmatrix} 2 & -1 \\ -5 & -2 \\ 4 & 3 \end{pmatrix}$; $A + B = \begin{pmatrix} -1 & 1 \\ 3 & 5 \\ -4 & -4 \end{pmatrix}$;

   $A - B = \begin{pmatrix} 3 & -1 \\ -7 & 1 \\ 4 & 2 \end{pmatrix}$; $3A + 2B = \begin{pmatrix} -1 & 2 \\ 4 & 13 \\ -8 & -9 \end{pmatrix}$

9. $\begin{pmatrix} 0 & 0 & 0 & 0 & 0 \\ 0 & 0 & 0 & 0 & 0 \\ 0 & 0 & 0 & 0 & 0 \end{pmatrix}$

11. (d) Both equal $\begin{pmatrix} 16 & -24 & 8 \\ -16 & 32 & 0 \end{pmatrix}$

    (e) Both equal $\begin{pmatrix} -4 & 16 & -4 \\ 12 & 16 & -4 \end{pmatrix}$

13. (a) False (b) False (c) True
    (d) True   (e) True   (f) True

15. (a)
	Washington	Illinois	Maryland	New York	Wisconsin
Registrations	261,000	5,952,000	2,259,000	7,319,000	2,472,000
Drivers	335,000	6,124,000	2,218,000	8,546,000	2,594,000

    $= A$

    (b)
	Washington	Illinois	Maryland	New York	Wisconsin
Registrations	263,000	6,174,000	2,346,000	7,458,000	2,578,000
Drivers	332,000	6,300,000	2,359,000	8,731,000	2,664,000

    $= B$

(c)
$$\begin{array}{c} \text{Registrations} \\ \text{Drivers} \end{array} \begin{pmatrix} \text{Washington} & \text{Illinois} & \text{Maryland} & \text{New York} & \text{Wisconsin} \\ 2{,}000 & 222{,}000 & 87{,}000 & 139{,}000 & 106{,}000 \\ -3{,}000 & 176{,}000 & 141{,}000 & 185{,}000 & 70{,}000 \end{pmatrix}$$

$= B - A$

The entries in $B - A$ represent the net changes in the number of registrations and licensed drivers in these five states between 1973 and 1974.

Section 3.3

1. 2×2 **3.** Undefined **5.** 3×4

7. $\begin{pmatrix} -14 & 6 & -2 \\ 16 & -6 & 4 \end{pmatrix}$ **9.** $\begin{pmatrix} 5 & 6 \\ 8 & -1 \end{pmatrix}$ **11.** $\begin{pmatrix} 14 & -15 \\ -5 & 8 \end{pmatrix}$

13. $A^2 = \begin{pmatrix} 3 & -5 \\ 5 & 8 \end{pmatrix}; A^3 = \begin{pmatrix} 1 & -18 \\ 18 & 19 \end{pmatrix}$

15. $A^2 = \begin{pmatrix} 1 & -4 & -1 \\ 0 & 9 & -1 \\ 0 & 0 & 4 \end{pmatrix}; A^3 = \begin{pmatrix} 1 & 14 & -7 \\ 0 & -27 & 7 \\ 0 & 0 & 8 \end{pmatrix}$

17. $I_2 = \begin{pmatrix} 1 & 0 \\ 0 & 1 \end{pmatrix}; I_5 = \begin{pmatrix} 1 & 0 & 0 & 0 & 0 \\ 0 & 1 & 0 & 0 & 0 \\ 0 & 0 & 1 & 0 & 0 \\ 0 & 0 & 0 & 1 & 0 \\ 0 & 0 & 0 & 0 & 1 \end{pmatrix}; 2I_3 = \begin{pmatrix} 2 & 0 & 0 \\ 0 & 2 & 0 \\ 0 & 0 & 2 \end{pmatrix}$

19. (a) Both matrices equal $\begin{pmatrix} 11 & -8 \\ 13 & 8 \end{pmatrix}$.

(b) The first two matrices equal $\begin{pmatrix} 1 & 5 & 19 \\ 9 & -3 & 15 \end{pmatrix}$;

the third and fourth matrices equal $\begin{pmatrix} 11 & 7 \\ 6 & 5 \\ 1 & -7 \end{pmatrix}$.

(c) Both matrices equal $\begin{pmatrix} 4 & -1 & 1 \\ 2 & 3 & -1 \end{pmatrix}$.

(d) All three matrices equal $\begin{pmatrix} 10 & -12 & -16 \\ -2 & 0 & -12 \end{pmatrix}$.

21.
$$\begin{array}{c} \text{Electricity} \\ \text{Natural gas} \\ \text{Oil} \end{array} \begin{pmatrix} A & B \\ 9 & 11 \\ 5 & 5 \\ 4 & 6 \end{pmatrix}$$

23. Tom spent $59; Steve spent $86.

25. 63.2 million voters; 78.2 million nonvoters

Section 3.4

1.
	John	Linda	Curtis	Mary	George	Lisa
John	0	0	1	1	1	0
Linda	0	0	0	1	0	1
Curtis	1	1	0	0	1	0
Mary	0	1	0	0	1	1
George	1	0	1	0	0	0
Lisa	1	1	0	1	0	0

3. 1 of each   5. Yes, 2 stages   7. No   9. No
11. Persons 1, 2, and 4 belong to at least one clique.
13. Persons 2, 3, 4, and 5 belong to at least one clique.
15. Everyone belongs to at least one clique.
17. Person 4 is the only liaison person.   19. There are no liaison persons.
21. Czechoslovakia is the only liaison country.
23. Person 3 dominates; person 2 is dominated.
25. Person 2 dominates; persons 1, 3, and 4 are dominated.
27. Persons 1, 2, and 3 dominate; person 4 is dominated.
29. Carr dominates; Kelly is dominated.
31. Canada, France, and Italy dominate; the United States, Canada, and France are dominated.

33. $$C^2 = \begin{pmatrix} 2 & 1 & 1 & 0 & 0 \\ 1 & 2 & 1 & 0 & 0 \\ 1 & 1 & 2 & 0 & 0 \\ 0 & 0 & 0 & 1 & 0 \\ 0 & 0 & 0 & 0 & 1 \end{pmatrix}; C^3 = \begin{pmatrix} 2 & 3 & 3 & 0 & 0 \\ 3 & 2 & 3 & 0 & 0 \\ 3 & 3 & 2 & 0 & 0 \\ 0 & 0 & 0 & 0 & 1 \\ 0 & 0 & 0 & 1 & 0 \end{pmatrix}$$

$$C^4 = \begin{pmatrix} 6 & 5 & 5 & 0 & 0 \\ 5 & 6 & 5 & 0 & 0 \\ 5 & 5 & 6 & 0 & 0 \\ 0 & 0 & 0 & 1 & 0 \\ 0 & 0 & 0 & 0 & 1 \end{pmatrix}$$

Section 3.5

1. $(3, 3)$ 3. $(-1, -2)$ 5. $(-2, -2)$ 7. $(6, 3)$
9. $(-\frac{5}{2}, 3)$ 11. $(-2, 2)$ 13. $(-1, 0)$ 15. $(-4, 2)$
17. $(5, 2)$ 19. $(1, -2)$ 21. $0.60
23. $7000 in bonds; $3000 in mutual funds   25. 8 lots of each
27. Canoe 24 times; sail 6 times

Section 3.6

1. $(2r - 6s - 4t + 7, r, s, 9 - 3t, t)$
3. $(2r + 28, r, -1, -5)$
5. $(8 - 7r + 5s, 4r - 3s - 3, r, 6 - 2s, s)$
7. $(2r - 1, 2 - 3r, r, 5, 4)$

9. $(4 - 2r + s, -5s - 3, 6 - 4r + 2s, r, -3s - 2, s)$
11. $(7, 1, -2)$ 13. No solutions
15. $(4, -3, -1)$ 17. $(2, 3, -2, -1)$
19. $(4r + s + 4, r, 2s + 1, s)$ 21. $(r - 6, r, -5, -2)$
23. No solutions 25. $(3 - r - 2s, 7 - 2r - 5s, r, s - 3, s)$
27. $(s + 2, 2r - 4s, r, -2s - 1, s)$
29. 9 gallons of the first herbicide; 5 gallons of the second; 2 gallons of the third
31. $8000 in the mutual fund; $7000 in stocks; $3000 in land
33. 14.5 pounds of peanuts; 17 pounds of cashews; 8.5 pounds of almonds
35. 70 acres of corn; 90 acres of soybeans; 40 acres fallow

Section 3.7

1. Data Processing: $8000; Maintenance: $11,000; Payroll: $5000; Calculators: $10,800; Typewriters: $10,700
3. Accounts Receivable: $40,000; Data Processing: $60,000; Maintenance: $20,000; Trousers: $42,000; Jackets: $36,000; Suits: $56,000
5. 770 units of electricity; 620 units of natural gas; 510 units of oil
7. 115 units of transportation; 170 units of food; 155 units of oil
9. Food earns 50%; housing earns 50%
11. Food earns 75%; housing earns 25%
13. Food earns 30%; oil earns 60%; transportation earns 10%
15. Food earns 50%; oil earns 40%; transportation earns 10%
17. 200 vehicles per hour
19. 300 shares of A, 400 shares of B, 400 shares of C, and 100 shares of D; or 600 shares of A, 0 shares of B, 0 shares of C, and 300 shares of D

Section 3.8

1. The product is I_2. 3. The product is I_2.
5. The product is I_3. 7. The product is I_3.
9. $\begin{pmatrix} 7 & 3 \\ -2 & -1 \end{pmatrix}$ 11. None 13. $\begin{pmatrix} -\frac{5}{2} & \frac{3}{2} \\ -2 & 1 \end{pmatrix}$
15. $\begin{pmatrix} -9 & 1 & 4 \\ 7 & -1 & -3 \\ 4 & -1 & -2 \end{pmatrix}$ 17. None 19. $\begin{pmatrix} 0 & -\frac{1}{2} & -2 \\ 2 & \frac{5}{2} & 9 \\ 1 & \frac{3}{2} & 5 \end{pmatrix}$
21. $\begin{pmatrix} 1 & -1 & 0 & 0 \\ 0 & -2 & 1 & 0 \\ 2 & -3 & 0 & -1 \\ 1 & -3 & 1 & -1 \end{pmatrix}$ 23. $(5, -2)$ 25. $(-8, -7)$
27. $(7, -5, -3)$ 29. $(2, -4, -1)$
31. 36, 64, 59, 91, 59, 97, 15, 25, 68, 109, 47, 75, 35, 66, 7, 13, 58, 89
33. ATTACK AT NOON

Review Exercises

1. (a) False (b) True (c) True (d) False
   (e) True (f) False (g) False (h) True
   (i) True (j) False (k) True (l) False
   (m) False (n) True (o) False (p) False
   (q) False (r) True

2. (a) $\begin{pmatrix} -1 & 4 & -1 \\ 1 & 0 & 4 \end{pmatrix}$ (b) $\begin{pmatrix} 3 & 4 & -5 \\ -5 & -2 & 6 \end{pmatrix}$
   (c) $\begin{pmatrix} 6 & 0 & -6 \\ -9 & -3 & 3 \end{pmatrix}$ (d) $\begin{pmatrix} 11 & 12 & -17 \\ -18 & -7 & 19 \end{pmatrix}$

3. (a) $\begin{pmatrix} -6 & 0 \\ -3 & 14 \end{pmatrix}$ (b) $\begin{pmatrix} -7 & 14 & 15 \\ 5 & -1 & 6 \end{pmatrix}$

   (c) $\begin{pmatrix} -4 & 6 \\ 9 & 11 \\ -12 & 4 \end{pmatrix}$ (d) $\begin{pmatrix} -8 & 13 \\ 23 & -12 \\ 8 & 1 \end{pmatrix}$

4. (a)

	Harry	George	Joan	Lisa	Nancy	Bruce
Harry	0	1	0	1	0	1
George	0	0	1	0	0	1
Joan	1	0	0	1	1	0
Lisa	1	0	0	0	1	1
Nancy	0	1	1	1	0	0
Bruce	1	0	1	1	0	0

   (b) Harry, Lisa, and Bruce belong to at least one clique.

5. Mary, Sam, and Linda
6. (a) $(3, -1, -2)$ (b) $(5, 4, 1)$ (c) No solutions
   (d) $(1, 2, -1, 4)$
7. Maintenance: $2000; Data Processing: $4000; Personnel: $3000; Frozen Food: $8400; Canned Food: $7100
8. 20 units of wool; 20 units of electricity; 10 units of food
9. (a) $(3r - 41s - 8, r, 34s + 8, 13s + 3, s)$
   (b) $(3r - 12s + 17, 2r - 5s + 8, r, 3s - 5, s)$
   (c) $(17 - 3r - 5s, 3r - 3s + 3, r, s - 2, 2s - 4, s)$
   (d) No solutions
10. (a) $\begin{pmatrix} -3 & 1 & 2 \\ -6 & 1 & 3 \\ -8 & 1 & 4 \end{pmatrix}$ (b) $\begin{pmatrix} -8 & 12 & 5 \\ 5 & -7 & -3 \\ 2 & -3 & -1 \end{pmatrix}$ (c) None
    (d) $\begin{pmatrix} 2 & 5 & 4 \\ \frac{1}{2} & 1 & 1 \\ \frac{1}{3} & \frac{4}{3} & 1 \end{pmatrix}$

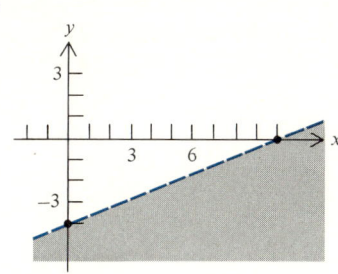

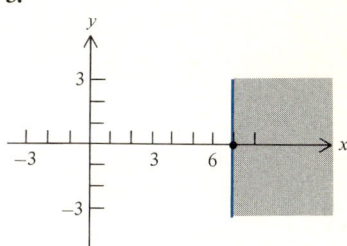

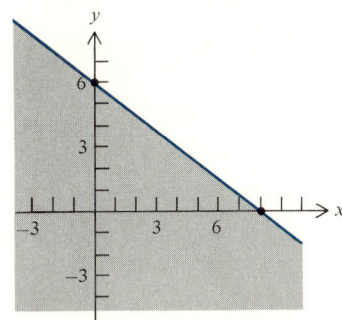

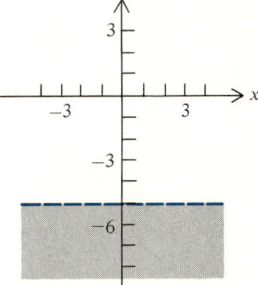

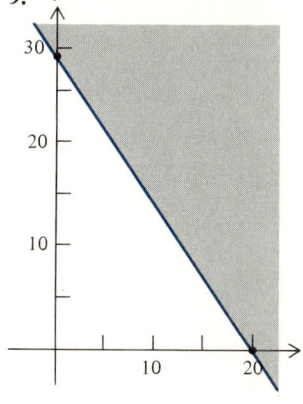

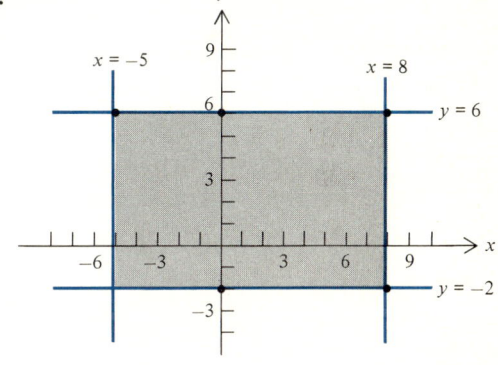

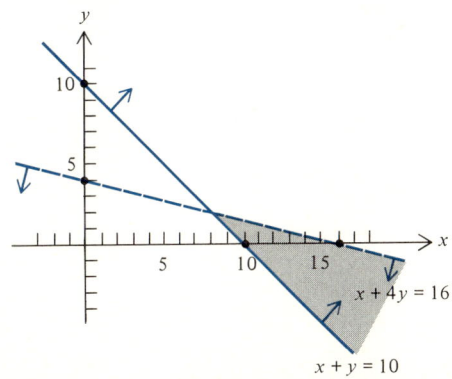

Chapter 4
Section 4.1

1.
3.
5.
7.
9.
11.
13.

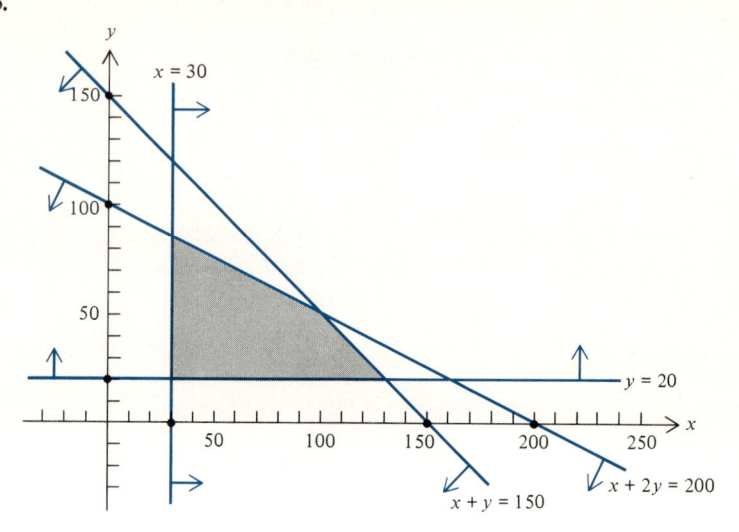

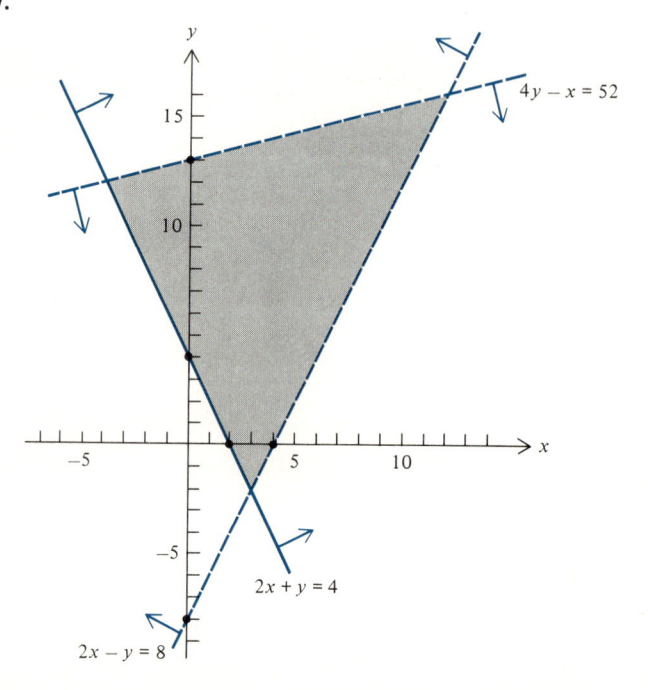

15.

17.

19.

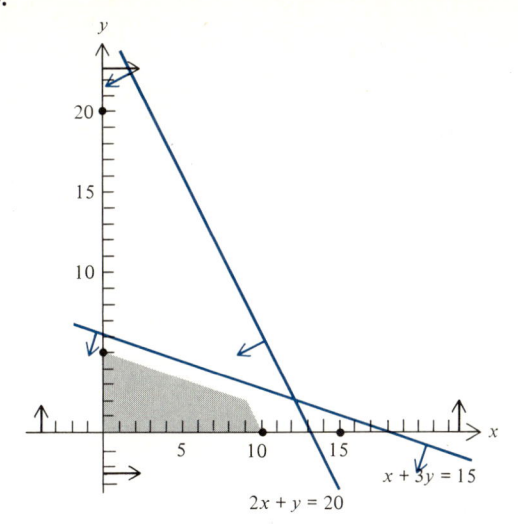

$2x + y = 20$
$x + 3y = 15$

21.

$2x + y = 18$
$x + 3y = 24$

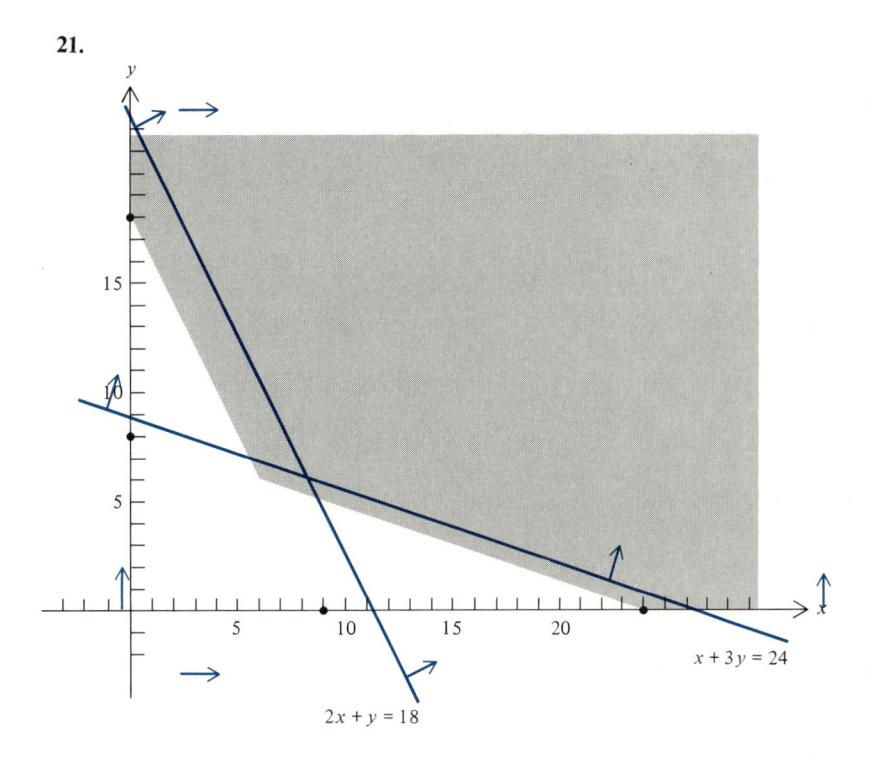

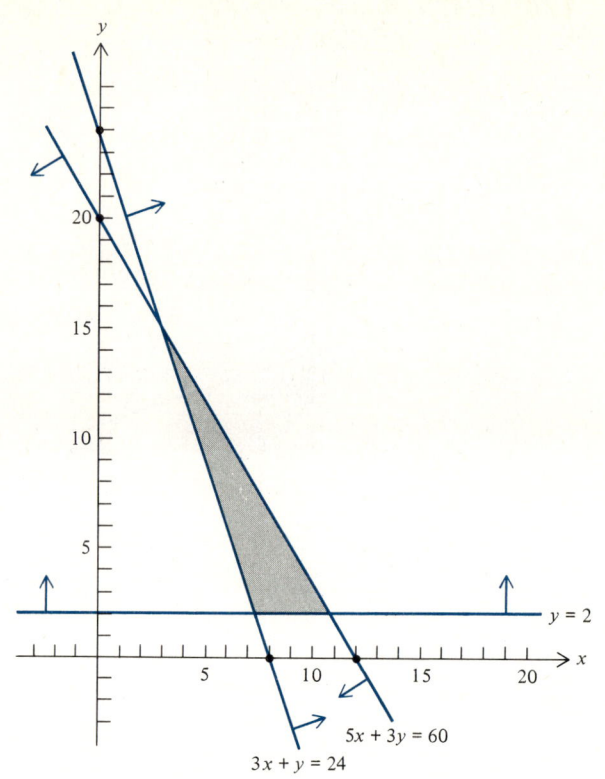

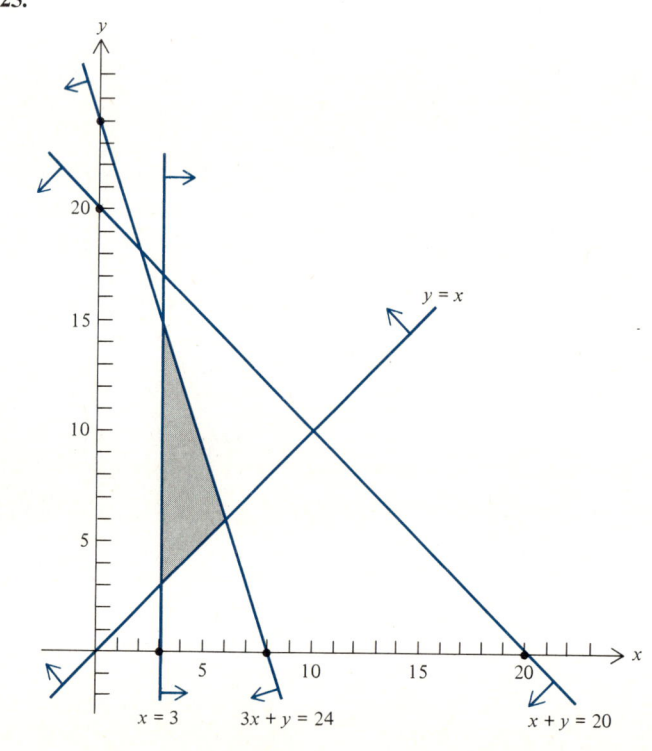

23.

25.

Section 4.2

1. Maximize $x + y$
   Subject to $12x + 8y \leq 240$
                  $10x + 15y \leq 300$
                         $x \geq 0$
                         $y \geq 0$

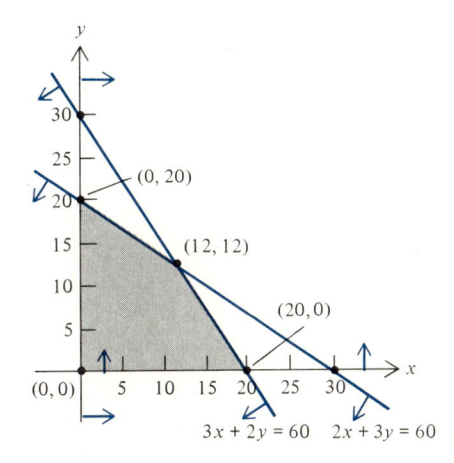

3. Minimize $200x + 150y$
   Subject to $800x + 300y \geq 6000$
                  $50x + 150y \geq 900$
                        $x \geq 0$
                        $y \geq 0$

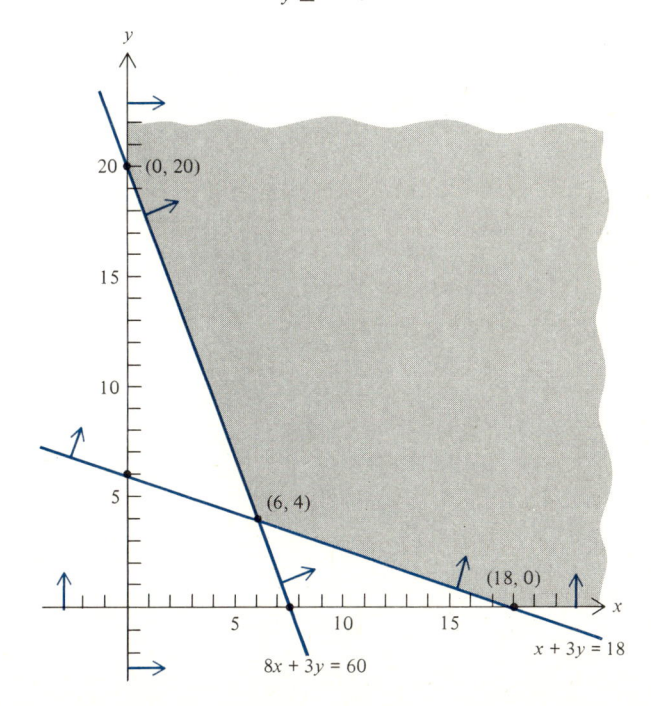

Answers to Odd-Numbered Exercises

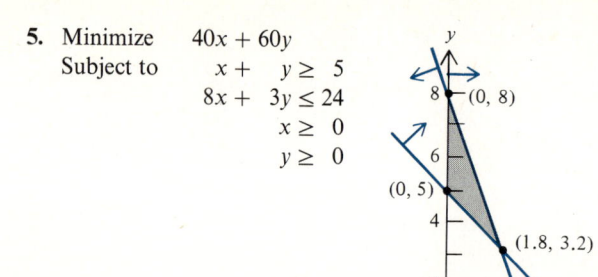

5. Minimize $\quad 40x + 60y$
Subject to $\quad x + y \geq 5$
$\qquad\qquad\quad 8x + 3y \leq 24$
$\qquad\qquad\quad x \geq 0$
$\qquad\qquad\quad y \geq 0$

Vertices: (0, 8), (0, 5), (1.8, 3.2)
Lines: $8x + 3y = 24$, $x + y = 5$

7. Maximize $\quad 0.70x + 0.75y$
Subject to $\quad x + y \leq 4000$
$\qquad\qquad\quad 2x + y \leq 6000$
$\qquad\qquad\quad y \leq 3000$
$\qquad\qquad\quad x \geq 0, y \geq 0$

Vertices: (0, 3000), (1000, 3000), (2000, 2000), (3000, 0), (0, 0)
Lines: $y = 3000$, $x + y = 4000$, $2x + y = 6000$

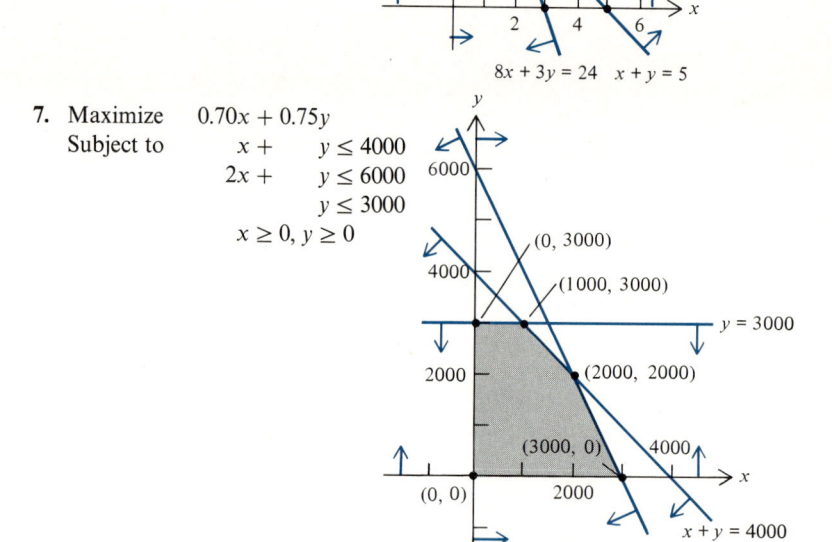

9. Maximize $\quad 5x + 4y$
Subject to $\quad 4x + 3y \leq 36{,}000$
$\qquad\qquad\quad 4x + 5y \leq 40{,}000$
$\qquad\qquad\quad 2x + 5y \leq 30{,}000$
$\qquad\qquad\quad x \geq 0, y \geq 0$

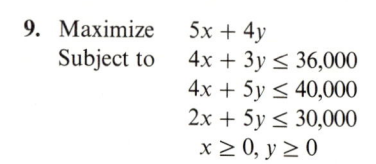

Vertices: (0, 6000), (5000, 4000), (7500, 2000), (9000, 0), (0, 0)
Lines: $4x + 3y = 36{,}000$, $4x + 5y = 40{,}000$, $2x + 5y = 30{,}000$

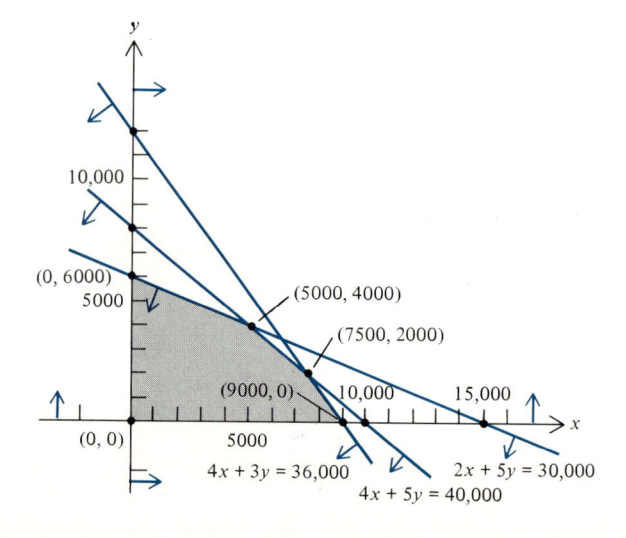

11. Minimize $500x + 200y$

Subject to

$$\begin{aligned} x + y &\geq 12 \\ x + y &\leq 15 \\ 2x - y &\geq 0 \\ x \geq 0,\ y &\geq 0 \end{aligned}$$

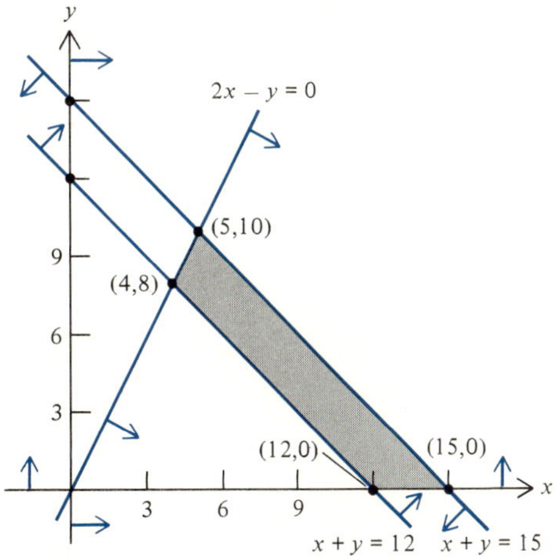

13. Minimize $x + y$

Subject to

$$\begin{aligned} 30x + 20y &\geq 3600 \\ x - 2y &\geq 0 \\ y &\geq 15 \\ x &\geq 0 \end{aligned}$$

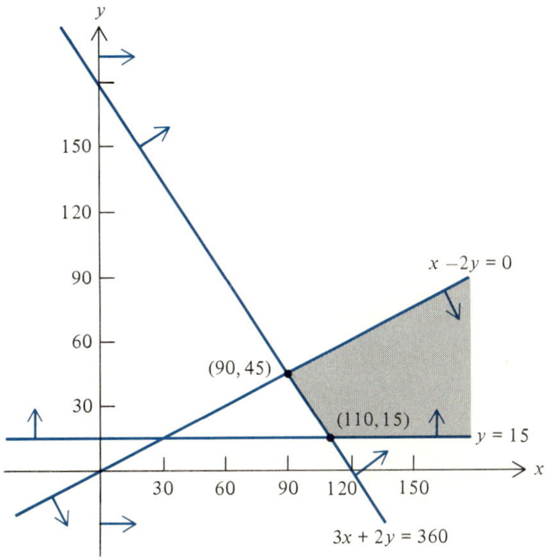

15. Maximize $220x + 195y$

Subject to

$$\begin{aligned} x + y &\leq 200 \\ 110x + 85y &\leq 18{,}700 \\ y &\geq 66 \\ 3x - y &\geq 0 \\ x &\geq 0 \end{aligned}$$

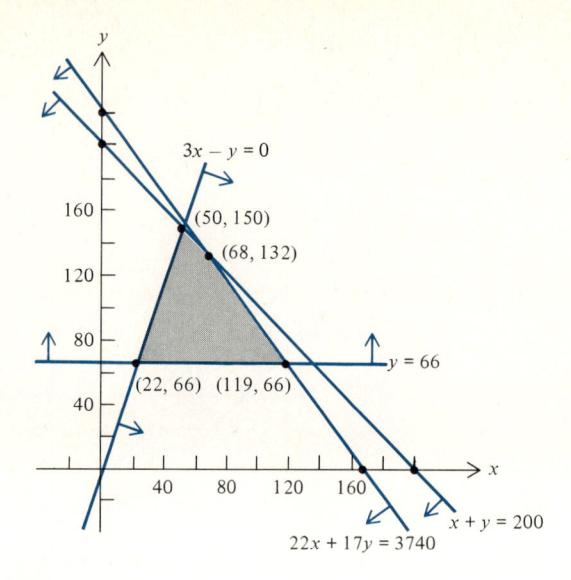

Section 4.3

1. The maximum of 480 occurs at $x = 60$ and $y = 45$.
3. The maximum of 840 occurs at $x = 120$ and $y = 0$.
5. The minimum of 1080 occurs at $x = 180$ and $y = 30$.
7. The minimum of 480 occurs at $x = 240$ and $y = 0$.
9. The maximum of 432 occurs at $x = 72$ and $y = 9$.
11. 12 rats and 12 mice; a maximum of 24 animals
13. 6 ounces of food 1 and 4 ounces of food 2; a minimum of 1800 calories
15. 1.8 tons of Illinois coal and 3.2 tons of western coal; a minimum of $264
17. 1000 units of product A and 3000 units of product B; a maximum of $2950
19. 7500 units of part A and 2000 units of part B; a maximum of $45,500
21. 4 hours of prime time and 8 hours of evening time; a minimum of $3600
23. 110 hours in the town and 15 hours in the rural area; a minimum of 125 hours
25. 68 acres of corn and 132 acres of soybeans; a maximum of $40,700

Section 4.4

1. $$\begin{aligned} x + 3y + r &= 200 \\ 2x + 5y + s &= 500 \\ -6x - 4y + P &= 0 \\ x \geq 0, y \geq 0, r \geq 0, s \geq 0 \end{aligned}$$

3. $$\begin{aligned} 2x + 4y + r &= 1200 \\ x + 3y + s &= 1000 \\ -3x - 8y + P &= 0 \\ x \geq 0, y \geq 0, r \geq 0, s \geq 0 \end{aligned}$$

5. $$\begin{aligned} 6x + 5y + r &= 600 \\ 3x + 4y + s &= 240 \\ -4.50x - 3.50y + P &= 0 \\ x \geq 0, y \geq 0, r \geq 0, s \geq 0 \end{aligned}$$

7. $$\begin{aligned} 3x + 4y + r &= 300 \\ x + 2y + s &= 120 \\ x + t &= 30 \\ -5x - 12y + P &= 0 \\ x \geq 0, y \geq 0, r \geq 0, s \geq 0, t \geq 0 \end{aligned}$$

9.
$$4x + 3y + r = 36{,}800$$
$$4x + 5y + s = 40{,}000$$
$$2x + 5y + t = 30{,}000$$
$$-5x - 4y + P = 0$$
$$x \geq 0,\, y \geq 0,\, r \geq 0,\, s \geq 0,\, t \geq 0$$

Section 4.5

1. $x = 200$; $y = 0$; maximum $= 1200$
3. $x = 0$; $y = 300$; maximum $= 2400$
5. $x = 80$; $y = 0$; maximum $= 360$
7. $x = 0$; $y = 60$; maximum $= 720$
9. $x = 8000$; $y = 1600$; maximum $= 46{,}400$
11. $x = 0$; $y = 30$; $z = 0$; maximum $= 120$
13. $x = 140$; $y = 55$; $z = 0$; maximum $= 725$
15. 0 units of the first product; 32 units of the second product; 20 units of the third product; maximum profit $= \$2000$
17. 40,000 gallons of the first product; 0 gallons of the second product; 40,000 gallons of the third product; maximum profit $= \$32{,}000$

19. (a)
$$\begin{array}{c} s \\ z \\ x \\ {} \end{array} \left(\begin{array}{cccccc|c} x & y & z & r & s & t & P \\ 0 & 0.2 & 0 & 0 & 1 & -0.5 & 0 16 \\ 0 & 2.0 & 1 & -5 & 0 & 7.5 & 0 140 \\ 1 & 0.0 & 0 & 5 & 0 & -2.5 & 0 100 \\ \hline 0 & 0.0 & 0 & 15 & 0 & 27.5 & 1 1980 \end{array}\right)$$

(b) $x = 100$; $y = 0$; $z = 140$; $P = 1980$
(c) There are multiple solutions.
(d) Multiple solutions occur when the entry in the bottom row of a column corresponding to a nonbasic variable is zero in an optimal tableau. In this case other basic feasible solutions can be obtained by performing additional pivots using any such column as the pivot column.

21. $x = 400$, $y = 0$, and $z = 400$; or $x = \frac{2800}{3}$, $y = \frac{400}{3}$, and $z = 0$; or $x = 1000$, $y = 0$, and $z = 0$; $P = 2000$
23. The objective function is unbounded on the feasible set.

Section 4.6

1. $x = 8$; $y = 12$; maximum $= 84$
3. $x = 200$; $y = 0$; maximum $= 600$
5. $x = 0$; $y = 400$; maximum $= 800$
7. $x = 30$; $y = 150$; maximum $= 840$
9. $x = 15$; $y = 45$; minimum $= 315$
11. $x = 30$; $y = 60$; minimum $= 420$
13. $x = 160$; $y = 0$; minimum $= 320$
15. $x = 70$; $y = 30$; minimum $= 330$
17. $x = 35$; $y = 0$; $z = 5$; minimum $= 95$
19. $x = 0$; $y = 7.2$; $z = 15.6$; minimum $= 54$
21. 10 rings, 0 stickpins, and 0 pendants; a minimum cost of $340

23. 25 grams of the first food, 0 grams of the second food, and 0 grams of the third food; a minimum cost of $1.00

25. Phase I ends with $P \neq 0$, and so the problem has no feasible vectors.

Section 4.7

1. Minimize $200y_1 + 500y_2$
   Subject to
   $$y_1 + 2y_2 \geq 6$$
   $$3y_1 + 5y_2 \geq 4$$
   $$y_1 \geq 0, y_2 \geq 0$$

3. Minimize $1200y_1 + 1000y_2$
   Subject to
   $$2y_1 + y_2 \geq 3$$
   $$4y_1 + 3y_2 \geq 8$$
   $$y_1 \geq 0, y_2 \geq 0$$

5. Minimize $600y_1 + 240y_2$
   Subject to
   $$6y_1 + 3y_2 \geq 4.50$$
   $$5y_1 + 4y_2 \geq 3.50$$
   $$y_1 \geq 0, y_2 \geq 0$$

7. Minimize $300y_1 + 120y_2 + 30y_3$
   Subject to
   $$3y_1 + y_2 + y_3 \geq 5$$
   $$4y_1 + 2y_2 \geq 12$$
   $$y_1 \geq 0, y_2 \geq 0, y_3 \geq 0$$

9. Minimize $36{,}800y_1 + 40{,}000y_2 + 30{,}000y_3$
   Subject to
   $$4y_1 + 4y_2 + 2y_3 \geq 5$$
   $$3y_1 + 5y_2 + 5y_3 \geq 4$$
   $$y_1 \geq 0, y_2 \geq 0, y_3 \geq 0$$

11. Maximize $100x_1 + 160x_2 + 260x_3$
    Subject to
    $$x_1 + x_2 + 2x_3 \leq 3$$
    $$x_1 + 4x_2 + 4x_3 \leq 4$$
    $$x_1 \geq 0, x_2 \geq 0, x_3 \geq 0$$

13. Maximize $24x_1 + 30x_2$
    Subject to
    $$x_1 - x_2 \leq 2$$
    $$-x_1 + 2x_2 \leq 1$$
    $$2x_1 + x_2 \leq 3$$
    $$x_1 \geq 0, x_2 \geq 0$$

15. $y_1 = 6; y_2 = 0;$ minimum $= 1200$
17. $y_1 = 2; y_2 = 0;$ minimum $= 2400$
19. $y_1 = 0; y_2 = 1.5;$ minimum $= 360$
21. $y_1 = 0; y_2 = 6; y_3 = 0;$ minimum $= 720$
23. $y_1 = \frac{9}{8}; y_2 = \frac{1}{8}; y_3 = 0;$ minimum $= 46{,}400$
25. $x_1 = 1; x_2 = 1;$ maximum $= 54$ **27.** $100   **29.** $100
31. $34   **33.** $0.04

Review Exercises

1. (a) False   (b) True   (c) False   (d) False
   (e) False   (f) True   (g) True   (h) True

Answers to Odd-Numbered Exercises   **499**

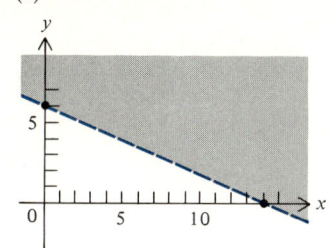

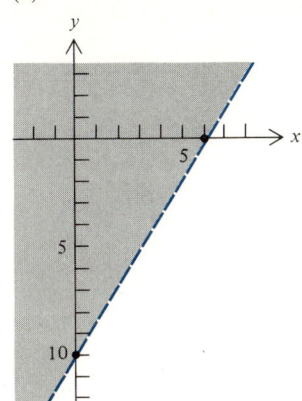

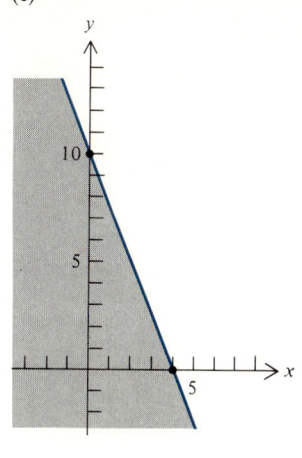

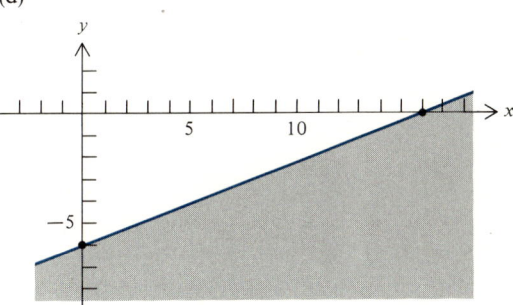

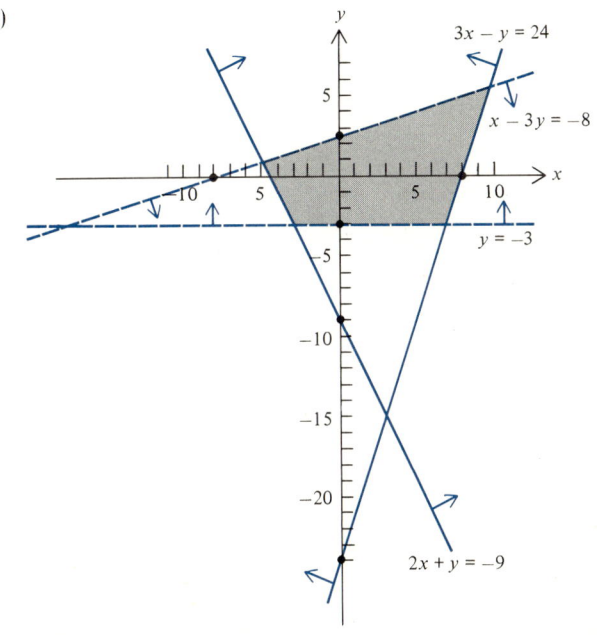

2. (a)

(b)

(c)

(d)

3. (a) $3x - y = 24$; $x - 3y = -8$; $y = -3$; $2x + y = -9$

(b)

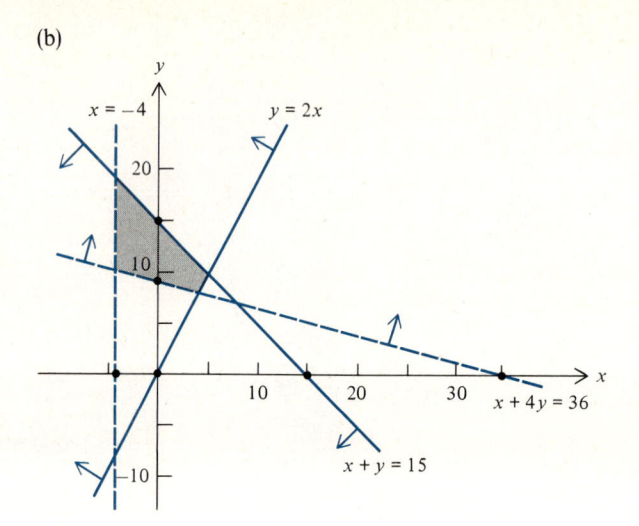

4. (a) $x = 90$; $y = 60$; maximum $= 960$
   (b) $x = 15$; $y = 20$; minimum $= 55$
5. 150 units of A; 200 units of B; maximum profit $= \$525$
6. 7 teams from Baltimore; 9 teams from Cleveland; minimum cost $= \$710$
7. (a) $x = 14$; $y = 35$; $z = 0$; maximum $= 364$
   (b) $x = 0$; $y = 15$; $z = 0$; minimum $= 60$
8. 80 small bottles; 20 medium bottles; 0 large bottles; maximum profit $= \$32$
9. 150 units in Boston; 0 units in Minneapolis; 1500 units in Seattle; minimum cost $= \$27,000$

Chapter 5

Section 5.1

1.

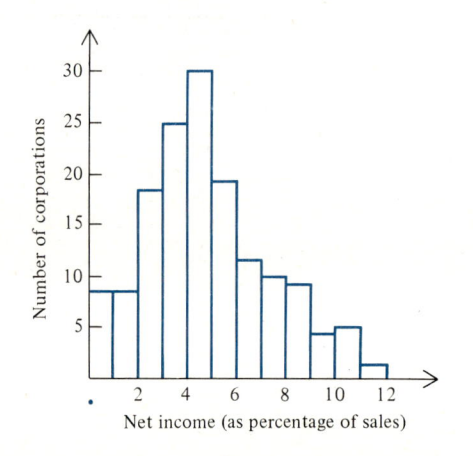

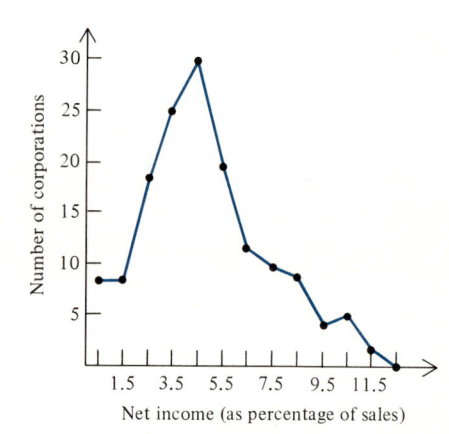

Answers to Odd-Numbered Exercises   501

3.

[Histogram: Number of Justices vs Years of service, bins at 6, 12, 18, 24, 30, 36]

[Line graph: Number of Justices vs Years of service, points at 4.5, 10.6, 16.5, 22.5, 28.5, 34.5]

5.

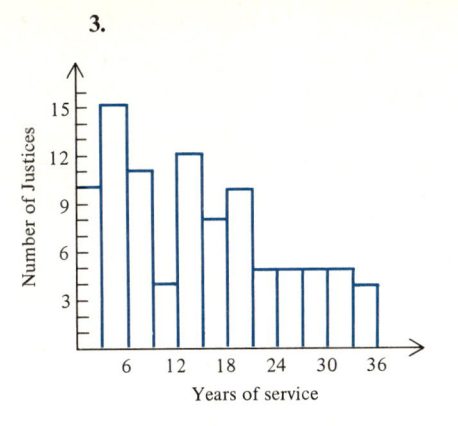

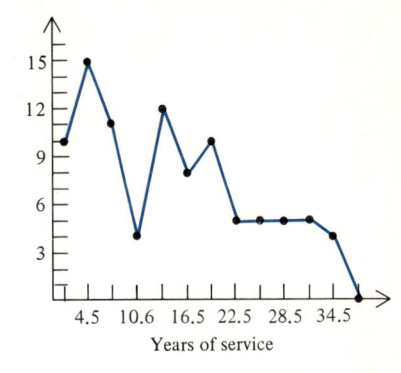

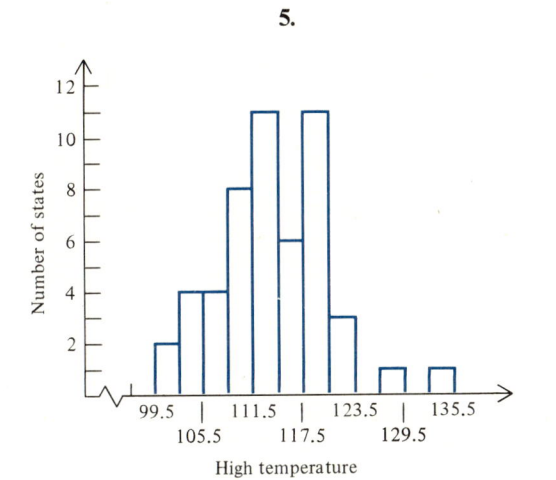

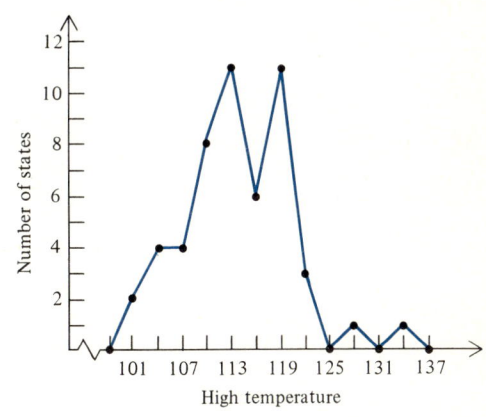

[Histogram: Number of states vs High temperature, bins at 99.5, 105.5, 111.5, 117.5, 123.5, 129.5, 135.5]

[Line graph: Number of states vs High temperature, points at 101, 107, 113, 119, 125, 131, 137]

7. One possibility is:

Interval	Frequency	Relative frequency
38.5–41.5	0	0.00
41.5–44.5	2	0.05
44.5–47.5	2	0.05
47.5–50.5	6	0.16
50.5–53.5	6	0.16
53.5–56.5	10	0.26
56.5–59.5	5	0.13
59.5–62.5	4	0.11
62.5–65.5	2	0.05
65.5–68.5	1	0.03
68.5–71.5	0	0.00

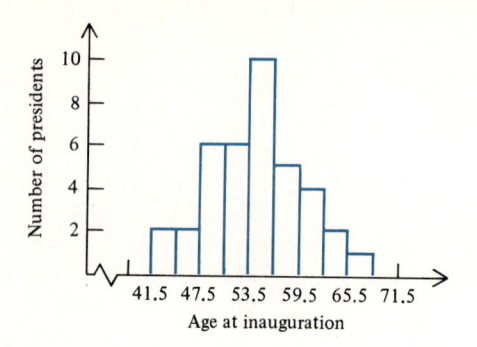

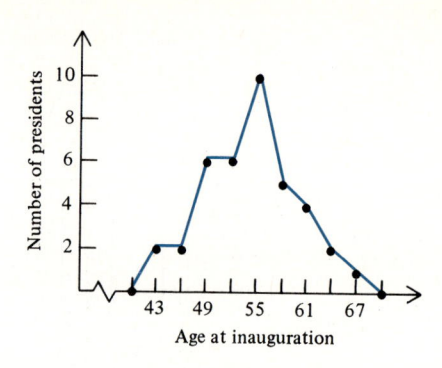

502 *Answers to Odd-Numbered Exercises*

9. One possibility is:

Interval	Frequency	Relative frequency
80.5–85.5	0	0.00
85.5–90.5	1	0.04
90.5–95.5	2	0.08
95.5–100.5	2	0.08
100.5–105.5	0	0.00
105.5–110.5	4	0.15
110.5–115.5	4	0.15
115.5–120.5	4	0.15
120.5–125.5	2	0.08
125.5–130.5	4	0.15
130.5–135.5	1	0.04
135.5–140.5	1	0.04
140.5–145.5	0	0.00
145.5–150.5	1	0.04
150.5–155.5	0	0.00

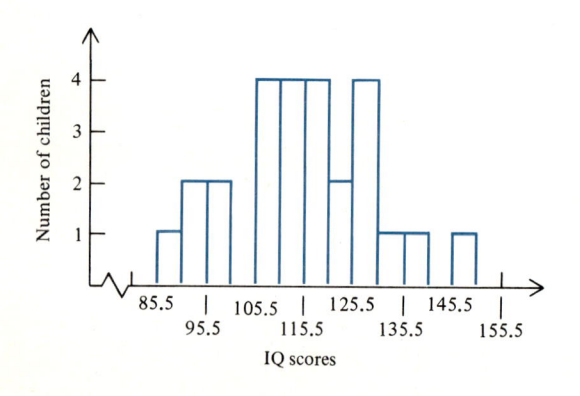

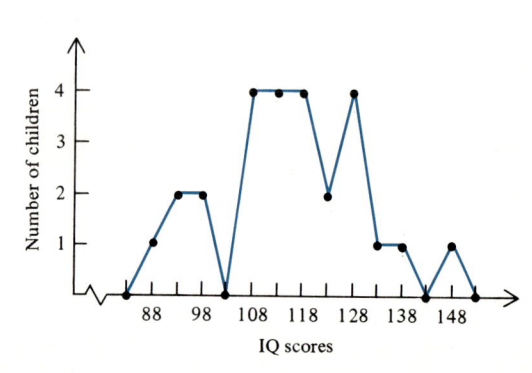

11. One possibility is:

Interval	Frequency	Relative frequency
17.5–21.5	0	0.00
21.5–25.5	2	0.05
25.5–29.5	0	0.00
29.5–33.5	9	0.21
33.5–37.5	8	0.19
37.5–41.5	4	0.10
41.5–45.5	10	0.24
45.5–49.5	6	0.14
49.5–53.5	1	0.02
53.5–57.5	0	0.00
57.5–61.5	2	0.05
61.5–65.5	0	0.00

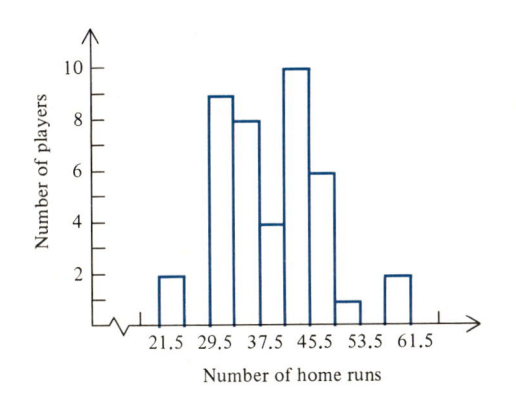

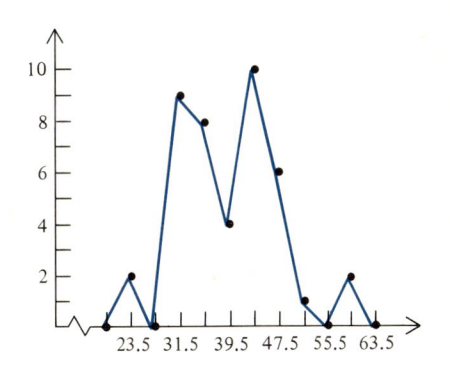

Section 5.2

1. Mean = 6; median = 7; mode = 7; standard deviation ≈ 2.19
3. Mean = 28; median = 29; no mode; standard deviation ≈ 8.12
5. Mean = 7; median = 7.5; modes: 4 and 9; standard deviation ≈ 2.45
7. Mean = 5; median = 6; mode = 2; standard deviation ≈ 2.40
9. $\mu \approx 4.87$; $\sigma \approx 2.52$ 11. $\mu \approx 14.62$; $\sigma \approx 9.80$
13. $\mu \approx 113.76$; $\sigma \approx 6.50$ 15. $\mu \approx 54.29$; $\sigma \approx 5.61$
17. $\mu \approx 115.50$; $\sigma \approx 14.23$ 19. $\mu \approx 39.60$; $\sigma \approx 8.02$

Section 5.3

1. 0.2852   3. 0.6349   5. 0.3795   7. 0.5987
9. 0.1292   11. 0.0621   13. −1.5   15. 1.8   17. 0.86
19. −2.6   21. 0.3413   23. 0.5138   25. 0.2295
27. 0.1605   29. 0.8944   31. 0.2266   33. 0.7611
35. 0.0808   37. 0.0548   39. 0.7888
41. A: 84.7–100; B: 78.9–84.6; C: 69.1–78.8; D: 63.3–69.0; F: 0–63.2

Section 5.4

1. $r \approx .874$
   $y = 2x + 10$

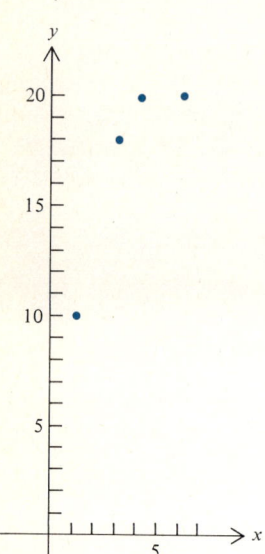

3. $r \approx -.998$
   $y = -\frac{8}{3}x + \frac{67}{3}$

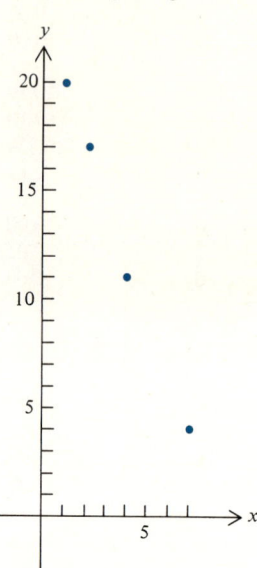

5. $r \approx .983$
   $y = 1.5x + 4$

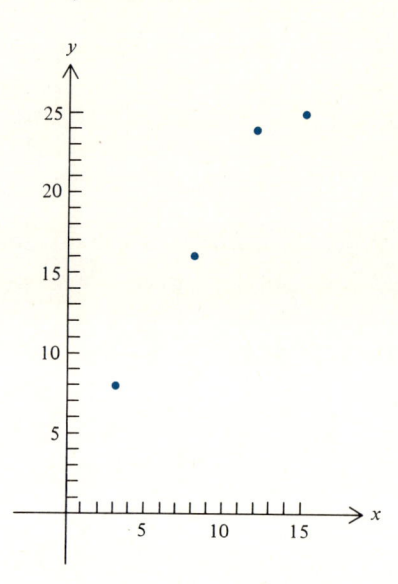

7. $r \approx -.996$
   $y = -3x + 34$

9. $r \approx .992$
   $y = 1.6x + 3.2$

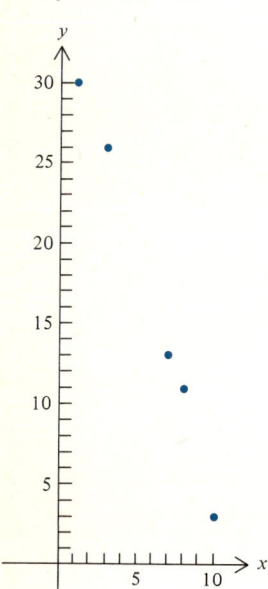

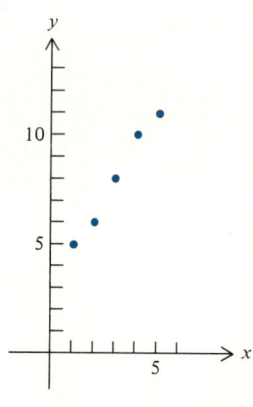

11. $r \approx .926$; $y = 9.23x + 114.72$

13. (a) $y = 83.69x + 660.11$ (b) $r \approx .994$ (c) 743.8 billion

15. (a) $y = 0.48x + 9.51$
    (b) 29.7 in 1925; 21.0 in 1926; 27.8 in 1927; 33.2 in 1928; 21.3 in 1929; 21.1 in 1930

Review Exercises

1. (a) True (b) True (c) True (d) False (e) False
   (f) False (g) False (h) True (i) False (j) True
   (k) True (l) True (m) True (n) False (o) False

2.

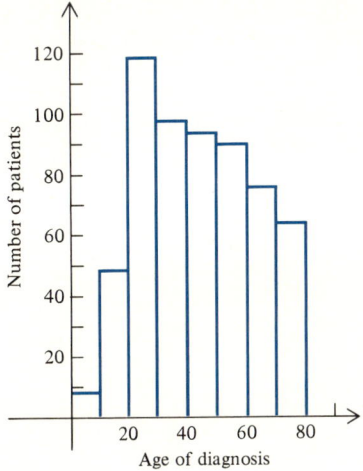

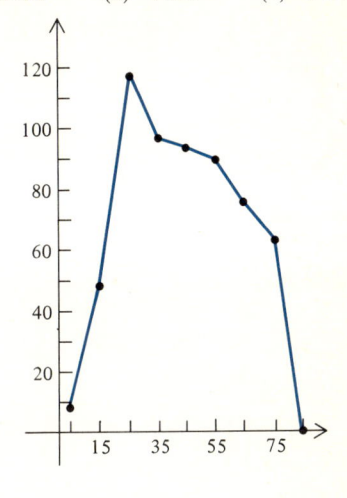

3. One possibility is:

Interval	Frequency	Relative frequency
40.5–45.5	0	0.00
45.5–50.5	2	0.06
50.5–55.5	1	0.03
55.5–60.5	6	0.17
60.5–65.5	5	0.14
65.5–70.5	6	0.17
70.5–75.5	5	0.14
75.5–80.5	5	0.14
80.5–85.5	2	0.06
85.5–90.5	3	0.09
90.5–95.5	0	0.00

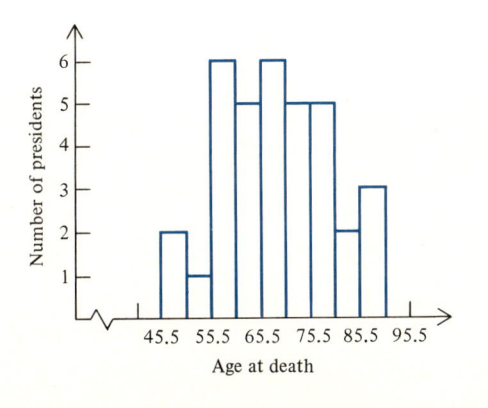

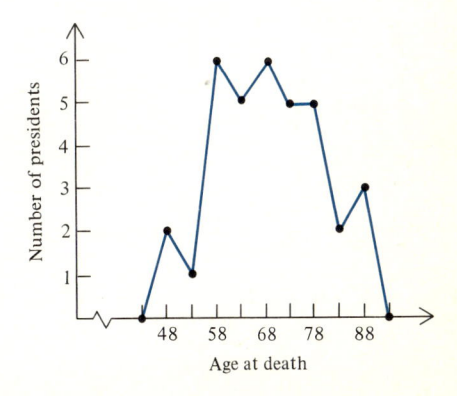

4. One possibility is:

Interval	Frequency	Relative frequency
18.5–22.5	0	0.00
22.5–26.5	1	0.02
26.5–30.5	4	0.10
30.5–34.5	4	0.10
34.5–38.5	6	0.14
38.5–42.5	5	0.12
42.5–46.5	10	0.24
46.5–50.5	7	0.17
50.5–54.5	5	0.12
54.5–58.5	0	0.00

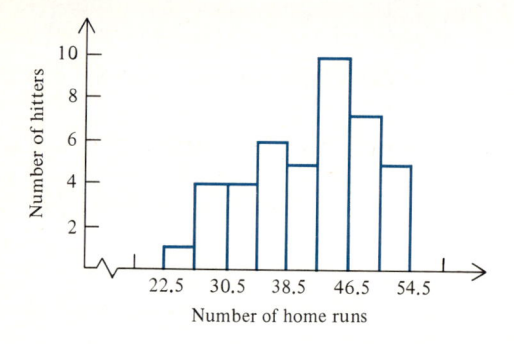

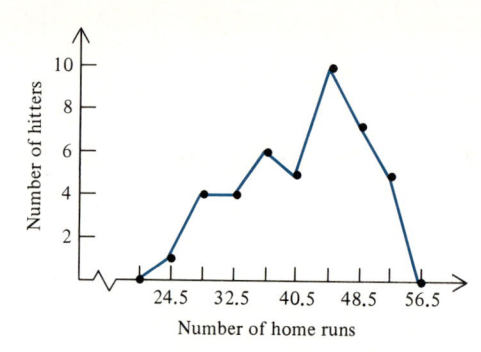

5. (a) Mean = 5; median = 5; modes: 2 and 7; standard deviation ≈ 2.27
(b) Mean = 6; median = 5.5; mode = 5; standard deviation ≈ 2.55

6. $\mu \approx 43.61$; $\sigma \approx 18.69$ **7.** $\mu \approx 68.71$; $\sigma \approx 10.70$

8. (a) 0   (b) 2   (c) −1.4   (d) 0.8

9. (a) 0.3944   (b) 0.4337   (c) 0.3153   (d) 0.3124
(e) 0.7734   (f) 0.4013

10. 0.0668   **11.** 0.4040

12. $r \approx .997$; $y = \frac{8}{7}x + \frac{4}{7}$ **13.** $r \approx .825$; $y = 0.84x + 0.61$

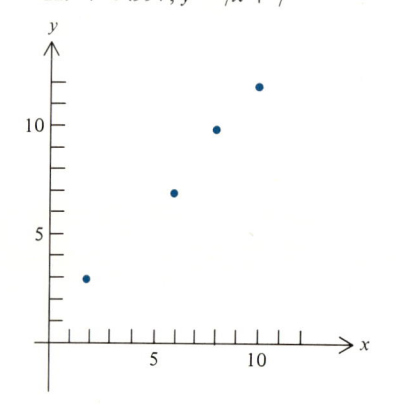

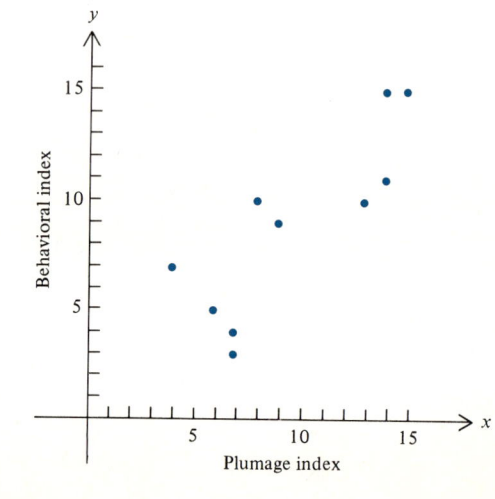

Chapter 6

Section 6.1

1. False 3. False 5. True 7. True
9. $\{6, 5, 4, 3, \ldots\}$ 11. $\{-2, -1, 0, 1, 2\}$
13. {Connecticut, Delaware, Georgia, Maryland, Massachusetts, New Hampshire, New Jersey, New York, North Carolina, Pennsylvania, Rhode Island, South Carolina, Virginia}
15. $\{x \mid x \text{ is an even integer between 1 and 11}\}$ 17. $\{y \mid 3 = |y|\}$
19. $\{z \mid z \text{ is a state bordering Mexico}\}$
21. Students at the university who are taking a business course or an economics course (or both)
23. Students at the university who are not taking mathematics
25. Students at the university who are taking a business course but not taking an economics course
27. Students at the university who are taking at least one course in business, economics, or mathematics
29. Students at the university who are taking a business course or who are taking courses in both economics and mathematics
31. $\emptyset, \{5\}$; 1 proper subset
33. $\emptyset, \{5\}, \{6\}, \{8\}, \{5,6\}, \{5,8\}, \{6,8\}, \{5,6,8\}$; 7 proper subsets
35. $A \cup B = \{1, 2, 3, 4\}; A \cap B = \{1\}; A' = \{0, 2, 4\}; B' = \{0, 3\}$
37. $A \cup B = \{-4, -3, 0, 1, 2, 5\}; A \cap B = \{-3, 1, 5\};$
    $A' = \{-5, -4, -2, -1, 0, 2, 3, 4\}; B' = \{-5, -2, -1, 3, 4\}$
39. $A \cup B = \{1, 2, 4, 6, 7, 8, 10, 12, 13, 14\}; A \cap B = \{4, 10\};$
    $A' = \{2, 3, 5, 6, 8, 9, 11, 12, 14, 15\}; B' = \{1, 3, 5, 7, 9, 11, 13, 15\}$
41. $A \cup B = \{x \mid x \text{ is a positive integer}\};$
    $A \cap B = \{x \mid x \text{ is an integer and } 10 \leq x \leq 100\};$
    $A' = \{x \mid x \text{ is a positive integer and } x < 10\};$
    $B' = \{x \mid x \text{ is an integer and } x > 100\}$
43. $A \cup B = \{x \mid x \text{ is an integer and } x > 20\};$
    $A \cap B = \{x \mid x \text{ is an integer and } x \geq 30\};$
    $A' = \{x \mid x \text{ is a positive integer and } x \leq 20\};$
    $B' = \{x \mid x \text{ is a positive integer and } x < 30\}$

Section 6.2

1.

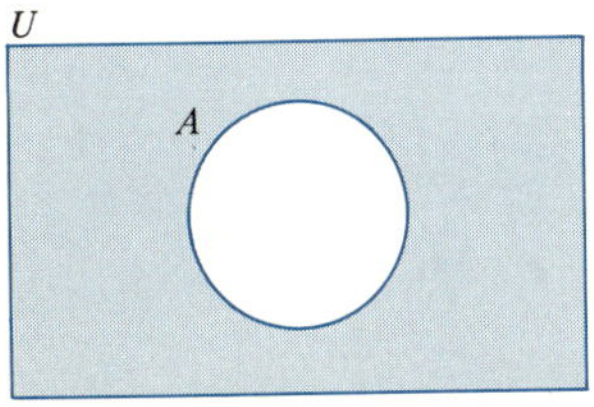

A'

3.

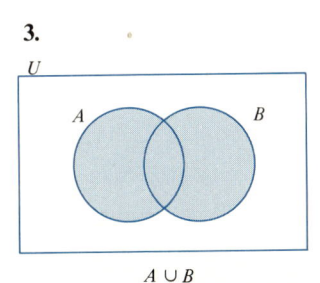

$A \cup B$

5.

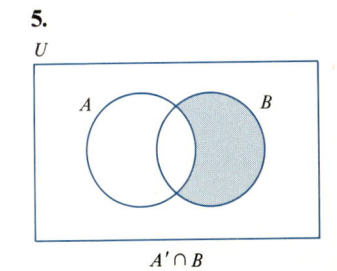

$A' \cap B$

Answers to Odd-Numbered Exercises

7. $(A \cap C) \cup B$

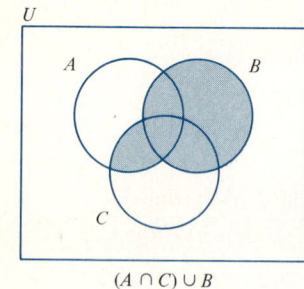

9. $(A \cup B)' \cap C$

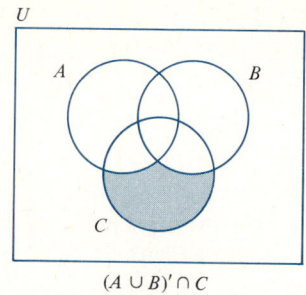

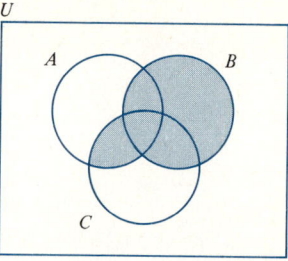

11. $(A \cup B) \cap (C \cup B)$

13. 6

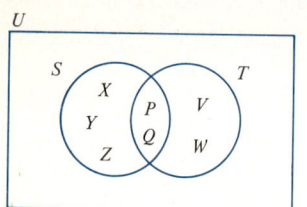

15.

15. Denote caseids by X, finbacks by Y, freshwater thecodonts by Z, land thecodonts by P, therapsids by Q, Cenozoic mammals by V, and dinosaurs by W.

17. 2603   19. (a) 7   (b) 5   (c) 2   21. 109

23. The data indicates a total of 910 new policyholders, but the company claims to have only 900.

Section 6.3

1. 35   3. $5^6 \cdot 2^4 = 250{,}000$

5. (a) $26^3 \cdot 10^3 = 17{,}576{,}000$ (b) $26 \cdot 25 \cdot 24 \cdot 10 \cdot 9 \cdot 8 = 11{,}232{,}000$
   (c) $26^2 \cdot 10^4 = 6{,}760{,}000$

7. 90

9. (a) $3 \cdot 2 \cdot 2 = 12$
   (b)

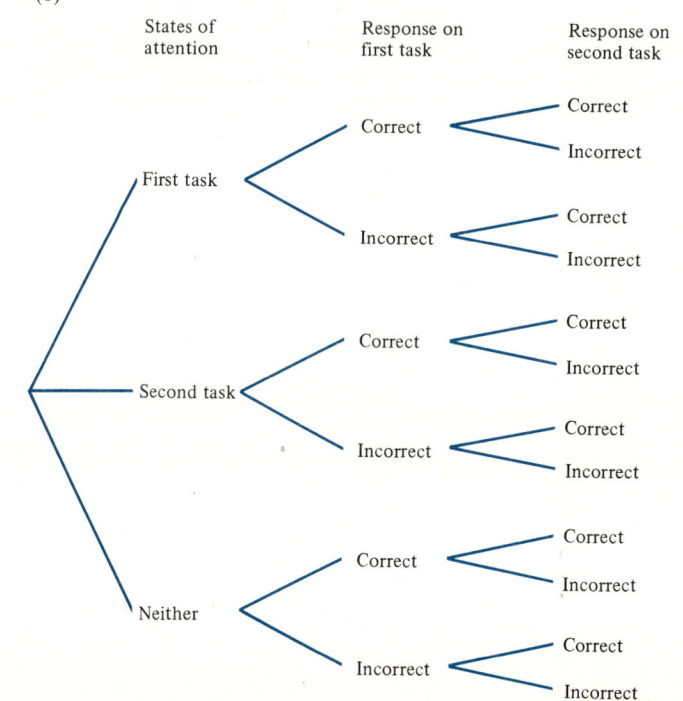

11. 2 **13.** $2^4 = 16$ **15.** $2^7 = 128$
17. (a) $2^{10} = 1024$ (b) $3^{10} = 59{,}049$
19. (a) 720 (b) 144 (c) 36 (d) 72 (e) 72

Section 6.4

1. 24 **3.** 40,320 **5.** 10 **7.** 120 **9.** 336
11. 126 **13.** n **15.** $n!$ **17.** $P(6,6) = 720$
19. $P(7,4) = 840$ **21.** (a) $P(5,5) = 120$ (b) $P(8,5) = 6720$
23. $\dfrac{7!}{2!2!} = 1260$ **25.** $\dfrac{10!}{3!3!2!} = 50{,}400$ **27.** $\dfrac{15!}{6!4!3!2!} = 6{,}306{,}300$
29. $\dfrac{20!}{5!5!5!5!} \approx 1.17 \times 10^{10}$ **31.** $C(832, 50) = \dfrac{832!}{782!50!}$
33. (a) $C(16,5) = 4368$ (b) $C(9,5) = 126$ (c) $C(7,5) = 21$
35. (a) $C(9,5) = 126$ (b) $C(4,3) \cdot C(5,2) = 40$
 (c) $C(4,1) \cdot C(5,4) = 20$ (d) $C(9,5) - C(4,4) \cdot C(5,1) = 121$
37. $C(3,1) \cdot C(5,2) \cdot C(6,2) = 450$
39. (a) $C(24,5) = 42{,}504$ (b) $C(10,5) = 252$
 (c) $C(8,2) \cdot C(10,3) = 3360$ (d) $C(6,1) \cdot C(8,2) \cdot C(10,2) = 7560$
41. (a) $C(36,5) = 376{,}992$ (b) $C(26,3) \cdot C(26,2) = 845{,}000$
 (c) $4 \cdot C(13,5) = 5148$ (d) $52 \cdot 48 \cdot 44 \cdot 40 \cdot 36 \approx 1.58 \times 10^8$
 (e) $4^5 = 1024$
43. $(n-1)!$

Review Exercises

1. (a) True (b) True (c) True (d) False
 (e) True (f) False (g) True (h) False
2. (a) $\{1,2,3,4,5,6,8\}$ (b) $\{2,5,6\}$ (c) $\{1,3,4,7,9,10\}$
 (d) $\{7,8,9,10\}$
3. U

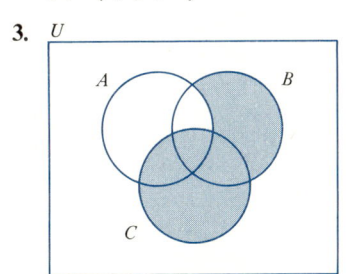

$(A' \cap B) \cup C$

4. 4 **5.** (a) 38 (b) 12 (c) 260
6. (a) 120 (b) 362,880 (c) 28 (d) 210 (e) 1680
 (f) 252 (g) 35 (h) 504
7. $C(13,3) = 286$ **8.** 440 **9.** $P(6,6) = 720$
10. $\dfrac{7!}{3!2!} = 420$ **11.** $C(10,4) = 210$ **12.** $P(12,3) = 1320$

13. (a) $P(11,4) = 7920$ (b) $C(11,4) = 330$ (c) $C(6,4) = 15$
    (d) $C(6,2) \cdot C(5,2) = 150$

Chapter 7

Section 7.1

1. $\{H, T\}$
3. {Jan., Feb., March, April, May, June, July, Aug., Sept., Oct., Nov., Dec.}
5. {1HH, 1HT, 1TH, 1TT, 2HH, 2HT, 2TH, 2TT, 3HH, 3HT, 3TH, 3TT, 4HH, 4HT, 4TH, 4TT, 5HH, 5HT, 5TH, 5TT, 6HH, 6HT, 6TH, 6TT}
7. $\{x | x \text{ is a nonnegative integer}\}$ 9. $\{y | y \text{ is a positive real number}\}$
11. $\{R, LL, LRR, LRLR, LRLL\}$
13. $E \cup F = \{HH, HT, TT\}$ is the event "the same side of the coin shows on both flips or the second flip is tails"; $E \cap F = \{TT\}$ is the event "the same side of the coin shows on both flips and the second flip is tails"; $E' = \{HT, TH\}$ is the event "different sides of the coin show on each flip"; $F' = \{HH, TH\}$ is the event "the second flip is heads."
15. $E \cup F$: an even number appears on the red die or a 5 or 6 appears on the white die; $E \cap F$: an even number appears on the red die and a 5 or 6 appears on the white die; E': an odd number appears on the red die; F': a number less than 5 appears on the white die.
17. $E \cup F$: at least one head appears or a number less than 3 is rolled; $E \cap F$: at least one head appears and a number less than 3 is rolled; E': no heads appear; F': a number greater than 2 is rolled.
19. $E \cup F = \{0, 1, 2, 3, 4, 5, 7, 9\}$; $E \cap F = \{1, 3\}$; $E' = \{5, 6, 7, 8, 9\}$; $F' = \{0, 2, 4, 6, 8\}$
21. F' 23. $F \cup G$ 25. $G \cap E'$ 27. $E \cup F \cup G$
29. Yes 31. No 33. No 35. .70 37. .75
39. .93 41. .28 43. $\frac{1}{6}$ 45. $\frac{1}{6}$ 47. $\frac{2}{9}$
49. (a) $\frac{5}{16}$ (b) $\frac{5}{16}$ (c) $\frac{13}{16}$ (d) $\frac{1}{16}$
51. $\frac{1}{4}$ 53. $\frac{11}{14}$ 55. $\frac{1}{28}$ 57. $\frac{3}{28}$
59. (a) $\frac{37}{61}$ (b) $\frac{24}{61}$ 61. $\frac{1}{70}$
63. (a) $\frac{14}{323}$ (b) $\frac{80}{323}$ (c) $\frac{135}{323}$
65. $\frac{6}{3003}$ 67. 0 69. $\frac{12}{143}$ 71. $\frac{200}{1001}$ 73. 1 to 2
75. 1 to 5 77. 1 to 5

Section 7.2

1. $Pr(E') = .4$; $Pr(F') = .8$; $Pr(E \cup F) = .7$
3. $Pr(E') = .5$; $Pr(F') = .7$; $Pr(E \cup F) = .65$
5. .78 7. 86% 9. Mutually exclusive
11. Mutually exclusive 13. Not mutually exclusive
15. Not mutually exclusive 17. Not mutually exclusive
19. Not mutually exclusive 21. Not mutually exclusive
23. $Pr(E') = .85$; $Pr(F') = .20$; $Pr(E \cup F) = .95$; $Pr(E \cap F) = 0$
25. $Pr(E') = .4$; $Pr(F') = .7$; $Pr(E \cup F) = .9$; $Pr(E \cap F) = 0$

27. (a) .3   (b) .8   (c) .9   29. $\frac{11}{26}$ 31. $\frac{2}{13}$ 33. $\frac{7}{13}$
35. $\frac{3}{4}$ 37. $\frac{5}{18}$ 39. $\frac{11}{36}$ 41. $\frac{7}{18}$ 43. $\frac{5}{9}$
45. (a) $\frac{17}{42}$ (b) $\frac{20}{21}$
47. (a) $(\frac{1}{7})^5$ (b) $1-(\frac{6}{7})^5$ (c) $120/7^5$ (d) $(\frac{5}{7})^5$

Section 7.3

1. $\frac{43}{176}$ 3. $\frac{67}{151}$ 5. $\frac{41}{160}$ 7. $\frac{1}{16}$ 9. $\frac{191}{626}$ 11. $\frac{62}{107}$
13. $\frac{67}{191}$ 15. No   17. No   19. (a) .12   (b) 0
21. (a) $\frac{1}{5}$ (b) $\frac{1}{4}$ (c) $\frac{1}{3}$ 23. Dependent
25. Dependent
27. With replacement: $\frac{25}{81}$; without replacement: $\frac{35}{117}$
29. With replacement: $\frac{20}{81}$; without replacement: $\frac{10}{39}$
31. With replacement: $\frac{41}{81}$; without replacement: $\frac{19}{39}$
33. $\frac{2}{3}$ 35. $\frac{65}{84}$ 37. $\frac{25}{102}$ 39. $\frac{1}{17}$ 41. $\frac{4}{663}$
43. $\frac{1}{221}$ 45. $\frac{25}{204}$
47. (a) .255   (b) .045   (c) .030   (d) .170
49. $\frac{2}{91}$ 51. $\frac{12}{65}$ 53. $\frac{4}{91}$ 55. $\frac{2}{21}$

57. (a) Both equal $\frac{57}{94}$ (b) Both equal $1 - \dfrac{n(E \cap F)}{n(F)}$

Section 7.4

1. $p = \frac{1}{3}; q = \frac{2}{3}$ 3. $p = \frac{1}{2}; q = \frac{1}{2}$ 5. $p = .85; q = .15$
7. $8(.8)(.2)^7 \approx .00008$ 9. $(.2)^8 \approx .000003$
11. $1 - 8(.8)(.2)^7 - (.2)^8 \approx .99992$
13. $(.2)^8 + 8(.8)(.2)^7 + 28(.8)^2(.2)^6 + 56(.8)^3(.2)^5 \approx .0104$
15. $6(\frac{1}{6})(\frac{5}{6})^5 \approx .402$ 17. $1 - (\frac{5}{6})^6 \approx .665$
19. (a) 3 consecutive tails   (b) 8 tails out of 11 flips
21. $495(.4)^8(.6)^4 \approx .042$; $12(.4)^{11}(.6)^1 + (.4)^{12} \approx .0003$
23. $120(.7)^7(.3)^3 \approx .267$; $120(.7)^7(.3)^3 + 45(.7)^8(.3)^2 + 10(.7)^9(.3) + (.7)^{10} \approx .650$
25. (a) $(\frac{2}{3})^4 \approx .198$ (b) $(\frac{1}{3})^4 \approx .012$ (c) $1 - (\frac{2}{3})^4 \approx .802$
   (d) $4(\frac{1}{3})(\frac{2}{3})^3 \approx .395$ (e) $1 - 4(\frac{1}{3})(\frac{2}{3})^3 - (\frac{2}{3})^4 \approx .407$
   (f) $4(\frac{2}{3})^3(\frac{1}{3}) + (\frac{2}{3})^4 \approx .593$
27. (a) $1 - (.9)^{10} - 10(.1)(.9)^9 \approx .264$
   (b) $1 - (.9)^{10} - 10(.1)(.9)^9 - 45(.1)^2(.9)^8 \approx .070$

Section 7.5

1. .55   3. .04   5. $\frac{16}{51}$ 7. .16   9. .31   11. .38
13. .37   15. .25   17. 70%   19. $\frac{13}{24}$
21. $Pr(E_1|F) = \frac{28}{31}$; $Pr(E_2|F) = \frac{3}{31}$
23. $Pr(E_1|F) = \frac{3}{19}$; $Pr(E_2|F) = \frac{16}{19}$
25. $Pr(E_1|F) = \frac{21}{37}$; $Pr(E_2|F) = \frac{12}{37}$; $Pr(E_3|F) = \frac{4}{37}$
27. $Pr(E_1|F) = \frac{7}{25}$; $Pr(E_2|F) = \frac{9}{25}$; $Pr(E_3|F) = \frac{9}{25}$
29. (a) $\frac{144}{241}$ (b) $\frac{6}{4759}$
31. East Side: $\frac{9}{35}$; Beach: $\frac{23}{56}$; Tragbaum: $\frac{93}{280}$

Section 7.6

1. 3.8
3. 0.4
5. 27.5
7. $\frac{55}{12}$
9. 2.96
11. $40,000
13. −$3.70
15. −$0.60
17. 1.5
19. 0.75
21. $\frac{9}{7}$
23. Mutual fund: $290; stock: $300

Review Exercises

1. (a) True (b) True (c) True (d) False
   (e) True (f) False (g) True (h) False
   (i) False (j) True (k) True (l) False
2. (a) {BBBB, BBBG, BBGB, BBGG, BGBB, BGBG, BGGB, BGGG, GBBB, GBBG, GBGB, GBGG, GGBB, GGBG, GGGB, GGGG}
   (b) $\frac{1}{2}$ (c) $\frac{1}{2}$ (d) $\frac{9}{16}$ (e) $\frac{1}{4}$ (f) $\frac{3}{8}$
3. (a) $\frac{351}{400}$ (b) $\frac{7}{10}$ (c) $\frac{5}{24}$ (d) $\frac{256}{351}$
4. $\frac{11}{75}$
5. (a) $\frac{1}{6}$ (b) $\frac{1}{30}$ (c) $\frac{3}{10}$ (d) $\frac{1}{2}$
6. $56(.6)^5(.4)^3 \approx .279$; $56(.6)^5(.4)^3 + 28(.6)^6(.4)^2 + 8(.6)^7(.4) + (.6)^8 \approx .594$
7. Large: $\frac{5}{8}$; red: $\frac{1}{4}$; yellow or green: $\frac{5}{12}$; yellow, blue, or green: $\frac{3}{4}$; small or green: $\frac{11}{24}$
8. .2
9. 86%; 27%
10. (a) $\frac{1}{8}$ (b) $\frac{1}{8}$ (c) $\frac{1}{4}$ (d) $\frac{7}{8}$
11. $\frac{2}{3}$
12. (a) $\frac{1}{17}$ (b) $\frac{2}{17}$ (c) $\frac{1}{17}$ (d) $\frac{11}{26}$ (e) $\frac{8}{16,575}$
    (f) $\frac{57}{1105}$ (g) $\frac{47}{85}$ (h) $\frac{1}{52}$ (i) $\frac{13}{102}$ (j) $\frac{25}{204}$
13. 7.1%
14. 100
15. −$0.20
16. 1
17. Make two cakes for an expected profit of $3.72.

Chapter 8

Section 8.1

1. Is a probability vector
3. Is not a probability vector
5. Is a probability vector
7. Is not a probability vector
9. Is not a transition matrix
11. Is a transition matrix
13. Is not a transition matrix
15. Is not a transition matrix
17. .45; (.45 .55)
19. .18; (.564 .436)
21. .28; (.250 .358 .392)
23. .5; (.3 .4 .3)
25. (a) The given probabilities (percentages) must remain the same from year to year.
    (b) One year
    (c)

	0 claims	1 claim	2 or more
0 claims	.92	.07	.01
1 claim	0	.85	.15
2 or more	0	0	1

27. 10.2% in February; 11.63% in March
29. 26.5% agricultural workers; 38% blue-collar workers; 35.5% white-collar workers
31. 25% in state 1; 29% in state 2; 21% in state 3; 24% in state 4

Section 8.2

1. Regular   3. Not regular   5. Regular   7. Not regular
9. (.6 .4)   11. $(\frac{4}{7}\ \frac{3}{7})$ 13. $(\frac{1}{7}\ \frac{2}{7}\ \frac{4}{7})$ 15. $(\frac{5}{28}\ \frac{5}{7}\ \frac{3}{28})$
17. The proportion of men in each age class will stabilize at 26.4% youth, 45.2% adult, and 28.4% senior citizen.
19. (a) .748   (b) 75%
21. (a) Subway: 20%; bus: 39%; automobile 41%
    (b) Subway: 20%; bus 60%; automobile 20%
23. (a) Urban: 26.5%; agriculture: 51%; unused: 22.5%
    (b) Urban: 40%; agriculture: 40%; unused: 20%

Section 8.3

1. Absorbing; state 2   3. Not absorbing
5. Absorbing; states 1 and 4   7. Absorbing; states 2 and 3

9. $\begin{pmatrix} 1 & 0 & 0 \\ .2 & .6 & .2 \\ .2 & .1 & .7 \end{pmatrix}; R = \begin{pmatrix} .2 \\ .2 \end{pmatrix}; Q = \begin{pmatrix} .6 & .2 \\ .1 & .7 \end{pmatrix}; (I-Q)^{-1} = \begin{pmatrix} 3 & 2 \\ 1 & 4 \end{pmatrix}$

11. $\begin{pmatrix} 1 & 0 & 0 \\ 0 & .5 & .5 \\ .2 & .1 & .7 \end{pmatrix}; R = \begin{pmatrix} 0 \\ .2 \end{pmatrix}; Q = \begin{pmatrix} .5 & .5 \\ .1 & .7 \end{pmatrix}; (I-Q)^{-1} = \begin{pmatrix} 3 & 5 \\ 1 & 5 \end{pmatrix}$

13. $\begin{pmatrix} 1 & 0 & 0 & 0 \\ 0 & 1 & 0 & 0 \\ .2 & .1 & .5 & .2 \\ 0 & .1 & .5 & .4 \end{pmatrix}; R = \begin{pmatrix} .2 & .1 \\ 0 & .1 \end{pmatrix}; Q = \begin{pmatrix} .5 & .2 \\ .5 & .4 \end{pmatrix}; (I-Q)^{-1} = \begin{pmatrix} 3 & 1 \\ \frac{5}{2} & \frac{5}{2} \end{pmatrix}$

15. $\begin{pmatrix} 1 & 0 & 0 & 0 \\ 0 & 1 & 0 & 0 \\ .6 & .2 & .1 & .1 \\ 0 & .2 & .4 & .4 \end{pmatrix}; R = \begin{pmatrix} .6 & .2 \\ 0 & .2 \end{pmatrix}; Q = \begin{pmatrix} .1 & .1 \\ .4 & .4 \end{pmatrix}; (I-Q)^{-1} = \begin{pmatrix} 1.2 & 0.2 \\ 0.8 & 1.8 \end{pmatrix}$

17. 5   19. 5   21. .6; .5   23. .48; .52   25. $\frac{50}{49}$ days
27. $\frac{95}{14}$ semesters
29. (a) 8 years   (b) 20 years   (c) $\frac{109}{150}$ (d) $\frac{3}{10}$
31. (a) $\frac{24}{11}$ (b) $\frac{62}{11}$ (c) $\frac{5}{11}$ (d) $\frac{8}{11}$

Section 8.4

1. (a) $\begin{matrix} & 0 & 1 & 2 \\ 0 \\ 1 \\ 2 \end{matrix} \begin{pmatrix} 1-c & 0 & 0 \\ 0 & 1-\frac{c}{2} & \frac{c}{2} \\ 0 & 0 & 1 \end{pmatrix}$ (b) $3/c$

3. (b) dh: $\frac{29}{6}$; dr: $\frac{20}{3}$
   (c) dh: $\frac{3}{4}$; dr: $\frac{1}{2}$; hh: $\frac{1}{2}$; hr: $\frac{1}{4}$
5. (a) $\begin{array}{c} \\ 0 \\ 1 \\ 2 \end{array} \begin{array}{ccc} 0 & 1 & 2 \\ \begin{pmatrix} 1 & 0 & 0 \\ \frac{1}{3} & \frac{1}{2} & \frac{1}{6} \\ 0 & 0 & 1 \end{pmatrix} \end{array}$ (b) 2 (c) $\frac{1}{3}$

7. (a) $\begin{pmatrix} 3 & \frac{12}{17} & \frac{2}{17} \\ 3 & \frac{36}{17} & \frac{6}{17} \\ 3 & \frac{20}{17} & \frac{26}{17} \end{pmatrix}$ (b) $\frac{6}{17}$ (c) $\frac{93}{17}$

Review Exercises

1. (a) False   (b) False   (c) True   (d) False   (e) True
   (f) True   (g) False   (h) False (i) True   (j) False
2. (a) Absorbing; (5)   (b) Neither   (c) Regular; ($\frac{4}{7}$ $\frac{3}{7}$)
   (d) Regular; (.72 .12 .16)   (e) Neither

   (f) Absorbing; $\begin{pmatrix} 1.4 & 0.1 \\ 1.0 & 1.5 \end{pmatrix}$

   (g) Regular; (.3 .3 .4)

   (h) Absorbing; $\begin{pmatrix} 1.8 & 0 & 0.4 \\ 1.1 & 5 & 0.8 \\ 0.4 & 0 & 1.2 \end{pmatrix}$

   (i) Neither   (j) Regular; ($\frac{3}{8}$ $\frac{7}{80}$ $\frac{1}{2}$ $\frac{3}{80}$)

   (k) Absorbing; $\begin{pmatrix} 1.6 & 1.2 & 0.4 \\ 0.6 & 2.2 & 0.4 \\ 0.4 & 0.8 & 1.6 \end{pmatrix}$

   (l) Neither
3. 0.625; 2.75
4. After two trials: $DP^2 = (.55 \; .31 \; .14)$; eventually: (.6 .3 .1)
5. After three trials: $DP^3 = (.225 \; .500 \; .275)$; eventually: (.2 .5 .3)
6. $\frac{17}{6}$; $\frac{8}{15}$ 7. 1; .45
8. After two trials: $DP^2 = (.1 \; .4 \; .5)$; eventually: (.1 .4 .5)
9. (a) $\begin{array}{c} \\ 0 \\ 1 \\ 2 \\ 3 \end{array} \begin{array}{cccc} 0 & 1 & 2 & 3 \\ \begin{pmatrix} .2 & .5 & .2 & .1 \\ .2 & .5 & .2 & .1 \\ 0 & .2 & .5 & .3 \\ 0 & 0 & .2 & .8 \end{pmatrix} \end{array}$

   (b) (.14 .39 .26 .21)
   (c) (.038 .152 .286 .524)

10. (a)
$$\begin{array}{c c} & \begin{array}{cccccc} 0 & 1 & 2 & 3 & 4 & 5 \end{array} \\ \begin{array}{c} 0 \\ 1 \\ 2 \\ 3 \\ 4 \\ 5 \end{array} & \begin{pmatrix} 1 & 0 & 0 & 0 & 0 & 0 \\ .3 & 0 & .7 & 0 & 0 & 0 \\ 0 & .3 & 0 & .7 & 0 & 0 \\ 0 & 0 & .3 & 0 & .7 & 0 \\ 0 & 0 & 0 & .3 & 0 & .7 \\ 0 & 0 & 0 & 0 & 0 & 1 \end{pmatrix} \end{array}$$

(b) $\frac{22170}{4141}$ years

(c) $\frac{3430}{4141}$

Chapter 9

Section 9.1

1. $XA = (-\frac{1}{12} \quad -\frac{1}{12})$; $AY = \begin{pmatrix} -\frac{1}{12} \\ -\frac{1}{12} \end{pmatrix}$; value $= -\frac{1}{12}$

3. $XA = (0 \quad 0)$; $AY = \begin{pmatrix} 0 \\ 0 \end{pmatrix}$; value $= 0$

5. $XA = (0.2 \quad 2.2 \quad 0.2)$; $AY = \begin{pmatrix} 0.2 \\ 0.2 \end{pmatrix}$; value $= 0.2$

7. $XA = (1.50 \quad 1.50 \quad 2.65)$; $AY = \begin{pmatrix} 1.5 \\ -1.0 \\ 1.5 \end{pmatrix}$; value $= 1.5$

9. $XA = (8 \quad 6 \quad 4 \quad 5)$; $AY = \begin{pmatrix} 2 \\ 4 \\ 2 \\ 3 \end{pmatrix}$; value $= 4$

11. Row 3; column 1   **13.** None   **15.** Column 1
17. Row 2; columns 1, 2, and 3; row 3
19. Column 4; row 1; column 2; row 3

21.
$$\begin{array}{c c} & \begin{array}{cc} \text{Heads} & \text{Tails} \end{array} \\ \begin{array}{c} \text{Heads} \\ \text{Tails} \end{array} & \begin{pmatrix} 9 & -6 \\ -6 & 4 \end{pmatrix} \end{array}$$

23.
$$\begin{array}{c c} & \begin{array}{ccc} \text{Scissors} & \text{Paper} & \text{Stone} \end{array} \\ \begin{array}{c} \text{Scissors} \\ \text{Paper} \\ \text{Stone} \end{array} & \begin{pmatrix} 0 & 1 & -1 \\ -1 & 0 & 1 \\ 1 & -1 & 0 \end{pmatrix} \end{array}$$

25.
$$\begin{array}{c c} & \begin{array}{cc} 0 & 1 \end{array} \\ \begin{array}{c} 0 \\ 1 \\ 2 \end{array} & \begin{pmatrix} 0 & 0 \\ 0 & 1 \\ 1 & -1 \end{pmatrix} \end{array}$$

27.
$$\begin{array}{c c} & \begin{array}{ccc} 5 & 6 & 7 \end{array} \\ \begin{array}{c} 1 \\ 2 \\ 3 \\ 4 \end{array} & \begin{pmatrix} -30 & -40 & -50 \\ -10 & -20 & -30 \\ 10 & 0 & -10 \\ 30 & 20 & 10 \end{pmatrix} \end{array}$$

516 *Answers to Odd-Numbered Exercises*

29.
$$\begin{array}{c c} & \begin{array}{ccc} 1 & 2 & 3 \end{array} \\ \begin{array}{c} 1 \\ 2 \\ 3 \end{array} & \begin{pmatrix} 5 & 4 & 6 \\ -4 & 5 & -2 \\ -6 & 2 & 5 \end{pmatrix} \end{array}$$

Section 9.2

1. $-3; (1\ 0\ 0); \begin{pmatrix} 0 \\ 1 \\ 0 \end{pmatrix}$ 3. None

5. $0; (0\ 0\ 1); \begin{pmatrix} 0 \\ 0 \\ 1 \end{pmatrix}$ 7. None

9. None 11. $2; (0\ 0\ 1\ 0); \begin{pmatrix} 0 \\ 1 \\ 0 \\ 0 \end{pmatrix}$

13. $3; (0\ 1\ 0\ 0); \begin{pmatrix} 1 \\ 0 \\ 0 \\ 0 \end{pmatrix}$ 15. None

17. $-1; (0\ 0\ 1\ 0); \begin{pmatrix} 0 \\ 1 \\ 0 \\ 0 \end{pmatrix}$ 19. None

21. $10{,}000; (0\ 0\ 0\ 1); \begin{pmatrix} 0 \\ 0 \\ 0 \\ 1 \end{pmatrix}$

Section 9.3

1. $(.7\ .3); \begin{pmatrix} .5 \\ .5 \end{pmatrix}; 0.5$ 3. $(\frac{3}{11}\ \frac{8}{11}); \begin{pmatrix} \frac{4}{11} \\ \frac{7}{11} \end{pmatrix}; -\frac{1}{11}$

5. $(\frac{2}{3}\ \frac{1}{3}); \begin{pmatrix} \frac{5}{9} \\ \frac{4}{9} \\ 0 \end{pmatrix}; -\frac{1}{3}$ 7. $(1\ 0); \begin{pmatrix} 0 \\ 1 \\ 0 \end{pmatrix}; 2$

9. $(\frac{2}{3}\ \frac{1}{3}); \begin{pmatrix} \frac{1}{3} \\ \frac{2}{3} \\ 0 \end{pmatrix}; 1$ 11. $(\frac{9}{16}\ \frac{7}{16}); \begin{pmatrix} 0 \\ \frac{5}{8} \\ \frac{3}{8} \end{pmatrix}; \frac{19}{8}$

13. $(.55\ 0\ .45); \begin{pmatrix} .5 \\ 0 \\ .5 \\ 0 \end{pmatrix}; 1.5$ 15. $(.2\ .8); \begin{pmatrix} .4 \\ 0 \\ 0 \\ .6 \end{pmatrix}; 0.2$

17. $(\frac{7}{12}\ \frac{5}{12}); \begin{pmatrix} 0 \\ 0 \\ \frac{3}{4} \\ \frac{1}{4} \end{pmatrix}; \frac{3}{2}$ 19. $(.4\ .6); \begin{pmatrix} .4 \\ .6 \end{pmatrix}; 0$

Answers to Odd-Numbered Exercises 517

21. $(.9 \quad .1 \quad 0); \begin{pmatrix} .1 \\ .9 \\ 0 \end{pmatrix}; 4.1$

Section 9.4

1. $(.65 \quad .35); \begin{pmatrix} .55 \\ .45 \end{pmatrix}; 0.85$ **3.** $(.5 \quad .5); \begin{pmatrix} .7 \\ .3 \end{pmatrix}; 1.5$

5. $(.6 \quad .4); \begin{pmatrix} .5 \\ 0 \\ .5 \end{pmatrix}; 5$ **7.** $(.7 \quad .3); \begin{pmatrix} .3 \\ .7 \\ 0 \end{pmatrix}; 1.1$

9. $(.4 \quad 0 \quad .6); \begin{pmatrix} .6 \\ 0 \\ .4 \end{pmatrix}; 3.2$ **11.** $(\frac{3}{5} \quad \frac{1}{7} \quad \frac{9}{35}); \begin{pmatrix} \frac{1}{5} \\ \frac{1}{2} \\ \frac{3}{10} \end{pmatrix}; -\frac{2}{5}$

13. $(0 \quad .5 \quad .5); \begin{pmatrix} .75 \\ 0 \\ .25 \\ 0 \end{pmatrix}; 1$ **15.** $(\frac{2}{9} \quad \frac{1}{12} \quad \frac{7}{36} \quad \frac{1}{2}); \begin{pmatrix} \frac{1}{6} \\ \frac{5}{12} \\ \frac{1}{4} \\ \frac{1}{6} \end{pmatrix}; \frac{5}{12}$

17. $(\frac{1}{3} \quad \frac{1}{3} \quad \frac{1}{3}); \begin{pmatrix} \frac{1}{3} \\ \frac{1}{3} \\ \frac{1}{3} \end{pmatrix}; 0$ **19.** $(\frac{17}{55} \quad \frac{28}{55} \quad \frac{2}{11}); \begin{pmatrix} \frac{9}{55} \\ 0 \\ \frac{3}{11} \\ \frac{31}{55} \end{pmatrix}; \frac{59}{55}$

Review Exercises

1. (a) False (b) True (c) True (d) False (e) True
(f) False (g) True (h) True (i) False (j) False
(k) True (l) True (m) True (n) True (o) False

2. $XA = (0 \quad 0 \quad \frac{1}{2}); \; AY = \begin{pmatrix} 0 \\ 0 \\ -\frac{19}{3} \end{pmatrix};$ value $= 0$

3. (a) Column 3 (b) None (c) Columns 3 and 4; rows 1 and 4
(d) Row 1; columns 1 and 4; row 2

4. (a) $(.5 \quad .5); \begin{pmatrix} 0 \\ .6 \\ .4 \end{pmatrix}; 1$ (b) $(.6 \quad .4); \begin{pmatrix} 0 \\ .5 \\ .5 \end{pmatrix}; 2$

5. (a) $(.5 \quad .5 \quad 0); \begin{pmatrix} .75 \\ .25 \\ 0 \end{pmatrix}; 3.5$ (b) $(.250 \quad .575 \quad .175); \begin{pmatrix} .2 \\ .5 \\ .3 \\ 0 \end{pmatrix}; 0.9$

6. (a)
	NW	SW
NE	8	2
SE	2	−4

(b) The independent station should be built on the northeast corner; the major company's station should be built on the southwest corner.

7. (a)

		Smaller bank			
		Suburb 1	Suburb 2	Suburb 3	Suburb 4
Larger bank	Suburb 1	6	−4	−3	7
	Suburb 2	4	6	7	11
	Suburb 3	3	−7	6	10
	Suburb 4	−7	−11	−10	6

(b) Larger bank: $(\frac{1}{6}\ \ \frac{5}{6}\ \ 0\ \ 0)$;

Smaller bank: $\begin{pmatrix} \frac{5}{6} \\ \frac{1}{6} \\ 0 \\ 0 \end{pmatrix}$; $54\frac{1}{3}\%$

Chapter 10

Section 10.1

1. Not an arithmetic progression
3. Arithmetic progression with difference 5; 27
5. Arithmetic progression with difference −4; −10
7. Not an arithmetic progression
9. 26 **11.** 2 **13.** 69 **15.** −93 **17.** 57 **19.** 715
21. 1566 **23.** 502.5 **25.** (a) $11,700 (b) $92,400
27. (a) 96 (b) 174 **29.** 10% **31.** 125,250 **33.** $600.00

Section 10.2

1. Geometric progression with ratio $\frac{1}{4}$; $\frac{1}{1024}$
3. Not a geometric progression
5. Not a geometric progression
7. Geometric progression with ratio $-\frac{2}{3}$; $-\frac{512}{9}$ **9.** −12
11. 207.36 **13.** −6 **15.** 128 **17.** 72 **19.** 1089
21. 1599.0227 **23.** −9555 **25.** Does not exist **27.** $-\frac{8}{3}$
29. 18 **31.** Does not exist **33.** $20 billion
35. $27,130.85; $279,311.68 **37.** 62 **39.** $5000

Section 10.3

1. $525 **3.** $19,200 **5.** $1080 **7.** $4200
9. $7321.14 **11.** $323.21 **13.** $862.30 **15.** $2827.79
17. 6.168% **19.** 7.186% **21.** $450 **23.** $6209.93
25. 6% compounded semiannually **27.** 16% **29.** $618
31. 19.56% **33.** $1538.46 **35.** 6.99% **37.** $1000 now
39. 6.7% rate of inflation

Section 10.4

1. 8, −24, 72, −216, 648 **3.** 0, −6, −12, −18, −24
5. −5, −11, −23, −47, −95 **7.** 4, −2, 4, −2, 4

9. $-2, 1, -11, 37, -155$ 11. $y_n = y_1(5)^{n-1}$
13. $y_n = (y_1 - \frac{1}{3})(-2)^{n-1} + \frac{1}{3}$ 15. $y_n = y_1 + 6(n-1)$
17. $y_n = (y_1 + \frac{4}{3})(-2)^{n-1} - \frac{4}{3}$ 19. $y_n = (y_1 - \frac{1}{6})(3)^{n-1} + \frac{1}{6}$
21. -1 23. -15.125 25. 154 27. -4.99904 29. -7
31. $38,737.89 33. $3810.56 35. $100(2^{23}) \approx 8.389 \times 10^8$
37. $390 billion

Section 10.5

1. $2682.42 3. $3933.61 5. $278.83 7. $203.38
9. $8516.06 11. $49,054.30 13. $199.29 15. $45.84
17. $14,131.26 19. $11,800.83 21. $87.76 23. $3024.55
25. $377.64 27. $246.71 29. Do not replace 31. $716.64

Section 10.6

1. $p_0 = 10$; the sequence approaches p_0

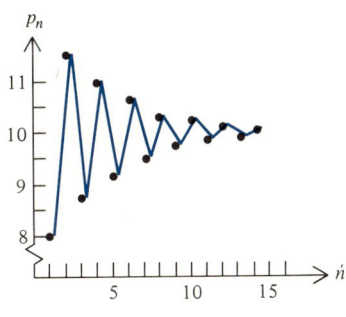

3. $p_0 = 12$; the sequence approaches p_0

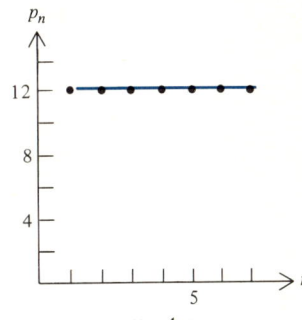

5. $Y_n = (2^{n-1})Y_1$

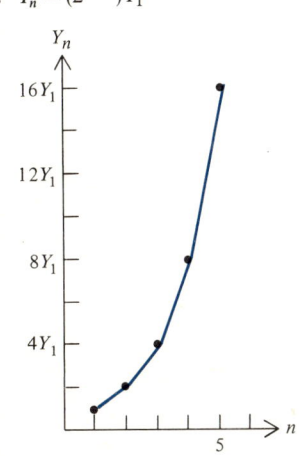

7. $Y_n = Y_1$

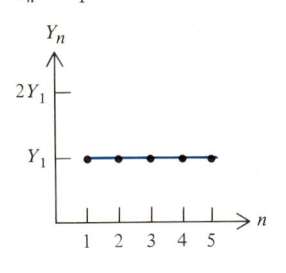

9. $Y_n = (-2)^{n-1}Y_1$

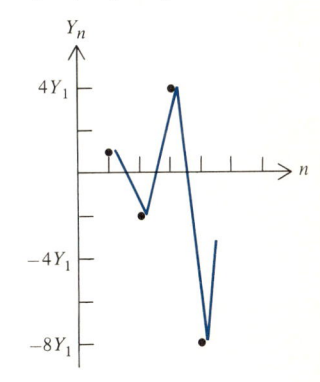

11. $b = 0$
13. The income Y_n oscillates between positive and negative values while $|Y_n|$ increases without bound.

15. (a) $Y_n = \dfrac{-a}{b-a-u} Y_{n-1} + \dfrac{v}{b-a-u}$

(b) $Y_n = \left(Y_1 - \dfrac{v}{b-u}\right)\left(\dfrac{-a}{b-a-u}\right)^{n-1} + \dfrac{v}{b-u}$

17. (a) $S_n = cS_{n-1}$ (b) $S_n = S_1 c^{n-1}$ (c) $S_\infty = \dfrac{S_1}{1-c}$

Section 10.7

1. $p_n = 0.5$

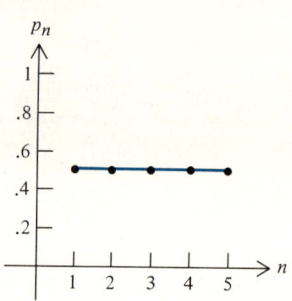

3. $p_n = -0.25(0.2)^{n-1} + 0.75$

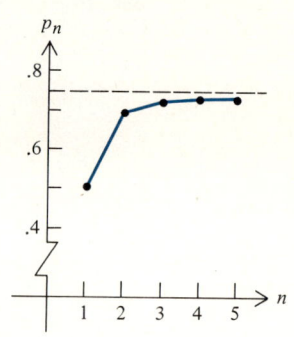

5. $p_n = \frac{1}{6}(0.4)^{n-1} + \frac{1}{3}$

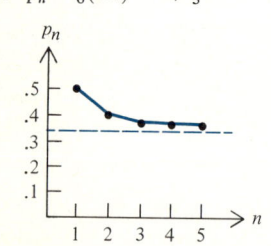

7. $p_n = (0.5)^n$

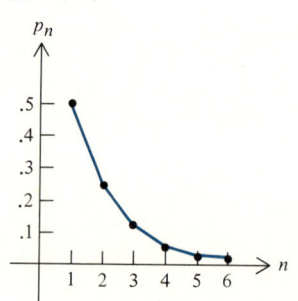

9. $p_n = -0.3(0.4)^{n-1} + 0.5$

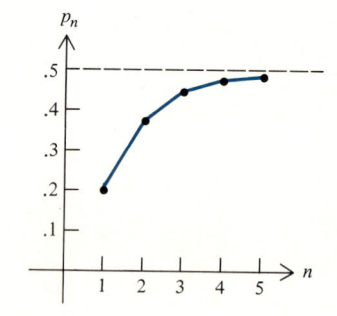

11. .5 13. 0 15. .75

17. Since $p_n = 1$ for each n, the desired response will always be performed because the subject is rewarded on each trial.

19. (b) $y_n = \left(y_1 - \dfrac{b'}{b'+c'}\right)(1 - b' - c')^{n-1} + \dfrac{b'}{b'+c'}$

(c) $\dfrac{b'}{b'+c'}$

21. $y_n = (y_1 - L)\left(\dfrac{R-1}{R}\right)^{n-1} + L$; the sequence approaches L.

23. $y_n = (y_1 - \pi)(1 - \theta)^{n-1} + \pi$

Review Exercises

1. (a) False (b) True (c) False (d) False (e) True
   (f) False (g) True (h) True (i) True (j) True
   (k) False (l) True

2. -73 **3.** 945 **4.** -3072 **5.** $\dfrac{1}{3(2^{14})} - \dfrac{64}{3} \approx -21.333$

6. 256 **7.** $7260 **8.** $3216.87 **9.** $5536.76
10. $1, -2, -11, -38, -119$ **11.** 2795.9505 **12.** $166.07
13. $20,931.01 **14.** $7210.15 **15.** $763.69 **16.** $10,800
17. (a) $35,852.78 (b) $328,491.78

Chapter 11

Section 11.1

1. [graph with vertices v_1, v_2, v_3, v_4] **3.** [graph with vertices v_1, v_2, v_3, v_4, v_5]

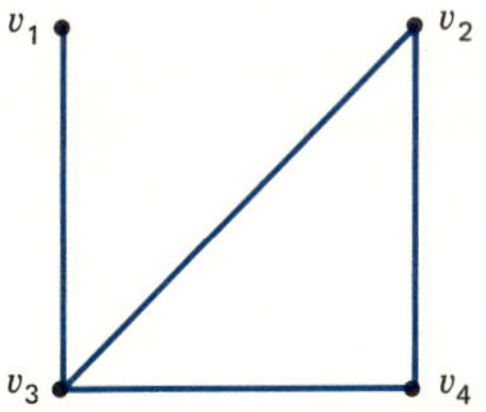

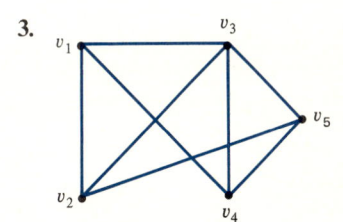

5. Only v_2 is adjacent to v_1; v_1 and v_3 have degree 1, and v_2 and v_4 have degree 2. The sum of the degrees and twice the number of edges are both 6.

7. Vertices v_2, v_5, and v_6 are adjacent to v_1; every vertex has degree 3. The sum of the degrees and twice the number of edges are both 18.

9. [graph with vertices v_1, v_2, v_3, v_4] **11.** [graph with vertices v_1, v_2, v_3, v_4, v_5]

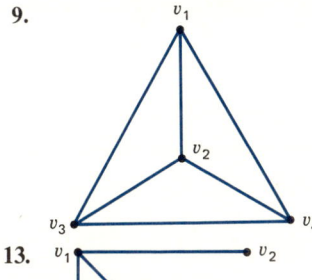

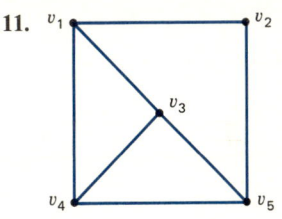

13. [graph with vertices v_1, v_2, v_3, v_4] **15.** Planar [pentagon graph with vertices v_1, v_2, v_3, v_4, v_5]

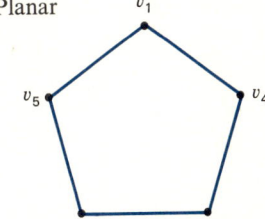

17. Not planar **19.** Planar [graph with vertices $v_1, v_2, v_3, v_4, v_5, v_6$]

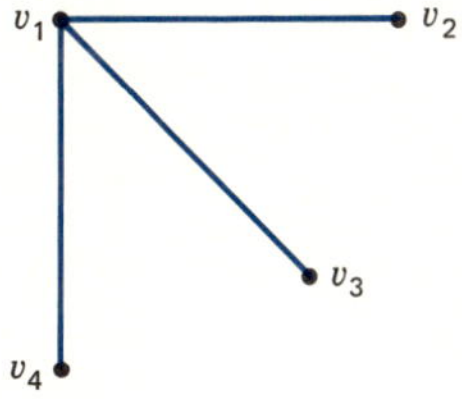

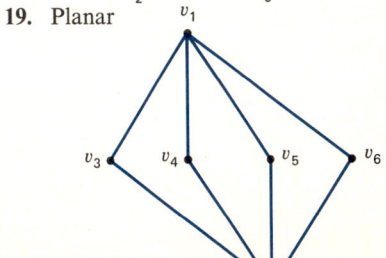

522 *Answers to Odd-Numbered Exercises*

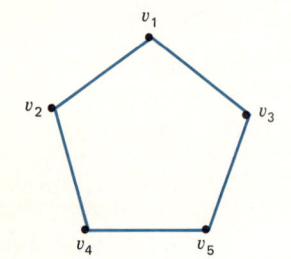

21. (a) Yes (b) Not possible **23.** **25.** $\frac{1}{2}n(n-1)$

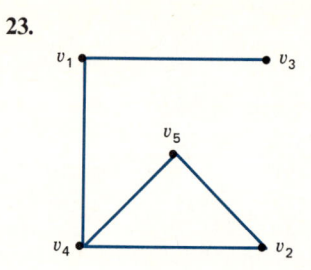

Section 11.2

1. Yes   3. Not a path   5. $v_1v_2v_3v_4v_8v_3v_7v_2v_6v_1v_5v_6v_7v_8$
7. No such path exists.
9. $v_1v_2v_3v_4v_8v_3v_4v_7v_8v_7v_3v_6v_2v_7v_6v_1v_2v_5v_6v_5v_1$
11. No such path exists.   13. No such path exists.
15. No such path exists.   17. No such path exists.
19. $v_1v_2v_3v_6v_5v_8v_9v_{12}v_{11}v_{10}v_7v_4$
21. $v_4v_3v_2v_1v_5v_6v_{10}v_9v_{12}v_{13}v_{14}v_{11}v_7v_8$ 23. $v_4v_2v_1v_3v_5$
25. No such path exists.   27. $v_6v_3v_1v_2v_5v_8v_9v_7v_4$
29. Such a path exists starting from any vertex.
31. Yes
33. (a)

(b) $v_5v_1v_2v_3v_4v_8v_7v_6v_2v_6v_7v_3v_7v_8v_4v_3v_2v_1v_5$

35. (a)

(b) No such route is possible.

37.

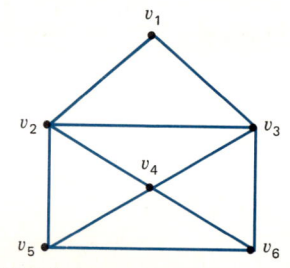

$v_5v_4v_3v_1v_2v_3v_6v_5v_2v_4v_6$

Section 11.3

1.

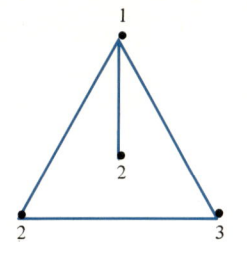

3.

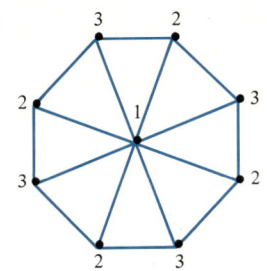

5.

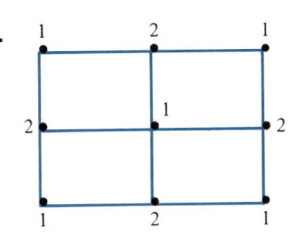

7.

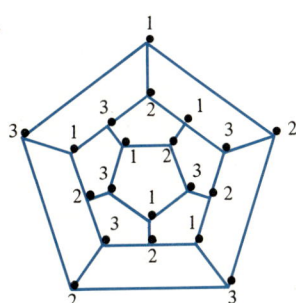

9.

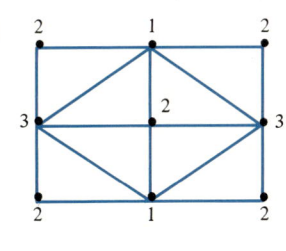

11.

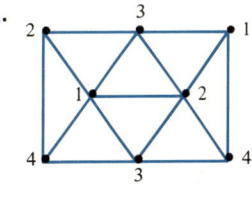

13.

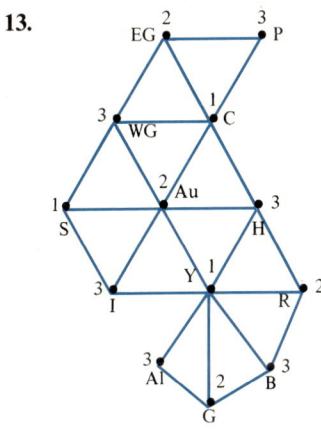

15. Two days are needed.
Day 1: Tours A, B, and E
Day 2: Tours C, D, and F

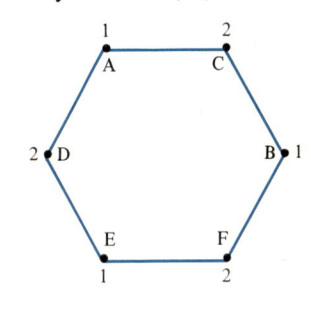

17. Three hours are needed.
Hour 1: abstract algebra and real analysis
Hour 2: linear algebra and complex analysis
Hour 3: differential geometry and sampling theory

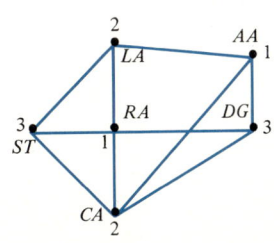

19. The hotel cannot accommodate all five conventions in two weeks.

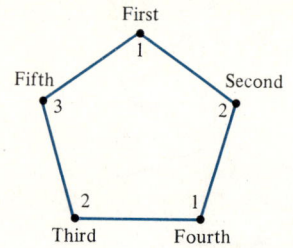

21. Three observatories are needed.

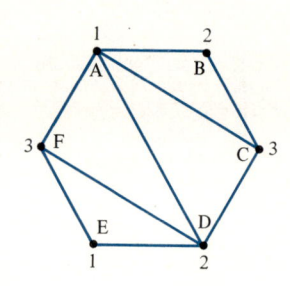

Section 11.4

1. 1   **3.** 2   **5.** 1   **7.** Undefined
9. $s(v_1) = 6$; $s(v_2) = 3$; $s(v_3) = 1$; $s(v_4) = 1$; $s(v_5) = 0$
11. $s(v_1) = 4$; $s(v_2) = 1$; $s(v_3) = 1$; $s(v_4) = 0$; $s(v_5) = 0$
13. $s(v_1) = 3$; $s(v_2) = 2$; $s(v_3) = 2$; $s(v_4) = 1$; $s(v_5) = 1$; $s(v_6) = 0$
15. Score sequence: $(1, 1, 1)$; 0 transitive triples; 1 cyclic triple
17. Score sequence: $(1, 1, 2, 2)$; 2 transitive triples; 2 cyclic triples
19. Score sequence: $(3, 1, 0, 2)$; 4 transitive triples; 0 cyclic triples
21.

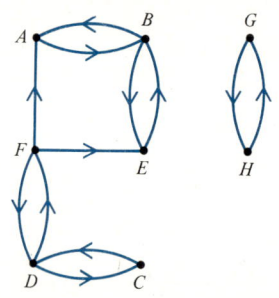

23. $s(P) = 13$; $s(VP_1) = s(VP_3) = 2$; $s(VP_2) = 1$; others have status 0.

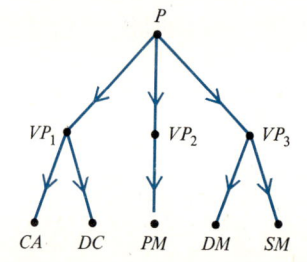

25. (a)

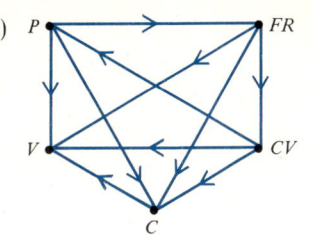

(b) (3, 3, 3, 1, 0)

(c) 9 transitive triples; 1 cyclic triple
(d) One scoop of peach, fudge ripple, and cherry vanilla

27. (a)

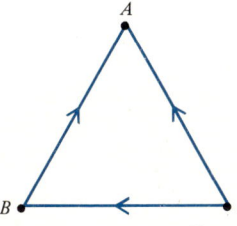

(b) In a two-way race, Carroll would defeat either Adams or Baker and Baker would defeat Adams. Yet in a three-way race, Adams would finish first, Baker second, and Carroll third.

29. (a)

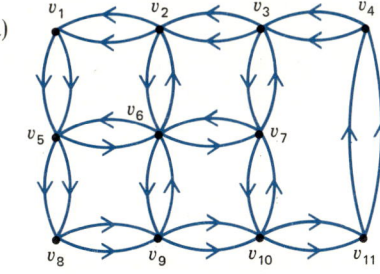

(b) $v_5 v_6 v_9 v_{10} v_7 v_6 v_2 v_1 v_5 v_8 v_9 v_6 v_7 v_3 v_2 v_1$
$v_5 v_8 v_9 v_{10} v_{11} v_4 v_3 v_7 v_{10} v_{11} v_4 v_3 v_2 v_6 v_5$

31. One possibility is

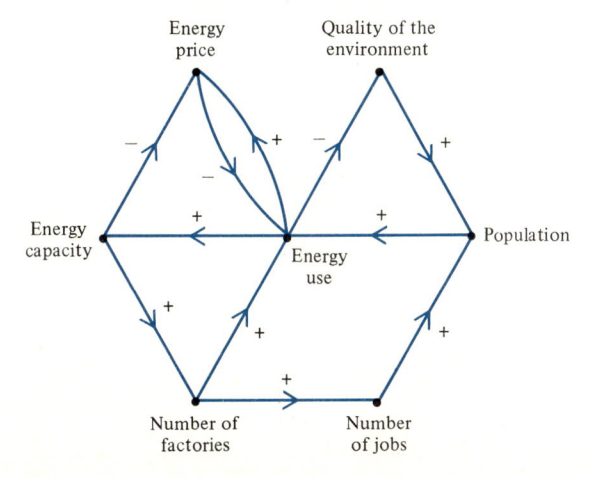

33. $\frac{1}{2} p(p-1)$

Review Exercises

1. (a) False (b) False (c) False (d) True (e) False
   (f) True (g) True (h) False (i) False (j) True
   (k) False (l) True (m) True

2. v_1 and v_3 are of degree 2; v_2, v_6, v_7, and v_8 are of degree 3; v_4 and v_5 are of degree 4

3. (a) Planar (b) Not planar

4. (a) Edge path: $v_3v_1v_4v_2v_3v_4v_5v_1v_6v_2v_5v_6$; vertex path: $v_3v_1v_4v_2v_5v_6$
   (b) No edge path; vertex path: $v_1v_3v_5v_7v_8v_6v_4v_2$
   (c) Edge path: $v_1v_7v_3v_4v_7v_6v_3v_5v_6v_1v_3v_2v_1$; vertex path: $v_1v_2v_3v_4v_7v_6v_5$

5. Day 1: engineering, budgeting, and maintenance; day 2: sales, data processing, payroll, and accounts receivable; day 3: personnel, quality control, and accounts payable

6. Day 1: Tours B and E; day 2: Tours A, F, and D; day 3: Tour C

7. $s(P) = 23$; $s(VPO) = 14$; $s(VPF) = 9$; $s(BM) = 7$;
   $s(LO) = 5$; $s(HT) = 2$; all others have 0 status

8. Score sequence: $(5, 1, 3, 1, 2, 3)$; 17 transitive triples; 3 cyclic triples

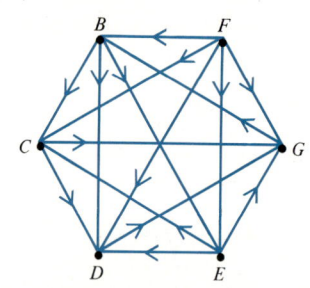

9. Indegrees: Angela, 2; Bill, 4; Courtney, 1; Dick, 4; Evelyn, 2; Forest, 2
   Outdegrees: Angela, 3; Bill, 2; Courtney, 1; Dick, 2; Evelyn, 4; Forest, 3

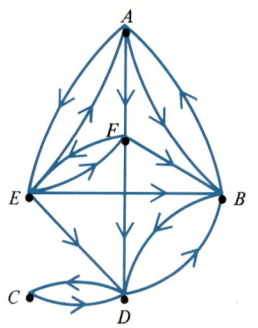

10. (a) No such sequence exists.
    (b) One possible sequence is EGCADBF.

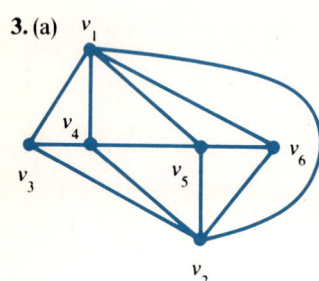

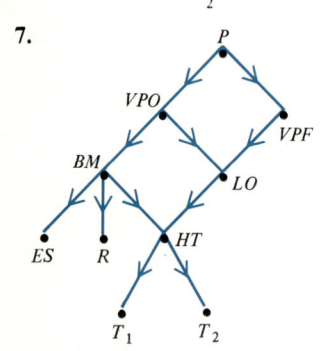

Index

Amortization, 401
Annuity, 397–401
    future value, 399
    present value, 397
Arithmetic progression, 374–378
    common difference, 375
    nth term, 375
    sum of the first n terms, 376–377
Augmented matrix, 86
Axis, 8

Battle of the Bismarck Sea, 350–351
Bayes' formula, 279–286
Biology
    ecosystem, 320–321
    food web, 444–445
    genetics, 304–305, 329–330
Block, 49
Blood type, 225–227, 269–270, 273
Book value, 37
Break-even analysis, 30–32
Break-even chart, 32
Break-even point, 32
Break-even quantity, 31
Business
    break-even analysis, 30–32
    decision making, 2–3
    financial leverage, 38–40
    interlocking directorate, 226
    model for allocating service charges, 94–96
    use of mathematical models, 2–3

Cartesian coordinate system. *See* Rectangular coordinate system
Clique, 69–70
Cobweb model, 403–405
Code. *See* Cryptography
Coefficient of correlation. *See* Linear regression
Coloring problems, 435–440
Column vector. *See* Vector
Combination, 235–238, 252, 276
Community change, 307–308
Constraint
    in linear programming problems, 127
    nonbinding, 134
Coordinates, 9
Cost, 30–32, 36–40, 95–96
    direct, 95–96
    fixed, 30
    indirect, 95–96
    variable, 30
Cost function, 30
Counting techniques, 222, 228–238
    combinations, 235–238
    multiplication principle, 229
    number of elements in the union of sets, 222
    permutations, 233–235
Cryptography, 110–111

Demand, 25–30, 403–405
Demography, 60–62
Dependent variable. *See* Variable

Depreciation, 37–38
Difference equation, 391–395
   definition of a solution, 391
   solution of a first-order linear equation, 392
Digraph, 444–449
   arc, 444
   arc progression, 446
   path, 446
   signed, 445
   vertices, 444
Dominance relation, 73–74, 447

Earnings
   before income and taxes, 38
   per share of common stock, 38
Earnings per share indifference point, 40
EBIT. *See* Earnings
Economics
   Harrod model for growth of national income, 406–408
   Leontief input-output model, 97–99
   market equilibrium, 25–30, 403–405
   supply and demand, 25–30, 403–405
Elementary row operations, 81–82, 107–110, 149–151
EPS. *See* Earnings
Equilibrium demand, 26, 404
Equilibrium price, 25, 404
Equilibrium supply, 26, 404
Ethiopia. *See* Galla tribes
Events in an experiment, 245–253
   dependent, 268
   equiprobable, 249–253
   impossible, 245
   independent, 268–271
   mutually exclusive, 260–262
   odds in favor of, 257
   probability of, 246–274
   simple, 245
Experiment, 243–292
   Bernoulli, 274
   binomial, 274–277
   deterministic, 243
   expected value, 288–292
   sample space, 244–253, 282–286
   stochastic, 243

Factorial notation, 233
Feasible set, 122–169
   bounded, 130
   unbounded, 130
   vertex of, 130–131, 142–143
Federal Reserve Board, 385
Financial leverage, 38–40

Fixed cost. *See* Cost
Food web, 444–445
Foreign trade, 76–77
Frequency distribution, 181–185
   frequency of an interval, 183
   frequency polygon, 185
   histogram, 183
   modal class, 192
   relative frequency of an interval, 183
Function, 6
   graph of a, 8
   linear, 16
   objective, 129
   probability, 246

Galla tribes, 303–304, 308
Gambler's ruin, 323–324
Game theory. *See* Matrix games
Gaussian elimination, 87–92
General form of the equation of a line, 17
Geometric progression, 380–383
   common ratio, 380
   nth term, 380
   sum of the first n terms, 381
   sum of the terms, 382
Graph, 417–449
   adjacency matrix, 425
   complete, 424–437
   components, 425
   connected, 425
   contraction, 422
   edge progression, 424
   edges of, 418
   hexagonal, 421
   path in, 425
   pentagonal, 421
   planar, 420
   vertices of, 418
Graph theory, 417–449
Gross national product, 8, 383, 396

Half-plane, 118–119
Hamiltonian circuit, 432
Hardy-Weinberg law, 304–305, 308
Histogram. *See* Frequency distribution

Identity matrix, 60, 97–99, 318–328, 365
Incidence matrix, 68–74
Independent variable. *See* Variable
Indifference chart, 38
Input-output matrix, 97–99
Input-output model
   closed, 98–99
   open, 97–98

Index

Instrumental conditioning, 410
Intercepts, 11
Interest, 385–389
  compound, 386
  effective rate, 388
  nominal rate, 388
  principal, 385
  rate of, 385
  simple, 385
Interlocking directorate, 226
Intersection of sets. See Sets
Inventory
  cost of, 11–15
  value of, 393–395
Inverse of a matrix, 105–111, 319–328

Königsberg bridge problem, 426

Land use, 312–313
Leading variable, 86
Learning
  mathematical theory of, 409–413
  paired-associate, 325–326, 328–329
Leontief, Wassily. See Input-output model
Liaison person, 71
Linear function, 16, 26–32
Linear inequalities, 118–125, 157–158
  graphing of, 120
  system of, 122–125
Linear method of depreciation. See Depreciation
Linear programming, 117–176, 353–369
  dual problem, 173
  geometric method, 134–140
  simplex method, 140–169
  used to solve matrix games, 353–369
Linear regression, 203–209
  coefficient of correlation, 206–207
  least squares line, 204
  linear regression equation, 204–205
  scatter diagram, 203
Lines, 17–25, 78
  equations, 17, 22, 23
  horizontal, 18
  parallel, 21, 78
  perpendicular, 25
  slope of, 20
  vertical, 18–19

Marginal propensity to consume, 383, 393–395
Market equilibrium, 25–30, 403–405
Markov chain, 298–328
  absorbing, 316–328
  absorbing state, 317
  canonical form, 318
  fixed probability vector, 309–313
  fundamental matrix, 319
  initial distribution vector, 301
  regular, 308–313
  states of, 298
  transition matrix, 299
Markup, 36
Matching pennies, 338, 343
Mathematical model, 2
Mathematics of finance, 385–401
Matrices, 45–176, 298–369
  adjacency, 425
  columns, 47
  diagonal of, 47
  difference of, 53
  entries, 46
  equality of, 48
  i, j entry, 47
  product of, 57
  rows, 47
  scalar product of, 52
  size of, 47
  square, 47
  sum of, 52
  transition, 299
Matrix games, 336–369
  algorithm for solving, 365
  dominated column, 344
  dominated row, 343–344
  fair, 343
  $m \times n$ matrix games, 361–369
  optimal strategies, 341–342
  payoff, 337
  payoff matrix, 338
  players, 337
  saddle point, 350–352
  strategies, 339–345
  strictly determined, 349–352
  $2 \times m$ matrix games, 353–360
  two-person zero-sum, 337
  value of, 341
Mean. See Measure of central tendency
Measure of central tendency, 189–192
  mean, 189–190
  median, 190
  modal class, 192
  mode, 191
Measure of dispersion, 189, 192–195
  standard deviation, 194
  variance, 193
Median. See Measure of central tendency
Method of elimination, 79–81
Method of substitution, 78–79
Michigan Supreme Court, 73–74
Minimax theorem, 341–342

Mode. *See* Measure of central tendency
Multigraph, 426
Multiplication principle, 228–231

National income, 383, 406–409
n-coloring of a graph, 435
New Zealand, 311–312
Normal distribution, 196–201
   equation, 197
   standard normal distribution, 197
   z score, 199
n-tuple, 6

Objective function, 129
Odds, 257
Operant behavior. *See* Instrumental conditioning
Ordered pair, 8

Paired comparisons, 448–449
Parallel lines. *See* Line
Parameter, 86, 143
Permutation, 233–235, 252–253
Perpendicular lines. *See* Line
Pivot column, 87, 148
Point-slope form of the equation of a line, 22
Present value, 389
Price, 25–30
Pricing, 36–37
Principal. *See* Interest
Probability, 243–292, 299
   of the complement of an event, 258
   conditional, 265–271
   of the intersection of events, 267–271
   of a simple event, 246
   of the union of events, 259–262
Probability vector. *See* Vector
Profit function, 32
Psychology
   conditioning, 315
   instrumental conditioning, 410
   learning, 412–413
   memory, 330–331
   paired-associate learning, 325–326, 328–329
   paired comparisons, 448–449
   Yerkes-Dodson law, 229
Public works jobs, 409

Rectangular coordinate system, 8
Regression analysis. *See* Linear regression
Revenue function, 30
Road network. *See* Traffic flow
Row echelon form, 86–88
Row vector. *See* Vector

Sample space. *See* Experiment
Scalar, 52
Scheduling problems, 435–440
Scissors-paper-stone, 347, 369
Selection
   without replacement, 273
   with replacement, 273
Service charges, 95–96
Sets, 215–226, 230
   complement of, 219
   disjoint, 218
   elements of, 215
   empty, 217
   equality of, 216
   intersection of, 218
   number of elements in the union of, 222
   proper subset, 217
   subset, 217, 230
   union of, 218
   universal, 218
   Venn diagrams, 220–221
Set braces, 216
Set of feasible solutions. *See* Feasible set
Simplex method, 140–169, 361–369
   algorithm for, 151
   artificial variable, 159–160
   basic feasible solution, 142
   basic variable, 142
   minimization, 166–169
   nonbasic variable, 142
   pivot, 149
   pivot column, 148
   pivot element, 149
   pivot row, 149
   simplex tableau, 147
   slack variable, 141
   two-phase method, 160–166
   used to solve matrix games, 361–369
Sinking fund, 398
Slope-intercept form of the equation of a line, 23
Slope of a line. *See* Line
Social science
   demography, 60–62
   sociological relations, 68–74
   use of mathematical models, 2–3
Sociology
   community change, 307–308
   conflict, 326–328
   conformity, 326–328
   organization theory, 446
   paired comparisons, 448–449
   status, 447
Solution of a system of linear equations, 78, 85

Standard deviation. *See* Measure of dispersion
Statistics, 181–209
Status, 447
Submatrix, 49
Subsidy, 29
Supply, 25–30, 403–405
System of linear equations, 77–101, 309–311
   applications of, 94–101
   in n unknowns, 85–92
   in two unknowns, 77–83
   used to find fixed probability vectors, 309–311

Tax, 27–28, 40
Terms of a sequence, 375, 391
Tournament, 447–449
   cyclic triple, 448
   score, 447
   score sequence, 447
   transitive triple, 448
Trade. *See* Foreign trade
Trade cycle, 409
Traffic flow, 99–101

Tree diagram, 228–230, 284
Two-finger morra, 347, 369
Two-phase method. *See* Simplex method

Union of sets. *See* Sets

Variable, 7
Variance. *See* Measure of dispersion
Vector, 47, 301, 309–310, 339–341
   column, 47, 340
   probability, 301, 309–310, 339–341
   row, 47, 339
Venn diagram, 220–221
Vertices, 418–430, 444–447
   adjacent, 418
   degree of, 418
   distance between, 447
   indegree of, 446
   outdegree of, 446
   reachable, 447
   status of, 447

Yerkes-Dodson law, 229

Zero matrix, 54

81 82 83 84 85 9 8 7 6 5 4 3 2 1